D1378171

ALGEBRA

ALGEBRA

EUGENE D. NICHOLS
RALPH T. HEIMER
E. HENRY GARLAND

DEPARTMENT OF MATHEMATICS EDUCATION
Florida State University

HOLT, RINEHART AND WINSTON, INC.   1966
New York · Chicago · San Francisco · Toronto · London

Preface

This text is a sequel to *Elementary Algebra* by E. D. Nichols but may be used successfully with any college students who have familiarity with the beginning notions of a modern elementary algebra course.

The following are a few of the important features of the textbook:

Even as new material is being introduced, a review of elementary algebra is incorporated within the first four chapters.

Throughout, there is emphasis on student discovery and proof. At the end of each chapter, there are found a vocabulary list, chapter review exercises, and a chapter text. Cumulative review exercises occur after each four chapters to aid in maintaining important concepts.

The exposition of new topics is complete and clear. It is important that each student read the textbook carefully. This is an important part of leading students to discover mathematical truths and patterns for themselves and to develop the ability to read mathematical discourses.

The authors wish to acknowledge their indebtedness to Miss Mary Clyde Johnson, Mrs. Janice Duncan, and Mrs. Geraldine Garland for typing the manuscript.

E. D. N.

Tallahassee, Florida   R. T. H.
December 1965   E. H. G.

Contents

vii

SYMBOL LIST

N	set of natural numbers	1
$\forall$	for every	1
ϵ	belongs to	1
$\cup$	union	3
$\rightarrow$	implies	9
$\frown$	it is not the case that	9
$\wedge$	and	13
$\vee$	or	13
$\exists$	there exists	14
ϕ	the empty set	14
I	set of integers	14
$|Y|$	absolute value	20
Q	set of rational numbers	34
R	set of real numbers	34
$\cap$	intersection	34
$\subset$	is a subset of	34
$|$	such that	156
A'	A inverse	164
$[x]$	greatest integer function	178
$\sum$	summation of	480
$!$	factorial	490
$P(E)$	probability of event E	521
$\overline{A}$	complement of A	522
$\vec{B}$	vector B	536

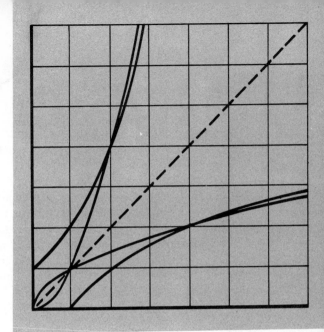

CHAPTER 1

Number Systems

THE SYSTEM OF NATURAL NUMBERS—CLOSURE

The numbers used for counting are 1, 2, 3, 4, ... The three dots indicate that not all of the numbers have been listed. They continue on and on. These numbers are called *natural numbers*. The set of natural numbers, which we designate by N, is an *infinite* set.

$$N = \{1, 2, 3, 4, \ldots\}$$

The numbers themselves are of not much use unless we can do something with them. The actions performed on numbers are called operations. You are familiar with at least four operations on numbers: addition, subtraction, multiplication, division.

You have undoubtedly observed that the result of adding any pair of natural numbers is a natural number. We state this as follows:

$$\forall_{a \epsilon N} \, \forall_{b \epsilon N} \, (a + b) \, \epsilon \, N$$

This abbreviated statement means the following: For every natural number a and for every natural number b, the sum of a and b belongs to the set of natural numbers. We say that the set of natural numbers is *closed* under the operation of addition.

1

■ *Closure Property of Natural Numbers under Addition*
   $\forall_{a \epsilon N} \, \forall_{b \epsilon N} \; (a + b) \, \epsilon \, N$ [abbreviated Cl PA]

Since the set of natural numbers is an infinite set, we are not able to verify this property on all numbers. We simply *assume* that it is true for all natural numbers.

It is easy to prove that the set of natural numbers is not closed under subtraction. For example, $4 - 7$ is not a member of the set of natural numbers. This one example is sufficient to prove the absence of the closure property for this operation, since for a property to hold it must apply in *every* instance. An example proving that a property does not hold is called a *counterexample*.

Let us consider a subset of the set of natural numbers, say the set of even numbers: $E = \{2, 4, 6, 8, \ldots\}$. Is E an infinite set? Does E have a smallest element? A largest element? We can examine a few cases to see whether the set of even numbers seems closed under addition.

$$2 + 4 = 6 \qquad 14 + 8 = 22 \qquad 16 + 20 = 36$$

It seems that the closure property does hold for the set of even numbers. We shall prove this later in this chapter.

For future reference we shall state a definition of even numbers. But first, observe that $2a$ is a natural number for every $a \, \epsilon \, N$. If a is 1, then $2a$ is 2; if a is 2, then $2a$ is 4, and so on.

■ *Definition of Even Natural Number*   Any natural number which can be given as the product of 2 and some natural number is an *even* number.

EXERCISES

1. Prove that the set of odd numbers is not closed under addition by citing one counterexample.

2. Prove that the set of natural numbers is not closed under division by citing one counterexample.

3. A *prime* number is a natural number which has exactly two natural number divisors (factors). Prove that the set of prime numbers is not closed under addition by giving one counterexample.

■ *Closure Property of Natural Numbers under Multiplication*
   $\forall_{a \epsilon N} \, \forall_{b \epsilon N} \; (a \cdot b) \, \epsilon \, N$ [Cl PM]

4. Prove that the set of prime numbers is not closed under multiplication by giving one counterexample.

5. A natural number which has more than two divisors is called a *composite* number. For example, 4 is a composite number; it has three divisors.
   a. List the three divisors of 4.
   b. List in order all composite numbers less than 15.
   c. By applying the definition of a prime number and the definition of a composite number, prove that 1 is neither a prime nor a composite number.

6. Which of the following pairs of sets are disjoint?

    a. {1}; {prime numbers}

    b. {1}; {composite numbers}

    c. {prime numbers}; {composite numbers}

    d. {even numbers}; {prime numbers}

    e. {odd numbers}; {composite numbers}

7. What is {1} $\cup$ {prime numbers} $\cup$ {composite numbers} equal to?

8. Prove that {1, 2} is not closed under

    a. addition   **b.** subtraction   **c.** multiplication   **d.** division

9. Prove that {1} is closed under

    a. multiplication   **b.** division

10. Prove that {1} is not closed under

    a. addition   **b.** subtraction

11. Using the definition: $\forall_{a \in N}$ $2a$ is an even number, prove that 50 is an even number.

12. Using the definition: $\forall_{a \in N}$ $2a - 1$ is an odd number, prove that 21 is an odd number.

Other properties of natural numbers

In addition to the closure properties of addition and multiplication, the system of natural numbers has other familiar properties.

■ *Commutative Property of Natural Numbers under Addition*
  $\forall_{a \in N} \forall_{b \in N}$ $a + b = b + a$ [CPA]

■ *Commutative Property of Natural Numbers under Multiplication*
  $\forall_{a \in N} \forall_{b \in N}$ $a \cdot b = b \cdot a$ [CPM]

■ *Associative Property of Natural Numbers under Addition*
  $\forall_{a \in N} \forall_{b \in N} \forall_{c \in N}$ $(a + b) + c = a + (b + c)$ [APA]

It is necessary to agree on the following: $a + b + c$ means $(a + b) + c$ and $a + b + c + d$ means $(a + b + c) + d$ which in turn means $[(a + b) + c] + d$. Generally, we can associate any finite number of terms in this way. The same agreement will hold for multiplication.

■ *Associative Property of Natural Numbers under Multiplication*
  $\forall_{a \in N} \forall_{b \in N} \forall_{c \in N}$ $(ab)c = a(bc)$ [APM]

■ *Left-Distributive Property of Natural Numbers for Multiplication over Addition*
  $\forall_{a \in N} \forall_{b \in N} \forall_{c \in N}$ $a(b + c) = (ab) + (ac)$ [LDPMA]

The last property is called "left-distributivity" to distinguish it from right-distributivity, which is

$$\forall_{a \epsilon N} \forall_{b \epsilon N} \forall_{c \epsilon N} \ (b + c)a = (ba) + (ca) \quad \text{[RDPMA]}$$

We now prove *right-distributivity* as a theorem.

Proof $(b + c)a = a(b + c)$ CPM
                         $= (ab) + (ac)$ LDPMA
                         $= (ba) + (ca)$ CPM
Hence $(b + c)a = (ba) + (ca)$

For several pages we have been using the relation *is equal to* abbreviated by =. We now state the meaning of this relation precisely, as well as the properties it possesses.

◼ *Definition of "is equal to"* a *is equal to* b, $a = b$, means that a and b are two names for the same thing.

The relation *is equal to* (=) has the following three properties.

◼ *Reflexive property*
$\forall_a \ a = a$

◼ *Symmetric property*
$\forall_a \forall_b$, if $a = b$, then $b = a$

◼ *Transitive property*
$\forall_a \forall_b \forall_c$, if $a = b$ and $b = c$, then $a = c$

◼ *Definition of Equivalence Relation*   Any relation which has the reflexive, symmetric, and transitive properties is called an *equivalence relation*.

◼ *Substitution Property*
If $a = b$, then a can be replaced by b and vice-versa in any statement and the truth-value of the new statement is the same as the value of the original statement.

[NOTE: Each statement has only one of the two truth-values, true or false. The truth-value of a true statement is *true* or T, and of a false statement is *false* or F.]

We now state a property which only the natural number 1 enjoys — no other natural number has this property.

◼ *Property of Natural Number 1 for Multiplication*
There exists a natural number, namely 1, for which it is true that
$\forall_{a \epsilon N} \ a \cdot 1 = a$ [P1M]

We call the natural number 1 the *multiplicative identity* of the set of natural numbers.

Now combining the relation *is equal to* with the operations of addition and multiplication, we can list four more familiar properties.

■ *Right-hand Addition Property*
$\forall_{a\epsilon N}\forall_{b\epsilon N}\forall_{c\epsilon N}$, if $a = b$, then $a + c = b + c$

■ *Right-hand Multiplication Property*
$\forall_{a\epsilon N}\forall_{b\epsilon N}\forall_{c\epsilon N}$, if $a = b$, then $ac = bc$

■ *Right-hand Cancellation Property over Addition*
$\forall_{a\epsilon N}\forall_{b\epsilon N}\forall_{c\epsilon N}$, if $a + c = b + c$, then $a = b$

■ *Right-hand Cancellation Property over Multiplication*
$\forall_{a\epsilon N}\forall_{b\epsilon N}\forall_{c\epsilon N}$, if $ac = bc$, then $a = b$

These are *properties of the set of natural numbers* over the *is equal to* relation. Remember for now we are restricted to natural numbers only.

These are basic properties of operations on natural numbers which we use very frequently and subsequently extend to numbers other than the natural numbers. From your previous study of algebra, you will recall applying some basic properties repeatedly when simplifying expressions. For example, in writing

$$(2n + 1)(2k + 1) = (2n + 1)(2k) + (2n + 1) \cdot 1$$
$$= 2n \cdot 2k + 1 \cdot 2k + 2n \cdot 1 + 1 \cdot 1$$
$$= 4nk + 2k + 2n + 1$$

we make use of a number of properties. Can you identify all of them?

EXERCISES

1. Which of the following properties hold and which do not hold for the relation $\neq$ (is not equal to): reflexive, symmetric, and transitive. Is $\neq$ an equivalence relation?

2. Which of the above three properties hold for the relation $>$ (is greater than)? Is the relation $>$ an equivalence relation?

3. Name the property illustrated by each of the following examples.

a. $3 + 7 = 7 + 3$

b. $4 \cdot 12 = 12 \cdot 4$

c. $7(a + 4) = (7a) + (7 \cdot 4)$

d. $(m + n) + p = m + (n + p)$

e. $(m + n) \cdot 2 = (m \cdot 2) + (n \cdot 2)$

f. 7×42 is a natural number

g. $(xy)z = x(zy)$ [CAUTION: There are two properties illustrated here.]

h. $7 + 25$ is a natural number

i. $12 + (3 + 4) = 12 + (4 + 3)$

j. $(1 \times 6) \times 12 = (6 \times 1) \times 12$

k. $\forall_x\forall_y$, if $x = y$, then $x + 1 = y + 1$

4. Prove that the square of an even number is an even number. [HINT: Study the example below. Consider squaring as multiplying.]

Example: You have undoubtedly discovered some time ago that *the product of two even numbers is an even number*. Now we can prove this. Study this proof because it will help you to prove other theorems.

$\forall_{a\epsilon N}$ $2a$ is an even number and $\forall_{b\epsilon N}$ $2b$ is an even number.
Thus, $\forall_{a\epsilon N}\forall_{b\epsilon N}$ $(2a) \cdot (2b)$ is the product of two even numbers.
Now we need to prove that it is an even number.

$$(2a) \cdot (2b) = (2 \cdot 2) \cdot (ab) = (2 \cdot 2) \cdot k$$

Observe that we replaced ab by k. We can do this because we know that $\forall_{a\epsilon N}\forall_{b\epsilon N}$ ab is a natural number (by what property?), which we call k. [This is a very useful technique which you will want to store in your memory for frequent use.]

$(2 \cdot 2) \cdot k = 2 \cdot (2k) = 2m$ [Rename the natural number $2k$ as m.]
So $(2a) \cdot (2b) = 2m$ and $\forall_m$ $2m$ is an even number [why?].
Q.E.D. [Quod Erat Demonstrandum, meaning that which was to be proved or demonstrated.]

5. Prove that the sum of two even numbers is an even number.

6. Some of the following equations have solutions in the set of natural numbers, others do not. Whenever the solution sets have their elements in the natural numbers, find them; in other cases where there is not a solution in N, designate the solution set as ϕ.

a. $y + 3 = 8$

b. $x + 5 = 2$

c. $2z + 3 = 15$

d. $2m + 3 = 3$

e. $2s + 1 = 5$

f. $5 + 3t = 1$

g. $3(2u - 5) = 15$

h. $v + 2 = 10 - v$

i. $3(n + 2) = n + 7$

j. $v - 1 = v + 2$

k. $2(k + 3) = 1$

l. $2(r - 1) + 3(r + 1) = 1$

m. $2x - 7 = 3x$

n. $4(2y - 3) + 4 = (y - 1) \cdot 7 + 1$

Ordering of the natural numbers

We make frequent use of natural numbers when comparing scores of two teams, ages of two individuals, incomes of two individuals, and so on. A relation which might be involved in making such comparisons is the relation *is less than*. We say, for example, that the distance from A to B *is less than* the distance from A to C and write it as $AB < AC$.

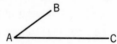

We need to define the relation *is less than*.

■ *Definition of "is less than" for the Natural Numbers*   For two natural numbers x and y, x *is less than* y, $x < y$, means that there is a natural number z for which $x + z = y$.

For example, $2 < 5$ means that there is a natural number n for which $2 + n = 5$. This number is 3, because $2 + 3 = 5$.

We will now state an important property of natural numbers, which involves both relations, $=$ and $<$.

■ *Trichotomy Property of Natural Numbers*

If x and y are natural numbers, then exactly one of the following is true.

$$x < y \qquad x = y \qquad y < x$$

This trichotomy property will help us prove some theorems concerning natural numbers.

Theorem 1 For any natural numbers x, y, z, if $x < y$, then $x + z < y + z$.

We know, by definition of $<$, that $x + z < y + z$ means that there is some natural number which when added to $x + z$ will give $y + z$. We need to prove the existence of this number.

To the right of each statement in the proof, reference is made to the statements which support what is said. Be sure to look up or recall each statement, so that you understand how it justifies what is said.

Proof

$x < y$	Given
$x + w = y \quad (w \epsilon N)$	Def. $<$
$(x + w) + z = y + z$	Rt. add. prop.
$x + (w + z) = y + z$	APA
$x + (z + w) = y + z$	CPA
$(x + z) + w = y + z$	APA
$x + z < y + z$	Def. $<$

In the sixth statement above we proved the existence of a natural number w for which $(x + z) + w = y + z$, therefore by the definition of the relation *is less than* it follows that $x + z < y + z$.

Theorem 2 For any natural numbers x, y, z, if $x < y$, then $xz < yz$.

Proof

$x < y$	Given
$x + w = y \quad (w \epsilon N)$	Def. $<$
$(x + w)z = yz$	Rt. mult. prop.
$(xz) + (wz) = yz$	RDPMA
$xz < yz$	Cl PM; def. $<$

In the fourth statement above we proved that there is a natural number wz for which $(xz) + (wz) = yz$; we know that wz is a natural number by the closure property of multiplication. By the definition of *is less than* it follows that $xz < yz$.

Theorem 3 For any natural numbers x, y, z, if $x < y$ and $y < z$, then $x < z$.

Proof

$x < y,\ y < z$	Given
$x + s = y,\ y + t = z \quad (s \epsilon N,\ t \epsilon N)$	Def. $<$
$(x + s) + t = z$	Subst. prop.; what substitution was made?
$x + (s + t) = z$	APA
$x < z$	Cl PA; def. $<$

In the fourth statement above why is $s + t$ a natural number? How does the last statement follow from the previous one?

Frequently we encounter a compound statement of this kind: $x < y$ or $x = y$. We abbreviate this as $x \leq y$, and read it: x is less than or equal to y.

Also, the compound statement $x < y$ and $y < z$ can be abbreviated to $x < y < z$. It is read: x is less than y and y is less than z.

EXERCISES

1. Using definition of $<$, tell the meaning of $5 < 7$.

2. Write in an abbreviated form each of the following:
    a. $5 < 7$ or $5 = 7$
    b. $10 < 11$ or $10 = 11$
    c. $3 < 5$ and $5 < 12$
    d. $1 < 2$ and $2 \leq 105$
    e. $3 \leq 3$ and $3 < 37$
    f. $5 \leq 9$ and $9 \leq 9$

3. Prove the following two theorems for all natural numbers.
    a. For all natural numbers x, y, z, if $x + z < y + z$, then $x < y$. [HINT: Use definition of $<$ and the right-hand cancellation property for addition.]
    b. For all natural numbers x, y, z, if $xz < yz$, then $x < y$. [HINT: First prove that $xz < yz$ means that there is a natural number wz for which $xz + wz = yz$.]

4. Using the theorems on inequalities, simplify each inequality. The replacement set for the variables is the set of natural numbers.

Examples: i.
$$2x + 1 < x + 5$$
$$x + x + 1 < x + 1 + 4$$
$$x + (x + 1) < 4 + (x + 1)$$
$$x < 4$$

ii.
$$3n + 12 < 21$$
$$3(n + 4) < 3 \cdot 7$$
$$(n + 4) \cdot 3 < 7 \cdot 3$$
$$n + 4 < 7$$
$$n + 4 < 3 + 4$$
$$n < 3$$

AGREEMENT: "$x > y$" means the same as "$y < x$." "$x > y$" is read: x is *greater than* y.

iii.
$$3(n + 1) > 2n + 7$$
$$2n + 7 < 3(n + 1)$$
$$2n + 7 < 3n + 3$$
$$2n + 4 + 3 < 3n + 3$$
$$2n + 4 < 3n$$
$$4 + 2n < n + 2n$$
$$4 < n$$

a. $3m + 2 < m + 8$

b. $6 + 9y < 4y + 11$

c. $2n + 6 > 4n + 2$

d. $15 > 4s + 12$

e. $4(n + 3) > 7(n + 1)$

f. $5t + 10 < 3t + 30$

g. $5(3 + k) > 3(9 + k)$

h. $7(2x + 1) < 3(2x + 10)$

Implication

You have already proved the two theorems

$$\forall_{x\epsilon N}\forall_{y\epsilon N}\forall_{z\epsilon N}, \text{ if } x < y, \text{ then } x + z < y + z$$

and

$$\forall_{x\epsilon N}\forall_{y\epsilon N}\forall_{z\epsilon N}, \text{ if } x + z < y + z, \text{ then } x < y$$

A glance at the two statements reveals that they are related. The first statement is of the form: "if p, then q," and the second statement is of the form: "if q, then p." The second statement is called the *converse* of the first statement.

■   *Definition of Implication*   A statement of the form: "if p, then q" is called an *implication* and is sometimes written as $p \rightarrow q$ [read: p *implies* q]. An implication is sometimes called a *conditional*.

There are three derived forms of implications which are of interest in mathematics. If we take $p \rightarrow q$ as our basic statement form, then the three derived forms are as follows:

$q \rightarrow p$ *converse*

$\sim p \rightarrow \sim q$ *inverse* [read: not p implies not q]

$\sim q \rightarrow \sim p$ *contrapositive*

The converse of the implication

If it is snow, then it can be melted.

is: If it can be melted, then it is snow.

The first statement is true. The second statement is false. This example shows that the converse of an implication which is true is not necessarily a true implication.

The inverse of the implication

If it is snow, then it can be melted.

is: If it is not snow, then it cannot be melted.

It is a false implication. Therefore, the inverse of a true implication is not necessarily true.

The contrapositive of the implication

If it is snow, then it can be melted.

is: If it cannot be melted, then it is not snow.

This implication is true. Is it the case that the contrapositive of every true implication is a true implication? We shall answer this question in the next section.

EXERCISES

1.   Write the converse, inverse, and contrapositive of each of the following implications.

    a. If $x + 2 = 5$, then $x = 3$.

    b. If two sides in a triangle are of the same length, then the angles opposite these sides have the same measure.

    c. If $5 > 3$, then $7 > 5$.

    d. If next Monday is Labor Day, then there will be no school next Monday.

    e. If Mary will do well in this algebra course, then she will be able to take trigonometry next year.

2. $\sim p$ [read: not p] is called the *negation* of p.   One simple way of obtaining the negation of any sentence is to prefix it by "it is not true that." Give the negation of each of the following obtained in this manner.

    a. It will rain tomorrow.

    b. Suzie is a good dresser.

    c. John is the best mathematics student in this school.

    d. Jack is not a good chess player.

    e. Debbie does not care to attend school parties.

    f. This class does not need to worry about doing well in mathematics.

    g. We do not enjoy doing a lot of homework.

3.   Give the negation of each sentence in problem **2** by negating the verb.   Problem **2a** is done for you.

    a. It will not rain tomorrow.

SOME PRINCIPLES OF LOGIC

Each of the following statements

$$5 = 7 \qquad 10 \neq 3 \qquad 2 < 1 \qquad 5 > 4 \qquad 2^3 = 4$$

can be classified as being either true or false.   We will write "$\text{tv}(5 = 7) = \text{F}$" to mean that the *truth-value* of the statement "$5 = 7$" is *false*.   Similarly, "$\text{tv}(10 \neq 3) = \text{T}$" means that the *truth-value* of "$10 \neq 3$" is *true*.

  ■ *Principle of the Truth-Value of a Statement*
Every statement has the truth-value of either T or F, but not both T and F.

  ■ *Principle of the Truth-Value of a Negation*
If $\text{tv}(p) = \text{T}$, then $\text{tv}(\sim p) = \text{F}$ and if $\text{tv}(p) = \text{F}$, then $\text{tv}(\sim p) = \text{T}$.

We show this in the form of a *truth-table* at the top of the following page.

p	$\sim p$
T	F
F	T

■ *Principle of the Truth-Value of a Double Negation*
$\mathrm{tv}(\sim \sim p) = \mathrm{tv}(p)$

The truth-table for this principle is

p	$\sim \sim p$
T	T
F	F

The first principle tells us that a statement cannot be both true and false. This is a comforting principle to have.

The principle of negation tells us that the negation of a statement does not have the same truth-value as the statement.

The principle of double negation establishes the truth-value of the negation of the negation [or double negation] of any statement to be the same as the truth-value of the statement.

There is one more important principle to be established. It is a principle concerning the truth-value of an implication. We need to be able to decide whether, for example, the statement: "If $2 = 5$, then $3 = 7$," is true or it is false.

■ *Principle of the Truth-Value of an Implication*
The implication $p \rightarrow q$ is false only if $\mathrm{tv}(p) = $ T and $\mathrm{tv}(q) = $ F.

There are four different combinations of truth-values of p and q. We show these by the following table.

p	q
T	T
T	F
F	T
F	F

The principle of implication tells us that in only one of the four cases the implication is false; it is true in the remaining three cases. The total truth table for an implication can be shown as follows:

p	q	$p \rightarrow q$
T	T	T
T	F	F
F	T	T
F	F	T

Using a truth-table, we can now easily show that the converse of a true implication is not necessarily true.

p	q	$p \rightarrow q$	$q \rightarrow p$
T	T	T	T
T	F	F	T
F	T	T	F
F	F	T	T

We notice that, in the case of $tv(p) = F$ and $tv(q) = T$, $p \rightarrow q$ is true, and the converse $q \rightarrow p$ is false.

Similarly, we can show that the inverse of a true implication is not necessarily true.

p	q	$p \rightarrow q$	$\sim p$	$\sim q$	$\sim p \rightarrow \sim q$
T	T	T	F	F	T
T	F	F	F	T	T
F	T	T	T	F	F
F	F	T	T	T	T

What are the truth-values of p and q for which $p \rightarrow q$ is true and $\sim p \rightarrow \sim q$ is false?

EXERCISES

1. Make a truth-table to show that $p \rightarrow q$ has the same truth-value as the contrapositive of $p \rightarrow q$; that is, $\sim q \rightarrow \sim p$. We say that a statement and its contrapositive are *logically equivalent*.

2. For each of the following statements tell whether it is true or it is false.

a. If $5 = 4 + 1$, then $5 + 7 = (4 + 1) + 7$

b. If $3 \neq 2 + 1$, then $2 = 2$

c. If $5 \neq 7$, then $3 \neq 1$

d. If $1 < 3$, then $3 > 1$

e. If $3 > 1$, then $3 < 1$

f. If $3 \not< 1$, then $3 \not> 1$

g. If $3 \not> 1$, then $1 \not< 3$

h. If $2 \geq 2$, then $5 > 1$

i. If $2 \geq 2$, then $1 > 5$

j. If $1 = 2$, then $2 = 1$

If and only if, And, Or

Consider the following true implication:

$$\text{If } 4 = 1 + 3, \text{ then } 4 + 5 = (1 + 3) + 5.$$

Using the form $p \rightarrow q$, it can be written as: $[4 = 1 + 3] \rightarrow [4 + 5 = (1 + 3) + 5]$.

It is easy to verify that the converse: $[4 + 5 = (1 + 3) + 5] \rightarrow [4 = 1 + 3]$, of this implication is also true. Thus, we have a true implication whose converse is also true. Such a two-way implication can be written in an abbreviated form: $4 = 1 + 3$ if and only if $4 + 5 = (1 + 3) + 5$.

This is further abbreviated as: $[4 = 1 + 3] \leftrightarrow [4 + 5 = (1 + 3) + 5]$.

An "if and only if" statement is sometimes called a *bi-conditional* (a two-way implication).

■   *Principle of the Truth-Value of a Bi-conditional*
A bi-conditional $p \leftrightarrow q$ is true only when either both p and q are true or both p and q are false.

There are two more forms of compound statements which you have considered in elementary algebra. One of these consists of two simple statements connected with "and"; the other consists of two simple statements connected with "or." The first is called a *conjunction* (and), the second a *disjunction* (or).

An example of a conjunction is: The sun is shining and all little children are playing.

An example of a disjunction is: $3 = 5$ or $1 + 1 = 2$.

We shall now state two principles which determine the truth-values of a conjunction and of a disjunction.

■   *Principle of the Truth-Value of a Conjunction*
The truth-value of a conjunction is T if and only if each of the component parts has the truth-value T.

The commonly used abbreviation for "and" is "$\wedge$". According to this last principle, the truth-table for the conjunction is as follows:

p	q	$p \wedge q$
T	T	T
T	F	F
F	T	F
F	F	F

■   *Principle of the Truth-value of a Disjunction*
The truth-value of a disjunction is F if and only if each of the component parts has the truth-value F.

The commonly used abbreviation for "or" is "$\vee$". We can reason that the truth-table for the disjunction is as follows:

p	q	$p \vee q$
T	T	T
T	F	T
F	T	T
F	F	F

EXERCISES

1. For each statement

    i. write its converse, then

    ii. write a bi-conditional, using both statements

  a. If Jack receives more than 75% on the test, then he will pass the course.

  b. If there are no clouds, then it is not raining.

  c. If Susan is a student of mathematics, then she knows algebra.

  d. If it is a fish, then it has scales.

  e. If two finite sets have the same number of elements, then they are matching sets.

  f. $\exists_{x \epsilon N}$, if $x + 2 = 3$, then $x = 1$. ["$\exists_x$" is read: "there exists an x such that"; it is called *an existential quantifier*, since it asserts the existence of a number.]

  g. $\exists_{x \epsilon N}$, if $x^2 = 16$, then $x = 4$.

  h. $\exists_{y \epsilon N}$, if $y + 1 < 2$, then $y < 1$.

  i. $\exists_{z \epsilon N}$, if $2z + 4 < 10$, then $z + 2 < 5$.

2. Make a complete truth-table for $p \leftrightarrow q$ by displaying the columns for $p \rightarrow q$, $q \rightarrow p$, and $(p \rightarrow q) \wedge (q \rightarrow p)$.

3. Tell the truth-value of each of the following:

  a. $(2 = 1 + 1) \wedge (7 = 3 + 4)$ **d.** $(9 = 7) \vee (5^2 = 25)$

  b. $(2 = 1 + 1) \vee (7 = 3 + 4)$ **e.** $(6 = 10) \wedge (1^3 = 4)$

  c. $(9 = 7) \wedge (5^2 = 25)$ **f.** $(6 = 10) \vee (1^3 = 4)$

  g. $[\forall_{x \epsilon N} \, (x + 3 = 1) \rightarrow (x + 6 = 4)] \wedge [\forall_{x \epsilon N} \, (x = 2) \rightarrow (x = 5)]$

  h. $[\forall_{x \epsilon N} \, (x + 3 = 1) \rightarrow (x + 6 = 4)] \vee [\forall_{x \epsilon N} \, (x = 2) \rightarrow (x = 5)]$

  i. $[\forall_{x \epsilon N} \, (x = 1) \rightarrow (x = 2)] \wedge [\forall_{x \epsilon N} \, (x = 2) \rightarrow (x^2 = 2)]$

  j. $[\forall_{x \epsilon N} \, (x = 1) \rightarrow (x = 2)] \vee [\forall_{x \epsilon N} \, (x = 2) \rightarrow (x^2 = 2)]$

THE SYSTEM OF INTEGERS

In the set of natural numbers, the equation

$$x + 5 = 2$$

does not have a solution. That is, the solution set in N of "$x + 5 = 2$" is the *empty* set, ϕ. This is because the set of natural numbers is not closed under subtraction, for $2 - 5$ is not a natural number.

    The set of integers

$$I = \{\ldots, -5, -4, -3, -2, -1, 0, 1, 2, 3, 4, 5, \ldots\}$$

with which you are already familiar *is* closed under subtraction. This means that the difference of any two integers is an integer.

The solution of the equation

$$x + 5 = 2$$

in the set of integers is -3, for "$-3 + 5 = 2$" is a true statement.

The set of integers possesses the properties of closure, associativity, commutativity, left-distributivity, and multiplicative identity, which we stated for the natural numbers. We restate them for the integers (in each case the range of the variable is the set of integers).

■ *Closure Property of Integers under Addition*
$\forall_{x \epsilon I} \forall_{y \epsilon I} (x + y) \epsilon I$ [Cl PA]

■ *Closure Property of Integers under Multiplication*
$\forall_{x \epsilon I} \forall_{y \epsilon I} xy \epsilon I$ [Cl PM]

■ *Commutativity under Addition*
$\forall_{x \epsilon I} \forall_{y \epsilon I} x + y = y + x$ [CPA]

■ *Commutativity under Multiplication*
$\forall_{x \epsilon I} \forall_{y \epsilon I} xy = yx$ [CPM]

■ *Associativity under Addition*
$\forall_{x \epsilon I} \forall_{y \epsilon I} \forall_{z \epsilon I} (x + y) + z = x + (y + z)$ [APA]

■ *Associativity under Multiplication*
$\forall_{x \epsilon I} \forall_{y \epsilon I} \forall_{z \epsilon I} (xy)z = x(yz)$ [APM]

■ *Left-Distributivity for Multiplication over Addition*
$\forall_{x \epsilon I} \forall_{y \epsilon I} \forall_{z \epsilon I} x(y + z) = (xy) + (xz)$ [LDPMA]

■ *Property of Integer 1 for Multiplication*
There exists an integer, namely 1, for which it is true that $\forall_{x \epsilon I} x \cdot 1 = x$ [P1M]

The integer 1 is the *multiplicative identity* of the set of integers.

The last property needs some explanation. First, we are using the symbol 1 as an abbreviation for $+1$ (positive one), since we are referring to the integer 1 and every non-zero integer is either positive or negative. Second, we need to resolve the issue of whether the natural number 1 and the integer 1 are the same number. The best way to resolve this issue would be to define the natural number 1 and the integer 1, and then we would know whether or not they are the same. But this would take us too far afield.

We resolve this issue by simply observing that positive integers $+1$, $+2$, $+3$, ... and natural numbers 1, 2, 3, ... "behave" exactly alike under the operations of addition and multiplication. This can be shown by displaying a one-to-one correspondence.

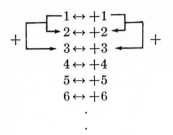

$$1 \leftrightarrow +1$$
$$2 \leftrightarrow +2$$
$$3 \leftrightarrow +3$$
$$4 \leftrightarrow +4$$
$$5 \leftrightarrow +5$$
$$6 \leftrightarrow +6$$

We observe that the sum of any two natural numbers, say 1 and 2, is 3, the number which corresponds to the sum $(+1) + (+2)$, which is $+3$.

Similarly, $2 \times 3 = 6$ and $(+2) \times (+3) = +6$. The natural number 2 is matched with $+2$, 3 is matched with $+3$, and the product 6 is indeed the number which is matched with $+6$. Thus we will not go wrong if we use a natural number in place of its corresponding positive integer.

■ *Definition of "Isomorphic"*   When two sets of elements "behave" exactly the same under their respective operations, then we say that the two sets are *isomorphic* under those operations.

The set of integers is a "richer" set than that of natural numbers. It also happens to have some properties which the set of naturals does not have.

Two of the properties are due to the existence of the integer 0. Remember that 0 is *not* a member of the set of natural numbers.

■ *Property of Zero for Addition*
There exists an integer, namely 0, for which it is true that $\forall_{x \epsilon I} \; x + 0 = x$. [PZA]
We call the integer 0 the *additive identity*.

■ *Property of Additive Inverse*
$\forall_{x \epsilon I}$, there exists a unique integer, $-x$, called the *additive inverse* of x, for which $x + (-x) = 0$. (The *additive inverse* is also called the *opposite*.)   [PAI]

■ *Order Property of Additive Inverse*
The additive inverse of a positive integer is a negative integer, the additive inverse of a negative integer is a positive integer, and the additive inverse of 0 is 0.

For example, the additive inverse of 5 is -5, the additive inverse of -9 is $-(-9)$ which is 9, and the additive inverse of 0 is 0. Zero is the only integer which is its own additive inverse.

You will recall from your previous study of algebra the property of zero under multiplication: $\forall_x \; x \cdot 0 = 0$. This property also holds for the integers.

■ *Property of Zero under Multiplication*
$\forall_{x \epsilon I} \; x \cdot 0 = 0$ [PZM]

Another property of integers, which has already been stated for natural numbers is the following:

■ *Right-hand Cancellation Property under Multiplication*
$\forall_{x \epsilon I} \; \forall_{y \epsilon I} \; \forall_{z \epsilon I, \; z \neq 0}$, if $xz = yz$, then $x = y$

Write the analogous property for addition.

Since the set of integers has all of these properties, it is an *integral domain*.

■ *Definition of An Integral Domain* An integral domain is a set of elements with the following properties

  i. closure, associativity, commutativity for multiplication and addition

  ii. left-distributivity of multiplication over addition

  iii. existence of unique multiplicative and additive identities

  iv. existence of an additive inverse for each element of the set

  v. right-hand cancellation over *is equal to* for multiplication

The following are also properties of an integral domain and therefore are properties of the integers.

■ *Right-hand Multiplication Property*
$\forall_{x \epsilon I} \forall_{y \epsilon I} \forall_{z \epsilon I}$, if $x = y$, then $xz = yz$

■ *Right-hand Addition Property*
$\forall_{x \epsilon I} \forall_{y \epsilon I} \forall_{z \epsilon I}$, if $x = y$, then $x + z = y + z$

We can now prove the theorem that the additive inverse of the additive inverse of any integer is that integer. Supply the reasons for each step.

Theorem 4 $\forall_{a \epsilon I}$ $-(-a) = a$

Proof
$$a + (-a) = 0$$
$$(-a) + [-(-a)] = 0$$
$$a + (-a) = (-a) + [-(-a)]$$
$$a + (-a) = [-(-a)] + (-a)$$
$$a = -(-a)$$

EXERCISES

1. List *all* of the properties which the set of natural numbers is lacking in order to be an integral domain.

2. Using I as the universal set, solve the following equations.

a. $x + 9 = 1$ **f.** $3(n + 2) = 2(n + 1)$

b. $3y + 7 = 10$ **g.** $4(z - 3) = 2z + 10$

c. $3m + 1 = 2m + 1$ **h.** $1 - 5u = 3u - 15$

d. $9s + 5 = 3s - 1$ **i.** $2(p + 6) - 7 = 3 - 2(p + 3)$

e. $3 - 5t = 10 + 2t$ **j.** $(v - 1)(v + 1) = (v + 1)(v + 2) + 3$

3. Give the additive inverse (opposite) for each of the following integers.

a. 5   **c.** 0   **e.** -2196

b. -12 **d.** 1014   **f.** -1

4. Tell which of the following equations have no solutions in the set of integers. If any of the following equations have integral solutions, find them.

    a. $3x = 102$ **d.** $12x + 3 = -9$ **g.** $2x - 1 = 4$

    b. $5x = 12$ **e.** $5(x + 2) = 7$ **h.** $9x = 8x$

    c. $12x + 3 = -8$ **f.** $4x - 5 = 5$ **i.** $3(x + 2) = 4(x + 2)$

5. In the set of natural numbers, is there a least natural number? If so, what is it?

6. Do you think that, in the set of integers, there is a least integer? If so, what is it?

7. Name any infinite subset of the set of natural numbers. Does this subset contain a member which is less than any other member? Do you think your answer would hold for any infinite subset of the set of natural numbers?

8. Do you think that you can choose an infinite subset of the set of integers which has no least member? If your answer is "yes," give an example of such a subset.

9. State and prove the right-distributive property of multiplication under addition for integers.

10. Prove that the sum of an even integer and an odd integer is an odd integer. [HINT: $\forall_{a \epsilon I} 2a$ is an even integer and $(2a + 1)$ is an odd integer; also every even integer can be given in the form $2a$ and every odd integer can be given in the form $(2a + 1)$, where a is some integer.]

11. Prove that the product of an even integer and an odd integer is an even integer.

12. Prove that the set of odd integers is closed under multiplication; that is, prove that the product of two odd integers is an odd integer.

13. Using the theorem you proved in problem **12,** prove that the square of an odd integer is an odd integer. [HINT: Think of squaring a number as multiplying the number by itself.]

Ordering of the integers

Let us consider three subsets of integers.

$$I_1 = \{1, 2, 3, 4, 5, \ldots\}$$
$$I_2 = \{0\}$$
$$I_3 = \{-1, -2, -3, -4, -5, \ldots\}$$

It is easy to see that the union of these three subsets is the set of integers.

$$I_1 \cup I_2 \cup I_3 = I$$

    $1, 2, 3, 4, 5, \ldots$ are called positive integers
    $-1, -2, -3, -4, -5, \ldots$ are called negative integers
    The integer 0 is non-negative *and* non-positive

We now state three definitions which are essential in order to perform operations with integers.

■ *Definition of "b − a" for Integers* $\forall_{a\epsilon I} \forall_{b\epsilon I}$, *"b − a" means "b + (−a)."*

■ *Definition of "a < 0," "0 < a" for Integers* $\forall_{a\epsilon I}$, *"a < 0" means "a is negative." "0 < a" means "a is positive."*

■ *Definition of "a < b" for Integers* $\forall_{a\epsilon I} \forall_{b\epsilon I}$, *"a < b" means "0 < b − a."*

In elementary algebra you learned that the product of a pair of positive integers is a positive integer, that the product of a pair of negative integers is also a positive integer, and that the product of a positive integer and a negative integer is a negative integer.

That the product of a pair of positive integers is a positive integer follows from the isomorphism between positive integers and natural numbers under multiplication. Explain.

Of course, from the isomorphism between these two sets of numbers under addition, it follows that the sum of two positive integers is a positive integer.

We will now *prove* that the product of a positive integer and a negative integer is a negative integer.

Theorem 5 $\forall_{a<0} \forall_{0<b}$ $ab < 0$

Proof		
	$a < 0$ means a is negative	Def. $a < 0$
	$0 < b$ means b is positive	Def. $0 < a$
	$-a$ is positive	Order prop. add. inv.
	$(-a)(b)$ is a positive integer	Why?

Since $(-a)(b) = -(ab)$, then the additive inverse of the product of a and b is a positive integer; therefore ab, which by Theorem 4 is the additive inverse of $-(ab)$, is a negative integer.

In the proof of Theorem 5 we assumed that $\forall_{a\epsilon I} \forall_{b\epsilon I} (-a)(b) = -(ab)$. You might have proved it in your previous study of algebra. Below is a proof of this statement. Supply the reasons for each step in this proof.

Proof $a + (-a) = 0$
$$[a + (-a)]b = 0 \cdot b = 0$$
$$(ab) + [(-a)b] = 0$$
$$(-a)b = -(ab)$$

We state one more property of integers with which you are already familiar.

■ *Trichotomy Property of Integers*
If a and b are integers, then exactly one of the following holds.

$$a < b \qquad a = b \qquad b < a$$

■ *Definition of Ordered Integral Domain* An integral domain in which the sum of a pair of positive elements is positive, and the product of a pair of positive elements is positive, and the trichotomy property holds for all elements is called an *ordered integral domain*.

We now state four additional properties of integers, which are analogous to Theorems 1, 2, and 3 which we proved for natural numbers.

■ *Right-hand Addition Property*
$\forall_{x \epsilon I} \forall_{y \epsilon I} \forall_{z \epsilon I}$, if $x < y$, then $x + z < y + z$

■ *Positive Right-hand Multiplication Property*
$\forall_{x \epsilon I} \forall_{y \epsilon I} \forall_{z \epsilon I, z>0}$, if $x < y$, then $xz < yz$

■ *Negative Right-hand Multiplication Property*
$\forall_{x \epsilon I} \forall_{y \epsilon I} \forall_{z \epsilon I, z<0}$, if $x < y$, then $xz > yz$

■ *Transitivity Property*
$\forall_{x \epsilon I} \forall_{y \epsilon I} \forall_{z \epsilon I}$, if $x < y$ and $y < z$, then $x < z$

NOTE: These are properties of the set of integers over the *is less than* relation.

There is one more concept associated with integers which you probably studied in elementary algebra. It is the concept of *absolute value*.

■ *Definition of Absolute Value* The *absolute value* of a, symbolized by $|a|$, means the following:

$$|a| = a \text{ if } 0 \leq a$$
$$|a| = -a \text{ if } a < 0$$

This definition tells us that the absolute value of a positive integer is that integer; that the absolute value of 0 is 0; and that the absolute value of a negative integer is the additive inverse of that integer.

For example
$$|6| = 6$$
$$|-25| = -(-25) = 25$$
$$|0| = 0$$

EXERCISES

1. Reread the proof of Theorem 5. Now prove the theorem $\forall_{a<0} \forall_{b<0} \ 0 < ab$. [HINT: If $a < 0$, then $0 < -a$; that is, $-a$ is positive. Recall that the product of a pair of positive integers is positive, and that $(-a)(-b) = ab$.]

2. Prove that $\forall_{a \neq 0} 0 < a^2$. [HINT: Recall that $a^2 = a \cdot a$.]

3. Choose a pair of integers. Show that the trichotomy property holds for these integers.

4. Choose three integers. Make a statement concerning these integers which illustrates the transitivity property of integers for *is less than*.

5. Solve each equation; the universal set is the set of integers.

Example:
$$|2x + 3| = 5$$

$2x + 3 = 5$ or $2x + 3 = -5$
$2x = 2$ or $2x = -8$
$x = 1$ or $x = -4$

CHECK: $|2 \cdot 1 + 3| = |2 + 3| = |5| = 5$
                   $|2 \cdot (-4) + 3| = |-8 + 3| = |-5| = 5$

               The solution set is $\{1, -4\}$

  a. $|x| = 7$ **c.** $|2n + 4| = 12$ **e.** $|s + 3| = 5$ **g.** $|3t - 4| = 2$

  b. $|y + 1| = 2$ **d.** $|2m + 3| = 1$ **f.** $|4z - 1| = 2$ **h.** $|2m + 1| = -1$

6. For each of the following, tell whether it is true or false.

  a. $|-6| \neq |6|$ **i.** $|-3| \cdot |-2| \neq |(-3)(-2)|$

  b. $|-10| < |0|$ **j.** $|9| \cdot |4| = |9 \times 4|$

  c. $|-3| > |3|$ **k.** $\forall_{a \epsilon I} \forall_{b \epsilon I} \; |a| \cdot |b| = |ab|$

  d. $|2 - 5| = |5 - 2|$ **l.** $|7 + 4| = |7| + |4|$

  e. $|10 - 1| \neq |1 - 10|$ **m.** $|9 + (-3)| < |9| + |3|$

  f. $|6 - 100| \leq |100 - 6|$ **n.** $|-2 + (-6)| = |-2| + |-6|$

  g. $\forall_{a \epsilon I} \forall_{b \epsilon I} |a - b| = |b - a|$ **o.** $|-4 + 10| \leq |-4| + |10|$

  h. $|5| \cdot |-6| = |5(-6)|$ **p.** $\forall_{a \epsilon I} \forall_{b \epsilon I} \; |a + b| \leq |a| + |b|$

7. Using the definition of $b - a$, (p. 19) and the theorem $\forall_a \forall_b \; (-a)b = -(ab)$, prove the Left-Distributive Property of Multiplication over Subtraction; that is

$$\forall_{a \epsilon I} \forall_{b \epsilon I} \forall_{c \epsilon I} \quad a(b - c) = (ab) - (ac)$$

THE SYSTEM OF RATIONAL NUMBERS

You have seen that the introduction of integers enabled us to find solutions to some equations which did not have solutions in the set of natural numbers. But the integers are not sufficient for solving some equations. For example, the equation

$$5x = 2$$

has no solution in the set of integers. You, no doubt, know that the solution to this equation is $\frac{2}{5}$, which is not an integer; $\frac{2}{5}$ is a *rational number*.

■   *Definition of Rational Number*   A *rational number* is a number which has a name of the form $\frac{a}{b}$ where a and b are integers $(b \neq 0)$.

It is easy to see that the set of integers is isomorphic to a subset of the set of rational numbers $\frac{a}{b}$ in which b is replaced by 1 under the operations which we shall perform. Under this isomorphism $\frac{5}{1}$ corresponds to the integer 5, and the rational number $\frac{-7}{1}$ corresponds to the integer -7.

We must now decide when two numerals of the form $\frac{a}{b}$ are names for the same rational number.

■   *Definition of Equality for Rational Numbers* $\forall_a \forall_{b, \; b \neq 0} \forall_c \forall_{d, \; d \neq 0} \; \frac{a}{b} = \frac{c}{d}$ if and only if $ad = bc$.

We shall assume that, whenever we write $\frac{a}{b}$, it is automatically understood that $b \neq 0$.

According to the definition of equality of rational numbers, $\frac{6}{7} = \frac{30}{35}$ because $6 \times 35 = 7 \times 30$.

From your work with rational numbers in elementary algebra, you will recall how to add and multiply rational numbers. For example

$$\frac{2}{3} + \frac{3}{4} = \frac{2 \times 4 + 3 \times 3}{3 \times 4} = \frac{8+9}{12} = \frac{17}{12}$$

$$\frac{3}{4} \times \frac{5}{7} = \frac{3 \times 5}{4 \times 7} = \frac{15}{28}$$

We state these as definitions.

■ *Definition of Addition of Rational Numbers* $\forall_a \forall_{b \neq 0} \forall_c \forall_{d \neq 0} \ \dfrac{a}{b} + \dfrac{c}{d} = \dfrac{ad+bc}{bd}$

■ *Definition of Multiplication of Rational Numbers* $\forall_a \forall_{b \neq 0} \forall_c \forall_{d \neq 0} \ \dfrac{a}{b} \times \dfrac{c}{d} = \dfrac{ac}{bd}$

Since rational numbers are defined in terms of integers, we can prove the basic properties of rational numbers, assuming the properties of integers which we stated previously. We present a few examples of these proofs.

Theorem 6 The set of rational numbers is closed under addition; that is

$$\forall_a \forall_{b \neq 0} \forall_c \forall_{d \neq 0} \ \frac{a}{b} + \frac{c}{d} = \frac{ad+bc}{bd} \text{ is a rational number.}$$

Proof   We know that $\dfrac{a}{b} + \dfrac{c}{d} = \dfrac{ad+bc}{bd}$ for all a, b, c, and d ($b \neq 0$, $d \neq 0$) by definition of addition of rational numbers. We must show that $\dfrac{ad+bc}{bd}$ is a rational number; that is, it is of the form $\dfrac{x}{y}$, where x and y are integers. But we know that $ad + bc$ is an integer [closure property of integers for addition and multiplication] and bd is an integer [why?].

Theorem 7 The set of rational numbers is commutative under addition; that is

$$\forall_a \forall_{b \neq 0} \forall_c \forall_{d \neq 0} \ \frac{a}{b} + \frac{c}{d} = \frac{c}{d} + \frac{a}{b}$$

Proof

$$\frac{a}{b} + \frac{c}{d} = \frac{ad+bc}{bd} \qquad \text{why?}$$

$$\frac{c}{d} + \frac{a}{b} = \frac{cb+da}{db} \qquad \text{why?}$$

$$ad + bc = cb + da \qquad \text{why?}$$

$$bd = db \qquad \text{why?}$$

$$\frac{ad+bc}{bd} = \frac{cb+da}{db} \qquad \text{why?}$$

and it follows that $\forall_a \forall_{b \neq 0} \forall_c \forall_{d \neq 0} \ \dfrac{a}{b} + \dfrac{c}{d} = \dfrac{c}{d} + \dfrac{a}{b}$.

Rational numbers possess one additional property which the integers do not have.

■ *Property of Multiplicative Inverse* [PMI]

For every non-zero rational number $\frac{a}{b}$ there exists a unique *multiplicative inverse* $\frac{b}{a}$, for which $\frac{a}{b} \times \frac{b}{a} = 1$. (The *multiplicative inverse* is also called the *reciprocal*.)

It is this property of rational numbers which allows the equations of the form $ax = b$ to have the solution $\frac{b}{a}$, since $a \cdot \left(\frac{b}{a}\right) = a \cdot \left(b \cdot \frac{1}{a}\right) = b \cdot \left(a \cdot \frac{1}{a}\right) = b \cdot 1 = b$.

A set of elements which is an integral domain and also has the multiplicative inverse property is called a *field*. Thus, *the set of rational numbers is a field*.

EXERCISES

1. Show how you can obtain the rational number which corresponds to the integer 1 by appropriate replacements in $\frac{a}{b}$.

2. State the property involving the rational number 1 which is analogous to the property of integer 1 for multiplication.

3. Show how you can obtain the rational number which corresponds to the integer 0 by appropriate replacements in $\frac{a}{b}$.

4. State the property involving the rational number 0 which is analogous to the property of zero for addition of integers.

5. State the property for rational numbers which is analogous to the property of additive inverse for integers.

6. Reread the proof of Theorem 6. Now prove that the set of rational numbers is closed under multiplication.

7. Reread the proof of Theorem 7. Now prove that multiplication of rational numbers is commutative.

8. Prove that addition of rational numbers is associative.

9. Prove that multiplication of rational numbers is associative.

10. Prove that multiplication of rational numbers is left-distributive over addition.

11. Add, using the definition for addition of rational numbers.

a. $\frac{2}{3} + \frac{1}{2}$

b. $\frac{-1}{3} + \frac{3}{4}$

c. $\frac{4}{-7} + \frac{-2}{3}$

d. $\frac{1}{9} + \frac{-4}{5}$

e. $\frac{1}{4} + \left(-\frac{4}{5}\right)$

$$\left[\text{HINT:} \quad -\frac{4}{5} = \frac{-4}{5} \right.$$

$$\left. \text{or} \quad -\frac{4}{5} = \frac{4}{-5} \right]$$

f. $-\frac{2}{7} + \frac{1}{3}$

g. $-\frac{3}{4} + \left(-\frac{9}{11}\right)$

h. $\frac{3}{4} + \left(-\frac{8}{9}\right)$

12. Multiply, using the definition of multiplication of rational numbers.

a. $\dfrac{3}{4} \times \dfrac{5}{9}$

d. $-\dfrac{5}{8} \times \dfrac{4}{3}$

g. $-\dfrac{5}{2} \times \left(-\dfrac{1}{7}\right)$

b. $\dfrac{-2}{3} \times \dfrac{5}{-3}$

e. $-\dfrac{3}{2} \times \left(-\dfrac{3}{5}\right)$

h. $-\dfrac{2}{5} \times \left(-\dfrac{3}{7}\right)$

c. $\dfrac{3}{-5} \times \dfrac{4}{9}$

f. $\left(\dfrac{3}{4} \times \dfrac{1}{2}\right) \times \left(-\dfrac{3}{4}\right)$

i. $-\dfrac{1}{3} \times \left(-\dfrac{1}{4}\right)$

Positive and negative rational numbers

We defined a rational number $\dfrac{a}{b}$ to be the quotient of the integers a and b ($b \neq 0$). You already observed that when a is replaced by 0 in $\dfrac{a}{b}$ we obtain the rational number 0. But what kind of a rational number do we obtain when, for example, a is a negative integer and b is a positive integer?

We will state two definitions which describe a way of telling whether a non-zero rational number is positive or negative.

■ *Definition of Positive Rational Number* $0 < \dfrac{a}{b}$ if and only if $0 < ab$.

This definition tells us that a rational number $\dfrac{a}{b}$ is positive whenever the product of the integers a and b is positive. But we already know that ab is positive if both a and b are negative or if both a and b are positive. For example

$\dfrac{-2}{-5}$ is positive   Why? $\left[\text{a simpler name for } \dfrac{-2}{-5} \text{ is } \dfrac{2}{5}.\right]$

$\dfrac{3}{7}$ is positive   Why?

■ *Definition of Negative Rational Number* $\dfrac{a}{b} < 0$ if and only if $ab < 0$.

According to this definition, a rational number $\dfrac{a}{b}$ is negative whenever the product of the integers a and b is negative. We know that ab is negative, if either a is positive and b is negative, or a is negative and b is positive. For example

$\dfrac{-3}{5}$ is negative   Why? $\left[\text{another name for } \dfrac{-3}{5} \text{ is } -\dfrac{3}{5}.\right]$

$\dfrac{2}{-7}$ is negative   Why? $\left[\text{another name for } \dfrac{2}{-7} \text{ is } -\dfrac{2}{7}.\right]$

EXERCISES

1. For each rational number, give a name of either the form $\dfrac{a}{b}$ or $-\dfrac{a}{b}$, where a and b are positive integers.

a. $\dfrac{-3}{-8}$

b. $\dfrac{-1}{5}$

c. $\dfrac{-2}{-9}$

d. $\dfrac{3}{-6}$

e. $\dfrac{-(-2)^{*}}{5}$ **g.** $\dfrac{-(-1)}{-(-4)}$ **i.** $\dfrac{5}{-8}$ **k.** $\dfrac{-(-3)}{17}$

f. $\dfrac{-(-5)}{-6}$ **h.** $\dfrac{6}{-(-5)}$ **j.** $\dfrac{-(-1)}{-1}$ **l.** $\dfrac{-(-(-4))^{**}}{-5}$

2. Prove: $\forall_{b \neq 0}\ 0 < \dfrac{1}{b}$ if and only if $0 < b$. [HINT: Use def. pos. rational number. What is a replaced by in this definition?]

3. Prove: $\forall_{b \neq 0}\ \dfrac{1}{b} < 0$ if and only if $b < 0$. [HINT: Use def. neg. rational number.]

4. Solve each equation. The universal set is the set of rational numbers.

Example:
$$2n + \frac{2}{3} = \frac{1}{2}$$
$$2n = \frac{1}{2} - \frac{2}{3}$$
$$2n = \frac{3}{6} - \frac{4}{6}$$
$$2n = -\frac{1}{6}$$
$$n = -\frac{1}{6} \times \frac{1}{2}$$
$$n = -\frac{1}{12} \qquad \text{The solution set is } \left\{-\frac{1}{12}\right\}.$$

a. $3x = 7$

b. $-2y = 9$

c. $-2m = -\dfrac{1}{3}$

d. $4z + 2 = -3$

e. $\dfrac{1}{2}t - \dfrac{1}{3} = 4$

f. $\dfrac{s+1}{3} = \dfrac{1}{3}$

g. $2(3p - 4) = 7$

h. $\dfrac{1}{3 + 2x} = \dfrac{1}{4}$

i. $\dfrac{2}{3 - y} = \dfrac{1}{y + 2}$

j. $\dfrac{2z + 3}{-2} = \dfrac{2 - 5z}{3}$

k. $\dfrac{3(x - 5)}{2} = \dfrac{2(3 - 5x)}{3}$

Ordering of the rationals

■ *Trichotomy Property of Rational Numbers*

Given rational numbers $\dfrac{a}{b}$ and $\dfrac{c}{d}$, one and only one of the following is true.

$$\frac{a}{b} < \frac{c}{d} \qquad\qquad \frac{a}{b} = \frac{c}{d} \qquad\qquad \frac{c}{d} < \frac{a}{b}$$

The definition of equality for rational numbers gave us a way of telling when $\dfrac{a}{b} = \dfrac{c}{d}$, namely, whenever $ad = bc$. But how can we tell whether, for example,

$$\frac{2}{-7} < \frac{3}{-8} \text{ is true?}$$

* Read: the additive inverse of negative two.
** Read: the additive inverse of the additive inverse of negative four.

To answer this question, let us first observe that every rational number has a name of the form $\frac{a}{b}$, where b is a positive integer. For example

$$\frac{2}{-5} = \frac{-2}{\boxed{5}} \qquad \frac{-1}{-7} = \frac{1}{\boxed{7}}$$

$$\uparrow \qquad\qquad\qquad \uparrow$$
$$\text{positive} \qquad\qquad \text{positive}$$

Now we shall write a few true statements which are arranged in pairs. Your task is to see how we obtained each statement on the right from the statement on the left.

$$\frac{1}{3} < \frac{1}{2} \qquad 1 \times 2 < 3 \times 1,\ (2 < 3)$$

$$\frac{-2}{5} < \frac{-1}{5} \qquad -2 \times 5 < 5 \times (-1),\ (-10 < -5)$$

$$\frac{-4}{7} < \frac{1}{10} \qquad -4 \times 10 < 7 \times 1,\ (-40 < 7)$$

By this time, you probably observed the pattern involved in the examples above. We state it as a definition.

■ *Definition of Ordering of the Rational Numbers* $\frac{a}{b} < \frac{c}{d}$ if and only if $ad < bc$ $(0 < b,\ 0 < d)$. Since $\frac{a}{b} < \frac{c}{d}$ means the same as $\frac{c}{d} > \frac{a}{b}$ and $ad < bc$ means the same as $bc > ad$, we have

$$\frac{c}{d} > \frac{a}{b} \text{ if and only if } bc > ad$$

and

$$\frac{c}{d} > \frac{a}{b} \text{ if and only if } cb > da$$

EXERCISES

1. True or false?

a. $\frac{2}{7} = \frac{3}{8}$ e. $\frac{-4}{5} < \frac{-5}{6}$ i. $\frac{2}{5} \not< \frac{5}{8}$ m. $-\frac{1}{2} > -\frac{1}{3}$

b. $\frac{1}{2} < \frac{4}{5}$ f. $\frac{3}{4} > \frac{3}{5}$ j. $\frac{7}{8} \not> \frac{5}{6}$ n. $\frac{-2}{-7} \not> \frac{-3}{-8}$

c. $\frac{-5}{6} > \frac{-6}{7}$ g. $\frac{0}{7} < \frac{-1}{2}$ k. $\frac{-3}{4} > \frac{1}{10,000}$ o. $-\frac{4}{7} < \frac{1}{99}$

d. $\frac{-1}{3} > \frac{-2}{4}$ h. $\frac{1}{3} \neq \frac{9}{27}$ l. $\frac{4}{-3} \not< \frac{5}{-4}$ p. $\frac{-6}{-5} \not< \frac{-5}{-4}$

2. Prove that $\forall_{b>0} \forall_{d>0} \frac{1}{b} < \frac{1}{d}$ if and only if $d < b$. [HINT: Use definition of ordering of rational numbers.]

3. Using definition of ordering of rational numbers, prove that every negative rational number is less than every positive rational number.

DENSITY OF RATIONAL NUMBERS

The sets of natural numbers and integers are frequently referred to as being *discrete* sets. This means that between two consecutive natural numbers there is no natural number. A similar situation exists for integers. For example, 5 and 6 are two consecutive integers, and there is no integer between 5 and 6.

Also, for any integer there is the next greater integer and the next lesser integer. What is the next integer greater than -5? What is the next integer less than -5? In general, if m is an integer, then $m + 1$ is the next greater integer, and $m - 1$ is the next lesser integer.

The set of rational numbers does not have this property of *discreteness*.

■ *Density Property*

Given two rational numbers a and b there is a third rational number c such that $a < c < b$ or $b < c < a$.

Thus, between any *two* rational numbers, there is another rational number. This means that, given a rational number, there is no next greater or next lesser rational number. Why?

It is rather easy to find a rational number which is between two given rational numbers. One way to do it is to compute the arithmetic *mean* (average) of the two numbers.

Example: Find a rational number between $\frac{2}{3}$ and $\frac{4}{7}$. We compute the arithmetic mean of $\frac{2}{3}$ and $\frac{4}{7}$, which is the sum of the two numbers divided by 2.

$$\frac{\frac{2}{3} + \frac{4}{7}}{2} = \frac{\frac{14 + 12}{21}}{2} = \frac{26}{42} = \frac{13}{21}$$

Use definition of ordering rationals to show that the following are true: $\frac{4}{7} < \frac{2}{3}$ and $\frac{4}{7} < \frac{13}{21} < \frac{2}{3}$.

We can prove that the arithmetic mean of two rational numbers is between the two numbers.

Theorem 8 For any two rational numbers $\frac{a}{b}$ and $\frac{c}{d}$,

if $\frac{a}{b} < \frac{c}{d}$, then $\frac{a}{b} < \dfrac{\frac{a}{b} + \frac{c}{d}}{2} < \frac{c}{d}$.

Proof Since we know by assumption that $\frac{a}{b} < \frac{c}{d}$ is true, we need only to

show that $\frac{a}{b} < \dfrac{\frac{a}{b} + \frac{c}{d}}{2}$ and $\dfrac{\frac{a}{b} + \frac{c}{d}}{2} < \frac{c}{d}$ are true.

First, we simplify $\dfrac{\frac{a}{b} + \frac{c}{d}}{2} = \dfrac{\frac{ad + bc}{bd}}{2} = \dfrac{ad + bc}{2bd}$

We will now show that $\dfrac{a}{b} < \dfrac{ad+bc}{2bd}$ follows from $\dfrac{a}{b} < \dfrac{c}{d}$. Supply the reason for each step.

$$\frac{a}{b} < \frac{c}{d} \qquad (b > 0, d > 0)$$

$$ad < bc$$

$$abd < bbc$$

$$abd + abd < abd + bbc$$

$$2abd < abd + bbc$$

$$a(2bd) < b(ad + bc)$$

$$\frac{a}{b} < \frac{ad + bc}{2bd}$$

Now prove the second part of this theorem.

$$\text{if } \frac{a}{b} < \frac{c}{d}, \text{ then } \frac{\frac{a}{b} + \frac{c}{d}}{2} < \frac{c}{d}$$

EXERCISES

1. Find the arithmetic mean of each pair of rational numbers.

   a. $\dfrac{1}{2}, \dfrac{1}{3}$ **b.** $\dfrac{3}{5}, \dfrac{4}{5}$ **c.** $\dfrac{9}{11}, \dfrac{11}{13}$ **d.** $\dfrac{1}{7}, \dfrac{1}{8}$

2. **a.** In problem **1**, order each set of three numbers (the given pair and their mean) by writing a statement of the form: $a < b < c$.

   b. Is the arithmetic mean in each case between the two given numbers?

3. The arithmetic mean of two numbers can be interpreted on the number line. The picture below shows the point which corresponds to the arithmetic mean of 2 and 4. It is the midpoint of the segment whose endpoints correspond to the numbers 2 and 4.

On a picture of the number line mark the points corresponding to the arithmetic mean of each of the following pairs of numbers.

   a. 2, 5 **b.** $-1, 2$ **c.** $-2, 3$ **d.** $0, -3$

4. For each pair of numbers a, b, compute $\dfrac{2a + b}{3}$ and mark the three points corresponding to a, $\dfrac{2a + b}{3}$, b, on a picture of the number line.

Example: $\quad -1, 5; \quad \dfrac{2a+b}{3} = \dfrac{2 \cdot (-1) + 5}{3} = \dfrac{-2+5}{3} = \dfrac{3}{3} = 1$

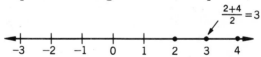

   a. $-2, 4$ **b.** $0, 3$ **c.** $1, 3$ **d.** $-2, -1$

5. For each pair of numbers in problem **4**, did you find that $\dfrac{2a+b}{3}$ is one-third of the way from a to b?

6. Prove that $\forall_a \forall_b$, if $a < b$, then $a < \dfrac{2a+b}{3} < b$.

7. For each pair of numbers a, b, given in problem **4**, compute $\dfrac{a+2b}{3}$ and mark the three points corresponding to a, $\dfrac{a+2b}{3}$, b, on a picture of the number line.

8. Prove that $\forall_a \forall_b$, if $a < b$, then $a < \dfrac{a+2b}{3} < b$.

9. For each pair of numbers $\dfrac{a}{b}$, $\dfrac{c}{d}$, such that $\dfrac{a}{b} < \dfrac{c}{d}$ $(b > 0, d > 0)$, compute $\dfrac{a+c}{b+d}$. Verify that $\dfrac{a}{b} < \dfrac{a+c}{b+d} < \dfrac{c}{d}$.

Examples: i. $\dfrac{1}{3}, \dfrac{1}{2}$ $\left(\dfrac{1}{3} < \dfrac{1}{2}\right)$; $\dfrac{a+c}{b+d} = \dfrac{1+1}{3+2} = \dfrac{2}{5}$

$\dfrac{1}{3} < \dfrac{2}{5}$ because $5 < 6$, $\dfrac{2}{5} < \dfrac{1}{2}$ because $4 < 5$

Therefore, $\dfrac{1}{3} < \dfrac{2}{5} < \dfrac{1}{2}$

ii. $-\dfrac{2}{3}, -\dfrac{1}{2}$ $\left(-\dfrac{2}{3} < -\dfrac{1}{2}\right)$

Since $-\dfrac{2}{3} = \dfrac{-2}{3}$ and $-\dfrac{1}{2} = \dfrac{-1}{2}$, $\dfrac{a+c}{b+d} = \dfrac{-2+(-1)}{3+2} = \dfrac{-3}{5}$

$\dfrac{-2}{3} < \dfrac{-3}{5}$ because $-10 < -9$, $\dfrac{-3}{5} < \dfrac{-1}{2}$ because $-6 < -5$

Therefore, $-\dfrac{2}{3} < -\dfrac{3}{5} < -\dfrac{1}{2}$

a. $\dfrac{2}{5}, \dfrac{1}{2}$ $\left(\dfrac{2}{5} < \dfrac{1}{2}\right)$ **c.** $-\dfrac{1}{2}, \dfrac{1}{4}$ $\left(-\dfrac{1}{2} < \dfrac{1}{4}\right)$ **e.** $-2,\ 0\,(-2 < 0)$

b. $-\dfrac{4}{5}, -\dfrac{4}{7}$ $\left(-\dfrac{4}{5} < -\dfrac{4}{7}\right)$ **d.** $0, \dfrac{1}{4}$ $\left(0 < \dfrac{1}{4}\right)$ **f.** $-\dfrac{3}{2}, 1$ $\left(-\dfrac{3}{2} < 1\right)$

10. Prove that for any two rational numbers $\dfrac{a}{b}$ and $\dfrac{c}{d}$ $(b > 0, d > 0)$, if $\dfrac{a}{b} < \dfrac{c}{d}$, then $\dfrac{a}{b} < \dfrac{a+c}{b+d} < \dfrac{c}{d}$.

11. For each pair of rational numbers $\dfrac{a}{b}, \dfrac{c}{d}$ $\left(\dfrac{a}{b} < \dfrac{c}{d}\right)$, compare $\dfrac{b}{a}$ with $\dfrac{d}{c}$.

Examples: i. $\dfrac{4}{5}, \dfrac{7}{8}$ $\left(\dfrac{4}{5} < \dfrac{7}{8}\right)$; $\dfrac{5}{4} > \dfrac{8}{7}$ because $35 > 32$

ii. $\dfrac{-2}{3}, \dfrac{-1}{2}$ $\left(\dfrac{-2}{3} < \dfrac{-1}{2}\right)$; $\dfrac{-3}{2} > \dfrac{-2}{1}$ because $-3 > -4$

iii. $\dfrac{-1}{3}, \dfrac{1}{2}$ $\left(\dfrac{-1}{3} < \dfrac{1}{2}\right)$; $\dfrac{-3}{1} < \dfrac{2}{1}$ because $-3 < 2$

a. $\dfrac{1}{2},\ 5\ \left(\dfrac{1}{2} < 5\right)$

b. $1,\ \dfrac{10}{3}\ \left(1 < \dfrac{10}{3}\right)$

c. $\dfrac{3}{5},\ \dfrac{11}{12}\ \left(\dfrac{3}{5} < \dfrac{11}{12}\right)$

d. $\dfrac{-4}{3},\ \dfrac{-1}{9}\ \left(\dfrac{-4}{3} < \dfrac{-1}{9}\right)$

e. $-10,\ -1\ (-10 < -1)$

f. $\dfrac{-7}{8},\ \dfrac{-6}{7}\ \left(\dfrac{-7}{8} < \dfrac{-6}{7}\right)$

g. $\dfrac{-1}{3},\ 7\ \left(\dfrac{-1}{3} < 7\right)$

h. $\dfrac{-1}{2},\ 1\ \left(\dfrac{-1}{2} < 1\right)$

i. $\dfrac{1}{4},\ \dfrac{1}{3}\ \left(\dfrac{1}{4} < \dfrac{1}{3}\right)$

j. $-1,\ \dfrac{2}{-3}\ \left(-1 < \dfrac{2}{-3}\right)$

12. Prove that for any two positive rational numbers $\dfrac{a}{b}$ and $\dfrac{c}{d}$, if $\dfrac{a}{b} < \dfrac{c}{d}$, then $\dfrac{b}{a} > \dfrac{d}{c}$.

RATIONAL NUMBERS AND DECIMAL NUMERALS

In order to find a name for a rational number in the form of a decimal numeral, we perform division.

Examples:

i. $\dfrac{1}{2} = .5$

$$2\overline{\smash{)}\,1.0} \quad \begin{array}{r} .5 \\ \hline 1\,0 \\ \hline 0 \end{array}$$

ii. $\dfrac{1}{4} = .25$

$$4\overline{\smash{)}\,1.00} \quad \begin{array}{r} .25 \\ \hline 8 \\ \hline 20 \\ 20 \\ \hline 0 \end{array}$$

iii. $\dfrac{1}{5} = .2$

$$5\overline{\smash{)}\,1.0} \quad \begin{array}{r} .2 \\ \hline 1\,0 \\ \hline 0 \end{array}$$

iv. $\dfrac{1}{25} = .04$

$$25\overline{\smash{)}\,1.00} \quad \begin{array}{r} .04 \\ \hline 1\,00 \\ \hline 0 \end{array}$$

Decimal numerals like .5, .25, −.2, and .04 are called *terminating decimal numerals*. They are obtained by dividing two integers and, at some point in the division process, a remainder of 0 is reached. Not all rational numbers have names which are terminating decimal numerals.

Examples:

i. $\dfrac{1}{3} = .33\overline{3}$

$$3\overline{\smash{)}\,1.000} \quad \begin{array}{r} .333\ldots \\ \hline 9 \\ \hline 10 \\ 9 \\ \hline 10 \\ 9 \\ \hline 1 \end{array}$$

ii. $\dfrac{1}{6} = .16\overline{6}$

$$6\overline{\smash{)}\,1.000} \quad \begin{array}{r} .166\ldots \\ \hline 6 \\ \hline 40 \\ 36 \\ \hline 40 \\ 36 \\ \hline 4 \end{array}$$

By placing a bar above 3 (above 6 in example *ii.*), we are indicating that the digit 3 (digit 6) repeats on and on indefinitely.

iii. $\frac{1}{7} = .142857\overline{142857}$

$$
\begin{array}{r}
.14285714\ldots \\
7\,\overline{)1.00000000} \\
7 \\
\hline
\text{(3)}0 \\
2\,8 \\
\hline
\text{(2)}0 \\
1\,4 \\
\hline
\text{(6)}0 \\
5\,6 \\
\hline
\text{(4)}0 \\
3\,5 \\
\hline
\text{(5)}0 \\
4\,9 \\
\hline
\text{(1)}0 \\
7 \\
\hline
\text{(3)}0
\end{array}
$$

We place a bar above the block of digits: $\overline{142857}$ to indicate that this block repeats indefinitely.

We see that from now on, we will have a repetition of the block of digits 142857.

Decimal numerals like $.33\overline{3}$, $.16\overline{6}$, and $.142857\overline{142857}$ are called *repeating non-terminating decimal numerals*.

It is reasonable now to ask whether, in dividing one integer by another, we will always get either a terminating decimal numeral or a repeating non-terminating decimal numeral. We already know that we can get terminating decimal names as well as repeating non-terminating decimal names. So, the question to be answered is whether it is possible to obtain a non-repeating decimal name when dividing one whole number by another. Let us reason out the answer by observing what happens when we divide a whole number by 7.

The important thing to observe is the remainders which are circled in the example above. Could any one of these remainders be 7 or more? The answer is "no." Explain. Thus, these remainders can be only 0, 1, 2, 3, 4, 5, 6. If the remainder at any point is 0, we have a terminating decimal numeral. Otherwise, we must get a repetition of the same remainder in at most the sixth step, since there are only six possible non-zero remainders. Once the same remainder occurs for the second time, we have a continuous repetition of previous steps from that point on.

Generally, if we divide a whole number by a whole number n, and if no remainder is 0, then we will have a repetition of a block of digits which will have *at most* $n - 1$ digits in it.

We now summarize our discussion.

■ *Property of Decimal Numerals for Rational Numbers*

Every rational number has a decimal name, which is either a terminating decimal numeral or a repeating non-terminating decimal numeral.

EXERCISES

1. Give a decimal numeral for each of the following rational numbers.

a. $\dfrac{4}{9}$ c. $\dfrac{3}{25}$ e. $\dfrac{11}{7}$ g. $-\dfrac{13}{8}$ i. $\dfrac{9}{13}$

b. $\dfrac{3}{11}$ d. $\dfrac{3706}{100}$ f. $3\dfrac{2}{15}$ h. $\dfrac{22}{7}$ j. $-5\dfrac{2}{3}$

2. Write an argument showing that a decimal name for $\frac{1}{21}$, if it is a repeating non-terminating decimal numeral, could not have more than 20 digits in the repeating block.

From a decimal numeral to a fractional numeral

In the previous section, we learned to find a decimal numeral for a rational number given in the form $\dfrac{a}{b}$; that is, in the form of a fractional numeral. We will now consider the reverse problem. Suppose we are given a decimal name for a rational number, and we wish to find a fractional numeral for the same number.

Example: $.5631 = \dfrac{5631}{10000}$

In the case of a terminating decimal numeral, it is easy to find a name of the form $\dfrac{a}{b}$ for the same rational number.

$$\text{Generally, } .a_1a_2\ldots a_n = \frac{a_1a_2\ldots a_n}{10^n}$$

Examples: i. $.44\overline{4} = ?$

Let $x = .44\overline{4}$;   then $10x = 4.44\overline{4}$

$$10x = 4.44\overline{4}$$
$$x = .44\overline{4}$$

$$10x - x = 4.44\overline{4} - .44\overline{4} \qquad \text{Subtracting}$$
$$9x = 4$$

$$x = \frac{4}{9}; \text{ and thus, } .44\overline{4} = \frac{4}{9}$$

ii. $7.44\overline{4} = ?$

We already know that $.44\overline{4} = \dfrac{4}{9}$.

Now $7.44\overline{4} = 7 + .44\overline{4} = 7 + \dfrac{4}{9} = 7\dfrac{4}{9} = \dfrac{67}{9}$

iii. $.56\overline{56} = ?$

Let $x = .56\overline{56}$;   then $100x = 56.56\overline{56}$

$$100x = 56.56\overline{56}$$
$$x = .56\overline{56}$$

$$99x = 56$$

$$x = \frac{56}{99}; \text{ and thus, } .56\overline{56} = \frac{56}{99}$$

iv. $.1231\overline{31} = ?$

Let $x = .1231\overline{31}$, then $100x = 12.31\overline{31}$

$$100x = 12.31\overline{31}$$
$$x = .12\overline{31}$$

$$99x = 12.19$$

$$x = \frac{12.19}{99} = \frac{1219}{9900}; \text{ and thus, } .1231\overline{31} = \frac{1219}{9900}$$

From the last four examples you should get a clue as to what power of 10 to use as a factor in order to do exercises of this kind successfully.

EXERCISES

Use the procedure of the above examples and give a fractional numeral for each of the following:

1.	$.\overline{7}$	**3.**	$.\overline{52}$	**5.**	$.1\overline{36}$	**7.**	$3.25\overline{162}$
2.	1.307	**4.**	-12.1003	**6.**	$-1.00\overline{3}$	**8.**	$-.\overline{142857}$

THE SYSTEM OF REAL NUMBERS

Although the system of rational numbers is the "richest" set we have considered so far, not every equation has a solution among the rational numbers. For example, the equation

$$x^2 - 2 = 0$$

has solutions $\sqrt{2}$ and $-\sqrt{2}$, which are not rational numbers. That is, $\sqrt{2}$ and $-\sqrt{2}$ have no names of the form $\frac{a}{b}$, where a and b are integers. Such numbers are called *irrational numbers*.

■ *Definition of Irrational Number* All the numbers associated with the number line that do *not* have names of the form $\frac{a}{b}$ ($b \neq 0$, $a\epsilon I$ and $b\epsilon I$) are *irrational numbers*.

We now give a proof that $\sqrt{2}$ is an irrational number. We shall use what is called an *indirect proof*, in which we assume the negation of that which is to be proved and show that this assumption leads to a contradiction.

Since every real number is either rational or irrational (see p. 34), let us assume that $\sqrt{2}$ is a rational number. Then it has a name of the form $\frac{a}{b}$, where a and b are relatively prime; that is, a and b have no common positive factors other than the number 1. (If they should have a common factor other than 1, then divide a and b by this factor.)

Thus, $\frac{a}{b} = \sqrt{2}$

$$\frac{a^2}{b^2} = 2 \qquad \text{why?}$$
$$a^2 = 2b^2 \qquad \text{why?}$$

Since $2b^2$ has a factor of 2, it is an even integer. Therefore, a^2 is an even integer. Since the only way to obtain an even integer by squaring is to square an even integer (the square of an odd integer is an odd integer), a is an even integer. Being an even integer, a is a product of 2 and some integer c, that is, $a = 2c$.

$$\text{Thus,} \quad (2c)^2 = 2b^2$$
$$4c^2 = 2b^2$$
$$2c^2 = b^2$$

Since $2c^2$ is an even integer, b^2 is an even integer. Therefore, b is an even integer.

Now we proved that both a and b are even integers. Since a and b cannot be *both* even integers *and* relatively prime, our original assumption that $\sqrt{2}$ is a rational number is false. Therefore, $\sqrt{2}$ is an irrational number.

We can obtain decimal *approximations* to irrational numbers, which are non-terminating non-repeating decimal numerals. For example, a seven-decimal place approximation to $\sqrt{2}$ is 1.4142135. This is *not equal to* $\sqrt{2}$ because $(1.4142135)^2$ is not 2. Rather

$$(1.4142135)^2 = 1.99999982358225$$

It is easy to display decimal numerals which are clearly non-terminating and non-repeating. For example

$$0.505005000500005000005\ldots$$

is such a decimal name. Explain why this decimal is non-repeating.

■ *Definition of Real Numbers*   The union of the set of all rational numbers and the set of all irrational numbers is the set of all *real numbers*.

If Q = the set of all rational numbers,
T = the set of all irrational numbers,
and R = the set of all real numbers,

then the following statements are true. (Explain each statement.)

$$Q \cup T = R \qquad Q \cap T = \phi \qquad Q \subset R \qquad T \subset R$$

We now list all of the properties of the set of real numbers under addition and multiplication, which make the set of real numbers a *field*.

$\forall_{x \in R} \forall_{y \in R} (x + y) \in R$ Cl PA

$\forall_{x \in R} \forall_{y \in R} (xy) \in R$ Cl PM

$\forall_{x \in R} \forall_{y \in R} x + y = y + x$ CPA

$\forall_{x \in R} \forall_{y \in R} xy = yx$ CPM

$\forall_{x \in R} \forall_{y \in R} \forall_{z \in R} (x + y) + z = x + (y + z)$ APA

$\forall_{x \in R} \forall_{y \in R} \forall_{z \in R} (xy)z = x(yz)$ APM

$\forall_{x \in R} \forall_{y \in R} \forall_{z \in R} x(y + z) = (xy) + (xz)$ LDPMA

There exists a unique real number 1, such that $\forall_{x \in R} x \cdot 1 = x$ P1M

There exists a unique real number 0, such that $\forall_{x \in R} x + 0 = x$ PZA

$\forall_{a \in R,\ a \neq 0}$ there exists a unique $b \in R$, such that $ab = 1$ PMI

$\forall_{x \in R}$, there exists a unique $y \in R$, such that $x + y = 0$ PAI

Although the system of real numbers is quite "rich," not all elementary equations have solutions among real numbers. For example, the equation

$$x^2 + 1 = 0$$

has no real numbers for its solutions. For this equation to have solutions, we need a still "richer" number system, which you will study in Chapter 9.

In addition to the eleven properties stated, the set of real numbers possesses the properties which were stated for the integers and rationals in the form of definitions, theorems, and properties. Review these at this time.

EXERCISES

1. For each statement name the property or properties it illustrates.

   a. $\sqrt{2} + 7 = 7 + \sqrt{2}$

   b. $3(9 + 1.5) = 3 \times 9 + 3 \times 1.5$

   c. $0 + 1.7 = 1.7$ [CAUTION: There are two properties involved here!]

   d. $(3.6 \times 1.5) \times 3.7 = 3.6 \times (1.5 \times 3.7)$

   e. $1 \times \sqrt{37} = \sqrt{37}$

   f. $\sqrt{5} \times 36 = 36\sqrt{5}$

   g. $3\sqrt{5} + 4\sqrt{5} = (3 + 4)\sqrt{5}$

   h. $(-3 + 1) + 0 = -3 + 1$

   i. $\sqrt{2} + (-\sqrt{2}) = 0$

   j. $\sqrt{20} [\sqrt{6} + (-\sqrt{6})] = \sqrt{20} \times 0$

   k. $9[7 + (-7)] = 0$

   l. $(5 + \sqrt{3}) + (-\sqrt{3}) = 5$

   m. $\sqrt{2} + [9 + (-\sqrt{2})] = 9$ [CAUTION: There are four properties involved here!]

2. For every real number x one and only one of the following is true

$$x < 0 \qquad x = 0 \qquad x > 0$$

This is the *Trichotomy Property of Real Numbers*. Write an argument showing that a square root of a negative number is not a real number. [Recall: $b^2 = a$ if and only if $b = \sqrt{a}$ or $b = -\sqrt{a}$.]

3. Prove that $\forall_a \forall_b (ab = 0) \leftrightarrow (a = 0 \text{ or } b = 0)$.
[HINT: Prove *i*. $(ab = 0) \rightarrow (a = 0 \text{ or } b = 0)$; *ii*. $(a = 0 \text{ or } b = 0) \rightarrow (ab = 0)$.]

4. Give an example showing that the set of irrational numbers is not closed under addition.

5. Give an example showing that the set of irrational numbers is not closed under multiplication.

6. Q = the set of all rational numbers
   T = the set of all irrational numbers
   R = the set of all real numbers

True or false?

   a. $\sqrt{17} \in Q$

   b. $1.\overline{12} \notin T$

   c. $Q \cap R = Q$

   d. $T \cap R = R$

   e. $Q \cup R = \phi$

   f. $T \cup R = R$

   g. $\sqrt{-16} \in R$

   h. $\sqrt[3]{27} \notin T$

   i. $\sqrt[3]{-27} \notin T$

7.   Find the solution set of each equation. Some equations have no solutions in the set of real numbers. In such cases write ϕ.

a. $x^2 - \dfrac{1}{4} = 0$

e. $m^2 + 1 = 2$

i. $z^2 - 3 = 5$

b. $y^2 + \dfrac{1}{4} = 0$

f. $\dfrac{3}{2s^2 - 1} = 3$

j. $5u^2 + 7 = 1$

c. $2n^2 + 3 = 0$

g. $\dfrac{5t^3 - 1}{3} = 4$

k. $\dfrac{2 - x^2}{3} = \dfrac{1}{3}$

d. $|m^2 + 1| = 2$

h. $3 - z^2 = 5$

l. $\dfrac{2y^2 - 3}{4} = \dfrac{y^2 - 1}{3}$

8.   Determine the solution set of each inequality. The properties of inequalities for real numbers are the same as those for rationals.

Examples: *i.*
$$3x + 2 < x - 7$$
$$3x + 2 + (-x) < x - 7 + (-x)$$
$$2x + 2 < -7$$
$$2x + 2 + (-2) < -7 + (-2)$$
$$2x < -9$$
$$(2x)\left(\frac{1}{2}\right) < (-9)\left(\frac{1}{2}\right)$$
$$x < -\frac{9}{2}$$
The solution set is $\left\{x \mid x < -\dfrac{9}{2}\right\}$.

ii.
$$\frac{2x - 1}{-3} < -2$$
$$\frac{2x - 1}{-3}(-3) > -2(-3)$$
$$2x - 1 > 6$$
$$2x - 1 + 1 > 6 + 1$$
$$2x > 7$$
$$2x\left(\frac{1}{2}\right) > 7\left(\frac{1}{2}\right)$$
$$x > \frac{7}{2}$$
The solution set is $\left\{x \mid x > \dfrac{7}{2}\right\}$.

a. $2x > 5$

d. $2 - 3t < t + 1$

g. $\dfrac{4s + 2}{3} < \dfrac{-2s - 1}{2}$

b. $-3y < 1$

e. $4(x - 2) > 5$

h. $\dfrac{2 - 3u}{4} > \dfrac{u - 5}{3}$

c. $4m - 1 > m + 2$

f. $\dfrac{3n - 1}{5} > 2$

i. $\dfrac{5(x + 2)}{3} < \dfrac{2(2x - 1)}{5}$

VOCABULARY

Use each of the following correctly in a sentence. Numerals in parentheses refer to pages where these words were used. If you are not sure of the meaning of any word, turn to the indicated pages.

absolute value (20)
additive identity (16)
additive inverse (16)
arithmetic mean (27)
associativity (3)
bi-conditional (13)
cancellation (16)
closure (2)
commutativity (3)
composite (2)
conditional (9)
conjunction (13)
contrapositive (9)
converse (9)
counterexample (2)
density (27)
discrete (27)
disjunction (13)
empty set (14)
even (2)
field (23)
implication (9)
infinite set (1)
integer (14)
integral domain (17)
inverse of a statement (9)
irrational number (33)

isomorphic (16)
left-distributivity (3)
multiplicative inverse (23)
natural number (1)
negation (10)
negative (19)
odd (2)
operation (1)
opposite (16)
ordering (6)
ordered integral domain (19)
positive (19)
prime (2)
rational number (21)
real number (34)
reciprocal (23)
reflexive (4)
repeating non-terminating
    decimal numeral (31)
right-distributivity (4)
substitution (4)
symmetric (4)
terminating decimal numeral (30)
transitive (4)
trichotomy (7)
truth-table (10)
truth-value (10)

REVIEW EXERCISES

1. Tell whether each set (**a–l** below) is closed under each of the following operations

    i. addition

    ii. subtraction

    iii. multiplication

    iv. division (except for division by zero)

a. N, the set of natural numbers

b. I, the set of integers

c. Q, the set of rational numbers

d. T, the set of irrational numbers

e. R, the set of real numbers

f. $\left\{ \dfrac{1}{3}, \dfrac{1}{9}, \dfrac{1}{27}, \dfrac{1}{81}, \cdots \right\}$

g. $\{1\}$

h. $\left\{\frac{1}{2}, 1, 2\right\}$

i. $\{0, 1\}$

j. E, the set of even natural numbers

k. F, the set of odd natural numbers

l. $\{1, 2, 3, \ldots, 10\}$

2. a. List the first ten *prime* natural numbers.

   b. List the first ten *composite* natural numbers.

3. Find a natural number n for which $n^2 - n + 41$ is *not* a prime natural number.

4. Complete with "odd" or "even."

   a. The sum of three odd numbers is ___?___ .

   b. The product of three odd numbers is ___?___ .

   c. The sum of four odd numbers is ___?___ .

   d. The product of four odd numbers is ___?___ .

5. Name the property illustrated by each of the following statements about real numbers.

   a. $7 \cdot 3 + 7 \cdot 12 = 7(3 + 12)$

   b. If $3 - 5 = -2$, then $-2 = 3 - 5$

   c. $3.6 + 2.3\overline{14}$ is a real number

   d. $\dfrac{3}{10} \cdot \dfrac{10}{3} = 1$

   e. $5 + (2 + 3) = (5 + 2) + 3$

   f. $4.62(1) = 4.62$

   g. $17 \cdot \pi = \pi \cdot 17$

   h. $17 \cdot \sqrt{2}$ is a real number

   i. $-9 + [-(-9)] = 0$

   j. $-\sqrt{17} + 0 = -\sqrt{17}$

   k. $(3 \cdot 7) + (12 \cdot 7) = (7 \cdot 3) + (12 \cdot 7)$

   l. $(3 \cdot \sqrt{11}) \cdot 6 = 3 \cdot (\sqrt{11} \cdot 6)$

   m. $(3 \cdot 7) + (12 \cdot 7) = (12 \cdot 7) + (3 \cdot 7)$

   n. If $6 \cdot 2 + 3 = 5 \cdot 3$ and $5 \cdot 3 = 16 - 1$, then $6 \cdot 2 + 3 = 16 - 1$.

6. a. Write an implication and its converse, such that one is true and the other is false.

   b. Write an implication and its converse, such that each is true.

   c. True or false?

   i. $[2 + 3 = 5] \leftrightarrow [(2 + 3) + 7 = (5) + 7]$

   ii. $[7 - 3 = 9] \leftrightarrow [(7 - 3) \cdot 8 = 9 \cdot 8]$

   iii. $[3 \cdot 0 = 5 \cdot 0] \leftrightarrow [3 = 5]$

   iv. Each implication and its converse have the same truth-value.

   v. Each implication and its contrapositive have the same truth-value.

7. Compute.

a. $-8 + (+12)$ e. $-8 - (+12)$ i. $(-8)(+12)$

b. $-8 + (-12)$ f. $-8 - (-12)$ j. $(-8)(-12)$

c. $+8 + (-12)$ g. $+8 - (-12)$ k. $(+8)(-12)$

d. $+8 + (+12)$ h. $+8 - (+12)$ l. $(+8)(+12)$

8. Find *all* of the *natural number* solutions of each of the following, if any such exist.

a. $x + 7 = 9$ d. $3x^2 = 27$ g. $3x < 18$

b. $3m - 4 = 23$ e. $2x + 9 = 7$ h. $2 + t < 7$

c. $38 - 4c = 10$ f. $x < 5$ i. $3 \le 2x < 11$

9. Find *all* of the *integer* solutions of each of the following, if any such exist.

a. $3x^2 = 27$ f. $7x = 64$

b. $4x = 5x$ g. $|x| \le 3$

c. $2x - 7 = 9 + 4x$ h. $x^3 = -8$

d. $17 - 2x = 9 + 2x$ i. $-3 \le x + 2 < 4$

e. $|x - 1| = 5$ j. $7 - 2x < 1$

10. Find *all* of the *rational number* solutions of each of the following, if any such exist.

a. $5x = 7$ c. $4 - 2x = 7$ e. $9x^2 = 4$

b. $7x = 5$ d. $5(2 - x) = 3(x + 4)$ f. $3x^2 = 6$

11. Use definitions of addition and multiplication of rational numbers to compute

a. $\dfrac{2}{7} + \dfrac{3}{10}$ b. $\dfrac{5}{13} \cdot \dfrac{4}{11}$ c. $\dfrac{3}{5} + \dfrac{7}{11}$ d. $\dfrac{3}{4} \cdot \dfrac{7}{10}$

12. Express $\frac{2}{7}$ as a repeating decimal numeral.

13. Express $4.2\overline{67}$ in the form $\dfrac{a}{b}$ such that $a \in I$ and $b \in I$.

14. Complete: For all statements p and q

a. the converse of $p \rightarrow q$ is __?__ .

b. the inverse of $p \rightarrow q$ is __?__ .

c. the contrapositive of $p \rightarrow q$ is __?__ .

15. Complete: Within the set of integers

a. the solutions of $x^2 = 64$ are __?__ .

b. the solution set of $x^2 = 64$ is __?__ .

16. For each number tell whether it is rational (r), irrational (i), or neither of the two (n).

a. $\dfrac{3}{7}$ d. $\sqrt{-9}$ g. $.717117111711117\ldots$

b. $\sqrt{5}$ e. 1.3 h. $\sqrt[3]{-64}$

c. $\sqrt{9}$ f. $1.3\overline{12}$ i. $\sqrt{-64}$

17. Make a truth-table for: $\sim p \rightarrow q$.

18.

a. Find the coordinate of T, the midpoint of segment $\overline{AB}$.

b. Find the coordinates of K and L, the trisection points of segment $\overline{AB}$.

c. Find the coordinate of M, the midpoint of segment $\overline{CD}$, in terms of a and b, the coordinates of C and D respectively.

d. Find the coordinates of R and E, the trisection points of segment $\overline{CD}$.

19. Complete by making use of the appropriate definitions.

a. $\dfrac{-3}{7} < \dfrac{-2}{5}$ because ___?___

b. $-5\dfrac{2}{3}$ is a rational number because $-5\dfrac{2}{3} = $ ___?___ and ___?___ $\epsilon\, I$ and ___?___ $\epsilon\, I$.

c. $\dfrac{3}{17} = \dfrac{9}{51}$ because ___?___

d. $\dfrac{-7}{-11}$ is positive because ___?___

20. Make a truth-table to prove it *false* that each implication and its converse have the same truth-value.

21. Of the sets (N, I, Q, R), studied in this chapter, which ones are *fields?* Which ones are *discrete? dense?*

22. Distinguish between rational numbers and irrational numbers in terms of their decimal names.

23. Solve each inequality in the set of real numbers.

a. $-2x + 3 > -2$

b. $\dfrac{m-2}{4} > \dfrac{2m+3}{5}$

c. $4(2y - 3) < 3(y + 2)$

d. $\dfrac{3(t+1)}{5} < \dfrac{-2(2-t)}{3}$

CHAPTER TEST

Each of the questions **1–20** is followed by five choices lettered **a, b, c, d,** and **e.** Choose the correct answers. There is *only one* correct choice to each question.

1. Which of the following is a *counterexample* to the statement: "The set of prime numbers is closed under addition"?

a. $2 + 3 = 5$ **c.** $5 + 7 = 12$ **e.** none of these

b. $4 + 3 = 7$ **d.** $6 + 9 = 15$

2. Which of the following proves that the set $\{-1, 0\}$ is *not* closed under multiplication?

a. $0 \times -1 = 0$ **c.** $-1 \times -1 = 1$ **e.** none of these

b. $-1 \times 0 = 0$ **d.** $0 \times 0 = 0$

3. Which of the following proves that the set $\{-\frac{1}{2}, 0, \frac{1}{2}\}$ is *not* closed under multiplication?

a. $0 \times 0 = 0$ **c.** $\frac{1}{2} \times 0 = 0$ **e.** none of these

b. $-\frac{1}{2} \times -\frac{1}{2} = \frac{1}{4}$ **d.** $-\frac{1}{2} \times 0 = 0$

4. $x \leq y$ means
  a. x is less than y and x is equal to y
  b. x is greater than y or x is equal to y
  c. x is greater than y and x is equal to y
  d. x is less than y or x is equal to y
  e. none of these

5. Which of the following is the *converse* of $a \rightarrow b$?
  a. $b \rightarrow a$ **b.** $\sim a \rightarrow \sim b$ **c.** $\sim b \rightarrow \sim a$ **d.** $\sim a \rightarrow b$ **e.** $\sim b \rightarrow a$

6. Which of the following is the *inverse* of $a \rightarrow b$?
  a. $b \rightarrow a$ **b.** $\sim a \rightarrow \sim b$ **c.** $\sim b \rightarrow \sim a$ **d.** $\sim a \rightarrow b$ **e.** $\sim b \rightarrow a$

7. Which of the following is the *contrapositive* of $a \rightarrow b$?
  a. $b \rightarrow a$ **b.** $\sim a \rightarrow \sim b$ **c.** $\sim b \rightarrow \sim a$ **d.** $\sim a \rightarrow b$ **e.** $\sim b \rightarrow a$

8. Which of the following is a *true* statement?
  a. If $4 = 7$, then $6 = 3 \times 2$. **d.** If $4 \not> 6$, then $6 \not> 4$.
  b. If $6 = 3 \times 2$, then $4 = 7$. **e.** none of these
  c. If $6 \not< 4$, then $4 \not< 6$.

9. Which of the following is *not true* for all integers x?
  a. $x \cdot 0 = x$ **c.** $x + (-x) = 0$ **e.** $x \cdot 1 = x$
  b. $x + 0 = x$ **d.** $x + x = 2x$

10. Which of the following results in a *true* statement when x is replaced by -3?
  a. $|x| = x$ **c.** $|x| > x$ **e.** none of these
  b. $|x| < x$ **d.** $|x| = 0$

In questions **11–13** the following abbreviations are used
$$Q = \text{the set of all rational numbers}$$
$$T = \text{the set of all irrational numbers}$$
$$R = \text{the set of all real numbers}$$

11. Which of the following tells us that Q and T are *disjoint* sets?
  a. $Q \cup T = R$ **c.** $Q \subset R$ **e.** none of these
  b. $Q \cap T = \phi$ **d.** $T \subset R$

12. Which of the following is *true*?
  a. $Q \subset R$ **b.** $R \subset Q$ **c.** $Q \subset T$ **d.** $T \subset Q$ **e.** none of these

13. Which of the following is *false*?
  a. $Q \subset R$ **b.** $T \subset R$ **c.** $R \not\subset T$ **d.** $R \not\subset Q$ **e.** $Q \subset T$

14. Which of the following statements is a *counterexample* to the statement: "The set of irrational numbers is closed under multiplication"?

a. $\sqrt{2} \times \sqrt{3} = \sqrt{6}$ **d.** $\sqrt{7} \times \sqrt{8} = \sqrt{56}$

b. $\sqrt{5} \times \sqrt{3} = \sqrt{15}$ **e.** none of these

c. $\sqrt{6} \times \sqrt{6} = \sqrt{36}$

15. Which of the following is *not* a rational number?

a. .2323323332...   **c.** $\dfrac{131}{169}$ **e.** none of these

b. .576576576...   **d.** .369705

16. In the universal set of *integers*, which of the following is the solution set of $2x + 3 = 4$?

a. $\left\{\dfrac{7}{2}\right\}$ **b.** $\left\{-\dfrac{1}{2}\right\}$ **c.** $\left\{\dfrac{1}{2}\right\}$ **d.** $\{0\}$ **e.** ϕ

17. In the universal set of *rational* numbers, which of the following is the solution set of $3x + 1 = 2$?

a. $\{1\}$ **b.** $\left\{-\dfrac{1}{3}\right\}$ **c.** $\left\{\dfrac{1}{3}\right\}$ **d.** $\{0\}$ **e.** ϕ

18. $.36\overline{36}$ is the same as

a. $\dfrac{3636}{10,000}$ **b.** $\dfrac{3636}{9900}$ **c.** $\dfrac{36}{99}$ **d.** $\dfrac{36}{100}$ **e.** none of these

19. Which of the following is an *irrational* number?

a. $\sqrt[3]{64}$ **b.** $\sqrt{144}$ **c.** $\sqrt[4]{16}$ **d.** $\sqrt{65}$ **e.** none of these

20. Which of the following is *between* $\dfrac{6}{7}$ and $\dfrac{7}{8}$?

a. $\dfrac{5}{6}$ **b.** $\dfrac{8}{9}$ **c.** $\dfrac{13}{15}$ **d.** $\dfrac{42}{56}$ **e.** none of these

21. State the density property of rational numbers.

22. State the trichotomy property of real numbers.

23. State the transitive property of $<$ for real numbers.

24. Define a rational number.

25. Define the sum of rational numbers $\dfrac{a}{b}$ and $\dfrac{c}{d}$.

26. Define the absolute value of the real number x.

27. State the three properties of an equivalence relation.

28. Prove that an implication and its contrapositive are logically equivalent. [Use a truth-table.]

29. Prove that for rational numbers $\dfrac{a}{b}$ and $\dfrac{c}{d}$ $(b > 0,\ d > 0)$, if $\dfrac{a}{b} < \dfrac{c}{d}$, then $\dfrac{a}{b} < \dfrac{a+c}{b+d} < \dfrac{c}{d}$.

For each example in the column on the left, choose the letter of the property illustrated by this example; properties are listed in the column on the right.

30. $5 \times 9 = 9 \times 5$

31. $(3 + 1) + 7 = 3 + (1 + 7)$

32. $(9 + 3) \times 2 = 9 \times 2 + 3 \times 2$

33. If $3 < 4$ and $4 < 7$, then $3 < 7$.

34. $(3 \times 9) \times 12 = 3 \times (9 \times 12)$

35. Of $2 < 4$, $2 = 4$, $2 > 4$, only $2 < 4$ is true.

36. $6 = 6$

37. If $5 = 2$, then $2 = 5$.

38. If 3 and 7 are natural numbers, then 21 is a natural number.

39. If $10 > 3$ and $3 = 2 + 1$, then $10 > 2 + 1$.

a. Symmetry

b. Associativity for multiplication [APM]

c. Trichotomy

d. Reflexivity

e. Commutativity for multiplication [CPM]

f. Closure of natural numbers under multiplication [Cl PM]

g. Substitution property

h. Associativity for addition [APA]

i. Transitivity

j. Right-hand distributivity [RDPMA]

For problems **40–43**, solve each inequality in the set of real numbers.

40. $-m + 2 < 3m - 7$

41. $\dfrac{2x - 1}{3} > \dfrac{2 - 5x}{2}$

42. $3(1 - t) < -2(3t + 4)$

43. $4(5s - 1) > -3(2 - 3s)$

BIBLIOGRAPHY

Barnett, I. A. *Some Ideas About Number Theory*. Washington: National Council of Teachers of Mathematics, 1961.

Brant, V. and Keedy, M. L. *Elementary Logic for Secondary Schools*. New York: Holt, Rinehart and Winston, Inc., 1962.

Dubisch, R. *The Nature of Number*. New York: Ronald Press Co., 1952.

Freitag, H. T. and Freitag, A. H. *The Number Story*. Washington: National Council of Teachers of Mathematics, 1960.

Johnson, D. A. *Logic and Reasoning in Mathematics*. St. Louis: Webster Publishing Co., 1963.

National Council of Teachers of Mathematics. *Enrichment Mathematics for High School*. Twenty-eighth Yearbook, Washington, 1963. pp. 34–55, 368–378.

Ringenberg, L. A. *A Portrait of 2*. Washington: National Council of Teachers of Mathematics, 1956.

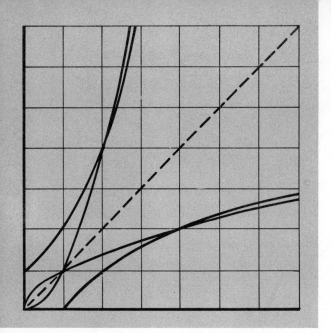

CHAPTER 2

Exponents and Radicals

BASIC PROPERTIES OF EXPONENTS

In your previous algebra course you studied a number of definitions and properties concerning exponents and radicals. To refresh your memory, we review them here for you.

■ *Definition of Natural Number Exponent*
$$\forall_{x\epsilon R} \forall_{n\geq 2,\, n\epsilon N} \quad x^n = \underbrace{x \cdot x \cdot x \cdot \ldots \cdot x}_{}$$

x used n times as a factor

To extend this definition, we define x^1 as follows:
$$x^1 = x$$

■ *Definition of Zero Exponent*
$$\forall_{x\neq 0} \quad x^0 = 1$$

■ *Definition of Negative Exponent*
$$\forall_{x\neq 0,\, x\epsilon R} \forall_{a>0,\, a\epsilon I} \quad x^{-a} = \frac{1}{x^a}$$

44

■ *Product of Powers Property*

$$\forall_{x \in R} \forall_{m \in I} \forall_{n \in I} \quad x^m \cdot x^n = x^{m+n}$$

We extended this property to more than two factors

$$x^a \cdot x^b \cdot \ldots \cdot x^z = x^{a+b+\ldots+z}$$

■ *Power of a Power Property*

$$\forall_{x \in R} \forall_{n \in I} \forall_{m \in I} \quad (x^n)^m = x^{nm}$$

■ *Power of a Product Property*

$$\forall_{x \in R} \forall_{y \in R} \forall_{n \in I} \quad (xy)^n = x^n y^n$$

We extended this property to include the power of a product of more than two factors

$$(a_1 a_2 \ldots a_k)^n = a_1{}^n a_2{}^n \ldots a_k{}^n$$

■ *Power of a Quotient Property*

$$\forall_{x \in R} \forall_{y \in R,\ y \neq 0} \forall_{n \in I} \quad \left(\frac{x}{y}\right)^n = \frac{x^n}{y^n}$$

Why did we state that $y \neq 0$?

■ *Quotient of Powers Property*

$$\forall_{x \in R,\ x \neq 0} \forall_{a \in I} \forall_{b \in I} \quad \frac{x^a}{x^b} = x^{a-b}$$

■ *Negative Exponent Properties*

$$\forall_{x \in R} \forall_{y \in R,\ y \neq 0} \forall_{a \in I,\ a>0} \quad x \cdot y^{-a} = \frac{x}{y^a}$$

$$\forall_{x \in R} \forall_{y \in I,\ y \neq 0} \forall_{a \in R,\ a>0} \quad \frac{x}{y^{-a}} = x y^a$$

■ *Order of Operations Agreements*

$$\forall_{x \neq 0,\ x \in R} \forall_{a \in I} \quad -x^a \text{ means } -(x^a)$$

$$\forall_{x \in R} \forall_{y \neq 0,\ y \in R} \forall_{a \in I} \quad xy^a \text{ means } x(y^a)$$

Do the exercises below to review the work with exponents based on the properties summarized above.

EXERCISES

1. Give the simplest equivalent number name involving no exponents.

a. 5^4

b. $(-3)^2$

c. -3^2

d. $\left(-\dfrac{2}{3}\right)^4$

e. $-\left(\dfrac{2}{3}\right)^4$

f. $3 \cdot 5^3$

g. $(0.1)^4$

h. $\left(-\dfrac{1}{5}\right)\left(-\dfrac{1}{5}\right)^3$

i. $(.003)^2$

2. Give a simpler equivalent expression for each of the following:

a. $x^7 x^8$

d. $(m^3)^4$

g. $\dfrac{a^2 b^3 c^7}{abc^5}$

b. $m^2 n^3 m^4$

e. $\dfrac{x^9}{x^3}$

h. $(-10)^3(-10)^5$

c. $a^2 x^3 a^{-2} x^{-3} y^4$

f. $\dfrac{6(x+y)^5}{9(x+y)^3}$

i. $\dfrac{(a+b+c)^7 x^4}{(a+b+c)^3 x^3}$

3. **a.** If a power has a positive number base and an odd number exponent, is the power a positive or a negative number?

b. If a power has a positive number base and an even number exponent, is the power a positive or a negative number?

c. If a power has a negative number base and an odd number exponent, is the power a positive or a negative number?

d. If a power has a negative number base and an even number exponent, is the power a positive or a negative number?

4. Using $\forall_{x \in R,\ x \neq 0} \dfrac{x}{x} = 1$, and the quotient of powers property, prove the definition of zero exponent.

5. For each of the following, give a simplified equivalent expression containing only *positive* exponents.

a. $\dfrac{5^{-4} \cdot 5^9}{5^3}$

e. $\dfrac{(x+y)^{-4}(x+y)^7}{(x+y)^{-2}(x+y)^{-1}}$

b. $\dfrac{(-3)^7(-3)^{-6}}{(-3)^{-4}}$

f. $\dfrac{-32(a+b+c)^{-3}(a+b)^{-1}}{16(a+b+c)^{-10}(a+b)^{-3}}$

c. $\dfrac{n^{-2} n^5}{n^9}$

g. $\dfrac{x^2(x+y)^3}{x^4(x+y)}$

d. $\dfrac{-18 a^3 d^3}{9 a^4 d^5}$

h. $\dfrac{(-3)^3(m+n)^{-2}}{(-3)^5(m+n)^{-5}}$

6. Prove each of the following:

a. $-2^4 \neq (-2)^4$

b. $-2^3 = (-2)^3$

7. For each of the following, write an equivalent expression which contains no negative exponents.

a. $5m^{-5}$

f. $\dfrac{(x+2)^{-2}}{(x+2)^{-7}}$

i. $\dfrac{9^{-2}}{-m^{-3}}$

b. $-4(x+y)^{-6}$

c. $9a(bc)^{-3}$

g. $\dfrac{9n}{a^{-2} n^{-5}}$

j. $\dfrac{-3x^4}{a^4 b^{-3}}$

d. $\dfrac{6}{x^{-4}}$

e. $\dfrac{3m^2}{-n^{-4}}$

h. $\dfrac{-4}{(axt)^{-2}}$

k. $\dfrac{(m-n)^{-3}}{(m-n)^{-4}}$

l. $\dfrac{5^3(x + y + z)^2}{5^{-1}(x + y + z)^{-3}}$

p. $\left(\dfrac{x^2}{x^{-4}}\right)^{-3}$

m. $\dfrac{-24(p + q)^{-2}(p + q + r)^6}{-8(p + q)^6(p + q + r)^{-2}}$

q. $\left(\dfrac{-2s^3}{-3r^2s^4}\right)^{-2}$

n. $\dfrac{(x + y)^{-3}(a - b)^{-4}}{(x + y)^4(a - b)^{-2}}$

r. $\left[\dfrac{(a + b)^2}{(a + b)^{-3}}\right]^{-4}$

o. $\dfrac{(m + n)^{-2}m^3n^{-5}}{m^2n^{10}}$

SQUARE ROOT

In your previous study of algebra you learned that the equation $x^2 = 64$ has two solutions: 8 and -8. Thus, 64 has two square roots, 8 and -8. To distinguish between the two square roots, we called the *positive* square root of 64 the *principal* square root of 64.

AGREEMENT: Whenever we use $\sqrt{x}\ (x \geq 0)$, we shall mean the *principal* square root of x.

You noticed that we made sure that in $\sqrt{x}$, x is non-negative. The following argument will show why this is necessary.

i. If $\sqrt{x}$ is a real number, then we want it to have the property that
$$\sqrt{x} \cdot \sqrt{x} = x$$

ii. Suppose x is negative.

iii. Then some real number multiplied by itself gives a negative number for the product.

iv. But each real number is either positive or negative or 0.
The product of a pair of positive numbers is a positive number
The product of a pair of negative numbers is a positive number
$0 \times 0 = 0$

v. Therefore, there is no real number which multiplied by itself results in a product which is a negative number.

vi. Hence, if $\sqrt{x}$ is a real number, then $x \geq 0$.

Later in this course you will learn about numbers whose squares are negative numbers.

We shall now state patterns involving square roots, which you encountered in your previous study of algebra.

■ *Product of Square Roots* (Distributivity of Square Root over Multiplication)
$$\forall_{x \geq 0} \forall_{y \geq 0} \sqrt{xy} = \sqrt{x}\sqrt{y}$$

An extension of this pattern to the n-th root is
$$\forall_{x \geq 0} \forall_{y \geq 0} \forall_{n \in N,\, n \geq 2} \sqrt[n]{xy} = \sqrt[n]{x}\sqrt[n]{y}$$

■ *Square Root in the Denominator* $\forall_{x>0} \dfrac{x}{\sqrt{x}} = \sqrt{x}$

■ *Quotient of Square Roots* $\forall_{x\geq0} \forall_{y>0} \sqrt{\dfrac{x}{y}} = \dfrac{\sqrt{x}}{\sqrt{y}}$

An extension of this pattern to the n-th root is

$$\forall_{x\geq0} \forall_{y>0} \forall_{n\epsilon N,\, n\geq2} \ \sqrt[n]{\dfrac{x}{y}} = \dfrac{\sqrt[n]{x}}{\sqrt[n]{y}}$$

For the purpose of simplifying computations of approximations involving the square root, we find names for such numbers as $\dfrac{\sqrt{2}}{\sqrt{5}}$ which do not have a radical sign in the denominator. When this is achieved, we say that we have "rationalized" the denominator. To rationalize the denominator in $\dfrac{\sqrt{2}}{\sqrt{5}}$, we proceed as follows:

$$\frac{\sqrt{2}}{\sqrt{5}} = \frac{\sqrt{2}\cdot\sqrt{5}}{\sqrt{5}\cdot\sqrt{5}} = \frac{\sqrt{10}}{5}$$

In $\dfrac{\sqrt{10}}{5}$, the denominator is a rational number.

More generally $\forall_{a\geq0} \forall_{b>0} \dfrac{\sqrt{a}}{\sqrt{b}} = \dfrac{\sqrt{a}\,\sqrt{b}}{\sqrt{b}\,\sqrt{b}} = \dfrac{\sqrt{ab}}{b}$

EXERCISES

Simplify each of the following, using the patterns shown in the examples.

Examples: i. $\sqrt{125} = \sqrt{25\cdot5} = \sqrt{25}\,\sqrt{5} = 5\sqrt{5}$

ii. $\sqrt[5]{64} = \sqrt[5]{32\cdot2} = \sqrt[5]{32}\cdot\sqrt[5]{2} = 2\sqrt[5]{2}$

iii. $\forall_{a\geq0} \forall_{b\geq0} \sqrt[4]{81a^7b^{12}} = 3\sqrt[4]{a^4\cdot a^3}\,\sqrt[4]{b^{12}} = 3a\sqrt[4]{a^3b^3} = 3ab^3\sqrt[4]{a^3}$

iv. $\forall_{x\neq0} \forall_y \dfrac{\sqrt[3]{y}}{\sqrt[3]{x^4}} = \dfrac{\sqrt[3]{y}}{x\sqrt[3]{x}} = \dfrac{\sqrt[3]{y}\cdot\sqrt[3]{x^2}}{x\sqrt[3]{x}\cdot\sqrt[3]{x^2}} = \dfrac{\sqrt[3]{x^2y}}{x\sqrt[3]{x^3}} = \dfrac{\sqrt[3]{x^2y}}{x^2}$

v. $16\sqrt{5} - 3\sqrt{125} = 16\sqrt{5} - 15\sqrt{5} = (16-15)\sqrt{5} = \sqrt{5}$

vi. $(7\sqrt{2} + \sqrt{3})(7\sqrt{2} - \sqrt{3})$
$$= (7\sqrt{2} + \sqrt{3})(7\sqrt{2}) - (7\sqrt{2} + \sqrt{3})\sqrt{3}$$
$$= 98 + 7\sqrt{6} - 7\sqrt{6} - 3 = 95$$

vii. $\dfrac{1+\sqrt{2}}{9-\sqrt{5}} = \dfrac{(1+\sqrt{2})(9+\sqrt{5})}{(9-\sqrt{5})(9+\sqrt{5})} = \dfrac{9+\sqrt{5}+9\sqrt{2}+\sqrt{10}}{81-5}$
$$= \dfrac{9+\sqrt{5}+9\sqrt{2}+\sqrt{10}}{76}$$

1. $\sqrt{150}$

2. $\sqrt{112}$

3. $\sqrt[3]{81}$

4. $\sqrt[4]{32}$

5. $\sqrt[4]{162}$

6. $\sqrt[5]{729}$

7. $\sqrt[5]{-96}$

8. $\sqrt{x^5}$

9. $\sqrt[3]{x^4 y^5}$

10. $\dfrac{\sqrt{18}}{\sqrt{5}}$

11. $\dfrac{\sqrt{26}}{\sqrt{5}}$

12. $\dfrac{\sqrt[3]{-64}}{\sqrt[3]{x^9}}$

13. $\dfrac{1}{\sqrt{7}}$

14. $\dfrac{\sqrt[3]{3x^6}}{\sqrt[3]{-27x^2}}$

15. $\dfrac{\sqrt[4]{243}}{\sqrt[4]{3}}$

16. $\sqrt[4]{16x^3} \cdot \sqrt[4]{xy^9}$

17. $9\sqrt{5} - 2\sqrt{5}$

18. $26\sqrt{2} + 10\sqrt{8}$

19. $\sqrt{7}(\sqrt{14} + \sqrt{7})$

20. $(1 + \sqrt{3})(1 - \sqrt{3})$

21. $(2 + \sqrt{7})(\sqrt{7} - 2)$

22. $(2\sqrt{10} + 3\sqrt{5})(2\sqrt{10} - 3\sqrt{5})$

23. $(a + \sqrt{b})(a - \sqrt{b})$

24. $(\sqrt{x} + \sqrt{y})(\sqrt{x} - \sqrt{y})$

25. $\left(a + \dfrac{1}{\sqrt{x}}\right)\left(a - \dfrac{1}{\sqrt{x}}\right)$

26. $\left(\dfrac{1}{\sqrt{x}} + \dfrac{1}{\sqrt{y}}\right)\left(\dfrac{1}{\sqrt{x}} - \dfrac{1}{\sqrt{y}}\right)$

27. $\dfrac{3 + \sqrt{5}}{2 - \sqrt{5}}$

28. $\dfrac{6(\sqrt{3} - 1)}{7(\sqrt{2} + 7)}$

29. $\dfrac{(\sqrt{2} + 3)^2}{(\sqrt{5} - 1)^2}$

30. $(1 + \sqrt{2})(\sqrt{3} - 1) - (\sqrt{5} + 6)(1 - \sqrt{3})$

RATIONAL NUMBER EXPONENTS

We now recall some of the properties which involve rational number exponents. They are based on the assumption that all of the properties and theorems for integer exponents are also true for *rational* number exponents.

$$\forall_{x \geq 0} \ \sqrt{x} = x^{\frac{1}{2}} \qquad \qquad \forall_x \ \sqrt{x^2} = |x|$$

Restricting ourselves to principal roots, we obtain further patterns involving rational number exponents.

$$\forall_{x \geq 0} \ \forall_{n \in N, \ n \geq 2} \ x^{\frac{1}{n}} = \sqrt[n]{x} \qquad \qquad \forall_{x \geq 0} \ \forall_{n \in N, \ n \geq 2} \ (\sqrt[n]{x})^n = x$$

Notice that $\qquad \qquad \sqrt[3]{-8} = -2$ and $\sqrt[5]{-243} = -3$

but that $\qquad \qquad \sqrt{-4}$ is *not* a real number

And generally

$$\forall_{x<0} \, \forall_{n \in N} \quad \text{if } n > 2 \text{ and } n \text{ is odd, then } \sqrt[n]{x} \text{ is a negative number}$$

$$\forall_{x<0} \, \forall_{n \in N} \quad \text{if } n \geq 2 \text{ and } n \text{ is even, then } \sqrt[n]{x} \text{ is not a real number}$$

$$\forall_{x \geq 0} \, \forall_{m \in N} \, \forall_{n \in N, \, n \geq 2} \quad \sqrt[n]{x^m} = x^{\frac{m}{n}}$$

$$\forall_{x \geq 0} \, \forall_{m \in N} \, \forall_{n \in N, \, n \geq 2} \quad \sqrt[n]{x^m} = (\sqrt[n]{x})^m$$

EXERCISES

1. Using the product of powers property, derive $\forall_{x \geq 0} \, \sqrt{x} = x^{\frac{1}{2}}$. [HINT: Use $m = \frac{1}{2}$ and $n = \frac{1}{2}$ in the product of powers property and $\sqrt{x} \cdot \sqrt{x} = x$.]

2. Using -5 and -7 for x, illustrate the pattern $\sqrt{x^2} = |x|$.

3. Show that $x^{\frac{1}{4}} = \sqrt[4]{x}$ $(x \geq 0)$ follows from the product of powers property and from

$$\forall_{x \geq 0} \quad \sqrt[4]{x} \, \sqrt[4]{x} \, \sqrt[4]{x} \, \sqrt[4]{x} = x$$

4. We use the following names in connection with roots. We call

$$\sqrt[n]{x} \quad \text{a } radical$$
$$\sqrt[n]{} \quad \text{a } radical \ sign$$
$$x \text{ in } \sqrt[n]{x} \quad \text{a } radicand$$
$$n \text{ in } \sqrt[n]{x} \quad \text{an } index$$

Test your knowledge of these words by telling for each statement whether it is true or false.

a. In $\sqrt[5]{-3}$, 5 is the radicand

b. In $\sqrt[5]{-3}$, -3 is the radicand

c. In $\sqrt[6]{17}$, 17 is the index

d. In $\sqrt[6]{17}$, 6 is the index

e. $\sqrt[3]{7}$ is a radical

f. $7^{\frac{1}{3}}$ is a radical

g. In $\sqrt[5]{7}$, $\sqrt[5]{}$ is a radical sign

h. In $\sqrt[12]{1}$, 12 is the index

i. $\sqrt{}$ means the same as $\sqrt[2]{}$

j. $\sqrt[2]{3}$ means the same as $\sqrt{3}$

5. Since $5^{\frac{1}{3}} = \sqrt[3]{5}$ and $5^{\frac{1}{3}} \times 5^{\frac{1}{3}} = 5^{\frac{2}{3}}$ and $\sqrt[3]{5} \times \sqrt[3]{5} = \sqrt[3]{5 \times 5} = \sqrt[3]{5^2}$, it follows that $\sqrt[3]{5^2} = 5^{\frac{2}{3}}$. Using a similar argument, show that $\sqrt[4]{12^7} = 12^{\frac{7}{4}}$.

6. Give a name which does not contain a square root sign ($\sqrt{}$) for each of the following:

Example: $\sqrt{(-7)^2} = |-7| = 7$

a. $\sqrt{(-3)^2}$

b. $\sqrt{\left(-\frac{2}{3}\right)^2}$

c. $\sqrt{5^2}$

d. $\sqrt{(-1.3)^2}$

7. For each of the following, write an equivalent symbol using a fractional exponent.

a. $\sqrt[3]{5}$

b. $\sqrt[4]{x^3}$

c. $\sqrt[8]{y^3}$

d. $\sqrt[9]{t^4}$

e. $\sqrt[4]{(x-y)^7}$

f. $\sqrt{(m+n)^3}$

8. For each of the following, write an equivalent symbol using a radical sign.

a. $7^{\frac{2}{5}}$ c. $a^{\frac{3}{4}}$ e. $(m+n)^{\frac{3}{7}}$

b. $9^{\frac{2}{3}}$ d. $c^{\frac{4}{5}}$ f. $(2x+y+z)^{\frac{9}{4}}$

9. Show that $\sqrt{\sqrt{256}} = 4$.

10. Show that $\forall_x \ \sqrt{\sqrt{x^2}} = \sqrt{|x|}$.

11. Show that $\forall_{x\epsilon R}\forall_{y\epsilon R} \ |x-y| \cdot |x-y| = (x-y)(x-y)$.

12. For each of the following, give the simplest name involving no exponents and no radical signs.

a. $\left(\dfrac{1}{2}\right)^{-5}$

b. 176^0

c. $27^{-\frac{2}{3}}$

d. $(-2)^{-4}$

e. $\dfrac{1}{4 \cdot 36^{-\frac{1}{2}}}$

f. $12 \cdot 27^{-\frac{1}{3}}$

g. $\left(\dfrac{1}{5}\right)^{-2}$

h. $\left(\dfrac{16}{9}\right)^{-\frac{1}{2}}$

i. $\dfrac{9^{-\frac{1}{2}}}{25^{-\frac{1}{2}}}$

j. $\left(\dfrac{1}{2}\right)^{-3}\left(\dfrac{1}{2}\right)^{-4}$

k. $(-1)^{137}$

l. $(-1)^{-12}$

13. Simplify. Do not use a negative exponent nor a radical sign.

a. $m^{\frac{5}{3}} \cdot m^{\frac{4}{3}}$

b. $x^{\frac{12}{7}} \cdot x^{-\frac{5}{7}}$

c. $n^{\frac{1}{4}} \cdot n^{\frac{9}{4}} \cdot n^{-\frac{1}{2}}$

d. $\dfrac{3x}{x^{\frac{5}{6}}}$

e. $\dfrac{y^{\frac{1}{8}}}{y^{\frac{1}{4}}}$

f. $\dfrac{(x+y)^{\frac{2}{3}}}{(x+y)^{\frac{1}{6}}}$

g. $\dfrac{(m-n)^{\frac{3}{7}}}{(m-n)^{\frac{1}{14}}}$

h. $\dfrac{-y^{-2}}{\frac{1}{2}}$

i. $\dfrac{m^{-3}x^{-2}}{x^{-3}}$

j. $\dfrac{1}{(x+y)^{-4}}$

k. $tx^{-2} + ux^{-1}$

l. $(27x^6y^9)^{-\frac{1}{3}}$

m. $(8a^{-3}b^{-6})^{-\frac{1}{3}}(16a^{-1}b^{-2})^2$

RADICAL EQUATIONS

You will recall, from your previous study of algebra, that an equation which contains a variable under a radical sign is called a *radical equation*. For example

$$\sqrt{x} - 3 = 1$$

is a radical equation. In solving radical equations we make use of the following:

$$\forall_{x\epsilon R} \ \forall_{y\epsilon R} \ \forall_{n\epsilon N}, \ \text{if } x = y, \text{ then } x^n = y^n$$

Some radical equations are solved for you below. Study these examples and observe what caution you must exercise when solving radical equations.

Examples: *i.* $\sqrt{x} - 3 = 1$

$$\sqrt{x} = 4$$
$$(\sqrt{x})^2 = 4^2$$
$$x = 16; \text{ the solution set } \textit{seems} \text{ to be } \{16\}$$

CHECK: $\sqrt{16} - 3 = 1$

$$4 - 3 = 1$$
$$1 = 1; \; \{16\} \textit{ is} \text{ the solution set}$$

ii. $\sqrt{n + 12} = \sqrt{-2n + 3}$

$$(\sqrt{n + 12})^2 = (\sqrt{-2n + 3})^2$$
$$n + 12 = -2n + 3$$
$$3n = -9$$
$$n = -3$$

Check to see whether $\{-3\}$ is the solution set of this equation.

iii. $3\sqrt{z} + 10 = 1$

$$3\sqrt{z} = -9$$
$$\sqrt{z} = -3$$
$$(\sqrt{z})^2 = (-3)^2$$
$$z = 9; \text{ the solution set } \textit{seems} \text{ to be } \{9\}$$

CHECK: $3\sqrt{9} + 10 = 1$

$$9 + 10 = 1$$
$$19 = 1 \text{ (false)}; \; \{9\} \text{ is } \textit{not} \text{ the solution set}$$

The solution set of $3\sqrt{z} + 10 = 1$ in the set of real numbers is ϕ. The equation $\sqrt{z} = -3$ implies that the principal square root of some real number is -3 (a negative number). Since the principal square root of any non-negative real number is a non-negative number, this equation has no real number solution.

You should note also that the technique used above in solving radical equations leads to new equations which may or may not be equivalent to the equation with which we started. In the first two examples we obtained equivalent equations, but in the third example the final equation ($z = 9$) was not equivalent to the original equation ($3\sqrt{z} + 10 = 1$).

EXERCISES

1.   Determine the real number solution sets for the following equations.

   a. $\sqrt{x} - 7 = -5$ **d.** $\sqrt{x + 1} = 12$

   b. $4\sqrt{p} + 1 = 25$ **e.** $\dfrac{\sqrt{2y - 1}}{3} = 1$

   c. $3 - 2\sqrt{n} = -5$ **f.** $\sqrt{2z + 1} = \sqrt{4z - 23}$

g. $\dfrac{\sqrt{m+4}}{2} = \dfrac{\sqrt{7m+1}}{4}$

i. $\sqrt{\dfrac{4+u}{3}} = \sqrt{\dfrac{7u+23}{6}}$

h. $\dfrac{\sqrt{t+2}}{12} = 0$

j. $\sqrt{\dfrac{1}{9-v}} = \sqrt{\dfrac{2}{17v+18}}$

2. The square root of a number is multiplied by 3 and 7 is subtracted from the product; the result is 5. What is the number?

3. A number is multiplied by 2 and 4 is added to the product. The square root of the sum is 4. What is the number?

4. The square root of the sum of a number and 2 is equal to the product of 6 and the square root of the difference of the number and 3. What is the number?

5. One-half of the square root of the sum of a number and $\frac{1}{4}$ is equal to $\frac{1}{6}$ of the square root of the product of the number and 12. What is the number?

SCIENTIFIC NOTATION

You may recall that we often employ scientific notation when dealing with very large or very small numbers. We say that a number is shown in scientific notation if it is given as the product of a number between 1 and 10 and the appropriate integer power of 10. For example, to show 135,000,000,000 in scientific notation, we write

$$1.35 \times 10^{11}$$

Since $1.35 \times 10^{11} = 135,000,000,000$, and $1 < 1.35 < 10$, and 10^{11} is the appropriate integer power of ten, 1.35×10^{11} is the correct name in scientific notation for 135,000,000,000.

Let us show a very small number in scientific notation.

$$.000000026 = 2.6 \times 10^{-8}$$

Explain why 2.6×10^{-8} is the correct name in scientific notation for .000000026.

EXERCISES

1. Show each of the following numbers in scientific notation.

   a. 3,900,000,000,000,000,000,000,000,000,000,000 ergs — the electromagnetic radiation which the sun emits every second (One erg is the amount of work required to raise $\frac{1}{981}$ of a gram vertically through one centimeter.)

   b. 93,000,000 miles — the distance of the earth from the sun

   c. 2,000,000,000,000,000,000,000,000,000,000 tons — the mass of the sun

   d. 1 light-year = 6,000,000,000,000 miles — the distance traveled by light in the course of one year

   e. 29,979,300,000 cm. per sec. — the velocity of light

f. 250,000,000 — the number of atoms which, when stretched in a row, would cover about an inch

g. 2,500,000,000,000 — the number of electrons which, when stretched in a row, would cover about an inch

h. 176,000,000 coulomb/gram — the ratio of charge to mass of an electron

i. 602,280,000,000,000,000,000,000 — the number of atoms in a gram-atom

j. 70,000,000,000 — the number of dollars representing the physical assets and endowment of gift-supported institutions in the United States in 1963

k. .000000000001 cm. — the maximum diameter of a region in which most of the mass and the positive charge of the gold atoms are concentrated

l. .0000001 cm. — the wave length of the longest x-rays

m. .0000000002 cm. — the wave length of γ-rays

n. .00000000000000000002 erg — the photon energy of radar waves

2. For each number, give its name in scientific notation.

a. 125.6   **c.** .42   **e.** .0000367

b. 30.003   **d.** .0029   **f.** .002056

3. Using the appropriate properties of exponents, simplify each of the following. Give the answer in scientific notation.

Example:
$$\frac{356 \times 10^5 \times 10^{-8}}{10^3 \times 10^{-9}} = \frac{356 \times 10^{-3}}{10^{-6}}$$
$$= 356 \times 10^{-3} \times 10^6$$
$$= 356 \times 10^3$$
$$= 3.56 \times 10^5$$

a. $10^9 \times 10^{-6} \times 27$

b. $\dfrac{796 \times 10^4 \times 10^{-2}}{10^{-7}}$

c. $\dfrac{1365.7 \times 10^3 \times 10^{-10}}{10^{-2} \times 10^9}$

d. $\dfrac{(13.5 \times 10^{-5})(2 \times 10^4)}{10^{-4}}$

VOCABULARY

Use each of the following correctly in a sentence. Numerals in parentheses refer to pages where these words were used. If you are not sure of the meaning of any word, turn to the indicated page.

exponent (44)

index (50)

negative exponent (44)

power of a power (45)

power of a product (45)

power of a quotient (45)

principal square root (47)

product of powers (45)

product of square roots (47)

quotient of powers (45)

quotient of square roots (48)

radical (50)

radical equation (51)

radical sign (50)

radicand (50)

rational number exponent (49)

scientific notation (53)

square root (47)

zero exponent (44)

REVIEW EXERCISES

1. Give equivalent expressions using a radical sign.

   a. $x^{\frac{4}{3}}$

   b. $[(3t)^2]^{\frac{1}{5}}$

   c. $\left[\left(\dfrac{x}{y^2}\right)^3\right]^{\frac{1}{4}}$

   d. $\left(\dfrac{-5n}{m^2}\right)^{\frac{2}{5}}$

   e. $\left(\dfrac{1}{3}x^{-2}\right)^{-\frac{1}{5}}$

   f. $\left[(xy^{-1}z^{-2})^{\frac{1}{2}}\right]^{\frac{2}{3}}$

2. True or false?

   a. $\sqrt[4]{-16} = -2$

   b. $\sqrt[3]{-8} = -2$

   c. $\left(\dfrac{1}{9}\right)^{-1} = 9$

   d. $\dfrac{\sqrt{5}}{\sqrt{7}} = \dfrac{5}{7}$

   e. $\dfrac{\sqrt{18}}{3} = \sqrt{2}$

   f. $\sqrt[3]{36} = 12$

   g. $\dfrac{\sqrt{28}}{\sqrt{14}} = 2$

   h. $\dfrac{\sqrt{8}}{\sqrt{2}} = 2$

   i. $\sqrt{10} \cdot \sqrt{5} = 5\sqrt{2}$

   j. $\left(\dfrac{4}{7}\right)^2 = \dfrac{8}{7}$

   k. $(5^2)^7 = 5^9$

   l. $\dfrac{5^8}{5^2} = 5^4$

   m. $(5\sqrt{5})^2 = 25\sqrt{5}$

   n. $(\sqrt{3})^3 = 3\sqrt{3}$

   o. $\sqrt[3]{2} + \sqrt[3]{2} = \sqrt[3]{4}$

   p. $7\sqrt{2} - 4\sqrt{2} = 3\sqrt{2}$

   q. $2\sqrt{2} \cdot 3\sqrt{2} = 6\sqrt{2}$

   r. $\dfrac{7\sqrt{2}}{2\sqrt{2}} = 5\sqrt{2}$

   s. $\dfrac{1}{\sqrt{2}} = \dfrac{\sqrt{2}}{2}$

   t. $\dfrac{1}{3\sqrt{3}} = \dfrac{\sqrt{3}}{9}$

3. For each number, give its name in scientific notation.

   a. 17.26

   b. 459.7

   c. .271

   d. .031

   e. .000329

   f. .000007601

4. Give equivalent expressions containing only positive exponents.

   a. $\dfrac{9a^{-3}}{a^{-5}}$

   b. $\dfrac{x^{-2}y^{-3}}{x^2y^3}$

   c. $\dfrac{x(a+b)^{-3}}{(a+b)^2}$

   d. $\dfrac{1}{x+y} \cdot (x^{-2}y^{-2})$

   e. $\dfrac{(a-b)^{-4}(a+b)^{-3}}{(a-b)^3(a+b)^{-4}}$

   f. $\dfrac{m^{-2}(x^{-2} + y^{-2})}{x+y}$

5. Give equivalent expressions containing fractional exponents.

a. $\sqrt{a+b}$

b. $\sqrt[3]{x-y}$

c. $\sqrt[5]{\dfrac{x}{y}}$

d. $\sqrt[4]{\dfrac{ax}{16}}$

e. $\sqrt[3]{\dfrac{-27}{(x+y)^2}}$

f. $\sqrt{(x+y)(m+n)}$

g. $\sqrt{\dfrac{a+b}{a-b}}$

h. $\sqrt[3]{x^4(x+y)^5}$

i. $\sqrt[7]{\dfrac{x^3}{(a+b)^4}}$

j. $\sqrt[5]{\dfrac{(x-y)^2}{x(x+y)^3}}$

6. Simplify.

a. $4m^{\frac{1}{4}} \cdot m^{\frac{1}{2}}$

b. $\dfrac{x^{-\frac{1}{4}}}{x^{\frac{1}{2}}}$

c. $(m+n)^{-4}(m+n)^3$

d. $\dfrac{(a-b)^{-3}(a+b)^4}{(a-b)^{-4}}$

e. $\dfrac{1}{x} \cdot x^{-3} \cdot x^9$

f. $[(a+b)^6(a-b)^4]^{\frac{1}{2}}$

7. Simplify each of the following, using the appropriate properties of exponents.

a. $\dfrac{10^7 \times 10^{-3}}{10^4}$

b. $\dfrac{10^2 \times 10^{-4} \times 10^8}{10^{-3} \times 10^9}$

c. $\dfrac{10^{-2} \times 10^{-3} \times 10^{-4}}{10^{-1} \times 10^{-5}}$

d. $10^{-4} \times \dfrac{1}{10^4} \times 10^3$

8. For each equation, determine its solution set in the set of real numbers.

a. $\sqrt{x+2} - 1 = 0$

b. $\sqrt{x+4} = \sqrt{2}$

c. $\sqrt{2x+1} = \sqrt{4x-9}$

d. $\sqrt{3-x} = \sqrt{4x-17}$

CHAPTER TEST

1. True or false?

a. $10^{-2} + 10^4 = 10^2$

b. $\dfrac{10^{-3}}{10^{-6}} = 10^3$

c. $\dfrac{10^{-4} \times 10^{-5}}{10} = 1$

d. $10^4 - 10^{-4} = 0$

e. $10^2 - 10^{-2} > 0$

f. $10^{-1} - 10 < 0$

g. $\sqrt[4]{-81} = -3$

h. $\sqrt[3]{-27} = -3$

i. $(1 - \sqrt{2})^2 = 3$

j. $(\sqrt{3} + 1)^2 = 2(\sqrt{3} + 2)$

k. $\dfrac{4^{-3}}{4^{-4}} = 4$

l. $\dfrac{\sqrt{12}}{\sqrt{3}} = 4$

m. $\dfrac{\sqrt{32}}{\sqrt{2}} = 4$

n. $\dfrac{5}{\sqrt{5}} = \sqrt{5}$

o. $\sqrt[3]{-\dfrac{1}{8}} = \dfrac{1}{2}$

p. $\sqrt{2} + \sqrt[4]{2} = \sqrt[6]{2}$

q. $\left(\dfrac{1}{2}\right)^7 \times \left(\dfrac{1}{2}\right)^{-7} = 0$

r. $\left(\dfrac{2}{3}\right)^{-2} = \dfrac{9}{4}$

s. $\sqrt{102} = 10\sqrt{2}$

t. $\sqrt{28} = 2\sqrt{7}$

u. $\left(\dfrac{3}{\sqrt{3}}\right)^2 = 3$

v. $8^{\frac{1}{4}} = 2$

w. $9^3 - 9 = 8 \times 81$

x. $\dfrac{\sqrt[3]{-8}}{\sqrt[3]{-2}} = \sqrt[3]{4}$

y. $\left(\dfrac{1}{2}\right)^{-4} = 16$

z. $3^2 - 3^3 = 3^{-1}$

2. Determine the real number solution sets.

a. $x^{-2} = 4$

b. $3x^3 = \dfrac{1}{9}$

c. $\sqrt{3x} = \sqrt{3}$

d. $\sqrt{2x+1} = \sqrt{7}$

e. $\sqrt{x^2+1} = 0$

f. $\dfrac{x}{2} = \sqrt{x+3}$

g. $\sqrt{25x+1} = -1$

h. $\sqrt{2x+3} = \sqrt{-x}$

i. $\sqrt{x+1} = \sqrt{x-1}$

j. $\dfrac{1}{\sqrt{x+2}} = \dfrac{1}{3}$

k. $\sqrt{x} = \sqrt{2x} + (1 - \sqrt{2})$

3. Simplify.

a. $4\sqrt{7} - 5\sqrt{7}$

b. $(\sqrt{2} - 1)(\sqrt{2} + 1)$

c. $\sqrt[3]{9a^2} \cdot \sqrt[3]{3a}$

d. $\sqrt[4]{16a^8b^{12}}$

e. $x^{\frac{1}{3}} \cdot x^{\frac{2}{3}} \cdot x$

f. $\dfrac{x^{\frac{2}{3}}}{x^{\frac{1}{3}} \cdot x}$

g. $(169m^3n^6)^{\frac{1}{2}}$

h. $\dfrac{c^{\frac{5}{2}}}{c^{-\frac{1}{2}}}$

i. $\left(\dfrac{48a^4b^3}{3a}\right)^{\frac{1}{3}}$

j. $\dfrac{r^{-4}}{\dfrac{1}{r^5}}$

4. Give equivalent expressions containing fractional exponents.

a. $\sqrt[7]{a^4}$

b. $\sqrt[4]{(mn)^3}$

c. $\sqrt[3]{4y^4z^2}$

d. $\sqrt[4]{\dfrac{x^3}{a^5}}$

e. $\sqrt[5]{\dfrac{(x-y)^2}{(x+y)^3}}$

f. $\sqrt{\dfrac{(a+b+c)^3}{(a+b)^5}}$

g. $\dfrac{\sqrt[3]{\left(\dfrac{2}{x}\right)^4}}{\sqrt[4]{\left(\dfrac{1}{n}\right)^5}}$

5. Give equivalent expressions containing only positive exponents and no radical signs.

a. $\dfrac{2m^4 \cdot m^{-2}}{m}$

b. $\dfrac{4x}{x^{-7}}$

c. $\dfrac{(x+a)^{-\frac{1}{2}}}{(x+a)^{\frac{5}{2}}}$

d. $\dfrac{3}{\dfrac{a}{x^{-2}}}$

e. $\dfrac{3ce^{-3}}{4c^{-1}e^{-4}}$

f. $\dfrac{(a+b+c)^{-3}}{(a+b)^{-4}}$

BIBLIOGRAPHY

Committee on the Undergraduate Program, Mathematical Association of America. *Universal Mathematics, Part I, Functions and Limits.* University of Kansas, 1954. pp. 336–337.

Heimer, R. T., Kocher, F., and Lottes, J. J. *A Program in Contemporary Algebra.* Book 5, Exponents, Radicals, and Quadratic Equations. New York: Holt, Rinehart and Winston, Inc., 1963.

Nichols, Eugene D. *Modern Elementary Algebra.* New York: Holt, Rinehart and Winston, Inc., 1965. Chapter 11.

Odom, Mary Margaret, and Nichols, Eugene D. (Consulting Editor). *Introduction to Exponents* (A Programed Unit). New York: Holt, Rinehart and Winston, Inc., 1964.

School Mathematics Study Group. *Applied Mathematics in the High School.* Studies in Mathematics, Volume X. Stanford: Stanford University, 1963. pp. 31-75.

School Mathematics Study Group. *First Course in Algebra.* New Haven: Yale University Press, 1961. pp. 247–311.

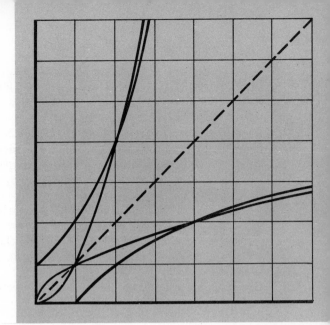

CHAPTER 3

Polynomials and Factoring

WHAT IS A POLYNOMIAL?

In this chapter we are going to study a very special kind of algebraic expression called a *polynomial*. Let us begin by defining polynomials in one variable, say x.

■ *Definition of a Polynomial in One Variable* Given the set consisting of all the real numbers and a single variable, say x, any element of this set or any expression which can be constructed from the elements of this set using only the operations of addition, subtraction, and multiplication is called a *polynomial in one variable* (also called a *polynomial in x.*)

It is important to note that the use of the variable x in the definition of a polynomial in x, rather than y or some other variable, is immaterial. Our primary objective is to define a polynomial in one variable. Here are four examples of polynomials in x.

$$2x + 5 \qquad\qquad 3x^2 + x + 1 \qquad\qquad 3x \qquad\qquad \frac{1}{2}x^2 - x - 1$$

Is $\frac{1}{2}x^2 + 1$ a polynomial in x? Why or why not? Notice that $x^2 + \frac{1}{x}$ is *not* a polynomial in x. Why not? $\frac{1}{3}$ is a polynomial in x. Why? [See definition of a polynomial on p. 59.]

Since polynomials may contain more than one variable, we have need for a more comprehensive definition which will cover all cases. Accordingly, we define a polynomial in n variables, n a natural number, as follows:

■ *Definition of a Polynomial in n Variables* Given the set consisting of all the real numbers and the n variables $x_1, x_2, \ldots, x_n$, any element of this set or any expression which can be constructed from the elements of this set using only the operations of addition, subtraction, and multiplication is called a *polynomial in n variables*.

Here are four examples of polynomials in two or more variables.

$$2xy + 3 \qquad\qquad x + y + z \qquad\qquad x^2y - 2x \qquad\qquad \frac{1}{2}x^2 + y^2$$

EXERCISES

1. Which of the following are *not* polynomials in one variable?

a. x **d.** $x^2 + 2x + 1$ **g.** $\frac{1}{3}x^2 - 2x + \frac{1}{2}$ **j.** $x^4 + 2x - 1$

b. $2x + 1$ **e.** $\dfrac{x + 1}{x}$ **h.** $\dfrac{3}{x} + 2$ **k.** y^2

c. 5 **f.** $2x^2 + \dfrac{3}{x}$ **i.** $\dfrac{1}{2}$ **l.** 0

2. Which of the following are *not* polynomials?

a. 2 **c.** $2x^2y^2$ **e.** $xy^2 - 1$ **g.** $\dfrac{2x^2}{y^2}$ **i.** $x + y + \dfrac{3}{z}$

b. $2x^2$ **d.** $\dfrac{2}{x}$ **f.** xyz^{-1} **h.** $\dfrac{4x^2y^2 + 1}{y}$ **j.** $x + \dfrac{y}{4}$

Some ways of classifying polynomials

Although polynomials may be classified in various ways, only four methods of classifying them are important to us at the present time. One obvious method is to classify polynomials according to the number of terms they contain. If a polynomial contains

> one term, then it is called a *monomial*
> two terms, then it is called a *binomial*
> three terms, then it is called a *trinomial*

For example, $-3x^2y$ is a monomial; $5x + 3y^2$ is a binomial; $t^2 - 3m + 4$ is a trinomial. It is customary to refer to a polynomial of four or more terms simply as a polynomial and to state the number of terms it contains.

A second method of classifying polynomials is according to the number of variables they contain. For example, each of the four polynomials

$$x \qquad\qquad 3t + 5 \qquad\qquad 2m^2 + m - 3 \qquad\qquad \frac{1}{2}y^3 + 5$$

is a polynomial in *one* variable. On the other hand, the three polynomials

$$x^2 + y \qquad\qquad xy + z \qquad\qquad 3tuv + w + 7$$

are polynomials in two, three and four variables, respectively.

A third method of classifying polynomials is with respect to degree. The *degree of a monomial in one variable* is given by the exponent of the variable in the monomial. For example

$3x$ is a *first* degree monomial since the exponent of x is understood to be 1
$5y^2$ is a *second* degree monomial since the exponent of y is 2
$2t^4$ is a *fourth* degree monomial since the exponent of t is 4

The degree of a monomial in more than one variable is given by the *sum* of the exponents of the variables. For example

$4xy^2$ is a third degree monomial
$2xy$ is a second degree monomial
$3xy^2z$ is a fourth degree monomial

The degree of a monomial, other than zero, which contains no variables is defined to be zero; that is, all non-zero real numbers are considered to be polynomials of degree zero. Extending the concept of degree to cover polynomials in general, we define the *degree of a polynomial* to be the same as that of its term of highest degree. For example

$2x^2 + 3$ is a second degree polynomial
$3xy + 1$ is a second degree polynomial
$4x^3 + xy + y^2$ is a third degree polynomial
$5t^2 + 6y^2t^2 - 7$ is a fourth degree polynomial
$\frac{2}{3}$ is a polynomial of degree zero

A fourth important method for classifying polynomials has to do with the numerical coefficients of the terms of the polynomial. If the numerical coefficient of each of the terms of a polynomial is an integer, then the polynomial is said to be a *polynomial over the integers.* For example, $2x^3 + 5x - 20$ is a polynomial over the integers, but $y^2 - 2y + \frac{1}{4}$ is not. If each of the numerical coefficients of the terms of a polynomial is an element of a specified set of numbers, the polynomial is said to be a polynomial over that set of numbers. Hence, since each numerical coefficient in the polynomial $2x^3 + 5x - 20$ is a rational number, this polynomial can be classified as a *polynomial over the rational numbers;* moreover, it is also a *polynomial over the real numbers.* Why? Indeed, since the set of integers is a proper subset of the set of rational numbers which is in turn, a proper subset of the set of real numbers, the relationship among the sets of polynomials over the integers, the rationals and the reals is shown by this diagram.

$$\boxed{\begin{array}{c} \text{Polynomials over the Reals} \\[4pt] \boxed{\begin{array}{c} \text{Polynomials over the Rationals} \\[4pt] \boxed{\text{Polynomials over the Integers}} \end{array}} \end{array}}$$

Thus, we see that every polynomial over the integers is also a polynomial over both the rationals and the reals. Moreover, every polynomial over the rationals is also a polynomial over the reals.

EXERCISES

1. True or false?

   a. Every monomial is a polynomial.

   b. Every polynomial is a trinomial.

   c. A binomial is a polynomial having four terms.

   d. Every polynomial is a monomial in one variable whose degree is at least one.

   e. $\dfrac{1}{x^2}$ is a monomial.

   f. 5 is a monomial.

   g. 9 is a polynomial.

   h. $2x + 3$ is a polynomial in one variable.

   i. $x + xy$ is a polynomial in two variables.

   j. $x^2 + \dfrac{3}{y} + y$ is a polynomial in two variables.

2. Give the degree of each of the following polynomials.

   a. $3x - 3$ **c.** $y^2 - 2y + 9$ **e.** $x - x^2y$

   b. t **d.** 1   **f.** $1 + x + x^2 + x^3 + x^4$

3. Classify each of the following as polynomials over the integers, rationals, or reals. Give the most descriptive classification in each case.

   a. $x^2 + \dfrac{1}{2}x + 4$ **c.** $y^2 + x$ **e.** $2\pi + x^4$

   b. $t^2 + 3t + 2$ **d.** $x^3 + x + \sqrt{2}$ **f.** $x^2 + 3x + \dfrac{1}{2}$

4. Which of the following are polynomials in

   i. two variables?

   ii. more than two variables?

   a. $3x_1x_2 + 2$ **d.** $5 - 7x + y$

   b. $x_1^2 + x_2^2 + x_3^2$ **e.** $y_1 + 7y_2$

   c. $x + 2y + 3z$ **f.** $x_1^2 + 2x_1x_2 + 1$

EVALUATION OF POLYNOMIALS

Suppose the replacement set for the variables in our discussion is R, the set of real numbers. Then, when you replace each variable in a polynomial by some element of R, you determine a real number. This process is called *evaluating* the polynomial or finding the *value* of the polynomial. For example, the value of the polynomial

$$3x - 5$$

when x is replaced by

2 is $[3 \cdot 2 - 5]$ or 1

0 is $[3 \cdot 0 - 5]$ or -5

-2 is $[3 \cdot (-2) - 5]$ or -11

$\dfrac{1}{3}$ is $\left[3 \cdot \left(\dfrac{1}{3}\right) - 5\right]$ or -4

-5.1 is $[3(-5.1) - 5]$ or -20.3

EXERCISES

For exercises **1–15,** evaluate the given polynomials for specified replacements.

1. $2x + 3$; 5 for x

2. x^2; 1 for x

3. $y^2 - y$; 1 for y

4. $t^2 - 3$; 0 for t

5. $2n^3 - n$; 2 for n

6. xy; 2 for x and (-2) for y

7. $x - y$; 3 for x and (-3) for y

8. $\dfrac{x}{3} + 1$; 6 for x

9. $2k - k^2$; 4 for k

10. x^2y; (-2) for x and 3 for y

11. $2(x - 3)$; 3 for x

12. $y^2 + 3$; (-3) for y

13. $\dfrac{1}{2}x - 1$; 1 for x

14. $x - y - z$; 2 for x, 1 for y and 0 for z

15. $xyz - 3$; 1 for x, 1 for y and 1 for z

16. Determine the value of the polynomial $3x^2 - x - 2$ if x is replaced by

    a. 0   **b.** .5   **c.** $\dfrac{1}{3}$ **d.** $-\dfrac{2}{3}$

17. Determine the value of the polynomial $\frac{1}{2}y^2 + \frac{11}{4}y - \frac{3}{2}$ if y is replaced by

    a. $\dfrac{1}{2}$ **b.** -6 **c.** 1   **d.** 2

18. Determine the value of the polynomial $\frac{1}{2}x^2y - x + y + 3z$ if

    a. x is replaced by 1, y is replaced by 2, and z is replaced by 3

    b. x is replaced by -1, y is replaced by -2, and z is replaced by $\frac{2}{3}$

    c. x is replaced by 2, y is replaced by $\frac{1}{4}$, and z is replaced by $\frac{1}{3}$

    d. x is replaced by $-\frac{4}{3}$, y is replaced by 0, and z is replaced by $-\frac{5}{6}$

ADDITION OF POLYNOMIALS

We have defined polynomials and have learned to classify them in several ways. We are now prepared to discuss the fundamental operations of addition, subtraction, multiplication, and division with polynomials.

To add polynomials, as illustrated by the following examples, we make use of the distributive, commutative, and associative properties of addition and multiplication for real numbers.

Examples:

i. $\forall_x \ 3x + 4x \quad = (3 + 4)x$ RDPMA

$= 7x$ Arith. fact

ii. $\forall_x \ 2x^2 + (x + 3x^2) = 2x^2 + (3x^2 + x)$ CPA

$= (2x^2 + 3x^2) + x$ APA

$= (2 + 3)x^2 + x$ RDPMA

$= 5x^2 + x$ Arith. fact

iii. (Supply reasons for each step.)

$\forall_x \ (3x^2 + 5x) + (4x^2 + x) = (3x^2 + 5x) + (x + 4x^2)$

$= [(3x^2 + 5x) + x] + 4x^2$

$= [3x^2 + (5x + x)] + 4x^2$

$= [3x^2 + (5x + 1x)] + 4x^2$

$= [3x^2 + (5 + 1)x] + 4x^2$

$= (3x^2 + 6x) + 4x^2$

$= 4x^2 + (3x^2 + 6x)$

$= (4x^2 + 3x^2) + 6x$

$= (4 + 3)x^2 + 6x$

$= 7x^2 + 6x$

The procedure for adding polynomials need not be as detailed as the last example might suggest. Since addition is both associative and commutative, we may use these properties several times without showing each step. We shall refer to this procedure as "sum (or term) rearrangement." Thus, applying the principle of sum rearrangement, the addition of the polynomials in the last example might appear like this

$$(3x^2 + 5x) + (4x^2 + x) = (3x^2 + 4x^2) + (5x + x)$$
$$= 7x^2 + 6x$$

For convenience, we often show one addend under the other like this

$$3x^2 + 5x$$
$$\underline{4x^2 + \ \ x}$$
$$7x^2 + 6x$$

Notice that similar terms (terms which are either identical or differ only in numerical coefficients) are arranged in columns, and hence, the distributive property may be applied in each column. Must $3x^2 + 5x$ be on the top line? Why or why not?

EXERCISES

1. Add.

a. $ax + 5$
$ ax - 4$

d. $xy + x + y + 2$
$ xy - 3$

g. $ n^3 + 8$
$-n^3 - n^2 - n - 8$

b. $3x^3 + 3x$
$4x^3 - 3x^2 - 7x + 10$

e. $c^2 - d^2$
$ c^2 + d^2$

h. $a^3 + b^3$
$a^3 - 3a^2b + 3ab^2 - b^3$

c. $x^2 + 2xy + y^2$
$x^2 - 2xy + y^2$

f. $a^3 + b^2 - c$
$ b^2 + c$

i. $ az^3 + bz^2 - z$
$-az^3 + z - 4$

2. Simplify.

a. $x + x$
b. $5y^2 + y^2$
c. $(3x^2 + 1) + (x^2 - 4)$
d. $(t^2 - t + 1) + t$
e. $(y^3 + 3y^2 + 2) + (y^4 + y^3 - y^2 + 5)$
f. $(4x^2y + 3xy + 7) + (x^3 + 3x^2y - 2xy - 5)$
g. $(4y^4 - 3y^3 - 2y^2 - y - 1) + (1 + y + y^2 + y^3 + y^4)$
h. $(3k^2 - k + 2) + (4k - 3)$
i. $b^3 + (3b^3 - c)$
j. $(x^4 - 1) + (x^3 - 3x^2)$

SUBTRACTION OF POLYNOMIALS

Since polynomials over the reals name real numbers for real replacements of the variables they contain, we define subtraction of polynomials in the same way that we define subtraction of real numbers.

■ *Definition of Subtraction of Polynomials* For any polynomial replacements of P and Q, the difference $P - Q$ is defined as follows:

$$P - Q = P + (-Q)$$

where $(-Q)$ is the additive inverse (opposite) of Q.

In other words, the difference $P - Q$ is equal to the sum of P and the additive inverse of Q. Remember, since Q and $(-Q)$ are additive inverses, their sum is zero; that is

$$Q + (-Q) = 0$$

The next question which we must answer is "What is $(-Q)$ for any particular polynomial replacement of Q?" For instance, if $Q = x^2 + 2x + 1$, then what is $(-Q)$? Here is an important theorem which answers this question.

Theorem 1 $\forall_X \forall_Y \ldots \forall_Z \quad -(X + Y + \ldots + Z) =$
$$(-X) + (-Y) + \ldots + (-Z)$$

In words, this theorem tells us that the additive inverse of a sum is equal to the sum of the additive inverses of the terms making up the sum. For example

$$-(x^2 + 2x + 1) = (-x^2) + (-2x) + (-1)$$

The proof of Theorem 1 is beyond the scope of this text, but a proof of a special case of the theorem will be shown. We shall prove that

$$\forall_X \forall_Y \quad -(X + Y) = (-X) + (-Y)$$

Proof $[X + Y] + [(-X) + (-Y)]$
$= [X + (-X)] + [Y + (-Y)]$ CPA and APA
$= 0 + 0$ PAI
$= 0$ PZA

Hence, $(-X) + (-Y) = -(X + Y)$ PAI
Q.E.D.

The definition of a difference, $P - Q$, and Theorem 1 provide us with all the tools we need to subtract any two polynomials.

Examples: i. $\forall_x \ (2x^3 + 5x) - (x^3 + 3x)$
$= (2x^3 + 5x) + [-(x^3 + 3x)]$ Def. diff. poly.
$= (2x^3 + 5x) + [(-x^3) + (-3x)]$ Theorem 1
$= x^3 + 2x$ Why?

    ii.   (Supply the reasons for each step.)
$\forall_y \ (3y^2 + y + 5) - (2y^2 - 3) = (3y^2 + y + 5) + (-2y^2 + 3)$
$= y^2 + y + 8$

    iii.   (Supply the reasons for each step.)
$\forall_t \ (3t^4 - t^2 + 2) - (-t^2 - 2) = (3t^4 - t^2 + 2) + (t^2 + 2)$
$= 3t^4 + 4$

For convenience in simplifying a difference, $P - Q$, of polynomials, we often write the polynomial Q under the polynomial P; the simplified expression of the difference is then easy to obtain. For instance, we might choose to simplify the difference

$$(5n^3 - 5n + 4) - (4n^3 - n - 2)$$

in the following way.

Subtract: $5n^3 - 5n + 4$
            $4n^3 - \ \ n - 2$
            $\overline{n^3 - 4n + 6}$

Note that we simply think of the additive inverse of $4n^3 - n - 2$, which is $-4n^3 + n + 2$, and write down the sum. Note also that the sum of $n^3 - 4n + 6$ and $4n^3 - n - 2$ is $5n^3 - 5n + 4$. This is no accident. By the definition of the difference $P - Q$

$$P - Q = P + (-Q)$$

observe that the sum of $P + (-Q)$ and Q is

$$[P + (-Q)] + Q = P + [(-Q) + Q] = P$$

This fact may be applied to check every subtraction.

EXERCISES

1. True or false?

  a. $\forall_x \; -(x+1) = -x+1$

  b. $\forall_n \; -(n^2 + 5n + 4) = -n^2 - 5n - 4$

  c. $\forall_x \forall_y \; -(x^3 - 3x^2y - 3xy^2 + y^3) = -x^3 - 3x^2y - 3xy^2 - y^3$

  d. $\forall_t \; -(-t^4 - 8) = t^4 + 8$

  e. $\forall_y \; -(-y^2) = y^2$

  f. $2^5 - 2^2 = 2^3$

  g. $10^7 - 10^3 = 10^4$

  h. $\forall_x \; x^{12} - x^3 = x^9$

  i. $\forall_m \forall_n \; -(3m - 4n) = 4n - 3m$

  j. $\forall_t \; -5t + 3t = -8t$

2. Subtract and check each answer by adding.

  a. $3x + 4$
     $\underline{x - 1}$

  b. $3x^2 - 2x - 1$
     $\underline{\quad\quad 5x + 6}$

  c. $1 - t + t^2$
     $\underline{\quad -t + t^2}$

  d. $4 - bcd$
     $\underline{\quad - bcd}$

  e. $-2n^4 - n^3 + n - 6$
     $\underline{\quad\quad n^3 \quad\quad +1}$

  f. $a - b$
     $\underline{a - b}$

  g. $x^2 + 2xy + y^2$
     $\underline{x^2 - 2xy + y^2}$

  h. $k^3 - k - 7$
     $\underline{k}$

  i. $x^3 - y^3$
     $\underline{x - 1}$

3. Simplify.

  a. $(6x^3 - 3x + 2) - (7x^3 + 3x + 7)$

  b. $(2 - x) - (x^2 + 3x + 3)$

  c. $y - (-y)$

  d. $(x^2 + 4xy + y^2) - (-x^2 + 4xy - 2y^2)$

  e. $(-2n^3 - n - 8) - (-7 - 2n^3)$

  f. $5t - t$

  g. $-t - (t)$

  h. $(4y + 5) - (-y - 3)$

MULTIPLICATION OF POLYNOMIALS

The procedures for multiplying polynomials are based on the distributive property and the commutative and associative properties of multiplication for real numbers. In the case of *multiplication of monomials*, we need employ only the latter two properties. The following example illustrates, in detail, the kinds of steps that are typically involved in the multiplication of monomials.

Example:

$$
\begin{aligned}
\forall_x \; (4x) \cdot (3x^2) &= 4[x(3x^2)] && \text{APM} \\
&= 4[(x \cdot 3)x^2] && \text{APM} \\
&= 4[(3 \cdot x)x^2] && \text{CPM} \\
&= 4[3(x \cdot x^2)] && \text{APM} \\
&= (4 \cdot 3) \cdot (x \cdot x^2) && \text{APM} \\
&= 12x^3 && \text{Arith. fact; Prod. of powers}
\end{aligned}
$$

The procedure for simplifying a product of monomials need not be as detailed as the above example might suggest. Since multiplication is both associative and commutative, we may use these properties several times without showing each step. We shall refer to this procedure as "factor (or product) rearrangement." Thus, using factor rearrangement, we have

$$\forall_x \ (4x) \cdot (3x^2) = 4 \cdot x \cdot 3 \cdot x^2$$
$$= (4 \cdot 3) \cdot (x \cdot x^2)$$
$$= 12x^3$$

In many cases, the product of two or more monomials can be determined mentally.

ORAL EXERCISES

Simplify mentally.

1. $(2x) \cdot (-3x)$

2. $(4x) \cdot (3y)$

3. $(-5a) \cdot (-7a^3)$

4. $(ab) \cdot (abc)$

5. $-r \cdot (rs) \cdot (rst)$

6. $(3n) \cdot (-2n^2 k) \cdot (k)$

7. $(x^2 y^3) \cdot (-5x) \cdot (-2y^2)$

8. $\left(\frac{1}{2} t^3 y\right) \cdot \left(\frac{1}{2} xy\right)$

9. $(2r)^2 \cdot (r^2 s)$

10. $a \cdot (2b) \cdot (3c)$

11. $(100x) \cdot (.1y)^2$

12. $(4t) \cdot (.5t^2)^2$

13. $-(n^2 t) \cdot (-3ntx)$

14. $(6x) \cdot \left(\frac{1}{2} xy\right) \cdot \left(\frac{1}{3} yz\right)$

15. $\left(\frac{1}{3} r^2 st\right) \cdot \left(\frac{2}{5} st\right)$

In considering *multiplication of polynomials* in general, we resort to the familiar distributive property. To see how the distributive property applies, consider the product $(a + b) \cdot (c + d)$.

Suppose we let $P = (a + b)$

Then $(a + b)(c + d) = P \cdot (c + d)$ Subst. prop.

$\qquad\qquad\qquad = P \cdot c + P \cdot d$ LDPMA

$\qquad\qquad\qquad = (a + b) \cdot c + (a + b) \cdot d$ Substitution

$\qquad\qquad\qquad = ac + bc + ad + bd$ RDPMA

The substitutions were introduced in the above example for the purpose of making the various steps easier to follow. Such substitutions are not necessary in practice. In brief, the steps in simplifying the given product were these.

$\qquad (a + b) \cdot (c + d) = (a + b) \cdot c + (a + b) \cdot d$ LDPMA

$\qquad\qquad\qquad\qquad = ac + bc + ad + bd$ RDPMA

Thus, we see that repeated applications of the distributive property produces the product. Here are six additional examples which illustrate procedures to follow when simplifying a product of polynomials. You supply the reason for each of the steps in the various examples.

Examples: *i.* $\forall_x \forall_y \ 2x \cdot (3x + y) = 2x \cdot 3x + 2x \cdot y = 6x^2 + 2xy$

        ii. $\forall_y \ y \cdot (y^2 + 2y + 1) = y \cdot y^2 + y \cdot 2y + y \cdot 1 = y^3 + 2y^2 + y$

Examples: *iii.* $\forall_t$ $3t^2 \cdot (t^3 + t^2 + t + 1) = 3t^2 \cdot t^3 + 3t^2 \cdot t^2 + 3t^2 \cdot t + 3t^2 \cdot 1$
$$= 3t^5 + 3t^4 + 3t^3 + 3t^2$$

    iv. $\forall_x$ $(x + 1) \cdot (x + 3) = (x + 1) \cdot x + (x + 1) \cdot 3$
$$= x \cdot x + 1 \cdot x + x \cdot 3 + 1 \cdot 3$$
$$= x^2 + 1 \cdot x + 3x + 3$$
$$= x^2 + 4x + 3$$

    v. $\forall_x\forall_y$ $(x + y) \cdot (y + 2) = (x + y) \cdot y + (x + y) \cdot 2$
$$= x \cdot y + y \cdot y + x \cdot 2 + y \cdot 2$$
$$= xy + y^2 + 2x + 2y$$

    vi. $\forall_x$ $(2x^2 + 5)(x^3 + x - 3) = (2x^2 + 5) \cdot x^3 + (2x^2 + 5) \cdot x$
$$- (2x^2 + 5) \cdot 3$$
$$= 2x^2 \cdot x^3 + 5 \cdot x^3 + 2x^2 \cdot x + 5 \cdot x$$
$$- 2x^2 \cdot 3 - 5 \cdot 3$$
$$= 2x^5 + 5x^3 + 2x^3 + 5x - 6x^2 - 15$$
$$= 2x^5 + 7x^3 - 6x^2 + 5x - 15$$

When multiplying polynomials, one may also place one polynomial below the other, apply the distributive property in the usual way, and arrange the terms of the products which are similar (terms which are identical or differ only in numerical coefficients) in the same column. The desired expression of the product is then easy to obtain. The following example illustrates this method.

Example: Multiply: $x^3 + x \ - 3$
                             $\underline{2x^2 + 5}$
                             $2x^5 + 2x^3 - 6x^2$
                             $\underline{+ 5x^3 \qquad\quad + 5x - 15}$
                             $2x^5 + 7x^3 - 6x^2 + 5x - 15$

EXERCISES

1.   True or false?

    a. $\forall_x$ $2x(x - 7) = 2x \cdot x - 7$

    b. $\forall_x$ $(4x + 1)(2x + 3) = (4x + 1) \cdot 2x + (4x + 1) \cdot 3$

    c. $\forall_x$ $(4x + 1)(2x + 3) = 4x \cdot (2x + 3) + (2x + 3)$

    d. $\forall_t$ $3t(t^2 - 2t - 1) = 3t^3 - 6t^2 - 3t$

    e. $\forall_x\forall_y$ $(x^2 + 2xy + y^2) \cdot x = x^3 + 2xy + y^2$

    f. $\forall_x\forall_y\forall_r\forall_s\forall_t$ $(x + y) \cdot (r + s + t) = x \cdot (r + s + t) + y \cdot (r + s + t)$

    g. $\forall_x\forall_y\forall_r\forall_s\forall_t$ $(x + y) \cdot (r + s + t) = (x + y) \cdot r + (x + y) \cdot s + (x + y) \cdot t$

    h. $\forall_c$ $(c + 3)^2 = (c + 3)(c + 3) = (c + 3) \cdot c + (c + 3) \cdot 3$

    i. $\forall_n$ $(n + 1)^2 = (n + 1) \cdot n + (n + 1)$

    j. $\forall_k$ $(k + 1)(k - 1) = (k + 1) \cdot k + (k + 1)$

    k. $\forall_x\forall_y$ $(1 - xy) \cdot (x^3y^2 - 3x + 2y - 5) = (x^3y^2 - 3x + 2y - 5) \cdot (1 - xy)$

    l. $\forall_m$ $2(3m) = (2 \cdot 3)(2 \cdot m)$

2.   Simplify.

    a. $3x(y + z)$

    b. $(t^2 - 1) \cdot 2t$

    c. $xy \cdot (2x^4y + x^2y^2 - 3xy^3)$

    d. $(x + 5)(x - 3)$

    e. $(x + 4)(y - 3)$

    f. $-4y^2(3y - 8)$

    g. $(k^3 - 2k)(4k^2 - 1)$

    h. $(ax^3 - bx^2 + c) \cdot (-3x)$

    i. $(3x + 4)(x^2 + 3x - 5)$

    j. $(4n^2 - 7n + 6)(5n^2 + 4n + 6)$

    k. $(y + 3)(y - 3)$

    l. $(3x - 4)(3x + 4)$

    m. $(a + b)(a - b)$

    n. $(t + 3)^2$

    o. $(2x + 5)^2$

    p. $(a + b + c)(d + e + f)$

3.   Multiply.

    a. $\begin{aligned} 5a &+ 7 \\ 2a &- 3 \end{aligned}$

    b. $\begin{aligned} 2x &+ 3y \\ x &- 4y \end{aligned}$

    c. $\begin{aligned} x^3 &- y^3 \\ 1 &- y \end{aligned}$

    d. $\begin{aligned} 4t^2 &- t + 3 \\ t &+ 3 \end{aligned}$

    e. $\begin{aligned} x^2 &+ xy + y^2 \\ x &- y \end{aligned}$

    f. $\begin{aligned} x^2 &- y^2 \\ x^2 &+ y^2 \end{aligned}$

    g. $\begin{aligned} t^3 &+ n^3 \\ t^3 &- n^3 \end{aligned}$

    h. $\begin{aligned} x &+ y \\ x &+ y \end{aligned}$

    i. $\begin{aligned} x^2 &- xy + y^2 \\ x &+ y \end{aligned}$

    j. $\begin{aligned} a^4 &+ a^2b^2 + b^4 \\ a^2 &- b^2 \end{aligned}$

    k. $\begin{aligned} x^2 &+ 5x - 7 \\ x^2 &- x + 4 \end{aligned}$

    l. $\begin{aligned} k^4 &- 2k^3 + 3k^2 - 4k + 5 \\ k &+ 2 \end{aligned}$

    m. $\begin{aligned} -n^3 &- 2n^2 - 3n - 4 \\ n^2 &+ n - 1 \end{aligned}$

    n. $\begin{aligned} ax^3 &+ bx^2 + c \\ ax^3 &- bx^2 + c \end{aligned}$

    o. $\begin{aligned} 2x^2y^2 &- 3x + 4y + 1 \\ 1 &- xy \end{aligned}$

    p. $\begin{aligned} r^2 &- 2r + 1 \\ 2r &- r^2 - 1 \end{aligned}$

Special products

We have learned how to find a simplified expression of the product of any two polynomials by applying — frequently more than once — the distributive property. There are certain pairs of polynomials, however, which you should be able to multiply instantly.

One special case is that where both polynomials are binomials, these binomials being the sum and difference, respectively, of the same two terms. For example, each of the products

$$(x + 5)(x - 5) \qquad\qquad (2x + 3)(2x - 3) \qquad\qquad (3x^2 + 1)(3x^2 - 1)$$

is of this special type. Observe the simplified forms of these products in relation to their factors.

$$\forall_x \ (x+5)(x-5) = (x+5) \cdot x + (x+5) \cdot (-5)$$
$$= x^2 + 5x - 5x - 25$$
$$= x^2 - 25$$

$$\forall_x \ (2x+3)(2x-3) = (2x+3) \cdot 2x + (2x+3) \cdot (-3)$$
$$= 4x^2 + 6x - 6x - 9$$
$$= 4x^2 - 9$$

$$\forall_x \ (3x^2+1)(3x^2-1) = (3x^2+1) \cdot 3x^2 + (3x^2+1) \cdot (-1)$$
$$= 9x^4 + 3x^2 - 3x^2 - 1$$
$$= 9x^4 - 1$$

This special case can be summarized by noticing that

$$\forall_X \forall_Y \ (X+Y) \cdot (X-Y) = X^2 - Y^2$$

In other words, any pair of binomials which pattern in the forms $(x+y)$ and $(x-y)$ will have a product which is equal to the square of the term corresponding to x minus the square of the term corresponding to y. Thus, for example,

$$\forall_t \ (5t+4) \cdot (5t-4) = (5t)^2 - (4)^2$$
$$= 25t^2 - 16$$

Another special case is the square of a binomial. The following examples should lead to a pattern for the square of a binomial.

Examples: i. $\forall_y \ (y+3)^2 = (y+3) \cdot (y+3)$
$$= (y+3) \cdot y + (y+3) \cdot 3$$
$$= y^2 + 3y + 3y + 9$$
$$= y^2 + 6y + 9$$

ii. $\forall_x \ (3x-1)^2 = (3x-1) \cdot (3x-1)$
$$= (3x-1) \cdot 3x - (3x-1) \cdot 1$$
$$= 9x^2 - 3x - 3x + 1$$
$$= 9x^2 - 6x + 1$$

Do you see the pattern? Here again, we summarize by observing that

$$\forall_X \forall_Y \ (X+Y)^2 = X^2 + 2XY + Y^2$$

In other words, when you square a binomial which patterns in the form $(x+y)$, the product may be expressed as the sum of three terms; two of the terms of the product, namely x^2 and y^2, correspond to the squares of the terms of the binomial, and the remaining term, namely $2xy$, is twice the product of the terms of the binomial. We see, for example, that

$$\forall_t \ (2t+5)^2 = (2t)^2 + 2(2t)(5) + (5)^2$$
$$= 4t^2 + 20t + 25$$

Moreover, since $\forall_X \forall_Y \ (X-Y) = [X+(-Y)]$, it follows that

$$\forall_X \forall_Y \ (X-Y)^2 = [X+(-Y)]^2$$
$$= X^2 + 2X(-Y) + (-Y)^2$$
$$= X^2 - 2XY + Y^2$$

Hence, we see that the expanded forms of $(X+Y)^2$ and $(X-Y)^2$ differ in only one detail; describe this point of difference and then study the following examples.

Examples: *i.* $\forall_x \forall_y \; (3x + 2y)^2 = (3x)^2 + 2(3x)(2y) + (2y)^2 = 9x^2 + 12xy + 4y^2$

          ii. $\forall_x \forall_y \; (xy - 3)^2 = (xy)^2 - 2(xy)(3) + (3)^2 = x^2 y^2 - 6xy + 9$

        iii. $\forall_t \; (-t - 7)^2 = (-t)^2 - 2(-t) \cdot 7 + (7)^2 = t^2 + 14t + 49$

EXERCISES

1. True or false?

a. $\forall_x \; x - 2 = 2 - x$

b. $\forall_x \; x - 2 = -2 + x$

c. $\forall_x \; x + 2 = 2 + x$

d. $\forall_x \; (x+2) \cdot (x-2) = (2+x) \cdot (-2+x)$

e. $\forall_x \; (2 + x) \cdot (-2 + x) = x^2 - 4$

f. $\forall_y \; (-y + 3) \cdot (-y - 3) = y^2 - 9$

g. $\forall_t \; (t + 7)^2 = t^2 + 7t + 49$

h. $\forall_k \; (3k - 2)^2 = 9k^2 + 12k + 4$

i. $\forall_n \; (2n - 1)^2 = 4n^2 - 4n + 1$

j. $\forall_a \forall_x \; (-a - x)^2 = a^2 + 2ax + x^2$

k. $\forall_t \; (t + 3)^2 = t^2 + 9$

l. $\forall_m \; (m - 6)^2 = (6 - m)^2$

2. Simplify.

a. $(4n + 3) \cdot (4n - 3)$

b. $(4n + 3)^2$

c. $(4n - 3)^2$

d. $(a + k) \cdot (a - k)$

e. $(x^2 - 6) \cdot (x^2 + 6)$

f. $(-2 + 5t) \cdot (-2 - 5t)$

g. $(-2 + 5t)^2$

h. $(-2 - 5t)^2$

i. $(x^2 + y) \cdot (x^2 - y)$

j. $[(a + b) + c] \cdot [(a + b) + c]$

k. $[x^2 + (x + 1)] \cdot [x^2 - (x + 1)]$

l. $[(a + 2b) + x] \cdot [(a + 2b) - x]$

m. $[(x + y) + 1]^2$

n. $[(2x + 1) - y]^2$

o. $[x + (y + z)] \cdot [x - (y + z)]$

p. $[x - (y - z)]^2$

3. Complete.

a. $\forall_x \forall_y \; x^2 - 4y^2 = (x - 2y) \cdot (\quad ? \quad)$

b. $\forall_t \; 9t^2 - 16 = (3t + 4) \cdot (\quad ? \quad)$

c. $\forall_n \; -25 + 49n^2 = (\quad ? \quad) \cdot (\quad ? \quad)$

d. $\forall_k \; 64k^2 - 81 = (\quad ? \quad) \cdot (\quad ? \quad)$

e. $\forall_x \; x^2 + 2x + 1 = (\quad ? \quad)^2$

f. $\forall_y \; y^2 + 4y + 4 = (\quad ? \quad)^2$

g. $\forall_k \; k^2 - 4k + 4 = (\quad ? \quad)^2$

h. $\forall_t \; t^2 - 6t + 9 = (\quad ? \quad)^2$

i. $\forall_n \; 4n^2 - 4n + 1 = (\quad ? \quad)^2$

j. $\forall_x \; 9x^2 + 24x + 16 = (\quad ? \quad)^2$

k. $21^2 = (20 + 1)^2 = 20^2 + 2 \cdot 20 \cdot 1 + 1^2 = (\quad ? \quad)$

l. $31^2 = (30 + 1)^2 = (\quad ? \quad)$

m. $52 \cdot 48 = (50 + 2) \cdot (50 - 2) = 50^2 - 2^2 = (\quad ? \quad)$

n. $63 \cdot 57 = (60 + 3)(60 - 3) = (\quad ? \quad)$

o. $35 \cdot 45 = (\quad ? \quad)$

DIVISION OF POLYNOMIALS

The definition of division of polynomials is similar to the definition of division of real numbers.

■ *Definition of Division of Polynomials* For any polynomials P, Q, and R,

$$Q \neq 0, \quad \frac{P}{Q} = R \quad \text{if and only if} \quad Q \cdot R = P.$$

To be able to divide any pair of polynomials, we shall first learn to divide one monomial by another. The definition of division tells us all we need to know in order to do this. For example, since $\forall_x \ 6x^2 \cdot 3x = 18x^3$, it follows that if $x \neq 0$

$$\frac{18x^3}{3x} = 6x^2 \quad \text{and} \quad \frac{18x^3}{6x^2} = 3x$$

As a second example

$$\forall_{x \neq 0} \ \frac{-8x^5}{2x} = -4x^4 \quad \text{since} \quad 2x \cdot (-4x^4) = -8x^5$$

EXERCISES

1. True or false?

a. $\forall_{x \neq 0} \ \dfrac{12x^3}{6x^2} = 2x$

b. $\forall_{y \neq 0} \ \dfrac{9y^2}{9y} = 1$

c. $\forall_{t \neq 0} \ \dfrac{t}{t} = t$

d. $\forall_{x \neq 0} \ \dfrac{24x^3}{-x^2} = -24x$

e. $\forall_{x \neq 0} \ \dfrac{-16x^4}{2x^2} = 8x^2$

f. $\forall_{x \neq 0} \ \dfrac{-x^5}{x^5} = -1$

g. $\forall_x \ \dfrac{4x}{4} = x$

h. $\forall_x \ \dfrac{12x}{0} = 0$

i. $\forall_{t \neq 0} \ \dfrac{0}{t^2} = 0$

j. $\forall_{x \neq 0} \forall_{y \neq 0} \ \dfrac{9x^2 y^2}{3x^2 y} = 3y$

2. Simplify; assume that all denominators are non-zero.

a. $\dfrac{22x^3}{x^3}$

b. $\dfrac{-14y^5}{7y}$

c. $\dfrac{-x^2 y^2}{xy}$

d. $\dfrac{8t^2}{-4t}$

e. $\dfrac{-a^2 b^3}{-ab^2}$

f. $\dfrac{64n^2}{16n}$

g. $\dfrac{3x^2 y^2}{xy^2}$

h. $\dfrac{0}{3x^2 y}$

i. $\dfrac{x^2 y^4}{y}$

j. $\dfrac{81t^3}{-27t^2}$

Division by monomials

We shall now consider the division of a polynomial (containing two or more terms) by a monomial.

The definition of division tells us that

$$\forall_{x \neq 0} \ \frac{6x^2 + 9x}{3x} = 2x + 3$$

since $\forall_x \ 3x(2x + 3) = 6x^2 + 9x$. The definition of division of polynomials does not give us much help, however, in simplifying a quotient like $\dfrac{6x^2 + 9x}{3x}$. As shown by the following examples, simplifying the quotient $\dfrac{P}{Q}$ where P is a polynomial and Q is a monomial involves the distributive property of multiplication over addition and the fact that

$$\forall_a \forall_{b \neq 0} \ \frac{a}{b} = a \cdot \frac{1}{b} = \frac{1}{b} \cdot a$$

Examples: i. $\displaystyle \forall_{x \neq 0} \ \frac{4x^3 + 2x^2}{2x} = \frac{1}{2x}(4x^3 + 2x^2)$

$$= \frac{4x^3}{2x} + \frac{2x^2}{2x} = 2x^2 + x$$

ii. $\displaystyle \forall_{x \neq 0} \ \frac{12x^2 + 9x}{3x} = \frac{1}{3x}(12x^2 + 9x)$

$$= \frac{12x^2}{3x} + \frac{9x}{3x} = 4x + 3$$

iii. $\displaystyle \forall_{x \neq 0} \ \frac{16x^4 + 12x^3 + 4x^2}{4x} = \frac{1}{4x}(16x^4 + 12x^3 + 4x^2)$

$$= \frac{16x^4}{4x} + \frac{12x^3}{4x} + \frac{4x^2}{4x} = 4x^3 + 3x^2 + x$$

iv. $\displaystyle \forall_{y \neq 0} \ \frac{25y^5 - 15y^3 - 10y^2 - 5y}{5y} = \frac{1}{5y}(25y^5 - 15y^3 - 10y^2 - 5y)$

$$= \frac{25y^5}{5y} - \frac{15y^3}{5y} - \frac{10y^2}{5y} - \frac{5y}{5y} = 5y^4 - 3y^2 - 2y - 1$$

EXERCISES

1.   True or false?

a. $\displaystyle \forall_{x \neq 0} \ \frac{18x^3 + 6x^2}{3x} = 6x^2 + 2$

b. $\displaystyle \forall_{y \neq 0} \ \frac{12y^2 + 6y}{3y} = 4y + 6y$

c. $\displaystyle \forall_{t \neq 0} \ \frac{12t^3 - 8t}{2t} = 6t^2 - 4$

d. $\displaystyle \forall_{n \neq 0} \ \frac{21n^5 - 12n^3 - 6n^2}{3n^2} = 7n^3 + 4n + 2$

e. $\displaystyle \forall_a \ \frac{-24a^4 + 8a^3 - 16}{-8} = 3a^4 - a^3 + 2$

f. $\displaystyle \forall_a \forall_{b \neq 0} \ \frac{a^2b + ab + 2b}{b} = a^2 + a + 2$

g. $\forall_n \forall_{m \neq 0} \dfrac{m^4 - m^3 n - m^3 n^2}{-m^3} = m + n + n^2$

h. $\forall_x \dfrac{4.25 x^2 - 2.75 x + 1.25}{.25} = 17 x^2 - 11 x + 5$

i. $\forall_x \forall_y \forall_z \dfrac{-x - y - z}{-1} = -(x + y + z)$

j. $\forall_a \forall_{x \neq 0} \dfrac{x^{2a} + x^{2a-1}}{x^a} = x^a + x^{a-1}$

2. Simplify and check by multiplication; assume that no divisor is zero.

a. $(3b^5 - 9b^4 + 6b^3) \div (3b^3)$

b. $(x^9 - x^7) \div (-x^7)$

c. $(4x^3 y + x^2 y^2 - xy) \div (xy)$

d. $(27 n^6 - 18 n^4) \div (-9 n^2)$

e. $(2x - 6x^2 + 8x^3 - 14x^5) \div (-2x)$

f. $(a^3 - a^2 b + ab^2) \div (-a)$

g. $(-x + y - z) \div (-1)$

h. $(1.2 t^2 - 2.1 t + .6) \div (-.3)$

i. $(x^{2n} - x^{3n}) \div x^n$

j. $(t^c - 2t^{c+2} + 3t^{c+4}) \div t^c$

Division by polynomials

We have learned to simplify the quotient $\dfrac{P}{Q}$ where P is any polynomial and Q is a monomial. Now we shall extend our discussion to quotients of polynomials in general.

The principles and procedures used in simplifying quotients of polynomials can be illustrated by examining division of numbers. To begin, let us consider the quotient $651 \div 31$. Recall that the symbol 651 is an abbreviation of $600 + 50 + 1$ and that 31 is an abbreviation of $30 + 1$. Hence, a more detailed way of showing

$$
\begin{array}{r}
21 \\
31 \overline{\smash{)}651} \\
62 \\
\hline
31 \\
31
\end{array}
\qquad \text{is to write} \qquad
\begin{array}{r}
20 + 1 \\
30 + 1 \overline{\smash{)}600 + 50 + 1} \\
600 + 20 \\
\hline
30 + 1 \\
30 + 1
\end{array}
$$

The last form reveals that $600 + 50 + 1 = (600 + 20) + (30 + 1)$, and so we are saying that

$$
\frac{651}{31} = \frac{600 + 50 + 1}{30 + 1} = \frac{(600 + 20) + (30 + 1)}{30 + 1} = 20 + 1 = 21
$$

For a second example, consider the quotient $1572 \div 12$. Proceeding as before, we have

$$
\begin{array}{r}
100 + 30 + 1 \\
10 + 2 \overline{\smash{)}1000 + 500 + 70 + 2} \\
1000 + 200 \\
\hline
300 + 70 + 2 \\
300 + 60 \\
\hline
10 + 2 \\
10 + 2
\end{array}
$$

We have found that

$$1000 + 500 + 70 + 2 = (1000 + 200) + (300 + 60) + (10 + 2)$$

and so we are saying that

$$\frac{1572}{12} = \frac{1000 + 500 + 70 + 2}{10 + 2} = \frac{(1000 + 200) + (300 + 60) + (10 + 2)}{10 + 2}$$

$$= \frac{1000 + 200}{10 + 2} + \frac{300 + 60}{10 + 2} + \frac{10 + 2}{10 + 2}$$

$$= 100 + 30 + 1$$

$$= 131$$

The methods employed in these two examples may be used to simplify quotients of polynomials. For example, consider the quotient $(5x^2 - 16x + 3) \div (x - 3)$. We write

$$x - 3 \enclose{longdiv}{5x^2 - 16x + 3}$$

Clearly, the first term of the simplified expression for the quotient is $5x$ since $\forall_x\ 5x \cdot x = 5x^2$. Now we multiply $(x - 3)$ by $5x$, place the terms of the product in the appropriate columns, and subtract.

$$
\begin{array}{r}
5x \\
x - 3 \enclose{longdiv}{5x^2 - 16x + 3} \\
5x^2 - 15x \\
\hline
-x + 3
\end{array}
$$

It still remains to divide $(-x + 3)$ by $(x - 3)$. The second term of the quotient, then, is -1. Continuing, we have

$$
\begin{array}{r}
5x - 1 \\
x - 3 \enclose{longdiv}{5x^2 - 16x + 3} \\
5x^2 - 15x \\
\hline
-x + 3 \\
-x + 3 \\
\hline
\end{array}
$$

Thus we have found that

$$\forall_{x \neq 3}\ \frac{5x^2 - 16x + 3}{x - 3} = 5x - 1$$

We can check our work by applying the definition of division of polynomials. Since $\forall_x\ (5x - 1)(x - 3) = 5x^2 - 16x + 3$, we know then that our work is correct.

For a second example, consider the quotient $(x^3 - 2x + 4) \div (x + 2)$. Notice that the dividend has no x^2-term; in such a case the coefficient of the missing term may be considered to be zero. Thus the problem could be written as

$$x + 2 \enclose{longdiv}{x^3 + 0 \cdot x^2 - 2x + 4}$$

or more simply as

$$x + 2 \enclose{longdiv}{x^3 - 2x + 4}$$

Notice, in this latter case, how the dividend is "spread out" so as to leave room for x^2-terms which may appear in our work. Study the completed work.

$$
\begin{array}{r}
x^2 - 2x + 2 \\
x + 2 \,\overline{\big)\, x^3 \qquad\quad\; - 2x + 4} \\
x^3 + 2x^2 \\
\hline
- 2x^2 - 2x \\
- 2x^2 - 4x \\
\hline
2x + 4 \\
2x + 4
\end{array}
$$

So far we have limited our attention to examples where the quotient of polynomials is also a polynomial. This is not always the case as will now be shown. The situation is again like that in arithmetic when you write

$$\frac{18}{7} = 2 + \frac{4}{7} \quad \text{or} \quad 2\frac{4}{7}$$

It is instructive to examine the computing procedure.

$$
\begin{array}{r}
2 \\
7 \,\overline{\big)\, 18} \\
14 \\
\hline
4
\end{array}
$$

Notice that the process terminates when the remainder is less than the divisor. Notice also that the quotient is $2 + \frac{4}{7}$ or $2\frac{4}{7}$.

In the case of division of polynomials, *let us agree to terminate the division procedure when a remainder is obtained whose degree is less than the degree of the divisor;* the remainder is shown as in ordinary (arithmetic) division. The procedure is illustrated by the following examples.

Examples: *i.*   Simplify the quotient $(2x^2 + 5x + 2) \div (2x - 1)$.

$$
\begin{array}{r}
x + 3 \\
2x - 1 \,\overline{\big)\, 2x^2 + 5x + 2} \\
2x^2 - x \\
\hline
6x + 2 \\
6x - 3 \\
\hline
5
\end{array}
$$

So, $\dfrac{2x^2 + 5x + 2}{2x - 1} = x + 3 + \dfrac{5}{2x - 1}$

Check that $\forall_{x \neq \frac{1}{2}} \; 2x^2 + 5x + 2 = (2x - 1)\left(x + 3 + \dfrac{5}{2x - 1}\right)$

ii.   Simplify the quotient $(4x + 5 - 3x^2) \div (2 + 3x)$.

$$
\begin{array}{r}
-x + 2 \\
3x + 2 \,\overline{\big)\, -3x^2 + 4x + 5} \\
-3x^2 - 2x \\
\hline
6x + 5 \\
6x + 4 \\
\hline
1
\end{array}
$$

So, $\dfrac{4x + 5 - 3x^2}{2 + 3x} = -x + 2 + \dfrac{1}{3x + 2}$

Notice that the terms of both the dividend and the divisor were arranged left to right according to descending degrees, beginning with the term of greatest degree. This procedure proves to be very helpful.

As in the first example, check this result.

iii. Simplify the quotient $(a^3 + 1) \div (a - 1)$.

$$
\begin{array}{r}
a^2 + a + 1 \\
a - 1 \overline{\smash{\big)}\, a^3 \qquad\qquad + 1} \\
\underline{a^3 - a^2} \\
a^2 \\
\underline{a^2 - a} \\
a + 1 \\
\underline{a - 1} \\
2
\end{array}
$$

So, $\dfrac{a^3 + 1}{a - 1} = (a^2 + a + 1) + \dfrac{2}{a - 1}$

As with previous examples, check this result.

EXERCISES

Simplify and check by multiplication; assume that no divisor is zero.

1. $(5x^2 - 6x - 8) \div (x - 2)$
2. $(3y^2 + 7y - 6) \div (y + 3)$
3. $(17n + 2n^2 + 21) \div (2n + 3)$
4. $(r^2 - 9) \div (r - 3)$
5. $(a^3 - 8) \div (a - 2)$
6. $(1 - 16t^4) \div (1 - 2t)$
7. $(2x^3 - 7x^2 + 9x - 3) \div (2x - 1)$
8. $(x^{2a} - 16) \div (x^a + 4)$
9. $(y^3 - 6y^2 + 12y - 8) \div (y^2 - 4y + 4)$
10. $(1 - r - 3r^2 - r^5) \div (r^2 + 2r + 1)$
11. $(x^2 + 5x + 4) \div (x + 2)$
12. $(2z^2 + 3z + 4) \div (z + 1)$
13. $(3a^3 - 2a + 3) \div (a - 2)$
14. $(t^3 - 1) \div (t + 1)$
15. $(3h^2 - 2h - 7) \div (h + 2)$
16. $(x^3 + x^2 + x + 1) \div (x^2 + x + 1)$
17. $(2n^4 - 3n^2 - 60) \div (n + 3)$
18. $(x^3 - y^3) \div (x - y)$
19. $(2 - t - t^3 + t^5) \div (3 + t^2)$
20. $(\frac{1}{27}x^{6c} + \frac{1}{8}y^{3c}) \div (\frac{1}{3}x^{2c} + \frac{1}{2}y^c)$

FACTORING POLYNOMIALS

In the section on multiplying polynomials of this chapter we learned how to simplify products of polynomials. For example, given the product $(5x - 2) \cdot (3x + 1)$ we learned how to show that

$$\forall_x \; (5x - 2) \cdot (3x + 1) = 15x^2 - x - 2$$

that is, that $(5x - 2) \cdot (3x + 1)$ and $15x^2 - x - 2$ are equivalent expressions. In general, given any two polynomials P and Q, we know how to find the polynomial R such that $P \cdot Q = R$. We now wish to reverse the problem: given a polynomial R, can we find polynomials P and Q such that $P \cdot Q = R$?

For any polynomials P, Q, and R, if $P \cdot Q = R$, then P and Q are *factors* of R. Furthermore, the process of finding the factors of a polynomial is called *factoring*. Also, if $P \cdot Q = R$, we refer to $P \cdot Q$ as a *factorization* of R. We have already seen that $(5x - 2) \cdot (3x + 1)$ is a factorization of $15x^2 - x - 2$ and that $(5x - 2)$ and $(3x + 1)$ are factors of $15x^2 - x - 2$.

As background we will briefly examine the factoring of integers. For example, to factor the integer 18, we could write

$$18 = 9 \cdot 2 \qquad\qquad 18 = 6 \cdot 3$$

$$18 = \frac{1}{2} \cdot 36 \qquad\qquad 18 = 1.8 \times 10$$

Thus, if the factoring of an integer means showing the integer as a product, the result is not unique. The uniqueness can be achieved if we agree that to factor an integer means to show its factorization using only *prime* numbers. This is called *the factorization* of a given integer. (Recall that a prime number is a positive integer which has *exactly two* positive integer divisors.) We will always get the same set of prime factors of a positive integer, no matter in what order we find them. For example, the prime factorization of 18 is $2 \cdot 3 \cdot 3$. The set of prime factors of 18 is $\{2, 3\}$. The prime factorization of 42 is $2 \cdot 3 \cdot 7$. What is the set of prime factors of 42?

The same problem arises when factoring polynomials. For instance, three factorizations of $4x^2 - 4y^2$ are

$$(2x - 2y)(2x + 2y)$$
$$2(x - y)(2x + 2y)$$
$$4(x - y)(x + y)$$

In most cases, we can be precise about what is wanted when we are instructed to factor polynomials by making the following agreements.

AGREEMENTS: The factors of a polynomial over the integers should also be polynomials over the integers.

Polynomials over the rationals should be factored as a product of a rational number and polynomials over the integers.

The process of factoring a polynomial is *not* considered to be *complete* until each factor is no longer factorable under the first two agreements.

The necessity for factoring polynomials over the reals which are not also polynomials over the rationals will not occur very frequently in this text. When the problem does arise, it will be understood that the factors, if any, should also be polynomials over the reals.

Example: i. According to our agreements, the complete factorization of $2x + 4y$ is $2(x + 2y)$.

Notice that a factorization like $4(\frac{1}{2}x + y)$ is *not* acceptable since it violates the first agreement. Explain why.

Examples: ii.   A factorization of $\frac{1}{2}x^2 - \frac{5}{4}xy + \frac{1}{2}y^2$ is $\frac{1}{4}(2x^2 - 5xy + 2y^2)$. But this is not a complete factorization according to the last agreement.   The complete factorization of $\frac{1}{2}x^2 - \frac{5}{4}xy + \frac{1}{2}y^2$ is $\frac{1}{4}(2x - y)(x - 2y)$. Notice that the factorization $(\frac{1}{2}x - y) \cdot (x - \frac{1}{2}y)$ is *not* acceptable since it violates the second agreement. Explain why.

iii.   According to our agreements, the complete factorization of $4x + 8$ is $4(x + 2)$.   Notice that the factorization $2(2x + 4)$ is *not* acceptable since it violates the last agreement. Explain why.

EXERCISES

1.   Classify each of the following as polynomials over the integers, the rationals, or the reals.

a. $x^2 + 3x + \dfrac{1}{2}$ **c.** $3r^2 - 2r - \sqrt{20}$ **e.** $-2n^2 - 3n - 4$

b. $t^2 - \sqrt{16}\, t + 2$ **d.** $\dfrac{1}{2}x^2 + \dfrac{1}{4}$ **f.** $3y - \dfrac{1}{5}$

2.   True or false?

a. $\forall_x\ 3x - 6 = 3(x - 2)$ **e.** One factor of 500 is 8.
b. $\forall_y\ y^2 + y = y(y - 1)$ **f.** One factor of 51 is 17.
c. $\forall_t\ t(t + 1) + 3(t + 1)$ **g.** 17 is not a prime factor of 51.
$= (t + 1)(t + 3)$ **h.** The set of prime factors of 8 is $\{2\}$.
d. $\forall_n\ n^2 + 2n + 1 = (n - 1)^2$ **i.** $\forall_x \forall_y\ x^2 - y^2 = (x - y)(x + y)$

j. $\forall_x\ (x - 2)$ is a factor of $(x^2 - 4)$.

k. If $\forall_x\ x^2 - x - 2 = (x - 2)(x + 1)$, then $\forall_{x \neq 2}\ \dfrac{x^2 - x - 2}{x - 2} = x + 1$.

l. If $\forall_x\ 2x^2 + 3x - 2 = (2x - 1)(x + 2)$, then $\forall_x\ \dfrac{2x^2 + 3x - 2}{x + 2} = 2x - 1$.

m. If $\forall_y\ 2y^2 + y - 3 = (2y + 3)(y - 1)$, then $\forall_y\ (y - 1)$ is a factor of $2y^2 + y - 3$.

n. The numbers 8 and 64 have the same set of prime factors.

o. The prime factorization of 24 is $2 \times 3 \times 4$.

Common factors

The basic property used in factoring polynomials is the distributive property. One should first look for a factor which is a factor of each term of the polynomial. Here are some examples which illustrate this procedure.

Examples: i. $\forall_x\ 5x + 15 = 5 \cdot x + 5 \cdot 3 = 5(x + 3)$

ii. $\forall_x \forall_y\ 2x^2 + 4xy = 2x \cdot x + 2x \cdot (2y) = 2x(x + 2y)$

iii. $\forall_a \forall_b \forall_c\ 12abc^2 - 6a^2bc + 18ab^2c = 6abc(2c - a + 3b)$

In the first example, 5 is called a *common factor* of each term of $5x + 15$. What is a common factor of each term of $2x^2 + 4xy$? Of $12abc^2 - 6a^2bc + 18ab^2c$? The above examples show how the distributive property is used in factoring certain polynomials over the integers; the distributive property is also useful in factoring certain polynomials over the rationals. Consider $\frac{1}{2}x^2 - \frac{1}{4}x$. By our agreements, we would factor this polynomial as

$$\frac{1}{2}x^2 - \frac{1}{4}x = \frac{1}{4} \cdot x(2x - 1)$$

Notice that the factored form is the product of a rational number and polynomials over the integers.

Examples: *i.* $\forall_y \ \frac{2}{3}y^2 - 2y = \frac{2}{3}y^2 - \frac{6}{3}y = \frac{2}{3}(y^2 - 3y) = \frac{2}{3}y(y - 3)$

   ii. $\forall_r \forall_s \forall_t \ \frac{1}{2}r + \frac{1}{3}s + \frac{1}{4}t = \frac{6}{12}r + \frac{4}{12}s + \frac{3}{12}t = \frac{1}{12}(6r + 4s + 3t)$

The use of the distributive property for factoring polynomials is more extensive than the above discussion would suggest. For example, consider the polynomial

$$x(y - 2) + 3(y - 2)$$

This polynomial is the sum of two polynomials each of which contains the binomial factor $(y - 2)$. Therefore, by the right distributive property of multiplication over addition

$$\forall_x \forall_y \ x(y - 2) + 3(y - 2) = (x + 3)(y - 2)$$

Many polynomials which contain four or more terms can be factored by applying the distributive property in this way. The following examples will illustrate the procedure.

Examples: *i.* $\forall_x \forall_y \ xy + x + y^2 + y$
            $= (xy + x) + (y^2 + y)$
            $= x(y + 1) + y(y + 1)$
            $= (x + y)(y + 1)$

   ii. $\forall_a \forall_b \forall_c \ 2ab - 2ac + 5b - 5c$
            $= (2ab - 2ac) + (5b - 5c)$
            $= 2a(b - c) + 5(b - c)$
            $= (2a + 5)(b - c)$

   iii. $\forall_x \forall_y \ 6xy - 1 + 2x - 3y$
            $= 6xy - 3y + 2x - 1$
            $= (6xy - 3y) + (2x - 1)$
            $= 3y(2x - 1) + 1 \cdot (2x - 1)$
            $= (3y + 1)(2x - 1)$

Notice that the first step in each of these examples was to "group" terms in pairs. Accordingly, this technique for factoring polynomials is often called the *grouping-by-pairs* method. Keep in mind, however, that the ultimate purpose of grouping is *to determine common factors* and then apply the distributive property.

EXERCISES

1. Factor each of the following polynomials as *completely* as possible by finding common factors and applying the distributive property.

a. $5t - 5$

b. $x^2 - x$

c. $-2y^2 + 8y$

d. $33x^3 - 121x^2$

e. $4x^2 + 8xy$

f. $6r^2t - 3rst$

g. $6a^3b^2 - 2a^2b^3$

h. $28xy - 42yz$

i. $6u^2v^2 - 9uv^3 + 3uv^2$

j. $\frac{1}{2}x - \frac{1}{3}y$

k. $\frac{1}{2}a^2b + 3a$

l. $\frac{2}{5}r^2 + 2rs - 4rt$

m. $x(x - y) + 3(x - y)$

n. $3a(m - n) - (m - n)$

o. $(x + 5) \cdot y - 2 \cdot (x + 5)$

p. $3(z - 3) + (z^2 - 3z)$

2. Factor by the "grouping-by-pairs" method.

a. $xy - y + 2x - 2$

b. $rs + 2r + 3s + 6$

c. $x^2 - 4x + 2x - 8$

d. $2xy + y - 6x - 3$

e. $5a + 3ab - 3b - 5$

f. $4y - xy - 20 + 5x$

g. $-2xy - 3 - 3y - 2x$

h. $3ax + 5bx - 3ay - 5by$

i. $2tx + 2ty - 4tz + 3x + 3y - 6z$

(HINT: Try two groups of three terms each.)

FACTORING TRINOMIALS

For all real number replacements of a, b, and c, $a \neq 0$, $ax^2 + bx + c$ is called a *quadratic polynomial*. Often the factorization of a quadratic polynomial is a product of two binomials. For example

$$\forall_x \ x^2 + 6x + 8 = (x + 2)(x + 4)$$

Although it is easy to determine that the product of the binomials $(x + 2)$ and $(x + 4)$ is $x^2 + 6x + 8$, it is sometimes more difficult to reverse the procedure to find that a factorization of $x^2 + 6x + 8$ is $(x + 2) \cdot (x + 4)$. The problem is simplified by recognizing certain patterns for multiplying binomials. The patterns we seek can be discovered by observing some examples.

Example:

$$
\begin{aligned}
\forall_x \ (x + 2)(x + 4) &= (x + 2)x + (x + 2)4 && \text{LDPMA} \\
&= (x^2 + 2x) + (4x + 8) && \text{RDPMA} \\
&= x^2 + (2x + 4x) + 8 && \text{Sum rearrangement} \\
&= x^2 + 6x + 8 && \text{RDPMA; Arithmetic fact}
\end{aligned}
$$

Notice that the first term of the product, namely x^2, is the product of the first terms of the given binomials; and the last term of the product, namely 8, is the product of the last terms of the given binomials. Finally, notice that the middle term of the product, namely $6x$, is the *sum* of the products $4x$ and $2x$.

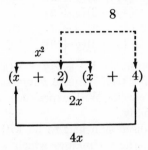

Examples: i. $\forall_x$ $(x + 1)(x + 5) = x^2 + x + 5x + 5$

$$= x^2 + 6x + 5$$

ii. $\forall_y$ $(2y + 1)(y - 2) = 2y^2 + y - 4y - 2$

$$= 2y^2 - 3y - 2$$

Now let us see how these examples aid us in factoring quadratic polynomials. As a first example, consider the trinomial $x^2 + 8x + 15$. From the preceding examples, we might try these as factorizations of $x^2 + 8x + 15$.

x^2 x^2

$(x + 15)(x + 1)$ and $(x + 5)(x + 3)$

15   15

Since $\forall_x$ $5x + 3x = 8x$ and $8x$ is the desired middle term, we know that $(x + 5)(x + 3)$ is the correct factorization. Prove that $(x + 15)(x + 1)$ is not a factorization of $x^2 + 8x + 15$.

As a second example, consider the trinomial $2x^2 - 7x + 6$. The only positive integer factors of 2 are 2 and 1, and the only positive integer factors of 6 are 1, 2, 3, and 6. Hence, we might look for the factorization of $2x^2 - 7x + 6$ among:

$(2x - 6)(x - 1)$; $(2x - 1)(x - 6)$; $(2x - 2)(x - 3)$; and $(2x - 3)(x - 2)$. Since $\forall_x$ $(-3x) + (-4x) = (-7x)$, the desired middle term, the fourth possibility above is the correct one.

As a third example, consider the trinomial $4y^2 + 5y - 6$. A little thought will reveal that each of the following products, in expanded form, will agree in first and last terms with the given trinomial.

$(4y + 6)(y - 1)$	$(4y + 3)(y - 2)$	$(2y + 6)(2y - 1)$
$(4y - 6)(y + 1)$	$(4y - 3)(y + 2)$	$(2y - 6)(2y + 1)$
$(4y - 1)(y + 6)$	$(4y + 2)(y - 3)$	$(2y + 3)(2y - 2)$
$(4y + 1)(y - 6)$	$(4y - 2)(y + 3)$	$(2y - 3)(2y + 2)$

The only correct factorization in the list is $(4y - 3)(y + 2)$. For many trinomials the number of possibilities for trial is quite large, but some binomials are very easily eliminated by a quick check. With experience, you will be able to recognize the correct factors rather rapidly.

Although the previous discussion had to do with the factoring of quadratic polynomials in one variable, the techniques which were presented work equally well for many other trinomials. For example, consider the trinomial $2a^2 + 5ab + 2b^2$. This time we must decide whether

$$\forall_a \forall_b\ 2a^2 + 5ab + 2b^2 = (2a + 2b)(a + b)$$

$$\text{or,} \quad \forall_a \forall_b\ 2a^2 + 5ab + 2b^2 = (2a + b)(a + 2b)$$

This last factorization is the correct one. Prove it.

There is one additional point which deserves special mention. Consider the trinomial $x^2 + 2x + 9$. The possibilities for factorizations of this trinomial are

$$(x + 9)(x + 1) \quad \text{and} \quad (x + 3)(x + 3)$$

neither of which is correct. Thus, the trinomial $x^2 + 2x + 9$ is *not* factorable in terms of factors which are polynomials over the integers. You will find that many trinomials are not factorable under our agreements.

EXERCISES

1.   True or false?

   a. $\forall_x\ x^2 + 4x + 3 = (x + 1)(x + 3)$

   b. $\forall_y\ y^2 + 9y - 14 = (y + 7)(y - 2)$

   c. $\forall_t\ t^2 - 9t + 18 = (t + 6)(t + 3)$

   d. $\forall_r\ r^2 + 3r - 10 = (r + 5)(r - 2)$

   e. $\forall_n\ n^2 - 5n + 6 = (n - 2)(n + 3)$

   f. $\forall_x\ 3x^2 + 17x + 10 = (3x + 2)(x + 5)$

   g. $\forall_y\ 6y^2 - y - 12 = (2y - 3)(3y + 4)$

   h. $\forall_t\ t^2 + 2t - 15 = (t - 5)(t + 3)$

   i. $\forall_k\ 2k^2 - 13k - 7 = (2k - 1)(k - 7)$

   j. $\forall_a \forall_b\ a^2 + ab - 2b^2 = (a + 2b)(a - b)$

   k. $\forall_x\ -x^2 + 4x + 5 = -(x - 5)(x + 1)$

   l. $\forall_y\ 1 - 4y + 4y^2 = (2y - 1)^2$

2. Factor completely, if possible.

a. $2x^2 + 9x + 4$

b. $y^2 - 10y - 11$

c. $r^2 - r + 12$

d. $8x^2 + 2x - 3$

e. $5z^2 + 10z - 15$
[HINT: Begin by identifying a common factor of each term.]

f. $6k^2 + 6k - 72$

g. $y^2 + 14y + 49$

h. $4t^2 - 12t + 9$

i. $\frac{1}{3}x^2 + \frac{1}{3}x - \frac{2}{3}$

$$\left[\text{HINT: } \frac{1}{3}x^2 + \frac{1}{3}x - \frac{2}{3} = \frac{1}{3}(x^2 + x - 2)\right]$$

j. $\frac{1}{5}t^2 + \frac{16}{5}t + 3$

k. $r^2 + \frac{r}{2} - \frac{3}{2}$

l. $2y^2 - \frac{1}{2}y - \frac{1}{4}$

m. $n^2 + \frac{n}{2} - 5$

A special pattern

Certain trinomials are factorable as the square of a binomial. Such a trinomial is called a *perfect square trinomial*. For example, $x^2 + 2x + 1$ is a perfect square trinomial since $\bigvee_x x^2 + 2x + 1 = (x + 1)^2$.

This suggests two questions: first, how do we determine whether a given trinomial is a perfect square trinomial? And, second, knowing that a trinomial is a perfect square, how do we factor it? The answers to both of these questions are obtained from studying the following:

$$\bigvee_a \bigvee_b (a + b)^2 = (a + b)(a + b)$$
$$= a^2 + ab + ab + b^2$$
$$= a^2 + 2(ab) + b^2$$

Thus, the trinomial $a^2 + 2(ab) + b^2$ is a perfect square trinomial since it is the square of the binomial $(a + b)$. The fact that

$$\bigvee_a \bigvee_b a^2 + 2(ab) + b^2 = (a + b)^2$$

can serve as a pattern for factoring any perfect square trinomial. That is, every perfect square trinomial fits the pattern $a^2 + 2(ab) + b^2$, and this fact enables us to recognize them. For example, the trinomial $x^2 + 8x + 16$ is a perfect square trinomial since x^2 and 16 are the squares of x and 4, respectively, and $8x = 2(4 \cdot x)$.

Since any trinomial which patterns in the form $a^2 + 2(ab) + b^2$ will have a factorization which patterns in the form $(a + b)^2$, we know that $\bigvee_x x^2 + 8x + 16 = x^2 + 2(4x) + 4^2 = (x + 4)^2$. The following examples illustrate this special pattern.

Example: *i.*   Factor the trinomial $y^2 + 6y + 9$.

Notice that $\bigvee_y y^2 + 6y + 9 = y^2 + 2(3 \cdot y) + 3^2$.

Thus, $y^2 + 6y + 9$ is a perfect square trinomial, and

$\bigvee_y y^2 + 6y + 9 = (y + 3)^2$.

Examples: ii.   Factor the trinomial $4t^2 + 12t + 9$.

Notice that $\forall_t\ 4t^2 + 12t + 9 = (2t)^2 + 12t + 3^2$
$$= (2t)^2 + 2(2t \cdot 3) + 3^2.$$

Thus, $4t^2 + 12t + 9$ is a perfect square trinomial, and $\forall_t\ 4t^2 + 12t + 9 = (2t + 3)^2$.

iii.   Factor the trinomial $4r^2 + 12rt + 9t^2$.

Notice that $\forall_r\forall_t\ 4r^2 + 12rt + 9t^2 = (2r)^2 + 12rt + (3t)^2$
$$= (2r)^2 + 2(2r \cdot 3t) + (3t)^2$$

Thus, $4r^2 + 12rt + 9t^2$ is a perfect square trinomial and $\forall_r\forall_t\ 4r^2 + 12rt + 9t^2 = (2r + 3t)^2$.

iv.   Factor the trinomial $x^2 + 5x + 4$.

Notice that $\forall_x\ x^2 + 5x + 4 = x^2 + 5x + 2^2$, but $2(x \cdot 2) \neq 5x$. Hence, $x^2 + 5x + 4$ is *not* a perfect square trinomial.

But in the section on factoring trinomials we did factor $x^2 + 5x + 4$: $\forall_x\ x^2 + 5x + 4 = (x + 4)(x + 1)$.

We have shown that $\forall_a\forall_b\ a^2 + 2ab + b^2 = (a + b)^2$. Replacing b in this statement by $(-c)$ we obtain the new pattern: $\forall_a\forall_c\ a^2 + 2a(-c) + (-c)^2 = [a + (-c)]^2$ which may be expressed as $\forall_a\forall_c\ a^2 - 2ac + c^2 = (a - c)^2$.

Thus we see that $a^2 - 2ac + c^2$ is another form of a perfect square trinomial; moreover, any trinomial which patterns in the form $a^2 - 2ac + c^2$ will have a factorization which patterns in the form $(a - c)^2$.

Examples: i.   Factor the trinomial $x^2 - 4x + 4$.

Notice that $\forall_x\ x^2 - 4x + 4 = x^2 - 4x + 2^2 = x^2 - 2(2x) + 2^2$.

Since $x^2 - 4x + 4$ is a perfect square trinomial which patterns in the form $a^2 - 2ac + c^2$, we know that $\forall_x\ x^2 - 4x + 4 = (x - 2)^2$.

ii.   Factor the trinomial $9x^2 - 6xy + y^2$.

Notice that $\forall_x\forall_y\ 9x^2 - 6xy + y^2 = (3x)^2 - 6xy + y^2$
$$= (3x)^2 - 2(3x \cdot y) + y^2.$$

Thus, $9x^2 - 6xy + y^2$ is a perfect square trinomial since it patterns in the form $a^2 - 2ac + c^2$, and we know that $\forall_x\forall_y\ 9x^2 - 6xy + y^2 = (3x - y)^2$.

EXERCISES

1.   True or false?
   a. $\forall_x\forall_y\ (x - y)^2 = x^2 - 2xy + y^2$
   b. $\forall_t\ (2t + 1)^2 = 4t^2 + 4t + 1$
   c. $\forall_r\ (3r - 2)^2 = 9r^2 - 12r + 4$
   d. $\forall_u\forall_v\ (2u + 3v)^2 = 4u^2 + 6uv + 9v^2$

e. $(r^2 + 2r + 4)$ is a perfect square trinomial.

f. $(4a^2b^2 - 8ab + 1)$ is a perfect square trinomial.

g. $\forall_y \ -(y + 3)^2 = -y^2 - 3y + 9$

h. $\forall_x \ -(3x - 1)^2 = -9x^2 + 6x - 1$

2. Factor completely.

a. $n^2 - 10n + 25$ **e.** $-k^2 + 12k - 36$ **i.** $x^2 + 3x + \dfrac{9}{4}$

b. $9y^2 + 30y + 25$ **f.** $2r^2 - 19r + 35$ **j.** $\dfrac{1}{5}y^2 - 2y + 5$

c. $16 + 8z + z^2$ **g.** $a^2 - ab - 6b^2$ **k.** $\dfrac{1}{3}y^2 + 2y + 3$

d. $4x^2 + 20x + 25$ **h.** $-9u^2 - 30uv - 25v^2$ **l.** $-\dfrac{4}{3}r^2 - 4rt - 3t^2$

FACTORING BINOMIALS

In the section on special products we learned that $\forall_a \forall_b \ (a + b)(a - b) = a^2 - b^2$. In other words, any pair of binomials which pattern in the forms $(a + b)$ and $(a - b)$ will have a product which patterns in the form $a^2 - b^2$; and conversely, any binomial which patterns in the form $a^2 - b^2$ will have a factorization which patterns in the form $(a + b)(a - b)$. We shall refer to a binomial which patterns in the form $a^2 - b^2$ as a *difference of squares*.

Examples: *i.*   Factor the binomial $y^2 - 16$.

$$\forall_y \ y^2 - 16 = y^2 - 4^2$$
$$= (y + 4)(y - 4)$$

     ii.   Factor the binomial $4x^2 - 9$.

$$\forall_x \ 4x^2 - 9 = (2x)^2 - 3^2$$
$$= (2x + 3)(2x - 3)$$

     iii.   Factor the binomial $9t^2 - 25r^2$.

$$\forall_t \forall_r \ 9t^2 - 25r^2 = (3t)^2 - (5r)^2$$
$$= (3t + 5r)(3t - 5r)$$

     iv.   Factor the polynomial $(a + b)^2 - 49$.

$$\forall_a \forall_b \ (a + b)^2 - 49 = (a + b)^2 - 7^2$$
$$= [(a + b) + 7] \cdot [(a + b) - 7]$$
$$= (a + b + 7)(a + b - 7)$$

     v.   Factor the polynomial $(x + y)^2 - (x - y)^2$.

$$\forall_x \forall_y \ (x + y)^2 - (x - y)^2$$
$$= [(x + y) + (x - y)] \cdot [(x + y) - (x - y)]$$
$$= [x + y + x - y] \cdot [x + y - x + y]$$
$$= (2x) \cdot (2y) = 4xy$$

vi. Factor the binomial $16t^4 - 1$.

$\forall_t \ 16t^4 - 1 = (4t^2)^2 - 1^2$
$= (4t^2 + 1)(4t^2 - 1)$

Notice that we have *not* factored completely since the second factor, $4t^2 - 1$, is a difference of squares. Continuing we see that

$\forall_t \ 16t^4 - 1 = (4t^2 + 1)(4t^2 - 1)$
$= (4t^2 + 1)[(2t)^2 - 1^2]$
$= (4t^2 + 1)(2t + 1)(2t - 1)$

EXERCISES

1. True or false?

   a. $(x + 5)$ is a factor of $x^2 - 25$.

   b. $(4r - 3)$ is a factor of $4r^2 - 9$.

   c. $(3y + 4)$ is a factor of $-(16 - 9y^2)$.

   d. $(2b - 5a)$ is a factor of $25a^2 - 4b^2$.

   e. $[(2x + y) - (2x + 3y)]$ is a factor of $(2x + y)^2 - (2x + 3y)^2$.

   f. $(x + y + 6)$ is a factor of $(x + y)^2 - 36$.

   g. $\forall_a \forall_b \forall_c \ a^2 - (b + c)^2 = (a - b + c)(a + b + c)$

   h. $(t^2 + 1)(t^2 - 1)$ is a complete factorization of $t^4 - 1$.

   i. $\forall_x \ 4x^2 - 25 = (4x + 5)(4x - 5)$

   j. $\forall_x \ 6x^2 - \dfrac{1}{6} = \dfrac{1}{6}(36x^2 - 1)$

2. Factor completely if the polynomial is factorable.

   a. $y^2 - x^2$

   b. $12x^2 - 3$

   c. $1 - 4n^2$

   d. $81a^2b^2 - b^2$

   e. $-49x^2 + 64y^2$

   f. $t^4 - 16$

   g. $25x^2 - x^2y^2$

   h. $y^2 - 3$

   i. $x^2 - (y + z)^2$

   j. $(2a - b)^2 - 25$

   k. $u^4 - v^4$

   l. $x^2 + 1$

   m. $3 - 48y^2$

   n. $(3r - 2)^2 - (2r + 1)^2$

   o. $(u^2 - v^2) - (u - v)$

   p. $\dfrac{1}{2}x^2 - 2y^2$

   q. $\dfrac{1}{9} - t^2$

   r. $\dfrac{1}{3}n^2 + 1$

   s. $\dfrac{1}{4}x - 4x^3$

   t. $7r^4 - \dfrac{1}{7}$

Factoring other special polynomials

It is possible to factor polynomials containing four or more terms if the terms of the polynomial can be "grouped" so that the resulting expression patterns as a difference of squares. The following examples illustrate this.

Examples: *i.* Factor the polynomial $x^2 - y^2 + 2x + 1$.
$$\forall_x \forall_y \ x^2 - y^2 + 2x + 1 = (x^2 + 2x + 1) - y^2$$
$$= (x + 1)^2 - y^2$$
$$= [(x + 1) + y] [(x + 1) - y]$$
$$= (x + y + 1)(x - y + 1)$$

ii. Factor the polynomial $9s^2 - 16 + 4t^2 - 12st$.
$$\forall_s \forall_t \ 9s^2 - 16 + 4t^2 - 12st = (9s^2 - 12st + 4t^2) - 16$$
$$= (3s - 2t)^2 - 4^2$$
$$= [(3s - 2t) + 4] [(3s - 2t) - 4]$$
$$= (3s - 2t + 4)(3s - 2t - 4)$$

There are other classes of binomials whose factors pattern in special ways. One such class is a *sum of two cubes*. Notice that

$$\forall_a \forall_b \ a^3 + b^3 = (a + b)(a^2 - ab + b^2)$$

(Multiply to verify this!) Thus, for example, we know that
$$\forall_t \ t^3 + 8 = t^3 + 2^3 = (t + 2)(t^2 - 2t + 4)$$

Another class of binomials whose factors pattern in a special way is a *difference of cubes*. Notice that

$$\forall_a \forall_b \ a^3 - b^3 = (a - b)(a^2 + ab + b^2)$$

(Verify this!) By observing this pattern we see, for example, that

$$\forall_x \ x^3 - 27 = x^3 - 3^3 = (x - 3)(x^2 + 3x + 9)$$

EXERCISES

1. True or false?

   a. $(x + 1)$ is a factor of $x^3 + 1$.

   b. $(2y + 1)$ is a factor of $8y^3 + 1$.

   c. $(t - 4)$ is a factor of $t^3 + 64$.

   d. $(2n - 3)$ is a factor of $8n^3 - 27$.

   e. $(a^2 + a + 1)$ is a factor of $a^3 - 1$.

   f. $(k^2 + 2k + 4)$ is a factor of $k^3 + 8$.

   g. $(3z + 2)$ is a factor of $27z^3 - 8$.

   h. $(x + y + 1)$ is a factor of $(x + y)^3 - 1$.

   i. $(n + 1)$ is a factor of $n^4 + 1$. [HINT: Divide $(n^4 + 1)$ by $(n + 1)$.]

   j. $(n - 1)$ is a factor of $n^5 - 1$.

2. Factor completely if the polynomial is factorable.

a. $x^3 + 125$

b. $y^3 - 125$

c. $27x^3 + 1$

d. $8y^3 - 1$

e. $-t^3 + 1$

f. $-n^3 - 64$

g. $24a^3 - 3b^3$

h. $(x + 2y)^3 - 8$

i. $27 + (x + 3)^3$

j. $(n + 4)^3 + (n - 1)^3$

k. $n^5 - 1$ [See problem **1j.**]

l. $u^2 + 10u + 25 - v^2$

m. $4a^2 - 4ab + b^2 - 9$

n. $x^2 - 16y^2 - 40y - 25$

o. $\frac{1}{2}x^2 + xy + \frac{1}{2}y^2 - 2$

A note on factoring polynomials over the rationals

In the section on factoring polynomials, we made several agreements about what we would accept as a factorization of a polynomial. We made these agreements in order for all of us to obtain the same result for any given polynomial. For many purposes, our second agreement that polynomials over the rationals should be factored as a product of a rational number and polynomials over the integers is too restrictive. We shall now relax this requirement and permit the factors of polynomials over the rationals to also be polynomials over the rationals. The consequences of this change in agreement are illustrated by the following examples.

Examples: *i.*   Factor the polynomial $x^2 - \frac{1}{9}$.

According to our original agreement, the expected factorization of $x^2 - \frac{1}{9}$ is $\frac{1}{9}(3x - 1)(3x + 1)$. By our new agreement, however, we consider the factorization $(x - \frac{1}{3})(x + \frac{1}{3})$ to be acceptable.

ii.   Factor the polynomial $x^2 - x + \frac{1}{4}$.

According to our original agreement, the expected factorization of $x^2 - x + \frac{1}{4}$ is $\frac{1}{4}(2x - 1)^2$. By our new agreement, the factorization $(x - \frac{1}{2})^2$ is acceptable.

EXERCISES

Factor in accordance with the changed agreement.

1. $a^2 - \frac{1}{4}$

2. $m^2 - \frac{1}{16}$

3. $n^2 + n + \frac{1}{4}$

4. $x^2 - \frac{4}{3}x + \frac{4}{9}$

5. $4y^2 - \frac{1}{9}$

6. $4s^2 - \frac{4}{7}s + \frac{1}{49}$

7. $x^3 - \frac{1}{8}$

8. $t^3 - \frac{1}{27}$

9. $m^3 + \frac{1}{64}$

10. $27t^3 + \frac{1}{.125}$

11. $\frac{1}{8}n^3 - \frac{1}{27}p^3$

12. $\frac{1}{125}a^3 - \frac{8}{27}b^3$

VOCABULARY

Use each of the following correctly in a sentence.   Numerals in parentheses refer to pages where these words were used. If you are not sure of the meaning of any word, turn to the indicated page.

additive inverse of a polynomial (65)

binomial (60)

degree of a monomial (61)

degree of a polynomial (61)

difference of cubes (89)

difference of squares (87)

monomial (60)

perfect square trinomial (85)

polynomial in n variables (60)

polynomial in one variable (59)

polynomial over the integers (61)

polynomial over the rationals (61)

polynomial over the reals (61)

sum of cubes (89)

trinomial (60)

value of a polynomial (63)

REVIEW EXERCISES

1.   Consider the following eight polynomials.

$i.$ $x^2 + 2$

$ii.$ $y^2 - 3y + 2$

$iii.$ $\frac{1}{2}xy$

$iv.$ $x^2 + 2xy + y^2$

$v.$ $u^3 + \sqrt{2}\,u$

$vi.$ z

$vii.$ $\frac{3}{2}x^2 - \frac{5}{2}x + \frac{1}{2}$

$viii.$ $t^4 + t^3 + t^2 + \frac{1}{2}$

a. Which of the above polynomials are monomials? binomials? trinomials? perfect square trinomials?

b. Give the degree of each of the above polynomials.

c. Which of the above polynomials are polynomials over the reals? over the rationals? over the integers?

d. Which of the above polynomials are polynomials in one variable? in two variables?

e. What is the value of the polynomial given under i if x is replaced by 0?

f. What is the value of the polynomial given under iii if x is replaced by 2 and y is replaced by 1?

g. What is the value of the polynomial given under ii if y is replaced by -1?

h. What is the value of the polynomial given under $viii$ if t is replaced by $-\frac{1}{2}$?

2.   True or false?

a. $\forall_x \ -(2x - 3) = -2x - 3$

b. $\forall_y \ -(-3y^2) = 3y^2$

c. $\forall_x \forall_y \ -(x^3 + x^2y - xy^2 - y^3) = -x^3 - x^2y - xy^2 - y^3$

d. $\forall_n \ -(-n^2 + 3n - 4) = n^2 - 3n + 4$

e. $\forall_a \forall_b \ -(-3 - ab) = ab + 3$

f. For all polynomials P and Q, $P - Q = P + (-Q)$.

g. $\forall_x \ (-3x^2)(-x) = 3x^3$

h. $\forall_x \forall_y \ (2x^2y)(-3x) = -6x^2y$

    i. $\forall_n \ (2n-1)(2n+1) = 2n(2n+1) - (2n+1)$

    j. $\forall_a\forall_b \ (2a+b)(a^2 - ab - 2b^2) = (2a+b)a^2 - (2a+b)(ab+2b^2)$

    k. $\forall_x \ (x-5) = -(5-x)$

    l. $\forall_r \ (3+r)(-3+r) = r^2 - 9$

    m. $\forall_x \ (2x+1)^2 = 4x^2 + 2x + 1$

    n. $\forall_t \ 2t(t-2) - 5(t-2) = (2t-5)(t-2)$

    o. $\forall_y \ (2y+3)(y-2) = 2y^2 + y - 6$

    p. The set of polynomials in x is closed under the operation of addition.

    q. The set of polynomials in x is closed under the operation of multiplication

    r. The set of polynomials in x is closed under the operation of division.

    s. The set $\{\ldots, -2x, -x, 0, x, 2x, \ldots\}$ is closed under the operation of addition.

    t. The set $\{x, x^2, x^3, \ldots\}$ is closed under the operation of multiplication.

3. Simplify.

    a. $(x^2 + x + 3) + (2x^2 - 2x - 4)$

    b. $2y^3 + (-y^3)$

    c. $(x^3 - 1) + (2x^2 + x + 1)$

    d. $(t^3 - 3t^2 - 2) + (t^4 - t^3 + t^2 - 5)$

    e. $(u^2 + 3uv - 7) + (2 - uv)$

    f. $(2x - 3) - (-3 + 2x)$

    g. $(7 - xy) - (-xy)$

    h. $3x^2 - (-x^2)$

    i. $(4 - t) - (-t^2 + t + 1)$

    j. $(3z^2 + z + 1) - (z^2 - 2z - 3)$

    k. $(4x + 7)(x - 2)$

    l. $(4x - 5)^2$

    m. $(3x - 1)(x^2 - x + 4)$

    n. $(x^2 - 3x + 2)(2x^2 + x + 5)$

    o. $(-x + 2)(x^5 - 3x^3 - x^2 - x + 2)$

    p. $(2x + 3y)(2x - 3y)$

    q. $\dfrac{4x^3y^3}{2xy^2}, \ (xy \neq 0)$

    r. $\dfrac{4x^4 - x^3}{2x}, \ (x \neq 0)$

    s. $(-6x^2 - x + 12) \div (2x + 3), \ \left(x \neq -\dfrac{3}{2}\right)$

    t. $(6x^4 + 4x^3 - 3x^2 + x + 2) \div (3x + 2), \ \left(x \neq -\dfrac{2}{3}\right)$

    u. $(-x^4 + 6x^3 + 2x - 12) \div (-x + 6), \ (x \neq 6)$

4. Factor completely if the polynomial is factorable.

a. $-3x^2 - 3$

b. $12t^2 - 27$

c. $x^2 - 2y - 2x + xy$

d. $2x^3 - 2y^3$

e. $2xy - 3y^2 - \frac{1}{3}x^2$

f. $x^2 - y^2 + 2x + 1$

g. $\frac{1}{3}x^2 - \frac{1}{3}x + 1$

h. $16r^3 - 54$

i. $4x^2 - \frac{1}{36}$

j. $t^3 + t^2 + \frac{1}{4}t$

CHAPTER TEST

1. Simplify.

a. $(t^2 + 3t - 3) + (-2t^2 - 4t + 5)$

b. $(3x^3 - x + 1) + (x^2 + 3x - 3)$

c. $-(-3x^2 + 4x - 5)$

d. $(y^2 - 5y) - (-y^2 - 4y + 4)$

e. $(x^4 - x^2 - 2) - (-2x^4 + x^3 + 1)$

f. $(5x - 7)(x + 2)$

g. $(-3x + 2)^2$

h. $(4x + 5y)(4x - 5y)$

i. $\dfrac{21x^3y^3z}{3x^2y^2z^2}, \quad (xyz \neq 0)$

j. $\dfrac{-6x^2 - 7x + 20}{-3x + 4}, \quad \left(x \neq \dfrac{4}{3}\right)$

k. $(n^4 + n^3 + n^2 + n + 1) \div (n + 1)$, $(n \neq -1)$

2. Determine the value of $x^2 - \frac{2}{3}x - 5$ when x is replaced by

a. 1   b. -1 c. 3   d. $\frac{1}{3}$ e. 0

3. Factor completely.

a. $xy^2 + x$

b. $4x^2 - 7x + 3$

c. $x^2 + 6x + 9$

d. $a^2 - 4a + 4$

e. $c^2 - 4d^2$

f. $3x^2 - 3$

g. $\frac{4}{5}r^2 - 5$

h. $9t^3 - 12t^2 + 4t$

i. $\frac{1}{4}x^2 + \frac{1}{3}x + \frac{1}{9}$

j. $64 + 27a^3$

k. $8n^3 - 27$

l. $4y - x^2 + 4x - xy$

m. $x^2 - y^2 - 2x + 1$

n. $\frac{1}{2}x^2 - \frac{5}{6}x - \frac{1}{3}$

4. Give the degree of each of the following polynomials.

a. $4x^3 - 9x + 5$ c. 7   e. $3 - 5xy^3 + 3x^2y^2 - xy + x$

b. $3x^2y - 4xy + 2x - y + 1$ d. $5t^3 - 4t^4 + t^2 - 2$

5. Classify each of the following as a monomial, a binomial, or a trinomial.

a. $5x - 3$ b. $2m^2$ c. $1 - 3y^3 + 4y$ d. 6   e. $\frac{1}{3}x^2 - \frac{1}{2}y^2$

6.   Which one of the following is a *perfect square* trinomial?

   a. $4x^2 + 6x + 9$ **c.** $4x^2 + 12x + 9$

   b. $4x^2 + 25x + 25$ **d.** $4x^2 + 4x + 4$

BIBLIOGRAPHY

Allendoerfer, C. B. and Oakley, C. O.   *Fundamentals of Freshman Mathematics.* New York: McGraw-Hill Book Co., Inc., 1959.   Chapter 3.

Heimer, R. T., Kocher, F. and Lottes, J. J. *A Program in Contemporary Algebra.* New York: Holt, Rinehart and Winston, Inc., 1963.   Book 4, Units I and II.

Rose, I. H.   *A Modern Introduction to College Mathematics.* New York: John Wiley & Sons, Inc., 1959.   pp. 279-287.

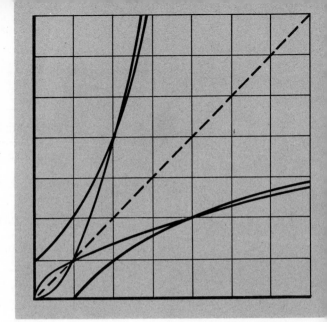

CHAPTER 4

Rational Expressions

WHAT IS A RATIONAL EXPRESSION?

The set of polynomials and the set of integers are similar in that each set is closed under the operations of addition, subtraction, and multiplication, and neither is closed under the operation of division. Thus, as each quotient $\dfrac{x}{y}$ of integers x and y $(y \neq 0)$ is called a rational number, we call each quotient $\dfrac{P}{Q}$ of polynomials P and Q $(Q \neq 0)$ a *rational expression*.

■ *Definition of Rational Expression* A rational expression is an expression that can be written in the form $\dfrac{P}{Q}$ where P and Q $(Q \neq 0)$ are polynomials.

Generally, every algebraic expression which is equivalent to a quotient of polynomials is said to be a rational expression. Since every polynomial P is equivalent to $\dfrac{P}{1}$, a quotient of polynomials, every polynomial is also a rational expression. The converse, of course, is not true. The relationship between the set of rational expressions and the set of polynomials is illustrated by the following diagram.

95

$$\boxed{\begin{array}{c} \text{Rational Expressions} \\[4pt] \boxed{\text{Polynomials}} \end{array}}$$

Explain the relationship suggested by the above diagram.

ORAL EXERCISES

Which of the following are rational expressions?

1. $x - 3$

2. 7

3. $\dfrac{x^2}{4}$

4. $\dfrac{x^2 + 3x + 2}{x + 3}$

5. $\sqrt{x^2 + 4x + 5}$

6. $\dfrac{x}{\sqrt{7}} + 2$

7. $y^2 + \dfrac{3}{y} - 2$

8. $\sqrt{t} - 2t - 4$

9. $\dfrac{2x + 3y - 7}{-x - 4y}$

SIMPLIFYING RATIONAL EXPRESSIONS

The procedure for simplifying fractional numerals is based on the following:

$$\forall_{c \neq 0} \forall_x \forall_{y \neq 0} \quad \frac{c \cdot x}{c \cdot y} = \frac{x}{y}$$

That is, for integer replacements of c, x, and y, $(c \cdot y \neq 0)$, $\dfrac{cx}{cy}$ and $\dfrac{x}{y}$ are two names for the same rational number. A similar fact underlies the simplifying of rational expressions.

Theorem 1 For all polynomials P, Q, and R, $Q \neq 0$, and $R \neq 0$, $\dfrac{R \cdot P}{R \cdot Q} = \dfrac{P}{Q}$

Proof   (Justify each step.)

$$\text{Let } T = \frac{P}{Q}$$

$$\text{Then } QT = P$$

$$\text{Hence } RQT = RP$$

$$\text{Thus } T = \frac{RP}{RQ}$$

$$\text{But } T = \frac{P}{Q}; \text{ therefore } \frac{RP}{RQ} = \frac{P}{Q}$$

Q.E.D.

Thus, simplifying a rational expression consists of *two* steps: factoring the numerator and denominator, and then applying Theorem 1. Here are some examples to illustrate the procedure.

Examples:

i. $\forall_{x \neq 0} \forall_{y \neq 0} \dfrac{4xy^2}{12x^2y} = \dfrac{4xy \cdot y}{4xy \cdot 3x} = \dfrac{y}{3x}$

ii. $\forall_{x \neq 1, \ x \neq 2} \dfrac{x^2 - 1}{x^2 - 3x + 2} = \dfrac{(x-1)(x+1)}{(x-1)(x-2)} = \dfrac{x+1}{x-2}$

iii. $\forall_{a \neq -2} \forall_{b \neq 1} \dfrac{a^2 b - a^2}{ab - a + 2b - 2} = \dfrac{a^2(b-1)}{(ab - a) + (2b - 2)}$

$$= \dfrac{a^2(b-1)}{a(b-1) + 2(b-1)}$$

$$= \dfrac{a^2(b-1)}{(b-1) \cdot (a+2)}$$

$$= \dfrac{a^2}{a+2}$$

iv. For every replacement of x and for every replacement of y such that $x^2 + 2xy + y^2 - 4 \neq 0$

$$\dfrac{x^2 + xy - 2x}{x^2 + 2xy + y^2 - 4} = \dfrac{x(x + y - 2)}{(x^2 + 2xy + y^2) - 4}$$

$$= \dfrac{x(x + y - 2)}{(x + y)^2 - 4}$$

$$= \dfrac{x(x + y - 2)}{(x + y - 2)(x + y + 2)} \quad \centerdot$$

$$= \dfrac{x}{x + y + 2}$$

v. For every replacement of u and for every replacement of v such that $u^2 + uv + v^2 \neq 0$

$$\dfrac{u^3 - v^3}{u^2 + uv + v^2} = \dfrac{(u - v)(u^2 + uv + v^2)}{u^2 + uv + v^2} = u - v$$

[CAUTION: It is important to recognize that the initial and terminal rational expressions in each of the above examples become names for the same number only for those replacements of the variables for which both rational expressions are defined.[1]] This is especially important to remember in instances where a rational expression is replaced by a simplified form in which all the restrictions on the replacements of the variables are no longer apparent. For example, the simplified form of $\dfrac{x^2 - 1}{x^2 - 3x + 2}$ is $\dfrac{x+1}{x-2}$ (see second example). Notice that the given rational expression is not defined if x is replaced by either 1 or 2; yet the simplified form *is* defined

---

[1] A rational expression is said to be *undefined* for any replacements of the variable or variables which make the value of the denominator zero.

if x is replaced by 1. Thus, if the expression $\dfrac{x^2 - 1}{x^2 - 3x + 2}$ is replaced by $\dfrac{x + 1}{x - 2}$, it must be specified that x (in the latter expression) may not be replaced by 1, in order for the two expressions to be considered equivalent.

EXERCISES

Simplify each of the following rational expressions; in each case, indicate the replacements which are not permissible.

1. $\dfrac{5x^2}{10x}$

2. $\dfrac{-4xy}{16x^2y^3}$

3. $\dfrac{3}{6x - 6}$

4. $\dfrac{r^2 - r^2t}{1 - t}$

5. $\dfrac{4n - 4}{n^2 - 1}$

6. $\dfrac{x^2 - 4x + 4}{x^2 - 4}$

7. $\dfrac{y^2 - y - 2}{2y^2 - 5y + 2}$

8. $\dfrac{z^2 - z + 1}{z^3 + 1}$

9. $\dfrac{xy - 2y + 2x - 4}{2x^2 - x - 6}$

MULTIPLICATION OF RATIONAL EXPRESSIONS

The product of two rational numbers, $\dfrac{a}{b}$ and $\dfrac{c}{d}$, was defined in Chapter 1 by the following:

$$\frac{a}{b} \cdot \frac{c}{d} = \frac{ac}{bd}$$

It is assumed that neither b nor d is equal to zero. The technique for *multiplying rational expressions* is similar to that for multiplying rational numbers. Since it can be proved, we state it as a theorem.

Theorem 2 For all polynomial replacements of P, Q, R, and S, $Q \neq 0$ and $S \neq 0$

$$\frac{P}{Q} \cdot \frac{R}{S} = \frac{P \cdot R}{Q \cdot S}$$

Proof   (Justify each step.)

$$\text{Let } x = \frac{P}{Q} \text{ and } y = \frac{R}{S}$$
$$\text{Then } x \cdot Q = P \text{ and } y \cdot S = R$$
$$(x \cdot Q) \cdot (y \cdot S) = P \cdot R$$
$$(x \cdot y) \cdot (Q \cdot S) = P \cdot R$$
$$x \cdot y = \frac{P \cdot R}{Q \cdot S}$$
$$\text{And } \frac{P}{Q} \cdot \frac{R}{S} = \frac{P \cdot R}{Q \cdot S}$$

Thus we find that the product of two rational expressions is also a rational expression; the numerator of the product is the product of the numerators of the given rational expressions; the denominator of the product is the product of the denominators of the given rational expressions.

In practice, it is usually desirable to factor, if possible, *the numerator and denominator of each rational expression before applying theorem 2.* By doing this, the product can be expressed in factored form and then simplified by applying Theorem 1. Here are some examples to illustrate the procedure.

Examples: i. $\forall_{x\neq0} \dfrac{5}{x} \cdot \dfrac{x^2 + x}{7} = \dfrac{5}{x} \cdot \dfrac{x(x + 1)}{7}$

$$= \frac{5x(x + 1)}{7x}$$

$$= \frac{5(x + 1)}{7} = \frac{5x + 5}{7}$$

ii. For every replacement of x and for every replacement of y such that $x^2 - 1 \neq 0$ and $xy \neq 0$

$$\frac{x}{x^2 - 1} \cdot \frac{x^2 + 4x + 3}{xy} = \frac{x}{(x - 1)(x + 1)} \cdot \frac{(x + 3)(x + 1)}{xy}$$

$$= \frac{x(x + 3)(x + 1)}{xy(x - 1)(x + 1)}$$

$$= \frac{x + 3}{y(x - 1)} = \frac{x + 3}{yx - y}$$

iii. For every replacement of x and for every replacement of y such that $y^3 + 2y \neq 0$ and $xy - 6 + 2y - 3x \neq 0$

$$\frac{y^2 - 6y + 9}{y^3 + 2y} \cdot \frac{xy^2 + 2x}{xy - 6 + 2y - 3x}$$

$$= \frac{(y - 3)^2}{y(y^2 + 2)} \cdot \frac{x(y^2 + 2)}{(xy - 3x) + (2y - 6)}$$

$$= \frac{(y - 3)^2}{y(y^2 + 2)} \cdot \frac{x(y^2 + 2)}{x(y - 3) + 2(y - 3)}$$

$$= \frac{(y - 3)^2}{y(y^2 + 2)} \cdot \frac{x(y^2 + 2)}{(y - 3)(x + 2)}$$

$$= \frac{x(y - 3)^2(y^2 + 2)}{y(y^2 + 2)(y - 3)(x + 2)} = \frac{x(y - 3)}{y(x + 2)} = \frac{xy - 3x}{xy + 2y}$$

EXERCISES

1. True or false?

a. $\forall_{x\neq0} \dfrac{7}{x} \cdot \dfrac{x^2}{14} = \dfrac{x}{2}$

b. $\forall_x \dfrac{3}{x - 2} \cdot \dfrac{x - 2}{x - 3} = \dfrac{3}{x - 3}$

c. $\forall_{y\neq4,\,y\neq-1} \dfrac{3(y + 1)}{y - 4} \cdot \dfrac{4y(y + 3)}{y + 1} = \dfrac{12y(y + 3)}{y - 4}$

d. $\forall_r \forall_{s \neq 0} \ \dfrac{-5r}{s} \cdot \dfrac{2rs}{-20} = \dfrac{-r^2}{2}$

e. $\forall_{t \neq \frac{1}{2}} \ \dfrac{1 - 2t}{2t - 1} = -1$

f. $\forall_{n \neq 0} \ \dfrac{5}{n} \cdot \dfrac{n}{5} = 1$

g. $\forall_{x \neq 0} \forall_{y \neq 0} \ \dfrac{x}{y^2} \cdot \dfrac{y^2}{x} = 1$

h. $\forall_{r \neq 2, \ r \neq -3} \ \dfrac{5(r - 2)}{7(r + 3)} \cdot \dfrac{7(r + 3)}{5(r - 2)} = 1$

i. $\forall_s \forall_t$ the reciprocal of $\dfrac{3s - t}{2s + 5t}$ is $\dfrac{1}{3s - t} \ (t \neq 3s, \ 2s \neq -5t)$

j. $\forall_{x \neq -\frac{4}{3}} \forall_{y \neq 0}$ the multiplicative inverse of $\dfrac{3x + 4}{2y}$ is $\dfrac{2y}{3x + 4}$

2. Simplify; assume that no denominator will have the value 0.

a. $\dfrac{x}{y} \cdot \dfrac{2x - 3y}{x^2}$

b. $\dfrac{t + 1}{t^2 - 1} \cdot \dfrac{t - 1}{2}$

c. $\dfrac{3y^2 - 12}{y} \cdot \dfrac{4y^2}{3y - 6}$

d. $\dfrac{3a^2 - 5a - 2}{2a^2} \cdot \dfrac{a}{a^2 - 4a + 4}$

e. $\dfrac{3s - 4}{2s^2 + 3s - 9} \cdot \dfrac{4s^2 - 12s + 9}{6s - 8}$

f. $\dfrac{y^2 - 4}{y^2 - y} \cdot \dfrac{3y}{2xy + 3y - 4x - 6}$

g. $\dfrac{x^2 - y^2}{x^2 + y^2} \cdot \dfrac{x + y}{x - y}$

h. $\dfrac{n^2 - 2n - 8}{n - 1} \cdot \dfrac{n^3 - 1}{n^2 + 4n + 4}$

i. $\dfrac{8r^3 + 27}{2r} \cdot \dfrac{6r^3}{4r^2 - 9}$

j. $\dfrac{10xy}{x + 2y - 2} \cdot \dfrac{x^2 + 4xy + 4y^2 - 4}{5y^3}$

DIVISION OF RATIONAL EXPRESSIONS

The definition of division for rational expressions is consistent with the definitions of division for real numbers and polynomials.

■ *Definition of Division of Rational Expressions*   For all rational expressions

$$R, \ S, \text{ and } T, \ S \neq 0, \ \dfrac{R}{S} = T \text{ if and only if } R = S \cdot T$$

Unfortunately, the definition given does not indicate how to divide rational expressions. A clue for simplifying a quotient of rational expressions is provided by the fact that for all real replacements of x and y, $(y \neq 0)$

$$\dfrac{x}{y} = x \cdot \dfrac{1}{y}$$

A similar result holds for rational expressions.

Theorem 3 If R and S are rational expressions, $S \neq 0$, then $\dfrac{R}{S} = R \cdot \dfrac{1}{S}$

Proof (Justify each step.)

$$\text{Let } x = \frac{R}{S}$$

$$\text{Then } x \cdot S = R$$

$$(x \cdot S) \cdot \frac{1}{S} = R \cdot \frac{1}{S}$$

$$x \cdot \left(S \cdot \frac{1}{S} \right) = R \cdot \frac{1}{S}$$

$$x = R \cdot \frac{1}{S}$$

$$\text{And } \frac{R}{S} = R \cdot \frac{1}{S}$$

Thus we see that a quotient $\dfrac{R}{S}$ of rational expressions R and S, $(S \neq 0)$, is equal to the product of R and the multiplicative inverse of S. Here are some examples which illustrate the technique of dividing rational expressions.

Examples:

i. $\forall_x \forall_{y \neq 0}\ x \div \dfrac{1}{y} = x \cdot \dfrac{y}{1} = xy$

ii. $\forall_{x \neq 3}\ \dfrac{x-3}{2} \div \dfrac{x-3}{2} = \dfrac{x-3}{2} \cdot \dfrac{2}{x-3}$

$$= \frac{2(x-3)}{2(x-3)} = 1$$

iii. $\forall_{y \neq 0} \forall_{x \neq 2,\ x \neq 3},\ \dfrac{x^2 - 2x}{y} \div \dfrac{x^2 - 5x + 6}{y^2}$

$$= \frac{x(x-2)}{y} \cdot \frac{y^2}{(x-3)(x-2)}$$

$$= \frac{xy^2(x-2)}{y(x-3)(x-2)}$$

$$= \frac{xy}{x-3}$$

Frequently a quotient of rational expressions appears in a form using the horizontal "division line" rather than the symbol ($\div$). For instance, the last example may be written as

$$\frac{\dfrac{x^2 - 2x}{y}}{\dfrac{x^2 - 5x + 6}{y^2}}$$

Notice the use of the heavy line to indicate that $\dfrac{x^2 - 2x}{y}$ and $\dfrac{x^2 - 5x + 6}{y^2}$ are the replacements of R and S, respectively, in $\dfrac{R}{S}$.

EXERCISES

1. True or false?

   a. $\forall_{x\neq0}\forall_{y\neq1}\ \dfrac{4}{x(y-1)}\cdot\dfrac{x(y-1)}{4}=1$

   b. $\forall_{x\neq0}\forall_{y\neq1}$ the reciprocal of $\dfrac{4}{x(y-1)}$ is $\dfrac{x(y-1)}{4}$

   c. $\forall_{x\neq0}\forall_{y\neq1}$ the multiplicative inverse of $\dfrac{4}{x(y-1)}$ is $\dfrac{x(y-1)}{4}$

   d. $\dfrac{5}{4}\div\dfrac{2}{3}=\dfrac{5}{4}\cdot\dfrac{3}{2}$

   e. $\dfrac{9}{5}\div\dfrac{3}{5}=\dfrac{5}{9}\cdot\dfrac{3}{5}$

   f. $\forall_{x\neq0}\forall_{y\neq0}\ \dfrac{x}{y}\div\dfrac{x}{y}=\dfrac{x^2}{y^2}$

   g. $\forall_{a\neq0}\forall_{b\neq0}\ \dfrac{a^2}{b^2}\div\dfrac{a}{b}=\dfrac{a}{b}$

   h. $\forall_a\forall_{b\neq0}\forall_{c\neq0}\forall_{d\neq0}\ \dfrac{a}{b}\div\dfrac{c}{d}=\dfrac{a}{b}\cdot\dfrac{d}{c}$

   i. For all permissible replacements of x and y
   $$\frac{x^2-y^2}{x}\div\frac{x-y}{y}=\frac{x^2-y^2}{x}\cdot\frac{y}{x-y}$$

   j. For all permissible replacements of r and s
   $$\frac{\dfrac{r^2+2rs+s^2}{rs}}{\dfrac{r+s}{s}}=\frac{r^2+2rs+s^2}{rs}\cdot\frac{r+s}{s}$$

2. Simplify; specify any restrictions concerning replacements.

   a. $\dfrac{2x^2-xy}{3}\div\dfrac{2x-y}{9}$

   b. $\dfrac{\dfrac{nt^2-4n}{2}}{\dfrac{t+2}{4}}$

   c. $(r^4-s^4)\div\dfrac{r^2+s^2}{r}$

   d. $\dfrac{3t^2+10t-8}{4t^2-12t+9}\div\dfrac{3t-2}{4t^2-9}$

   e. $\dfrac{4t^2+6t+9}{3t-2}\div\dfrac{8t^3-27}{9t^2-4}$

   f. $\dfrac{-xy^2}{1-x}\div\dfrac{2y}{x-1}$

   g. $\dfrac{2x^2-3y^2}{x^2}\div\dfrac{3y^2-2x^2}{x}$

   h. $\dfrac{6y-y^2}{3y+4}\div\dfrac{2y^2-9y-18}{27y^3+64}$

   i. $\dfrac{uv^3+v^4}{-u^2+v^2}\div\dfrac{u+v}{v^2-u^2}$

   j. $\dfrac{2rs-12-3s+8r}{r+s+2}\div\dfrac{s^2-16}{r^2-4+2rs+s^2}$

ADDITION OF RATIONAL EXPRESSIONS

The addition of rational expressions makes use of the distributive property and of Theorem 3 which states that for any polynomials P and Q, $Q \neq 0$, $\frac{P}{Q} = P \cdot \frac{1}{Q} = \frac{1}{Q} \cdot P$. The following theorem provides the basic information.

Theorem 4 For all polynomials P, Q, and R, $Q \neq 0$, $\dfrac{P}{Q} + \dfrac{R}{Q} = \dfrac{P+R}{Q}$

Proof (Justify each step.)

$$\frac{P}{Q} + \frac{R}{Q} = P \cdot \frac{1}{Q} + R \cdot \frac{1}{Q}$$

$$= (P+R) \cdot \frac{1}{Q}$$

$$= \frac{P+R}{Q}$$

In words, Theorem 4 tells us that the sum of two rational expressions which have a common denominator is also a rational expression; its numerator is the sum of the numerators; and its denominator is the common denominator. Here are some examples which illustrate the use of the theorem.

Examples:

    i. $\forall_{y \neq 0} \dfrac{5}{y} + \dfrac{7}{y} = \dfrac{5+7}{y} = \dfrac{12}{y}$

    ii. $\forall_x \forall_{y \neq 0} \dfrac{x+5}{y} + \dfrac{x-5}{y} = \dfrac{(x+5) + (x-5)}{y}$

$$= \frac{(x+x) + (5-5)}{y} = \frac{2x}{y}$$

    iii. $\forall_t \dfrac{2t+1}{t^2-2} + \dfrac{t-3}{t^2-2} = \dfrac{(2t+1) + (t-3)}{t^2-2}$

$$= \frac{3t-2}{t^2-2} \ (t^2 - 2 \neq 0)$$

    iv. $\forall_r \dfrac{3r-4}{r^2-3r+2} + \dfrac{5-3r}{r^2-3r+2}$

$$= \frac{(3r-4) + (5-3r)}{r^2-3r+2}$$

$$= \frac{1}{r^2-3r+2} \ (r^2 - 3r + 2 \neq 0)$$

Theorem 4 does not cover the case where the rational expressions to be added have different denominators. We can overcome the problem by finding equivalent rational expressions which have the same denominator. This can always be done by resorting to Theorem 1 which states that for all polynomial replacements of P, C, and Q, $C \neq 0$ and $Q \neq 0$

$$\frac{P}{Q} = \frac{C \cdot P}{C \cdot Q}$$

This result and Theorem 4 show us a way to add any two rational expressions. The following examples illustrate the procedure.

Examples: *i.* $\forall_{x \neq 0,\ x \neq -1}\ \dfrac{2}{x(x+1)} + \dfrac{3}{x} = \dfrac{2}{x(x+1)} + \dfrac{3(x+1)}{x(x+1)}$

$$= \dfrac{2 + 3(x+1)}{x(x+1)} = \dfrac{3x+5}{x(x+1)}$$

ii. $\forall_{x \neq 0} \forall_{y \neq 0}\ \dfrac{2}{x} + \dfrac{-3}{y} = \dfrac{2y}{xy} + \dfrac{-3x}{xy} = \dfrac{2y - 3x}{xy}$

iii. $\forall_{y \neq 4,\ y \neq -4}\ \dfrac{3y}{y^2 - 16} + \dfrac{2}{y+4} = \dfrac{3y}{(y+4)(y-4)} + \dfrac{2}{y+4}$

$$= \dfrac{3y}{(y+4)(y-4)} + \dfrac{2(y-4)}{(y+4)(y-4)}$$

$$= \dfrac{3y + 2(y-4)}{(y+4)(y-4)} = \dfrac{5y - 8}{(y+4)(y-4)}\ .$$

It should be noticed in example *iii.* that one important step in adding rational expressions with different denominators is to find a suitable common denominator. As in adding fractional numbers, it is better to find the *least common denominator*. When seeking the least common denominator (LCD) of a set of rational expressions the following steps are taken.

   i. Factor completely each denominator.

   ii. Form the LCD as the product of all the different factors. The exponent of each factor should be the greatest exponent associated with that factor in the various denominators.

For example, to find the LCD of

$$\dfrac{2y}{y^2 - 9}, \quad \dfrac{y^2 + 1}{y^2 + 6y + 9}, \quad \text{and} \quad \dfrac{5}{y^2 - 3y}$$

first factor each denominator completely.

$$\dfrac{2y}{(y+3)(y-3)}, \quad \dfrac{y^2 + 1}{(y+3)^2}, \quad \text{and} \quad \dfrac{5}{y(y-3)}$$

Verify that, according to step *ii* above, we obtain $y(y-3)(y+3)^2$ as the LCD in this example.

EXERCISES

1. True or false?

   a. The LCD for $\dfrac{1}{x^2}$ and $\dfrac{5}{xy}$ is xy.

   b. The LCD for $\dfrac{a}{x}$ and $\dfrac{b}{y}$ is xy.

   c. The LCD for $\dfrac{x}{x+y}$ and $\dfrac{4}{x}$ is $x + y$.

d. The LCD for $\dfrac{2r}{r+2}$ and $\dfrac{s}{r-2}$ is $(r+2)(r-2)$.

e. The LCD for $\dfrac{3t+1}{(t-1)^2}$ and $\dfrac{2t-3}{t^2-1}$ is $(t+1)(t-1)^2$.

f. The LCD for $\dfrac{2n+1}{n^2+2n+1}$ and $\dfrac{n}{n+1}$ is $(n+1)^2$.

g. The LCD for $\dfrac{1}{x}$, $\dfrac{2}{x^2y}$ and $\dfrac{3}{xyz^3}$ is xyz^3.

h. The LCD for $\dfrac{-2}{2x^2-5x}$, $\dfrac{-3x}{2x-5}$ and $\dfrac{5}{x^2}$ is $x^2(2x-5)$.

i. $\forall_a \forall_b \forall_{c\neq0}\ \dfrac{a}{c} + \dfrac{b}{c} = \dfrac{a+b}{c}$

j. $\forall_a \forall_c \forall_{b\neq0} \forall_{d\neq0}\ \dfrac{a}{b} + \dfrac{c}{d} = \dfrac{ad+bc}{bd}$

2. Simplify; assume that no denominator has the value 0.

a. $\dfrac{2x^2}{x^2y} + \dfrac{-x^2}{x^2y}$

b. $\dfrac{x^2}{x^2+1} + \dfrac{1}{x^2+1}$

c. $\dfrac{a}{x} + \dfrac{b}{y}$

d. $\dfrac{y}{y^2-1} + \dfrac{1}{y-1}$

e. $\dfrac{2t}{t^2-4} + \dfrac{1}{t^2+5t+6}$

f. $\dfrac{3n}{n^2+2n+1} + \dfrac{2n-1}{n^2+3n+2}$

g. $\dfrac{x}{2x^2+7x-15} + \dfrac{x+1}{2x^2-11x+12}$

h. $\dfrac{2}{r} + \dfrac{1}{r+1} + \dfrac{3}{r^2-1}$

i. $\dfrac{2y}{4y^2+4y+1} + \dfrac{-1}{2y+1}$

j. $\dfrac{1}{xy-3x-3y+9} + \dfrac{-1}{y-3} + \dfrac{-1}{x-3}$

SUBTRACTION OF RATIONAL EXPRESSIONS

Since the set of polynomials is a subset of the set of rational expressions, we must define the difference of two rational expressions in a way which is consistent with the definition of the difference of polynomials. The following definition meets this requirement.

■ *Definition of Subtraction of Rational Expressions* For all rational expressions

$$\frac{P}{Q} \text{ and } \frac{R}{S}, \quad \frac{P}{Q} - \frac{R}{S} = \frac{P}{Q} + \left(-\frac{R}{S}\right) \text{ where}$$

$-\dfrac{R}{S}$ is the additive inverse of $\dfrac{R}{S}$.

Thus, the difference $\dfrac{P}{Q} - \dfrac{R}{S}$ is defined to be the sum of $\dfrac{P}{Q}$ and the additive inverse of $\dfrac{R}{S}$.

As indicated in the definition of the difference of rational expressions, the additive inverse of the rational expression $\frac{P}{Q}$ is denoted by $-\frac{P}{Q}$. For example, $\left(-\frac{x^2}{x^2-1}\right)$ is the additive inverse of $\frac{x^2}{x^2-1}$. There are other equivalent symbols for the additive inverse of a rational expression; the following theorem tells how to obtain them.

Theorem 5 For all polynomials P and Q, $Q \neq 0$, $-\frac{P}{Q} = \frac{-P}{Q}$

Proof   (Justify each step.) Suppose that the rational expressions

$$\frac{P}{Q} \text{ and } \frac{R}{Q}$$

are additive inverses. That is

$$\frac{P}{Q} + \frac{R}{Q} = 0 \qquad \left(\text{or } -\frac{P}{Q} = \frac{R}{Q}\right)$$

But $\frac{P}{Q} + \frac{R}{Q} = \frac{P+R}{Q}$

$\therefore \quad \frac{P+R}{Q} = 0$

Hence $P + R = 0$ and so $R = (-P)$

$\therefore \quad -\frac{P}{Q} = \frac{-P}{Q}$

A corollary conclusion is in order: for all polynomials P and Q, $Q \neq 0$

$$\frac{-P}{Q} = \frac{P}{-Q}$$

This result follows from Theorem 1. Thus, we find that there are three acceptable ways of denoting the additive inverse of a rational expression $\frac{P}{Q}$. They are

$$-\frac{P}{Q}, \quad \frac{-P}{Q}, \text{ and } \quad \frac{P}{-Q}$$

The definition of the difference of rational expressions and Theorem 5 provide all the new information that is necessary to simplify a difference of rational expressions. The following examples illustrate the correct procedures.

Examples: *i.* $\forall_x \dfrac{x^3}{3} - \dfrac{x}{3} = \dfrac{x^3}{3} + \left(-\dfrac{x}{3}\right)$ Def. subt. rational express.

$\qquad\qquad = \dfrac{x^3}{3} + \dfrac{-x}{3}$ Theorem 5

$\qquad\qquad = \dfrac{x^3 + (-x)}{3}$ Theorem 4

$\qquad\qquad = \dfrac{x^3 - x}{3}$ Def. diff. polynomials

ii. $\forall_{x \neq 0}$ $\dfrac{2}{x} - \dfrac{x-3}{2x} = \dfrac{2}{x} + \dfrac{-(x-3)}{2x}$ [Notice the insertion of parentheses.]

$$= \dfrac{2}{x} + \dfrac{-x+3}{2x}$$

$$= \dfrac{4}{2x} + \dfrac{-x+3}{2x} = \dfrac{4+(-x)+3}{2x} = \dfrac{7-x}{2x}$$

iii. $\forall_{t \neq 1,\ t \neq -4}$ $\dfrac{2-t^2}{t^2+3t-4} - \dfrac{-t-1}{t+4}$

$$= \dfrac{2-t^2}{(t+4)(t-1)} - \dfrac{-t-1}{t+4} \qquad \text{Factoring}$$

$$= \dfrac{2-t^2}{(t+4)(t-1)} + \dfrac{t+1}{t+4} \qquad \forall_t\ -(-t-1) = t+1$$

$$= \dfrac{2-t^2}{(t+4)(t-1)} + \dfrac{(t+1)(t-1)}{(t+4)(t-1)} \qquad \text{LCD is } (t+4)(t-1).$$

$$= \dfrac{2-t^2}{(t+4)(t-1)} + \dfrac{t^2-1}{(t+4)(t-1)}$$

$$= \dfrac{2-t^2+t^2-1}{(t+4)(t-1)} = \dfrac{1}{(t+4)(t-1)}$$

EXERCISES

1. True or false?

a. $\forall_x$ $-\dfrac{x-2}{3} = \dfrac{-x+2}{3}$

b. $\forall_{r \neq 0}$ $-\dfrac{r^2+1}{r} = \dfrac{r^2+1}{-r}$

c. $\forall_{t \neq 0}$ $\dfrac{t^2+2t-1}{t} = \dfrac{-t^2+2t-1}{-t}$

d. $\forall_y$ $\dfrac{y(-y+1)}{2} = \dfrac{y(y-1)}{-2}$

e. $\forall_{x \neq 1,\ x \neq 2}$ $\dfrac{x+3}{(x-1)(x-2)} = -\dfrac{x+3}{(x-1)(2-x)}$

f. $\forall_{x \neq 0}$ $\dfrac{5}{2x} - \dfrac{7}{x} = \dfrac{5}{2x} + \dfrac{7}{x}$

g. $\forall_{x \neq 0}\forall_{y \neq 0}$ $\dfrac{4}{x} - \dfrac{3}{y} = \dfrac{4}{x} + \dfrac{-3}{y}$

h. $\forall_{n \neq 2,\ n \neq -2}$ $\dfrac{n}{n-2} - \dfrac{-3}{-n-2} = \dfrac{n}{n-2} + \dfrac{3}{n+2}$

i. $\forall_{a \neq 1}$ $\dfrac{2}{a-1} - \dfrac{3}{1-a} = \dfrac{2}{a-1} + \dfrac{3}{a-1}$

j. $\forall_{x \neq 3,\ x \neq -2}$ $\dfrac{x^2}{(x-3)(x+2)} - \dfrac{2}{(3-x)(x+2)} = \dfrac{x^2+2}{(x-3)(x+2)}$

2. Simplify; assume no demominator has the value 0.

a. $\dfrac{x^2}{y} - \dfrac{5}{y}$

b. $\dfrac{2u}{3v} - \dfrac{1}{v}$

c. $\dfrac{3x}{y} - \dfrac{4}{xy}$

d. $\dfrac{3x+3}{x^2-1} - \dfrac{2}{x-1}$

e. $\dfrac{4-a}{4a^2-9} - \dfrac{3a-1}{9-4a^2}$

f. $\dfrac{x}{3+x} - \dfrac{x-3}{x}$

g. $\dfrac{5}{y^2+y-6} - \dfrac{-3}{y^2-4y+4}$

h. $\dfrac{4}{x^2-x} - \dfrac{3}{1-x} - \dfrac{1}{x}$

i. $\dfrac{4}{2-r} - \dfrac{6}{-r-2} - \dfrac{-16}{r^2-4}$

j. $\dfrac{x^2+6x+9}{x-3} - (x-3)$

COMPLEX RATIONAL EXPRESSIONS

Expressions like

$$\frac{\dfrac{2x}{x-1}}{\dfrac{x^2}{x+1}}, \quad \frac{\dfrac{x}{y}+\dfrac{y}{x}}{xy}, \quad \frac{2-\dfrac{7}{r}}{\dfrac{3}{r}}, \quad \text{and} \quad \frac{\dfrac{x^2}{2}+3}{x^2}$$

are called *complex rational expressions*. Some techniques for simplifying complex rational expressions are illustrated by the following examples. As you study each example, think of the reason(s) for every step.

Example:

METHOD 1

$$\forall_{x\neq0}\forall_{y\neq0}\quad \frac{\dfrac{x}{y}+\dfrac{y}{x}}{xy} = \frac{\dfrac{x^2+y^2}{xy}}{\dfrac{xy}{1}} = \frac{x^2+y^2}{xy}\cdot\frac{1}{xy} = \frac{x^2+y^2}{x^2y^2}$$

METHOD 2

$$\forall_{x\neq0}\forall_{y\neq0}\quad \frac{\dfrac{x}{y}+\dfrac{y}{x}}{xy} = \frac{\left(\dfrac{x}{y}+\dfrac{y}{x}\right)(xy)}{(xy)(xy)} = \frac{x^2+y^2}{x^2y^2}$$

Example:

METHOD 1

$$\forall_{r\neq0}\quad \frac{2-\dfrac{7}{r}}{\dfrac{3}{r}} = \frac{\dfrac{2r-7}{r}}{\dfrac{3}{r}} = \frac{2r-7}{r}\cdot\frac{r}{3} = \frac{r(2r-7)}{3r} = \frac{2r-7}{3}$$

METHOD 2

$$\forall_{r\neq0}\quad \frac{2-\dfrac{7}{r}}{\dfrac{3}{r}} = \frac{\left(2-\dfrac{7}{r}\right)\cdot r}{\dfrac{3}{r}\cdot r} = \frac{2r-7}{3}$$

You have probably discovered that by method 1 the basic steps to follow in simplifying complex rational expressions consist of expressing, if necessary, both the numerator and denominator as "simple" rational expressions, and then applying theorem 3. Describe the basic steps used in method 2.

EXERCISES

Simplify; specify in each case the limitations on the replacements of the variables.

1. $\dfrac{2 + \dfrac{x}{y}}{\dfrac{x}{y^2}}$

2. $\dfrac{\dfrac{u^2}{v^2}}{1 + \dfrac{1}{v}}$

3. $\dfrac{3 + \dfrac{a}{b}}{1 + \dfrac{1}{b}}$

4. $\dfrac{\dfrac{x^2}{y} - x}{\dfrac{x - y}{4}}$

5. $\dfrac{\dfrac{2}{x} + \dfrac{3}{y}}{3x + 2y}$

6. $\dfrac{\dfrac{1}{r} + \dfrac{1}{s}}{\dfrac{1}{r} - \dfrac{1}{s}}$

7. $\dfrac{(x + y) - \dfrac{x}{2}}{\dfrac{x}{2} - (x + y)}$

8. $\dfrac{3x + \dfrac{11x - 2}{x - 4}}{\dfrac{3x + 2}{x}}$

9. $\dfrac{\dfrac{2}{\sqrt{3}} + \dfrac{5}{\sqrt{12}}}{\sqrt{27}}$

VOCABULARY

Use each of the following correctly in a sentence. Numerals in parentheses refer to pages where these words were used. If you are not sure of the meaning of any word, turn to the indicated page.

additive inverse of a rational
  expression (105)
complex rational expression (108)
least common denominator (LCD) (104)

multiplicative inverse of a rational
  expression (101)
rational expression (95)

REVIEW EXERCISES

1. True or false?

a. $\forall_y \dfrac{2y}{y} = 2$

b. $\forall_y \forall_{x \neq 1} \dfrac{xy^2 - y^2}{1 - x} = -y^2$

c. $\forall_y \forall_{x \neq 0} \dfrac{-4y}{x} \cdot \dfrac{3xy}{-8} = \dfrac{3y^2}{2}$

d. $\forall_y \forall_{x \neq 0} (x^2 - xy) \div (-x) = x + y$

e. $\forall_x \forall_{y \neq 2} \dfrac{x}{y - 2} \div (y - 2) = \dfrac{x}{y - 2} \cdot \dfrac{1}{y - 2}$

f. $\forall_{x \neq 0} \dfrac{4 - x}{x} + \dfrac{2}{x} = \dfrac{6 - x}{2x}$

g. If R_1 and R_2 are rational expressions and $R_1 + R_2 = 1$, then R_1 and R_2 are additive inverses.

h. If R_1 and R_2 are rational expressions and $R_1 \cdot R_2 = 0$, then R_1 and R_2 are multiplicative inverses.

i. If R_1 and R_2 are rational expressions and $R_1 + R_2 = 1$, then R_1 and R_2 are multiplicative inverses.

j. If R_1 and R_2 are rational expressions and $R_1 \cdot R_2 = 0$, then R_1 and R_2 are additive inverses.

2. Simplify. Specify in each instance the limitations on the replacements of the variables.

a. $\dfrac{x^2 - 4}{2x - 4}$

b. $\dfrac{x^3 - y^3}{x^2 - y^2}$

c. $\dfrac{x - 4}{x - 2} + \dfrac{2 - 2x}{2 - x}$

d. $3x + 1 + \dfrac{7x - 2}{2x + 3}$

e. $\dfrac{3y - 1}{y - 2} - \dfrac{y + 1}{y - 2}$

f. $\left(\dfrac{x^2 - 1}{x^2 + 2x - 3} \cdot \dfrac{x - 2}{x} \right) + \dfrac{x + 2}{x + 3}$

g. $\dfrac{y}{y - 2} \cdot \left(\dfrac{2y^2 - y - 3}{y^2 + 5y + 6} \div \dfrac{2y - 3}{y - 2} \right)$

h. $\dfrac{\dfrac{2}{x} + \dfrac{3}{y}}{\dfrac{x}{y} + \dfrac{y}{x}}$

i. $\left(2 + \dfrac{1}{x} \right) \div \left(\dfrac{2}{x} \cdot \dfrac{4x^2 + 4x + 1}{x - 4} \right)$

j. $\left(\dfrac{2u^2 - uv - 3v^2}{uv^3 + v^4} \div \dfrac{u^2 + 4uv - 5v^2}{uv + 5v^2} \right) \div \dfrac{2u - 3v}{v^2}$

3. Given that $\left(3x - \dfrac{1}{3x} \right) \cdot P = 1$ for all real replacements of x for which $\left(3x - \dfrac{1}{3x} \right)$ is defined and non-zero. Express P in terms of x in the simplest form.

4. Given that $\left(\dfrac{x - 3y}{y^2} \right) + Q = 0$ for all real replacements of x and for all non-zero replacements of y. Express Q in terms of x and y.

CHAPTER TEST

1. Find all real numbers, if any, for which each of the following rational expressions is *undefined*.

a. $\dfrac{x-2}{x^2-6x+9}$

c. $\dfrac{3x^2+3}{4x^2-1}$

b. $\dfrac{x^2-4}{2x^2-3x}$

d. $\dfrac{-3x^2-5x+2}{3x^2+5x-2}$

2. Simplify. Assume that no denominator will have zero value.

a. $\dfrac{3}{2x}+\dfrac{4}{y}$

f. $\dfrac{2x}{y}\cdot\dfrac{xy}{4}$

b. $\dfrac{3}{2x-4}+\dfrac{5}{x^2-4}$

g. $\dfrac{x+3}{x^2-1}\cdot\dfrac{12}{x^2-9}\cdot\dfrac{2x-2}{9}$

c. $\dfrac{-1}{x-y}-\dfrac{1}{x+y}$

h. $\dfrac{4y^2-9}{2y^2-6y}\div\dfrac{9-12y+4y^2}{-y^3+y^2+6y}$

d. $\dfrac{7}{2x-3}+\dfrac{-2}{3-2x}$

i. $\dfrac{\dfrac{1}{x}-\dfrac{1}{y}}{xy}$

e. $\dfrac{1}{x-1}+\dfrac{1}{x-2}-\dfrac{2}{3}$

j. $-\dfrac{6-2t}{t-3}$

3. True or false?

a. $\forall_{x\neq0}\forall_{y\neq0}\ \dfrac{\dfrac{1}{x}}{\dfrac{x}{y}}=\dfrac{y}{x}$

e. $\forall_a\forall_b\ \dfrac{a-b}{b-a}=1\ (a\neq b)$

b. $\forall_{x\neq0}\forall_{y\neq0}\ \dfrac{x}{y}\cdot\dfrac{y}{x}=1$

f. $\forall_{x\neq0}\ \dfrac{x}{5}\div\dfrac{x}{2}=\dfrac{x}{5}\cdot\dfrac{2}{x}$

c. $\forall_a\forall_b\forall_{x\neq0}\ \dfrac{a}{x}-\dfrac{b}{x}=\dfrac{a-b}{2x}$

g. $\forall_y\forall_{x\neq0}\ \dfrac{2xy-3}{x^2}=\dfrac{2y-3}{x}$

d. $\forall_x\forall_{y\neq0}\ -\dfrac{-x}{y}=\dfrac{-x}{-y}$

h. $\forall_x\forall_y\ x-\dfrac{y}{5}=5x-y$

CUMULATIVE REVIEW

The following exercises cover the material in Chapters 1 through 4.

1. Name the property illustrated by each of the following statements about real numbers.

a. $(2\cdot\sqrt{3})\cdot3=2\cdot(\sqrt{3}\cdot3)$

b. If $3+2\cdot5=13$ and $13=2\cdot5+3$, then $3+2\cdot5=2\cdot5+3$.

c. $-\sqrt{2}+[-(-\sqrt{2})]=0$

d. $\sqrt{3}+\left(\dfrac{1}{2}+3\right)=\left(\sqrt{3}+\dfrac{1}{2}\right)+3$

e. $5\sqrt{2} + 6\sqrt{2} = (5+6)\sqrt{2}$ **i.** $13^5 \cdot 1 = 13^5$

f. $\sqrt{2} \cdot \sqrt{7}$ is a real number

g. $3 \cdot \sqrt{2} = \sqrt{2} \cdot 3$ **j.** $\dfrac{12}{7} \cdot \dfrac{7}{12} = 1$

h. $9 + 0 = 9$ **k.** If $3 - 4 = -1$, then $-1 = 3 - 4$.

2. True or false?

a. The number $4^{\frac{1}{3}}$ is rational.

b. The number $16^{\frac{1}{4}}$ is rational.

c. Each implication and its contrapositive have the same truth-value.

d. The number 31 is prime.

e. The number 27 is not composite.

f. The number $5.0\overline{67}$ is irrational.

g. The real number solution set of $x^2 = 16$ is $\{4, -4\}$.

h. The real number solution set of $\sqrt{x} = 2$ is $\{4, -4\}$.

i. $\sqrt{\dfrac{4}{16}} = \dfrac{1}{2}$

j. $\sqrt{50} = 5\sqrt{2}$

k. $(3^2)^4 = 3^6$

l. $\sqrt[5]{-1} = -1$

m. $\left(\dfrac{1}{4}\right)^{-1} = 4$

n. $\sqrt[5]{2^4} = 2^{\frac{4}{5}}$

o. $\forall_x \ |x| = x$

p. $125.6 = 1.256 \times 10^3$

q. $\dfrac{10^{-4}}{10^{-2}} = 10^{-2}$

r. $4a^2 + 5$ is a polynomial over the integers.

s. $\forall_x \forall_y \ \dfrac{x+y}{2} = \dfrac{x}{2} + \dfrac{y}{2}$

t. $\forall_{x \neq 0} \forall_{y \neq 0} \ \dfrac{2}{x+y} = \dfrac{2}{x} + \dfrac{2}{y}, \ (x+y \neq 0)$

u. $\forall_{x \neq 0} \ \dfrac{5-2x}{x} + \dfrac{x-4}{x} = \dfrac{1-x}{x}$

v. $\forall_{a \neq 0} \forall_{b \neq 0} \ \dfrac{2}{\frac{a}{b}} = \dfrac{b}{2a}$

w. $\forall_{x \neq 0} \ \dfrac{x}{2} \div \dfrac{1}{x} = \dfrac{x^2}{2}$

x. $\forall_m \forall_{n \neq 0} \dfrac{m}{n} + 1 = \dfrac{m+1}{n}$

y. $|-4 - 3| = |-4| - |-3|$

z. $(5 - \sqrt{3})^2 = 28 - 10\sqrt{3}$

3. Simplify. State all restrictions concerning values of variables.

a. $\dfrac{xy^2}{x^2 - 1} \div \dfrac{yx^2}{x - 1}$

d. $\dfrac{3}{x^2 + 2x - 8} - \dfrac{1}{x + 4}$

b. $\left(\dfrac{x^2 - x - 2}{x^2 + 2}\right) \times \left(\dfrac{x + 2}{x + 1}\right)$

e. $(3x^3 - 5x + 7) \div (x - 1)$

c. $\dfrac{1}{x + 1} + \dfrac{2}{x^2 - 1}$

f. $\dfrac{3}{x - 2} - \dfrac{2}{2 - x}$

4. Consider the following eight polynomials:

    i. x

    ii. $3st$

    iii. $y^4 + \sqrt{2}\,y$

    iv. $t^4 + \dfrac{1}{2}t^2 + \dfrac{1}{3}$

    v. $x^2 - 2xn + n^2$

    vi. $m^2 + \sqrt{3}$

    vii. $-\dfrac{1}{2}ps + 3s^2$

    viii. $x^6 + 1$

a. Which of the polynomials are monomials? binomials? trinomials? perfect square trinomials?

b. Give the degree of each polynomial.

c. Which polynomials are polynomials over the reals? over the rationals? over the integers?

d. Which polynomials are polynomials in one variable? in two variables?

e. What is the value of the polynomial in *viii* if x is replaced by -1?

f. What is the value of the polynomial in *vi* if m is replaced by 0?

g. What is the value of the polynomial in *iv* if t is replaced by $\sqrt{2}$?

h. What is the value of the polynomial in *ii* if s is replaced by $-\frac{1}{3}$ and t is replaced by $\frac{1}{3}$?

i. Factor the polynomial in *v*.

5. For each number, give its name in scientific notation.

a. 47.7   b. .47   c. .0025   d. .00000106

6. Determine the real number solution sets.

a. $\sqrt{2x} = 4$

c. $\sqrt{2 - x} = \sqrt{x + 5}$

b. $\sqrt{1 - 3t} = 1$

d. $\sqrt{\dfrac{2}{1 + y}} = \sqrt{\dfrac{1}{2 - 2y}}$

7. Simplify.

a. $\dfrac{4a^2b^3}{8a^{-3}b^{-2}}$

b. $\dfrac{x^{-4}}{\dfrac{1}{2x^5}}$

c. $p^{\frac{1}{3}} \cdot p^{\frac{5}{3}}$

d. $(9x^4y^6)^{\frac{1}{2}}$

8. Determine the solution set of each inequality in the set of real numbers.

   a. $5x + 3 > 2x$

   b. $2(m - 2) < 3(2m + 1)$

   c. $\dfrac{y - 1}{3} > \dfrac{2 - 2y}{5}$

   d. $\dfrac{4(s + 1)}{3} < \dfrac{-3(2 - s)}{2}$

9. State the property which the set of integers is lacking in order to be a field.
10. Explain why $1.35235223522235\ldots$ is an irrational number.
11. Prove that the sum of two *even* natural numbers is an *even* natural number.
12. Give a counterexample to disprove each of the following.
    a. The set of natural numbers is closed under subtraction.
    b. The set of rational numbers is closed under the operation of taking square root.
    c. The set of integers is closed under division.
13. Order each three numbers listed below, by writing a statement of the form: $a < b < c$.

    a. $\dfrac{3}{11}, \dfrac{2}{7}, \dfrac{9}{32}$

    b. $-\dfrac{9}{13}, -\dfrac{5}{7}, -\dfrac{2}{3}$

14. Determine the additive inverse and the multiplicative inverse of $\dfrac{t - 4}{7}$ for each $t \neq 4$.

BIBLIOGRAPHY

Allendoerfer, C. B. and Oakley, C. O. *Fundamentals of Freshman Mathematics.* New York: McGraw-Hill Book Co., Inc., 1959. Chapter 4.

Heimer, R. T., Kocher, F. and Lottes, J. J. *A Program in Contemporary Algebra.* New York: Holt, Rinehart and Winston, Inc., 1963. Book 4, Units IV and V.

Rose, I. H. *A Modern Introduction to College Mathematics.* New York: John Wiley & Sons, Inc., 1959. pp. 287-293.

School Mathematics Study Group. *Mathematics For High School: Intermediate Mathematics, Part I.* New Haven: Yale University Press, 1961, pp. 95-102.

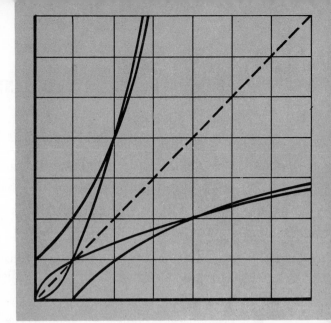

CHAPTER 5

Introduction to Coordinate Geometry

ALGEBRA AND PLANE GEOMETRY

In this chapter we will center our study around two central topics.

i. We will use what we know about the *algebra* of real numbers to study some portions of plane geometry

ii. We will use our knowledge of *plane geometry* to provide a model which illustrates some parts of algebra

In particular, for a given geometric condition concerning a set of points, we will obtain a corresponding algebraic condition, usually an equation or an inequality, whose solution set contains exactly the coordinates of the geometric set of points; for a given algebraic condition, we will determine the set of all points whose coordinates are exactly the members of the solution set of the algebraic condition. Furthermore, we will use algebra to prove some of the theorems usually encountered in a geometry course.

This "wedding" of geometry and algebra began with its discovery by Rene Descartes (1596-1650), a French mathematician. You may wish to read about this man in an encyclopedia or in a book concerning the lives of mathematicians.

A COORDINATE SYSTEM ON A LINE

From your first course in algebra, you are probably familiar with the *one-to-one correspondence* that exists between the *points* of a line and the *real numbers.*

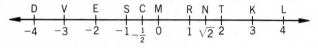

Fig. 1

Such a one-to-one correspondence is called a *coordinate system on a line.* From figure 1, notice that the number 3 has been paired with the point labeled K. What number has been paired with E? With S? To shorten such sentences we introduce the following definition.

■ *Definition of Coordinate* The number assigned to a point P by such a one-to-one correspondence is called the *coordinate* of P.

With reference to figure 1, verify the following examples.

Examples:　　*i.*　The coordinate of point V is the number -3.

　　　　　　ii.　The number 2 is the coordinate of the point labeled T.

　　　　　　iii.　$-1\frac{1}{2}$ is the coordinate of the point halfway between points E and S.

　　　　　　iv.　The coordinate of the point halfway between the points T and K is the number 2.5.

With reference to figure 1, note that the distance between the points K and E is 5 and that the coordinates of K and E are 3 and -2, respectively. With these facts, observe that

$$|(3) - (-2)| = |5| = 5 \text{ and that}$$
$$|(-2) - (3)| = |-5| = 5 \text{ also}$$

This suggests the following definition.

■ *Definition of Distance Between Two Points on a Real Number Line* The *distance* between any two points A and B on a real number line is the absolute value of the difference of the coordinates of A and B.

Furthermore, we shall denote such a distance by the letter-couple AB. Hence, $KE = 5$ and $EK = 5$.

EXERCISES

1. With reference to figure 1, determine each of the following. Write the *simplest* answer without absolute value bars.

Example:　　　　Determine RK. $RK = |(1) - (3)| = |-2| = 2$

a. *KR*	f. *VC*	k. *RE*	p. *DN*
b. *ML*	g. *CV*	l. *CT*	q. *ND*
c. *LM*	h. *VM*	m. *TC*	r. *LD*
d. *DE*	i. *MV*	n. *RN*	s. *VN*
e. *ED*	j. *ER*	o. *NR*	t. *NV*

2. True or false?

   a. $\forall_x \forall_y \; x - y = y - x$
   b. $\forall_x \forall_y \; |x - y| = |y - x|$
   c. $\forall_x \forall_y \; (x - y)^2 = (y - x)^2$
   d. $\forall_x \forall_y$, if $x > y$, then $x - y > 0$
   e. For each two points A and B, $AB = BA$.

Consider the line in figure 2 below and the corresponding coordinate system.

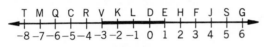

Fig. 2

One part of the figure has been heavily shaded; this part corresponds to the set of points V, E, and all points of the line *between* V and E. Such a set of points is called a *segment* and is denoted by the letter-couple naming its endpoints and a bar placed above the letter-couple. In this case we have been discussing the segment with endpoints V and E, which is denoted by $\overline{VE}$. We shall agree that any point X is between V and E if and only if $VX + XE = VE$. For example, L is between V and E since $VL = 2$, $LE = 2$, $VE = 4$, and $2 + 2 = 4$. C is not between V and E since $VC = 2$, $CE = 6$, $VE = 4$ and $2 + 6 \neq 4$. Does D belong to $\overline{VE}$? Why or why not? Does F belong to $\overline{VE}$? Why or why not? Does F belong to $\overline{GH}$? Why or why not? Notice that $\overline{CK}$ is a segment, a set of points; but that CK is a number, a positive number, the distance between points C and K.

EXERCISES

1. With reference to figure 1, determine the *coordinates* of the following points.

   a. the midpoint of $\overline{RK}$, the segment whose endpoints are R and K
   b. the midpoint of $\overline{VS}$
   c. the midpoint of $\overline{ML}$
   d. the midpoint of $\overline{MD}$
   e. the midpoint of $\overline{VR}$
   f. the midpoint of $\overline{TD}$
   g. the midpoint of $\overline{LR}$
   h. the midpoint of $\overline{VM}$
   i. the midpoint of $\overline{ER}$
   j. the midpoint of $\overline{TV}$
   k. the two *trisection* points of $\overline{KM}$
   l. the two trisection points of $\overline{MV}$
   m. the two trisection points of $\overline{RL}$
   n. the two trisection points of $\overline{DS}$

2. Given that the coordinate of a point A is the real number p and the coordinate of a point B is the real number q, determine the *coordinate* of the midpoint of $\overline{AB}$ in terms of p and q.

3. Given that the coordinate of a point A is the real number p and the coordinate of a point B is the real number q, determine the coordinate of one trisection point of $\overline{AB}$; the coordinate of the other trisection point of $\overline{AB}$.

4. Suppose that a coordinate system is established on a line. For each pairing, a point and its coordinate, tell whether B is closer to A or to C; that is, determine whether $AB < BC$ or $AB >$ BC.

a.	**b.**	**c.**	**d.**
$A \leftrightarrow 100$	$A \leftrightarrow 10^2$	$A \leftrightarrow 10^9$	$A \leftrightarrow 10^{23}$
$B \leftrightarrow 1000$	$B \leftrightarrow 10^3$	$B \leftrightarrow 10^8$	$B \leftrightarrow 10^{22}$
$C \leftrightarrow 10,000$	$C \leftrightarrow 10^4$	$C \leftrightarrow 10^6$	$C \leftrightarrow 10^{19}$

A COORDINATE SYSTEM ON A PLANE

We may establish a *coordinate system on a plane*, (see figure 3),

i. by selecting *any* line x in a plane and establishing a coordinate system on that line

ii. by selecting *the* line y (in that plane) which is *perpendicular* to that line x at the point on line x which corresponds to zero

iii. by establishing a coordinate system on the line y, having zero assigned to the point of intersection

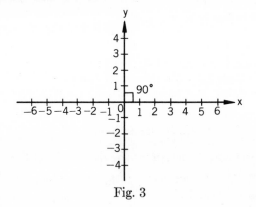

Fig. 3

The line x is called the *x-axis* and the line y is called the *y-axis*. The *point* 0 at which the lines x and y intersect is called the *origin*. The point 0 will correspond to zero for the coordinate system on the line y; in this chapter we will use the same *scale* on the line y that we have used on the line x. The arrowheads in the picture (figure 3) indicate the assigned positive direction along the axes.

We are now ready to establish a one-to-one correspondence between all the *points* of the *plane* and all *ordered pairs of real numbers*.

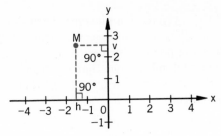

Fig. 4

For any point M in the plane, its perpendicular *projection* into the x-axis will be a point corresponding to a unique first real number h; and the perpendicular projection of M into the y-axis will be a point corresponding to a unique second real number v. Thus, to each point M in the plane is assigned a unique *ordered pair* of real numbers (h, v). Recall that $(h, v) = (s, t)$ if and only if $h = s$ and $v = t$, for all real numbers h, v, s, and t.

Conversely for each ordered pair of real numbers (h, v) there is exactly one point M in the plane corresponding to (h, v). Describe how to determine this unique point M for a given ordered pair of real numbers (h, v).

■ *Definition of x-coordinate; y-coordinate* The number h, determined as above, is called the *first coordinate* or *x-coordinate* of M; and the number v, determined as above, is called the *second coordinate* or *y-coordinate* of M.

Because of this one-to-one correspondence between points in a plane and ordered pairs of real numbers, when we mean that the point P *corresponds* to the ordered pair of real numbers $(7, -3)$, we may say

the point $(7, -3)$, or

$P(7, -3)$, or

$P = (7, -3)$

EXERCISES

1. For each point listed below and with reference to the coordinate system of figure 5, list the ordered pair of real numbers corresponding to the point. For some answers you will have to make estimates. The first problem has been answered for you.

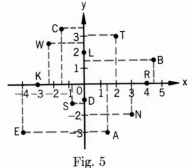

Fig. 5

a. N; $(3, -2)$ **e.** B **i.** R

b. T **f.** D **j.** L

c. E **g.** C **k.** W

d. K **h.** S **l.** O

2. Whenever a coordinate system on a plane has been established, as seen below, the two axes separate the plane into four sets of points. One such set of points, called *Quadrant I*, is the set of points which are in a one-to-one correspondence with all ordered pairs (x, y) of real numbers such that $x > 0$ and $y > 0$; i.e., $\{(x, y) \mid x > 0$ and $y > 0\}$. Describe the set of ordered pairs (x, y) that are in a one-to-one correspondence with the points of

a. Quadrant II

b. Quadrant III

c. Quadrant IV

d. the x-axis

e. the y-axis

f. the origin

(figure: coordinate plane with Quadrant II and Quadrant I above the x-axis, Quadrant III and Quadrant IV below; y-axis labeled, x-axis labeled, with 1 marked on each axis and 0 at the origin)

3. What points of the plane belong to no quadrant?

4. Use a sheet of graph paper and establish a coordinate system on the plane; then *plot* the following points by marking a heavy dot and writing the corresponding letter near it.

a. $A(-3, 0)$ **d.** $C(5.3, -2.8)$ **g.** $D(-4, -4)$ **j.** $B(-\sqrt{4}, 0)$

b. $M(-5, -4)$ **e.** $T(0, 6)$ **h.** $R(2\frac{1}{2}, 0)$ **k.** $E(-3, 3)$

c. $K(3, 5)$ **f.** $L(-3.3, 6.4)$ **i.** $F(3, -3)$ **l.** $O(0, 0)$

5. You may be familiar with the *Pythagorean Relation*, which states that for any right triangle ABC with the right angle at C, $(AC)^2 + (BC)^2 = (AB)^2$.

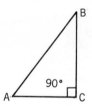

Examples: *i.* Triangle ABC is a right triangle with $\angle C$ the right angle, $AC = 3$ and $BC = 4$; determine AB.

$$(AC)^2 + (BC)^2 = (AB)^2$$
$$3^2 + 4^2 = (AB)^2$$
$$9 + 16 = (AB)^2$$
$$25 = (AB)^2$$
$$5 = AB$$

ii. Triangle KLM is a right triangle with $\angle M$ the right angle, $KM = 5$ and $LM = \sqrt{7}$; determine KL.

$$(KM)^2 + (LM)^2 = (KL)^2$$
$$5^2 + (\sqrt{7})^2 = (KL)^2$$
$$25 + 7 = (KL)^2$$
$$32 = (KL)^2$$
$$\sqrt{32} = KL$$
$$4\sqrt{2} = KL$$

iii. Triangle RST is a right triangle with $\angle T$ the right angle, $RS = 6$ and $RT = 3$; determine ST.

$$(RT)^2 + (ST)^2 = (RS)^2$$
$$3^2 + (ST)^2 = 6^2$$
$$9 + (ST)^2 = 36$$
$$(ST)^2 = 27$$
$$ST = \sqrt{27}$$
$$ST = 3\sqrt{3}$$

For each right triangle ABC with $\angle C$ the right angle, the lengths of two sides are given. Use the Pythagorean Relation to determine the length of the third side. Express your answer in the simplest form.

a. $AC = 5$; $BC = 12$

b. $AC = 1$; $BC = 1$

c. $AC = 3$; $BC = 3$

d. $AC = \sqrt{2}$; $BC = \sqrt{5}$

e. $AC = 1$; $BC = 1\frac{1}{3}$

f. $AC = 5$; $AB = 7$

g. $AB = \sqrt{15}$; $AC = \sqrt{7}$

h. $AB = 10$; $BC = 6$

i. $AC = 9$; $BC = 8$

j. $AC = x$; $BC = y$ [$x > 0$; $y > 0$]

k. $AC = 3x$; $BC = 4x$ [$x > 0$]

l. $AC = 4t + 4$; $BC = 3t + 3$ [$t > -1$]

6. Using a sheet of graph paper, establish a coordinate system on the plane and draw the square $ABCD$ with $A(2, 3)$; $B(6, 3)$; $C(6, 7)$; $D(2, 7)$.

a. What is the length of each side of the square $ABCD$?

b. What are the coordinates of the midpoint of $\overline{AB}$? Of $\overline{CD}$? Of $\overline{BC}$? Of $\overline{DA}$?

c. Determine the length of the diagonal $\overline{AC}$. [Hint: use the Pythagorean Relation which states that for any right triangle PQR with right angle at Q, $(PQ)^2 + (QR)^2 = (PR)^2$.]

d. What are the coordinates of the point of intersection of the two diagonals, $\overline{AC}$ and $\overline{BD}$?

7. Draw the rectangle $KLMN$ with $K(-4, -2)$; $L(-4, 4)$; $M(6, 4)$; $N(6, -2)$.

a. What is the length of each side?

b. What are the coordinates for the midpoint of each side?

c. What is the length of one diagonal?

d. What are the coordinates of the point of intersection of the two diagonals?

e. What are the coordinates of each point at which the rectangle intersects an axis?

8. One vertex of a square is at $P(5, -5)$; its diagonals intersect at the origin. Draw such a square.

a. What are the coordinates of each of the other three vertices?

b. What is the length of each side of the square?

c. What is the length of each diagonal of the square?

9. The midpoint of $\overline{AB}$ is the origin and the coordinates of A are $(2, 3)$. What are the coordinates of B?

THE DISTANCE BETWEEN ANY TWO POINTS

Use figure 6 below to help you answer the questions beneath the figure.

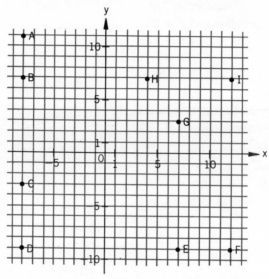

Fig. 6

What are the coordinates of each of the nine labeled points: $A, B, C, D, E, F, G, H, I$?

Determine each of the distances: AB; AC; CD; BD; EG; FI.

Determine each of the distances: HI; BH; BI; DE; EF; FE; FD.

You should notice that $A, B, C,$ and D have the same *first* coordinate, namely -8, and this makes it relatively easy to determine $AB, AC, CD,$ and BD. Also, since $F, E,$ and D have the same *second* coordinate, namely -9, it is easy to determine $DE, FE,$ and FD.

The preceding work suggests the following definition for the distance between two points with either the same first coordinate or the same second coordinate.

■ *Definition of Distance Between Two Points Having the Same First Coordinate or the Same Second Coordinate* For any two points $P(x, c)$ and $Q(x, d)$, $PQ = |c - d|$; and for any two points $S(m, y)$ and $T(n, y)$, $ST = |m - n|$.

EXERCISES

In each case below, determine AB (the length of $\overline{AB}$). Use graph paper if you must. Give the simplest answer; use absolute value bars only when necessary.

1. $A(5, 8)$ and $B(5, 12)$
2. $A(3, 1)$ and $B(3, 9)$
3. $A(-5, 2)$ and $B(-5, 14)$
4. $A(2, -5)$ and $B(2, 5)$

5. $A\left(3,\dfrac{1}{2}\right)$ and $B\left(3,6\dfrac{1}{2}\right)$

6. $A(2,4)$ and $B(2,-7)$

7. $A(8,726)$ and $B(8,634)$

8. $A(-7,-19)$ and $B(-7,27)$

9. $A(x,a)$ and $B(x,b)$ [for real numbers a, b, x]

10. $A(14,3)$ and $B(2,3)$

11. $A(-6,7)$ and $B(8,7)$

12. $A(83,-4)$ and $B(-5,-4)$

13. $A(s,y)$ and $B(t,y)$ [for real numbers s, t, y]

14. $A(3t+5,-7)$ and $B(2t+6,-7)$ [$t \neq 1$]

We have learned to find the distance between two points which have either the same first coordinate or the same second coordinate. We will now seek a way to determine the distance between two points which have different first coordinates and different second coordinates. That is, we will learn to determine PQ for any two points $P(r,s)$ and $Q(t,v)$ for which $r \neq t$ and $s \neq v$. Use figure 7 to help you answer the questions below.

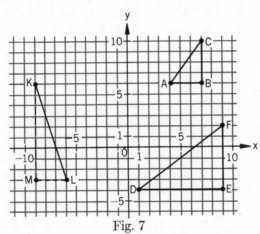

Fig. 7

What are the coordinates of A? of B? of C? Determine AB; BC. Is $\triangle ABC$ a right triangle? Why or why not? Use the Pythagorean Relation to determine AC.

What are the coordinates of D? of E? of F? Determine DE and EF. Is $\triangle DEF$ a right triangle? Why or why not? Use the Pythagorean Relation to determine DF.

Verify the following with respect to figure 7. The coordinates of K are $(-9,6)$ and the coordinates of L are $(-6,-3)$. The coordinates of M are $(-9,-3)$ and $\triangle KLM$ is a right triangle.

$$ML = |-9-(-6)| = |-3| = 3$$
$$MK = |-3-(6)| = |-9| = 9$$
$$(ML)^2 + (MK)^2 = (KL)^2 \qquad \text{(why?)}$$
$$3^2 + 9^2 = (KL)^2$$
$$9 + 81 = (KL)^2$$
$$90 = (KL)^2$$
$$\text{Therefore, } KL = \sqrt{90} = \sqrt{9} \cdot \sqrt{10} = 3\sqrt{10}$$

To generalize, consider figure 8 below.

Proof

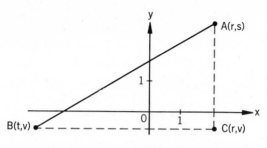

Fig. 8

Let $A(r, s)$ and $B(t, v)$ be two points in the plane $[r \neq t$ and $s \neq v]$; let C and A have the same projection into the x-axis; let B and C have the same projection into the y-axis. This establishes that $\triangle ABC$ is a right triangle, C is the vertex of right angle ACB, and the coordinates of C are (r, v).

Study the following with reference to the preceding:

$BC = |t - r|$ Def. dist. bet. two pts., same second coordinate

$AC = |v - s|$ Def. dist. bet. two pts., same first coordinate

$(BC)^2 + (AC)^2 = (AB)^2$ Pythagorean Relation

$(|t - r|)^2 + (|v - s|)^2 = (AB)^2$ Subst. Prop. [Tell what substitutions were made.]

Hence we have proved the following theorem.

Theorem   For every two points $A(r, s)$ and $B(t, v)$
$$AB = \sqrt{(t - r)^2 + (v - s)^2}$$

This is often referred to as the *Distance Formula*; it gives the distance between any two points with coordinates (r, s) and (t, v) respectively.

Example: Compute KT with $K(1, -7)$ and $T(5, 3)$
$$KT = \sqrt{(5 - 1)^2 + (3 - (-7))^2} = \sqrt{16 + 100}$$
$$= \sqrt{116} = \sqrt{4} \cdot \sqrt{29} = 2\sqrt{29}$$

EXERCISES

1.   Use the distance formula to compute the *distance* between the pairs of points whose coordinates are listed below. Express each answer in simplest form.

    a. $(9, 2)$ and $(6, 8)$ **e.** $(8, 7)$ and $(8, -6)$

    b. $(5, -3)$ and $(-2, 4)$ **f.** $(3, 12)$ and $(7, 12)$

    c. $(2, 5)$ and $(0, 0)$ **g.** $(100, -203)$ and $(97, -200)$

    d. $(-6, -3)$ and $(2, 1)$ **h.** $(-3, 8)$ and $(-4, 7)$

2. The coordinates of the endpoints of one diameter of a circle are $(3, 1)$ and $(-2, 5)$. What is the length of a *radius* of this circle?

3. Determine the *perimeter* of $\triangle ABC$ with $A(3, 7)$; $B(5, 2)$; $C(-7, 3)$. Prove that $\triangle ABC$ is a right triangle by using the converse of the Pythagorean Relation. Find the area of $\triangle ABC$.

4. Find the lengths of the *diagonals* of quadrilateral $PQRS$ with $P(-2, 3)$; $Q(5, 5)$; $R(6, -6)$; $S(-3, -3)$.

5. Prove that $\triangle KLM$ with $K(2, 8)$; $L(10, 11)$; $M(5, 0)$ is isosceles, but is *not* equilateral.

6. Prove that $B(-2, 5)$ is *between* $A(-5, -1)$ and $C(1, 11)$. [Hint: prove that $AB + BC = AC$.] Then prove that B is half-way between A and C. Remember, a drawing does not constitute a proof!

7. Prove that quadrilateral $ABCD$ with $A(-2, -2)$; $B(-1, 2)$; $C(8, 6)$; $D(7, 2)$ is a parallelogram. Prove that its diagonals are *not* equal in length.

8. Prove that points $P(-4, 1)$, $Q(2, 3)$, and $R(11, 6)$ are collinear. [A picture is not a proof!]

THE MIDPOINT OF A SEGMENT

Use figure 9 to help you answer the questions below the figure.

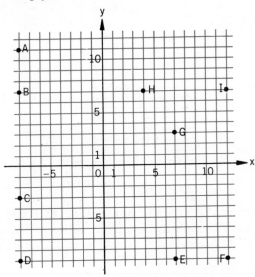

Fig. 9

What are the coordinates of each of the nine labeled points: A, B, C, D, E, F, G, H, I?

Verify that the coordinates of the midpoint of $\overline{AB}$ are $(-8, 9)$.

Determine the coordinates of the midpoint of each of the following segments: $\overline{CD}$, $\overline{BC}$, $\overline{AD}$, $\overline{AC}$, and $\overline{BD}$.

Verify that the coordinates of the midpoint of $\overline{HI}$ are $(8, 7)$.

Determine the coordinates of the midpoint of each of the following segments: $\overline{BH}$, $\overline{BI}$, $\overline{DE}$, $\overline{EF}$, and $\overline{DF}$.

You should notice that A, B, C, and D have the same *first* coordinate, namely -8, and this made it relatively easy to determine the coordinates of the midpoints of $\overline{BC}$, $\overline{CD}$, $\overline{AC}$, and $\overline{AD}$. Also, since D, E, and F have the same *second* coordinate, namely -9, it was easy to determine the coordinates of the midpoints of $\overline{DE}$, $\overline{EF}$, and $\overline{DF}$.

EXERCISES

Determine the coordinates of the midpoint of $\overline{AB}$ in each case below. The coordinates of A and B are given. Use graph paper only if necessary.

1. $A(5, 8)$ and $B(5, 12)$
2. $A(3, 1)$ and $B(3, 9)$
3. $A(-5, 2)$ and $B(-5, 14)$
4. $A\left(3, \frac{1}{2}\right)$ and $B\left(3, 6\frac{1}{2}\right)$
5. $A(2, -5)$ and $B(2, 5)$
6. $A(2, 4)$ and $B(2, -7)$
7. $A(8, 726)$ and $B(8, 634)$
8. $A(-7, -19)$ and $B(-7, 27)$

9. $A(x, a)$ and $B(x, b)$, [for real numbers a, b, x]
10. $A(14, 3)$ and $B(2, 3)$
11. $A(-6, 7)$ and $B(8, 7)$
12. $A(83, -4)$ and $B(-5, -4)$
13. $A(s, y)$ and $B(t, y)$ [for real numbers s, t, y]
14. $A(3t + 5, -7)$ and $B(t + 7, -7)$, $[t \neq 1]$

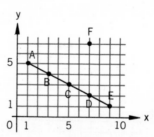

Fig. 10

In figure 10, consider $\overline{AE}$ with $A(1, 5)$ and $E(9, 1)$. We seek the coordinates of the midpoint of $\overline{AE}$. This point must be *i.* between A and E *and ii.* equidistant from A and E. Consider $B(3, 4)$. Is B the midpoint of $\overline{AE}$? B is between A and E since

$$AB = \sqrt{5}, BE = \sqrt{45} = 3\sqrt{5}, \text{ and } AE = \sqrt{80} = 4\sqrt{5}$$
and hence $AB + BE = AE$

But B is not equidistant from A and E since

$$AB = \sqrt{5}, BE = \sqrt{45}, \text{ and } \sqrt{5} \neq \sqrt{45}$$

Consider $F(7,7)$. Is F the midpoint of $\overline{AE}$? F is equidistant from A and E since
$$AF = \sqrt{40} = 2\sqrt{10} \text{ and } EF = \sqrt{40} = 2\sqrt{10}$$
and hence $AF = EF$

But F is not between A and E since
$$AF = 2\sqrt{10},\ EF = 2\sqrt{10}, \text{ and } AE = 4\sqrt{5}$$
and hence $AF + EF = 4\sqrt{10} \neq AE$

Consider $C(5,3)$. Is C the midpoint of $\overline{AE}$? C is between A and E since,
$$AC = \sqrt{20} = 2\sqrt{5},\ CE = 2\sqrt{5}, \text{ and } AE = 4\sqrt{5}$$
and hence $AC + CE = 4\sqrt{5} = AE$

C is also equidistant from A and E since
$$AC = 2\sqrt{5} = CE$$

Hence, C is the midpoint of $\overline{AE}$ according to the definition which follows:

■ *Definition of Midpoint of a Line Segment* M is the *midpoint* of $\overline{PQ}$ if and only if (*i.*) M is between P and Q $[PM + MQ = PQ]$ and (*ii.*) M is equidistant from P and Q $[MP = MQ]$.

We now seek a formula for determining the coordinates of M, the midpoint of $\overline{PQ}$ with $P(a,b)$ and $Q(c,d)$. That is, we are to express the coordinates of M in terms of a, b, c, and d. Let (x,y) be the coordinates of M, the midpoint of PQ.

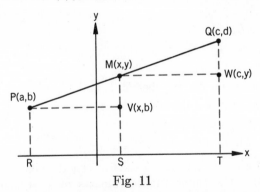

Fig. 11

Proof   With reference to figure 11, consider the perpendiculars from P, M, and Q to the x-axis at R, S, and T, respectively. Also consider the perpendiculars from P to $\overline{MS}$ at V and from M to $\overline{QT}$ at W. We have thus determined two congruent (same size and shape) right triangles: PVM and MWQ, such that $PV = MW$ and $MV = QW$. Since $PV = MW$ and $MV = QW$, it follows that
$$x - a = c - x \quad \text{and} \quad y - b = d - y$$
$$2x = a + c \quad \text{and} \quad 2y = b + d$$
$$x = \frac{a+c}{2} \quad \text{and} \quad y = \frac{b+d}{2}$$

We have just proved the following theorem.

Theorem   *Midpoint Formula.* For any two points $P(a, b)$ and $Q(c, d)$, the midpoint of $\overline{PQ}$ is $M\left(\dfrac{a + c}{2}, \dfrac{b + d}{2}\right)$.

Example: Determine the coordinates of T, the midpoint of $\overline{KL}$ with $K(-2, 7)$ and $L(8, 12)$.

Using the midpoint formula, the coordinates of T are $\left(\dfrac{-2 + 8}{2}, \dfrac{7 + 12}{2}\right)$ or $(3, 9.5)$.

EXERCISES

1. Given: A, B, and C with $A(3, 5)$; $B(7, 2)$; $C(11, 5)$. True or false?

   a. $AB = BC$ **b.** B is between A and C.   **c.** B is the midpoint of $\overline{AC}$.

2. Determine the coordinates of the midpoint of $\overline{AB}$ in each problem.

   a. $A(7, 16)$; $B(7, 28)$
   b. $A(-3, -5)$; $B(7, -5)$
   c. $A(0, 0)$; $B(8, 20)$
   d. $A(-5, -9)$; $B(0, 0)$
   e. $A(8, 6)$; $B(4, 10)$
   f. $A(8, -6)$; $B(4, -8)$
   g. $A(-8, -6)$; $B(4, 2)$
   h. $A(-8, 12)$; $B(-4, -4)$
   i. $A(-5, -9)$; $B(9, -5)$
   j. $A(a, b)$; $B(a, c)$, for real numbers a, b, and c
   k. $A(m, r)$; $B(n, r)$, for real numbers m, n, and r
   l. $A(0, 0)$; $B(s, t)$, for real numbers s and t
   m. $A(f, t)$; $B(c, k)$, for real numbers f, t, c, and k

3. The center of a given circle is at $F(-2, 6)$. One diameter of this circle has an endpoint at $V(3, 8)$. Determine the coordinates of T, the other endpoint of diameter $\overline{TV}$.

4. Given $\triangle ABC$ with $A(-3, -1)$; $B(3, 5)$; $C(-5, 13)$.

   a. Determine the length of the *median* from B for $\triangle ABC$. (A *median* of a triangle is a segment which has one endpoint at a vertex of the triangle and the other endpoint at the midpoint of the side opposite that vertex.)
   b. Determine AB, BC, and AC.
   c. Determine the coordinates of the midpoints K, L, and M of $\overline{AB}$, $\overline{BC}$, and $\overline{AC}$, respectively.
   d. Determine LM, KM, and KL.

e. Compare your answers to question **b** with those of question **d.** What does this comparison suggest to you?

f. What is the perimeter of $\triangle ABC$? Of $\triangle KLM$? Compare the perimeters.

5. True or false?

  a. For any 3 points A, B, and C, B is the midpoint of $\overline{AC}$ if and only if $AB + BC = AC$.

  b. For any 3 points A, B, and C, B is the midpoint of $\overline{AC}$ if and only if $AB = BC$.

6. Given segment $\overline{AB}$ with $A(r, s)$ and $B(m, n)$, determine the coordinates of T and V, the trisection points of $\overline{AB}$ in terms of r, s, m, and n.

7. Prove that $PM + MQ = PQ$, if $P(a, b)$; $M\left(\dfrac{a+c}{2}, \dfrac{b+d}{2}\right)$; $Q(c, d)$.

8. Prove that $PM = MQ$, if $P(a, b)$; $M\left(\dfrac{a+c}{2}, \dfrac{b+d}{2}\right)$; $Q(c, d)$.

SLOPE OF A LINE

Consider the line L_1 pictured in figure 12 and five of its points $A(-3, -6)$, $B(-1, -3)$, $C(1, 0)$, $D(3, 3)$, and $E(5, 6)$. For several pairs of these points, call them $P(x_1, y_1)$ and $Q(x_2, y_2)$, we shall compute $y_1 - y_2$, $x_1 - x_2$, and $\dfrac{y_1 - y_2}{x_1 - x_2}$.

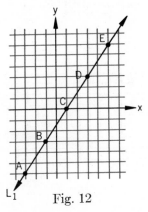

Fig. 12

$A(-3, -6)$ and $B(-1, -3)$: $y_1 - y_2 = -6 - (-3) = -3$

$$x_1 - x_2 = -3 - (-1) = -2$$

$$\frac{y_1 - y_2}{x_1 - x_2} = \frac{-3}{-2} = \frac{3}{2}$$

$E(5, 6)$ and $C(1, 0)$: $y_1 - y_2 = 6 - 0 = 6$

$$x_1 - x_2 = 5 - 1 = 4$$

$$\frac{y_1 - y_2}{x_1 - x_2} = \frac{6}{4} = \frac{3}{2}$$

$B(-1, -3)$ and $D(3,3)$: $y_1 - y_2 = -3 - 3 = -6$

$$x_1 - x_2 = -1 - 3 = -4$$

$$\frac{y_1 - y_2}{x_1 - x_2} = \frac{-6}{-4} = \frac{3}{2}$$

$D(3,3)$ and $B(-1, -3)$: $y_1 - y_2 = 3 - (-3) = 6$

$$x_1 - x_2 = 3 - (-1) = 4$$

$$\frac{y_1 - y_2}{x_1 - x_2} = \frac{6}{4} = \frac{3}{2}$$

Now, compute $y_1 - y_2$, $x_1 - x_2$ and $\dfrac{y_1 - y_2}{x_1 - x_2}$ for the next few pairs.

$A(-3, -6)$ and $D(3,3)$

$E(5,6)$ and $B(-1, -3)$

$B(-1, -3)$ and $E(5,6)$

You should notice that for every pair considered, although $y_1 - y_2$ and $x_1 - x_2$ may have had different values, $\dfrac{y_1 - y_2}{x_1 - x_2}$ always had the same value, namely $\frac{3}{2}$. In the case of L_1, $\frac{3}{2}$ is called the *slope* of L_1.

■ *Definition of Slope of a Line* For any two points

$$P(x_1, y_1) \text{ and } Q(x_2, y_2) \ [x_1 \neq x_2],$$

$\dfrac{y_1 - y_2}{x_1 - x_2}$ is the *slope* of the line through P and Q.

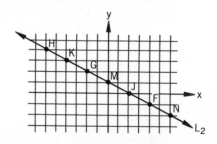

Fig. 13

Consider the line L_2 pictured in figure 13. Select five pairs of points on this line and for each pair compute $y_1 - y_2$, $x_1 - x_2$, and $\dfrac{y_1 - y_2}{x_1 - x_2}$. As one example, consider $K(-4,3)$ and $F(4, -1)$: $y_1 - y_2 = 3 - (-1) = 4$, $x_1 - x_2 = -4 - 4 = -8$, and $\dfrac{y_1 - y_2}{x_1 - x_2} = \dfrac{4}{-8} = -\dfrac{1}{2}$. In each of the five cases what did you find as the value of $\dfrac{y_1 - y_2}{x_1 - x_2}$? You should have found the same value in each case, namely $-\frac{1}{2}$. Therefore, by the definition of slope, we say that the slope of the line L_2 is $-\frac{1}{2}$.

In figure 14, $y_1 - y_2 = 0$ for each pair of points on the line L_3. Therefore, $\dfrac{y_1 - y_2}{x_1 - x_2} = 0$ and the slope of the line L_3 is zero.

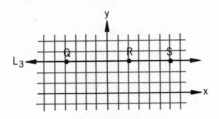

Fig. 14

In figure 15, $x_1 - x_2 = 0$ for each pair of points on the line L_4; therefore, $\dfrac{y_1 - y_2}{x_1 - x_2}$ is undefined and we say that the slope of the line L_4 is undefined.

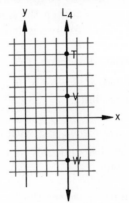

Fig. 15

EXERCISES

Determine $\dfrac{y_1 - y_2}{x_1 - x_2}$, the slope of the line passing through the two points whose coordinates are given.

1. $(8, 2)$ and $(3, 7)$
2. $(3, 7)$ and $(8, 2)$
3. $(8, 3)$ and $(2, 7)$
4. $(3, 8)$ and $(2, 7)$
5. $(-6, 8)$ and $(5, -3)$
6. $(-2, -5)$ and $(-4, -9)$
7. $(3, -2)$ and $(5, -6)$
8. $(2, 7)$ and $(9, 7)$

9. $(-6, 17)$ and $(3, 17)$
10. (a, b) and (c, b) for real numbers a, b, and c
11. $(5, 3)$ and $(5, 9)$
12. $(-2, -4)$ and $(-2, 3)$
13. (x, y) and (x, t), for real numbers x, y, and t
14. $(13, 11)$ and $(0, 0)$

We shall introduce the following notation to simplify our writing about lines and slopes.

NOTATION: The line which passes through two points P and Q will be denoted by $\overleftrightarrow{PQ}$, a letter-couple with $\leftrightarrow$ above it.

NOTATION: For any line L_1 through $P(a, b)$ and $Q(c, d)$, the slope of L_1, $\dfrac{b - d}{a - c}$, will be denoted by m_1.

For example

In figure 12, $L_1 = \overleftrightarrow{BD}$ and $m_1 = \frac{3}{2}$

In figure 13, $L_2 = \overrightarrow{KF}$ and $m_2 = -\frac{1}{2}$

In figure 14, $L_3 = \overleftrightarrow{RQ}$ and $m_3 = 0$

In figure 15, $L_4 = \overrightarrow{TV}$ and m_4 is not defined.

In certain problems you have already found that for a line $\overleftrightarrow{PQ}$, if $y_1 - y_2 = 0$ then the slope is zero, and if $x_1 - x_2 = 0$ then the slope is undefined. These kinds of lines are given special names by the following definitions.

◼ *Definition of Horizontal Line* For each $\overleftrightarrow{PQ}$ with $P(a, b)$ and $Q(c, d)$, the slope of $\overleftrightarrow{PQ}$ is zero if and only if $b = d$. In such a case, $\overleftrightarrow{PQ}$ is called a *horizontal* line.

◼ *Definition of Vertical Line* For each $\overleftrightarrow{PQ}$ with $P(a, b)$ and $Q(c, d)$, the slope of $\overleftrightarrow{PQ}$ is undefined if and only if $a = c$. In such a case, $\overleftrightarrow{PQ}$ is called a *vertical* line.

From the two previous definitions we see that (*i.*) if the slope of a line is zero, then the line is horizontal; and (*ii.*) if the slope of a line is undefined, then the line is vertical. But if the slope of a line is neither zero nor undefined, then the line is *oblique*, that is, neither horizontal nor vertical. If we are given a slope $m_1 \neq 0$, then either $m_1 > 0$ or $m_1 < 0$. Knowing whether $m_1 > 0$ or $m_1 < 0$, we can tell whether the line "slants up to the right" or "down to the right".

Study the following:

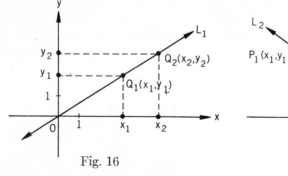

Fig. 16

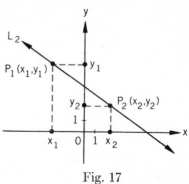

Fig. 17

In figure 16, the line L_1 "slants up to the right". Notice that $y_2 > y_1$ and $x_2 > x_1$; hence $y_2 - y_1 > 0$, $x_2 - x_1 > 0$, and $m_1 = \dfrac{y_2 - y_1}{x_2 - x_1} > 0$. But in figure 17, the line L_2 "slants down to the right". Notice that $y_1 > y_2$ but $x_1 < x_2$; hence $y_1 - y_2 > 0$, $x_1 - x_2 < 0$, and $m_2 = \dfrac{y_1 - y_2}{x_1 - x_2} < 0$.

We summarize these results as follows:

If $m = 0$, then the line is horizontal.
If m is undefined, then the line is vertical.
If $m > 0$, then the line "rises to the right".
If $m < 0$, then the line "falls to the right".

Do you see why $\dfrac{y_2 - y_1}{x_2 - x_1} = \dfrac{y_1 - y_2}{x_1 - x_2}$ for any particular non-vertical line?

EXERCISES

Return to exercises **1-14** on page 131 and determine whether each line is horizontal, vertical, or oblique; and if oblique, then whether it rises or falls to the right.

PARALLEL LINES AND PERPENDICULAR LINES

In figure 18, L_1 and L_2 have the same slope. What is it? L_3 and L_4 have the same slope. What is it? Do L_5 and L_6 have the same slope, different slopes, or undefined slopes? The pairs: L_1 and L_2, L_3 and L_4, L_5 and L_6, have a special relationship stated by the definition at the top of the next page.

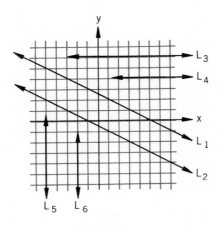

Fig. 18

■ *Definition of Parallel Lines* Two non-vertical lines are *parallel* if and only if they have the same slope; and each two vertical lines are parallel.

From this definition we can determine whether or not two lines are parallel if we know their slopes. But can we determine if two oblique lines are *perpendicular* by knowing their slopes? Study the following and be prepared to justify each statement.

Proof

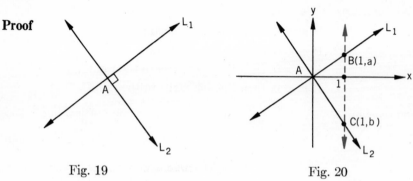

Fig. 19   Fig. 20

Given two lines, L_1 and L_2, intersecting at A such that $L_1 \perp L_2$, as in figure 19. Follow the argument below and supply reasons where necessary.

Establish a coordinate system on the plane as in figure 20 with $\overleftrightarrow{BC}$ passing through the point of the x-axis which is paired with 1 and such that $\overleftrightarrow{BC}$ is parallel to the y-axis.

$\triangle ABC$ is a right triangle, $\angle BAC$ being a right angle.

The coordinates of B are $(1, a)$, the coordinates of C are $(1, b)$, and the coordinates of A are $(0,0)$ for some real numbers a and b.

$AB = \sqrt{1 + a^2}$; $AC = \sqrt{1 + b^2}$; $BC = |a - b|$

$(AB)^2 + (AC)^2 = (BC)^2$

$(1 + a^2) + (1 + b^2) = (a - b)^2 = a^2 - 2ab + b^2$

$2 + a^2 + b^2 = a^2 + b^2 - 2ab$

$ab = -1$

m_1, the slope of L_1, is equal to a.

m_2, the slope of L_2, is equal to b.

The product of the slopes of the two oblique lines is -1. Thus, if two oblique lines are perpendicular, then the product of their slopes is -1.

Is the converse of the last statement true? That is, if the product of the slopes of two oblique lines is -1, then must the lines be perpendicular? To answer this, in figure 21 consider L_1 for which $m_1 = a$ and L_2 for which $m_2 = b$ and such that L_1 and L_2 intersect at point A and $(m_1)(m_2) = a \cdot b = -1$.

Proof

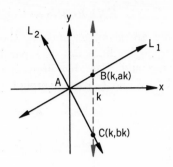

Fig. 21

We establish a coordinate system on the plane such that the origin is at A and neither L_1 nor L_2 is parallel to an axis.

Select any line that is parallel to the y-axis. It will intersect the x-axis at a point whose coordinates are $(k, 0)$ for some $k \neq 0$.

This line will intersect L_1 at a point B and will intersect L_2 at a point C.

The coordinates of A, the origin are $(0, 0)$; the coordinates of B are (k, ak); and the coordinates of C are (k, bk). Why?

We then note the following:

$AB = \sqrt{(ak)^2 + k^2}$ and $(AB)^2 = (ak)^2 + k^2$

$AC = \sqrt{(bk)^2 + k^2}$ and $(AC)^2 = (bk)^2 + k^2$

$BC = |ak - bk|$ and $(BC)^2 = (ak)^2 - 2abk^2 + (bk)^2 = (ak - bk)^2$

$ab = -1$, $2ab = -2$ and $-2ab = 2$

We can deduce the following by using the results from above:

$$
\begin{aligned}
(AB)^2 + (AC)^2 &= [(ak)^2 + k^2] + [(bk)^2 + k^2] \\
&= (ak)^2 + 2k^2 + (bk)^2 \\
&= (ak)^2 - 2abk^2 + (bk)^2, \ [2 = -2ab] \\
&= (ak - bk)^2 \\
&= (BC)^2
\end{aligned}
$$

Hence, $(AB)^2 + (AC)^2 = (BC)^2$

Triangle ABC is a right triangle with its right angle at A by the converse of the Pythagorean Relation. Hence, L_1 is perpendicular to L_2, and if two oblique lines have -1 as the product of their slopes, then the lines are perpendicular.

We have just outlined the proof of the following theorem.

Theorem Two oblique lines are perpendicular if and only if the product of their slopes is -1.

EXERCISES

1. In each problem, you are given m_1 and m_2, the slopes of lines L_1 and L_2, respectively. Tell whether the lines are (*i*.) parallel, (*ii*.) perpendicular, or (*iii*.) neither parallel nor perpendicular; then draw L_1 and L_2 for each problem such that L_1 passes through $A(3, 4)$ and L_2 passes through $B(5, 2)$.

a. $m_1 = \dfrac{2}{3}$; $m_2 = \dfrac{3}{2}$

e. $m_1 = -\dfrac{9}{2}$; $m_2 = \dfrac{2}{9}$

b. $m_1 = \dfrac{5}{7}$; $m_2 = \dfrac{10}{14}$

f. $m_1 = 3\dfrac{2}{8}$; $m_2 = 3.25$

c. $m_1 = \dfrac{3}{2}$; $m_2 = -\dfrac{3}{2}$

g. $m_1 = 0$; m_2 is undefined

d. $m_1 = -1$; $m_2 = 1$

h. m_1 is undefined; $m_2 = 0$

2. Without using the Distance Formula, prove that quadrilateral $ABCD$ is a parallelogram if $A(-5, -2)$; $B(1, -1)$; $C(4, 4)$; $D(-2, 3)$.

3. Without using the Distance Formula, prove that $\triangle ABC$ is a right triangle if $A(-2, 5)$; $B(6, 8)$; $C(1, -3)$.

4. Determine x so that the line through $A(x, 3)$ and $B(-2, 1)$ is parallel to the line through $C(5, -2)$ and $D(1, 4)$.

5. Determine x so that the line through $A(x, 3)$ and $B(-2, 1)$ is perpendicular to the line through $C(5, -2)$ and $D(1, 4)$.

6. Given quadrilateral $ABCD$ with $A(-5, 5)$; $B(5, 10)$; $C(3, -1)$; and $D(-7, -6)$.

    a. A *rhombus* is an equilateral quadrilateral. Prove that $ABCD$ is (or is not) a rhombus by using the Distance Formula.

    b. Prove that the diagonals are (or are not) perpendicular by using the Slope Formula.

    c. Is $ABCD$ a parallelogram? a rectangle? a square? Prove each of your answers.

7. Given quadrilateral $ABCD$ with $A(3, 1)$; $B(2, 4)$; $C(7, 6)$; and $D(8, 3)$.

    a. Prove that quadrilateral $ABCD$ is (or is not) a rhombus.

    b. Prove that the diagonals are (or are not) perpendicular by using the Slope Formula.

    c. Is quadrilateral $ABCD$ a parallelogram? a rectangle? a square? Prove each of your answers.

8. Determine the slope of the line through $P(x, y)$ and $Q(y, x)$, $[x \neq y]$. Determine the slope of each line perpendicular to $\overleftrightarrow{PQ}$, if all lines are in the plane.

9. Determine the slope of the line which passes through $A(2, 7)$ and

    a. is parallel to the x-axis.   **c.** passes through the origin.

    b. is parallel to the y-axis.

PROOFS USING COORDINATE GEOMETRY

At the beginning of this chapter, we mentioned that coordinate geometry could be used to prove some of the theorems of ordinary geometry. You will need to make use of

    i. the algebra that you have studied previously

    ii. the formulas and definitions of this chapter, especially those involving distance, midpoint, and slope

Example: By way of example, we shall prove that the segment between the midpoints of two sides of any triangle is (*i*.) parallel to the third side and (*ii*.) its length is half the length of that third side. Given *any* triangle ABC as in figure 22 below, we establish a coordinate system on the plane according to the procedures of the third section of this chapter.

One convenient way to do this is shown in figure 22 at the right. B is selected as the origin and $\overline{BC}$ is contained in the x-axis. A coordinate system is established on the x-axis by pairing C and 2. Since the same scale is to be used on the y-axis, we arbitrarily assign $(2a, 2b)$ to the point A to be sure that we are considering all triangles in general and not a particular case. Study the following:

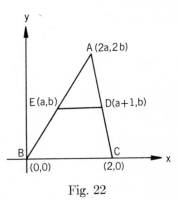

Fig. 22

D, the midpoint of $\overline{AC}$, has coordinates $(a+1, b)$ by the Midpoint Formula.

E, the midpoint of $\overline{AB}$, has coordinates (a, b) by the Midpoint Formula.

The slope of $\overline{DE}$ is zero and the slope of $\overline{BC}$ is zero by the Slope Formula.

$\overline{DE}$ is parallel to $\overline{BC}$ (why?) which was to be proved.

$DE = |(a+1) - a| = 1$, by the distance between two points definition.

$BC = |0 - 2| = 2$, by the distance between two points definition.

From the last two statements, $DE = \frac{1}{2} \cdot BC$, which was to be proved.

Repeat the proof of the previous theorem but with $B(0,0)$, $C(1,0)$, and $A(a, b)$. What disadvantage do you see in this second proof that was not involved in the proof above?

Example: As a second example, we shall use the method of coordinate geometry to prove that the diagonals of a parallelogram bisect each other.

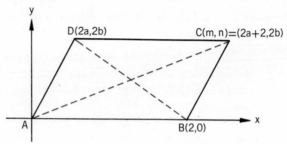

Fig. 23

Given any parallelogram $ABCD$, we establish a coordinate system on the plane as shown in figure 23, with $A(0,0)$; $B(2,0)$; $C(m,n)$; $D(2a,2b)$. Since $\overline{AB}$ is parallel to $\overline{CD}$ and the slope of $\overline{AB}$ is zero, it follows that $n = 2b$; and since $\overline{AD}$ is parallel to $\overline{BC}$, it follows that $m = 2a + 2$ (why?). Using the Midpoint Formula

$$\text{the midpoint of } \overline{AC} = K\left(\frac{2a + 2}{2}, \frac{2b}{2}\right) = K(a + 1,\ b)$$

$$\text{the midpoint of } \overline{BD} = R\left(\frac{2a + 2}{2}, \frac{2b}{2}\right) = R(a + 1,\ b)$$

From these equations, $K = R$ and the theorem has been proved since the two diagonals have the same midpoint.

EXERCISES

Use coordinate geometry to prove each of the following theorems.

1. The median of a trapezoid is parallel to a base of the trapezoid. (The *median* of a trapezoid is a segment whose endpoints are the midpoints of the non-parallel opposite sides of the trapezoid.)

2. The midpoint of the hypotenuse of a right triangle is equidistant from the triangle's three vertices.

3. The diagonals of a rhombus are perpendicular. (A rhombus is an equilateral parallelogram.)

4. The diagonals of a rectangle are congruent (have the same length).

5. The midpoints of the sides of an isosceles trapezoid are the vertices of a rhombus.

6. The midpoints of the sides of a rhombus are the vertices of a rectangle.

7. The segments whose endpoints are midpoints of opposite sides of a quadrilateral bisect each other.

8. If the diagonals of a parallelogram are congruent (have the same length), then the parallelogram is a rectangle.

9. If two medians of a triangle are equal in length, then the triangle is isosceles.

10. If two coplanar lines are each perpendicular to a third line, then the first two lines are parallel.

11. The opposite sides of a parallelogram have the same length.

EQUATIONS THAT DESCRIBE GEOMETRIC CONDITIONS

Suppose, as in figure 24 below, that we are given two points $A(3, 2)$ and $B(6, -2)$ and that we are asked to determine an *equation* in x and y which selects all points $P(x, y)$ such that each point P is equidistant from A and B.

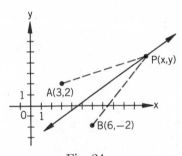

Fig. 24

(If you have already studied plane geometry, then you may recall that the set of all such points P is the line which is the perpendicular bisector of $\overline{AB}$.)

Consider *any* point $P(x, y)$ which is equidistant from A and B; thus,

$AP = PB$ [Why?]

$\sqrt{(x - 3)^2 + (y - 2)^2} = \sqrt{(x - 6)^2 + (y - (-2))^2}$ [Distance Formula]

$x^2 - 6x + 9 + y^2 - 4y + 4 = x^2 - 12x + 36 + y^2 + 4y + 4$

$6x - 8y = 27$

and $6x - 8y = 27$ is an equation in x and y of the line of points $P(x, y)$ each of which is equidistant from $A(3, 2)$ and $B(6, -2)$.

Suppose, as in figure 25 below, that we are given a point $C(5, -3)$ and asked to write either $(i.)$ an equation of the vertical line L_1 through C or $(ii.)$ an equation of the horizontal line L through C.

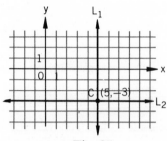

Fig. 25

Since each point $P(x, y)$ of L_1 has 5 as its *first* coordinate and no point not on L_1 has 5 as its first coordinate, an equation of L_1 is $x = 5$.

Since each point $P(x, y)$ of L_2 has -3 as its *second* coordinate and no point not on L_2 has -3 as its second coordinate, an equation of L_2 is $y = -3$.

EXERCISES

1.   Write a "simple" equation in x and y that selects all points $P(x, y)$ which are

a. equidistant from $A(3, 2)$ and $B(4, -3)$.

b. equidistant from $A(-2, -6)$ and $B(-3, 7)$.

c. equidistant from $A(3, 0)$ and $B(7, 0)$.

d. equidistant from $A(-4, 0)$ and $B(6, 0)$.

e. equidistant from $A(0, 8)$ and $B(0, -4)$.

f. equidistant from $A(0, -3)$ and $B(0, 3)$.

g. equidistant from $A(5, 0)$ and $B(-5, 0)$.

h. equidistant from $A(2, -5)$ and $B(-1, -3)$.

i. equidistant from $A(m, n)$ and $B(c, d)$. $[A \neq B]$

2.   Write $(i.)$ an equation of the vertical line; and $(ii.)$ an equation of the horizontal line which passes through

a. $T(5, 9)$

b. $A(-4, 2)$

c. $K(-3, -9)$

d. $E(37, -16)$

e. the origin

f. $R(5, 0)$

g. $M(0, -2)$

h. the midpoint of $\overline{AB}$ with $A(5, -6)$; $B(1, -10)$

i. $P(c, k)$, (for all real numbers c and k)

EQUATIONS OF CIRCLES

Suppose, as in figure 26 below, we are given a point $A(4, 5)$ and we are asked to determine an equation in x and y selecting all points $P(x, y)$ such that each point P is 3 units from A.

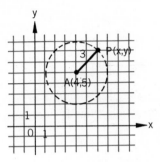

Fig. 26

(If you have already studied plane geometry, then you may recall that the set of all such points P is a *circle* whose *center* is A and whose *radius* is 3.)

Consider any point $P(x, y)$ which is 3 units from A.

$$AP = 3 \qquad \text{Why?}$$
$$\sqrt{(x - 4)^2 + (y - 5)^2} = 3 \qquad \text{Distance formula}$$
$$(x - 4)^2 + (y - 5)^2 = 9 \qquad \text{Why?}$$

and $(x - 4)^2 + (y - 5)^2 = 9$ is an equation in x and y which selects all points $P(x, y)$ that are 3 units from $A(4, 5)$.

EXERCISES

1. Write an equation in x and y of all points $P(x, y)$ which are

a. 3 units from $T(4, 6)$.

b. $\sqrt{7}$ unit from T(1, 4).

c. $\dfrac{1}{2}$ unit from $T(5, 2)$.

d. 6 units from $T(-2, 3)$.

e. $\dfrac{2}{3}$ unit from $T(3, -5)$.

f. $2\sqrt{5}$ units from $T(-2, -6)$.

g. 5 units from $T(0, 0)$.

h. 40 units from the origin.

i. r units from the origin, (for each real $r > 0$).

j. r units from $T(h, k)$, (for all reals r, h, and k; $r > 0$).

k. the points of the circle which is tangent to the x-axis at $A(4, 0)$ and tangent to the y-axis at $B(0, 4)$.

2. Write an equation in x and y for the circle which has a diameter $\overline{AB}$, with $A(-2, 6)$ and $B(8, -4)$.

3. The graph of each equation in x and y below is a circle. Determine $(i.)$ the coordinates of the center of the circle and $(ii.)$ the radius of the circle.

a. $(x - 2)^2 + (y - 3)^2 = 25$

b. $(x + 3)^2 + (y - \frac{1}{2})^2 = 16$

c. $(x - 7)^2 + (y + 3)^2 = 9$

d. $(x + 6)^2 + (y + 5)^2 = 4$

e. $4(x - 2)^2 + 4(y + 5)^2 = 36$

f. $a(x - h)^2 + a(y - k)^2 = b$, $(a > 0;$ $b > 0)$

g. $x^2 + (y - 4)^2 = 9$

h. $(x + 7)^2 + y^2 = 12$

i. $x^2 + y^2 = 25$

EQUATIONS OF OBLIQUE LINES

Suppose that a coordinate system has been established on a plane. Which of the following sets of conditions "determines" one and only one oblique line L in the plane?

  $i.$ knowing one point of L

  $ii.$ knowing two points of L

  $iii.$ knowing the slope of L

  $iv.$ knowing the slope of L and one point of L

  $v.$ knowing the distance between two points of L

You should have found that the correct answers are those under $(ii.)$ and $(iv.)$. We shall consider $(ii.)$ first, for $A(3, 2)$, $B(5, 1)$, and any other point $P(x, y)$ on L (as pictured in figure 27).

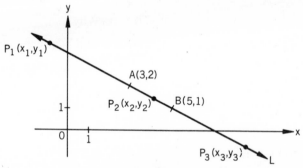

Fig. 27

Note that the slope of $\overline{AB} = \dfrac{2 - 1}{3 - 5}$ and the slope of $\overline{PA} = \dfrac{y - 2}{x - 3}$. Since the slope of all segments of a nonvertical line is the same real number, it follows that

$$\frac{2 - 1}{3 - 5} = \frac{y - 2}{x - 3} \quad [x \neq 3]$$

$$\frac{1}{-2} = \frac{y - 2}{x - 3}$$

$$x - 3 = 4 - 2y, \quad [x \neq 3]$$

$$x + 2y = 7$$

and $x + 2y = 7$ is a "simple" equation of the line through $A(3, 2)$ and $B(5, 1)$.

EXERCISES

Write a simple equation in x and y of the line passing through

1. $A(5,4)$ and $B(2,7)$
2. $A(-3,2)$ and $B(3,-2)$
3. $A(6,1)$ and $B(-2,-5)$
4. $A(0,0)$ and $B(4,-5)$

5. $A(-4,7)$ and $B(4,-7)$
6. $A(227,634)$ and $B(231,629)$
7. $A(5,8)$ and $B(7,8)$
8. $A(3,7)$ and $B(3,12)$

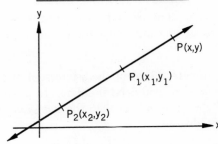

Generalizing the work of the preceding problems **1-6**, you were given the coordinates (x_1, y_1) and (x_2, y_2) of two points on an oblique line. The slope of this line is $\dfrac{y_1 - y_2}{x_1 - x_2}$ which we have designated as m. But if $P(x,y)$ is any third point of this line, then its slope is $\dfrac{y - y_1}{x - x_1}$. Since $\dfrac{y_1 - y_2}{x_1 - x_2} = \dfrac{y - y_1}{x - x_1} = m$, it follows that $y - y_1 = m(x - x_1)$. "$y - y_1 = m(x - x_1)$" is called the *point-slope* form for an equation of *the* line through $P_1(x_1, y_1)$ with slope m.

Example: Write a simple equation of the line through $C(-5, 2)$ which has

slope $m = \dfrac{2}{3}$.

Using the point-slope form, $y - y_1 = m(x - x_1)$

$y - 2 = \dfrac{2}{3}[x - (-5)]$

$3y - 6 = 2x + 10$

$3y = 2x + 16$

EXERCISES

Write a simple equation in x and y of the line with the given slope m and passing through the point C whose coordinates are given.

1. $m = \dfrac{3}{7}$; $C(7, 2)$

2. $m = \dfrac{-2}{5}$; $C(1, 4)$

3. $m = 4$; $C(10, -2)$

4. $m = \dfrac{-3}{4}$; $C(6, -2)$

5. $m = \dfrac{3}{-4}$; $C(6, -2)$

6. $m = -\dfrac{3}{4}$; $C(6, -2)$

7. $m = -\dfrac{5}{3}$; $C(-3, -4)$

8. $m = \dfrac{1}{3}$; $C(9,9)$

9. $m = 0$; $C(2,6)$

10. $m = 0$; $C(5,219)$

11. m is undefined; $C(3,7)$

12. $m = 2$; $C(0,6)$

13. $m = 5$; $C(0,8)$

14. $m = 3$; $C(0,51)$

15. $m = 4$; $C(0,210)$

16. $m = m_1$; $C(0,b)$

■ *Definition of y-intercept*   The second coordinate of the point at which any non-vertical line intersects the y-axis is called the *y-intercept* of the line.

If we knew the coordinates $(0, b)$ of the y-intercept of a line, then the point-slope form: $y - y_1 = m(x - x_1)$ could be simplified to $y - b = m(x - 0)$ or more simply: $y = mx + b$. "$y = mx + b$" is called the *slope-intercept* form for an equation of a nonvertical straight line.

Example: Write a simple equation of the line whose slope is $\frac{2}{3}$ and whose y-intercept is 4.

Using the slope intercept form: $y = mx + b$
$y = \frac{2}{3}x + 4$ or $3y = 2x + 12$

EXERCISES

1.   Write a simple equation in x and y of the line given (*i.*) its slope and (*ii.*) its y-intercept.

a. (*i.*) 5   (*ii.*) -2

b. (*i.*) -4 (*ii.*) 10

c. (*i.*) $\dfrac{2}{3}$ (*ii.*) 3

d. (*i.*) $-\dfrac{3}{7}$ (*ii.*) $\dfrac{2}{7}$

e. (*i.*) 0   (*ii.*) -6

f. (*i.*) 0   (*ii.*) 0

g. (*i.*) 0   (*ii.*) 4

h. (*i.*) π (*ii.*) π

i. (*i.*) $\dfrac{2}{\sqrt{3}}$ (*ii.*) $-\sqrt{27}$

j. (*i.*) -1 (*ii.*) -17

k. (*i.*) 1   (*ii.*) -17

l. (*i.*) $\dfrac{1}{2+\sqrt{3}}$ (*ii.*) $2 - \sqrt{3}$

2.   For each equation, (*i.*) write an equivalent one in slope-intercept form, (*ii.*) determine the slope of the corresponding line, (*iii.*) determine the y-intercept, and (*iv.*) draw the graph of the line.

Example: $5x + 3y = 6$

$5x + 3y = 6$

$3y = -5x + 6$

$y = -\frac{5}{3}x + 2$

i. $y = -\frac{5}{3}x + 2$ is an equivalent equation in slope-intercept form $[y = mx + b]$.

ii. The slope of this line is $-\frac{5}{3}$. $[m = -\frac{5}{3}]$

iii. the y-intercept is 2. $[b = 2]$

iv. First, we plot the point determined by the y-intercept, $A(0, 2)$. Second, since the slope $m = -\frac{5}{3} = \frac{-5}{3}$, let $y_1 - y_2 = -5$ and $x_1 - x_2 = 3$ to locate $B(3, -3)$ another point of the line. Third, having plotted A and B, two points of this line, it is an easy matter to draw the line (see figure 28).

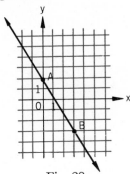

Fig. 28

a. $2y = 6x + 8$

b. $3x + 5y = 6$

c. $3y = x$

d. $x = \dfrac{y}{2}$

e. $18x + 6y - 12 = 0$

f. $2x - 5y - 7 = 0$

g. $8 - 2y = 5x$

h. $(x - 4)^2 + y = (x + 2)^2 + 6$

i. $3y = 6$

j. $(y + 3)^2 = (y + 4)^2$

3. Return to problem **2** and determine the slope of every line (in the plane) that is perpendicular to each of the lines **a-j.**

4. Write a simple equation in x and y of the line that is perpendicular to the graph of $y = \frac{2}{3}x - 17$ and also passes through $T(3, 1)$.

5. Write an equation of each line: L_1, L_2, L_3, L_4, L_5 and L_6 of figure 29.

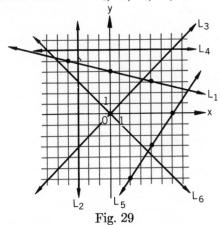

Fig. 29

PARABOLAS

In each of the three figures below, we have selected a *line D* and a *point F* which is *not* on line *D*. Then, in each case, we selected and plotted many points *P* such that each point *P* is equidistant from the line *D* and the point *F*. The curve which is the set of all such points is called a *parabola*.

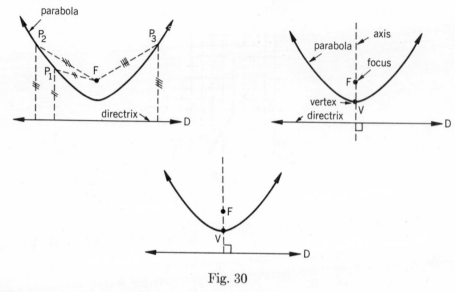

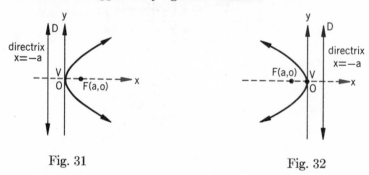

Fig. 30

The point *F* is called the *focus* or the *focal point*. The line *D* is called the *directrix*. The line through *F* and perpendicular to *D* is called the *axis* of the parabola. The axis intersects the parabola at a point *V* called the *vertex* of the parabola.

■ *Definition of Parabola* A *parabola* is a set of all points *P* in a plane such that each point *P* is equidistant from a given line *D* and a given point *F* (not on *D*) in the same plane.

Given a parabola, its focus *F*, and its directrix *D*, we may establish a coordinate system on the plane as suggested by figures 31 and 32.

Fig. 31   Fig. 32

i. Select the axis of the parabola as the x-axis

ii. Select the line perpendicular to the x-axis and passing through the vertex as the y-axis

iii. Assign $(a, 0)$ to the focus F (for some real number a)

Can you answer the following questions in terms of a?

What is the distance between F and the origin?

What is the distance between V and the directrix?

What is the distance between F and the directrix?

What are the coordinates of V?

What is an equation of the directrix?

What is an equation of the axis of the parabola?

From the definition of a parabola, we shall develop a standard form for equations in x and y of parabolas whose vertex is at the origin and whose focus belongs to the x-axis. Refer to figures 33 and 34 as you study the development beneath the figures.

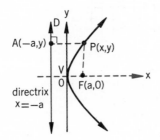

Fig. 33   Fig. 34

For each $P(x, y)$ belonging to the parabola

$FP = PA$	Why?
$PA = \|x - (-a)\|$	Why?
$FP = \sqrt{(x - a)^2 + (y - 0)^2}$	Why?
$\sqrt{(x - a)^2 + (y - 0)^2} = \|x - (-a)\|$	Why?
$x^2 - 2ax + a^2 + y^2 = x^2 + 2ax + a^2$	Supply the missing steps.
$y^2 = 4ax$	Supply the missing steps.

Thus, $y^2 = 4ax$ is an equation of the parabola

whose focus is at $F(a, 0)$

whose directrix has an equation: $x = -a$

whose vertex is at the origin

whose axis is the x-axis

for each real number $a \neq 0$.

Example: i. Given $y^2 = 8x$, an equation of a parabola, we know that $y^2 = 8x$ is of the form $y^2 = 4ax$ with $a = 2$; and thus

the focus is at $F(2, 0)$

an equation of the directrix is $x = -2$

the vertex is at the origin

Some ordered pairs (x, y) that satisfy $y^2 = 8x$ are $(0, 0)$, $(\frac{1}{2}, 2)$, $(\frac{1}{2}, -2)$, $(2, 4)$, $(2, -4)$, $(4\frac{1}{2}, 6)$ and $(4\frac{1}{2}, -6)$. Now one can sketch the graph of this parabola, its focus, and its directrix.

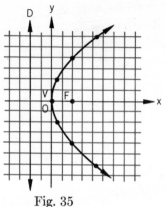

Fig. 35

Example: ii. Given $2y^2 + 12x = 0$, an equation of a parabola, we know that $2y^2 + 12x = 0$ is equivalent to $y^2 = -6x$ which is of the form $y^2 = 4ax$ with $a = -\frac{6}{4} = -\frac{3}{2}$

the focus is at $F(-\frac{3}{2}, 0)$

an equation of the directrix is: $x = \frac{3}{2}$

the vertex is at the origin

Some ordered pairs (x, y) that satisfy $y^2 = -6x$ and therefore satisfy $2y^2 + 12x = 0$ are $(0, 0)$, $(-\frac{2}{3}, 2)$, $(-\frac{2}{3}, -2)$, $(-\frac{3}{2}, 3)$, $(-\frac{3}{2}, -3)$, $(-2\frac{2}{3}, 4)$ and $(-2\frac{2}{3}, -4)$. Now one can quickly sketch the graph of this parabola, its focus, and its directrix.

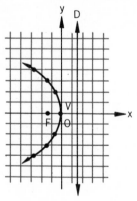

Fig. 36

EXERCISES

Each equation below is an equation of a parabola. For each equation and the corresponding parabola

a. write an equivalent equation in the form $y^2 = 4ax$, for some real number a

b. determine the coordinates of the focus

c. write an equation of the directrix

d. list at least seven ordered pairs that satisfy the equation and that will help you draw a graph of the parabola

e. draw a graph of the parabola, its focus, and its directrix

1. $y^2 = 12x$ **4.** $-y^2 = 12x$ **7.** $y^2 = x$ **10.** $y^2 = -4x$

2. $y^2 = 7x$ **5.** $3y^2 = 12x$ **8.** $y^2 = -x$ **11.** $y^2 = 40x$

3. $y^2 = -8x$ **6.** $2y^2 = -9x$ **9.** $y^2 = 4x$ **12.** $y^2 = -40x$

VOCABULARY

Use each of the following correctly in a sentence. Numerals in parentheses refer to pages where these words were used. If you are not sure of the meaning of any word, turn to the indicated page.

between (117)

circle (141)

coordinate (116)

coordinate system on a plane (118)

coordinate system on a line (116)

horizontal; vertical; oblique (132)

midpoint (127)

one-to-one correspondence (116)

ordered pair of real numbers (119)

parabola; focus; directrix; vertex; axis (146)

parallel lines (134)

perpendicular lines (134)

plotting (120)

point-slope form (143)

quadrant I; quadrant II, quadrant III;
    quadrant IV (120)

segment (117)

slope-intercept form (144)

slope (130)

x-axis; y-axis; origin (118)

y-intercept (144)

FORMULAS TO KNOW

See if you know the following formulas. Look them up if you have to.

1. For $\overline{AB}$ with $A(a, b)$ and $B(c, d)$

    a. the coordinates of the midpoint of $\overline{AB}$

    b. the slope of $\overline{AB}$ if $a = c$; if $b = d$; if $a \neq c$ and $b \neq d$

    c. AB if $a = c$; if $b = d$; if $a \neq c$ and $b \neq d$

2. For $\overleftrightarrow{AB}$ and $\overleftrightarrow{MN}$ with $A(a, b)$; $B(c, d)$; $C(e, f)$; and $D(g, h)$

    a. the conditions if $\overleftrightarrow{AB} \parallel \overleftrightarrow{MN}$

    b. the conditions if $\overleftrightarrow{AB} \perp \overleftrightarrow{MN}$

3. An equation in x and y of the straight line
  a. each of whose points $P(x, y)$ is equidistant from $A(x_1, y_1)$ and $B(x_2, y_2)$ $(A \neq B)$
  b. through $A(x_1, y_1)$ and $B(x_2, y_2)$, $(A \neq B)$
  c. whose slope is m_1 and passes through $A(x_1, y_1)$
  d. which is vertical and passes through $A(x_1, y_1)$
  e. which is horizontal and passes through $A(x_1, y_1)$
  f. whose slope is m_1 and passes through $T(0, b)$

4. An equation in x and y of the circle whose center is at $A(h, k)$ and whose radius is r, $(r > 0)$.

5. For a parabola with an equation in x and y of the form $y^2 = 4ax$
  a. the coordinates of the foxus; of the vertex
  b. an equation of the directrix; of the axis of the parabola
  c. distance between focus and vertex
  d. distance between focus and directrix

REVIEW EXERCISES

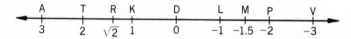

1. Suppose that a coordinate system has been established on a line as illustrated in the figure above.

  a. Determine TL.   **d.** Does $\overline{TL} = \overline{LT}$?   **g.** Determine TR.
  b. Determine LT.   **e.** Does $\overleftrightarrow{TL} = \overleftrightarrow{LT}$?   **h.** Does $TK = DL$?
  c. Does $TL = LT$?   **f.** Determine PR.   **i.** Does $\overline{TK} = \overline{DL}$?

  j. Determine the coordinate of the midpoint of $\overline{AR}$.

2. True or false?
  a. $\forall_x$, if $(x - 2)^2 = (3x - 4)^2$, then $x - 2 = 3x - 4$
  b. $\forall_x \forall_y$ $(x - y)^2 = (y - x)^2$
  c. $\forall_{x \neq 3}$ $\dfrac{x - 7}{3 - x} = \dfrac{7 - x}{x - 3}$
  d. $\forall_a \forall_b$ $\sqrt{a^2 + b^2} = a + b$
  e. For each point A and for each point B, if $A \neq B$, then $AB = BA$ and $\overline{AB} = \overline{BA}$.
  f. There is a one-to-one correspondence between the members of N and the members of I. $[N = \{1, 2, 3, \ldots\}]; [I = \{\ldots, -2, -1, 0, 1, 2, \ldots\}]$
  g. $\forall_t$ $|t - 3t| = |3t - t|$

h. 10^5 is closer to 10^6 than to 10^2.

i. $(\sqrt{9}, 36) \neq (2+1, 6^2)$

j. There is a triangle whose dimensions are

    i. 7 inches, 4 inches, and 12 inches

    ii. one mile, 1760 yards, and 5082 feet

k. $A(2,7)$ is between $B(5,4)$ and $C(-2,11)$.

l. $A(2,7)$ is midway between $B(5,4)$ and $C(-2,11)$.

m. $\forall_{a \geq 2} \forall_{b \geq 3}$, if $\sqrt{a-2} = \sqrt{b-3}$, then $a-2 = b-3$.

n. $\forall_a \forall_b$, if $(a-2)^2 = (b-3)^2$, then $a-2 = b-3$.

3. Given square $ABCD$ with $A(2a+1, m)$; $B(2a+1, 3m)$; and $C(2a+5, 3m)$

  a. determine the coordinates of D.

  b. determine AC, AB, and BC.

  c. determine the coordinates of R, S, and T, the midpoints of $\overline{AC}$, $\overline{AB}$, and $\overline{BC}$ respectively.

  d. determine the slopes of $\overline{AC}$, $\overline{AB}$, and $\overline{BC}$.

4. Given triangle ABC with $A(2,7)$; $B(5,4)$; and $C(-1,-3)$

  a. determine the perimeter of triangle ABC.

  b. determine the slopes of $\overline{AB}$ and of $\overline{BC}$.

  c. is triangle ABC right? isosceles? scalene?

  d. determine the coordinates of the midpoint of $\overline{AB}$; of $\overline{BC}$; of $\overline{AC}$.

  e. determine AD, the length of a median of triangle ABC.

5. Define.

  a. B is between A and C

  b. B is the midpoint of $\overline{AC}$

  c. The slope of $\overline{AB}$, with $A(a,b)$ and $B(c,d)$

    i. if $a = c$

    ii. if $b = d$

    iii. if $a \neq c$ and $b \neq d$

  d. $\overleftrightarrow{PQ}$ is horizontal

  e. $\overleftrightarrow{MN}$ is vertical

  f. $\overleftrightarrow{FG}$ is oblique

  g. circle

  h. parabola

6. Select the one correct response.

  a. The slopes of parallel non-vertical lines are

    i. reciprocals   *iii.* equal   *v.* always positive

    ii. additive inverses   *iv.* undefined

  b. The slopes of perpendicular oblique lines

    i. are equal   *iv.* have negative one as their product

    ii. have zero as their sum   *v.* have zero as their product

    iii. have one as their product

7. Write a simple equation in x and y of the line of points $P(x, y)$ such that
   a. the line passes through $A(2, -3)$ and $B(5, 1)$.
   b. the line has a slope of $\frac{3}{4}$ and passes through $C(-4, 2)$.
   c. the line has a slope of zero and passes through $C(-4, 2)$.
   d. the line has its slope undefined and passes through $C(-4, 2)$.
   e. the line has a slope of $\frac{-5}{12}$ and passes through $(0, 12)$.
   f. each point P is equidistant from $A(2, -3)$ and $B(5, -1)$.

8. Write an equation in slope-intercept form that is equivalent to $5x - 4y = 20$ and then draw a graph of the line of points $P(x, y)$.

9. Consider the set of points $P(x, y)$ whose coordinates satisfy $(x - 5)^2 + (y + 3)^2 = 7$.
   a. What is the name of this curve?
   b. What are the coordinates of its center?
   c. What is the length of a radius?
   d. What is the length of a diameter?
   e. Do any of its points belong to quadrant II? quadrant I?
   f. Compute its circumference.
   g. Compute the area of its interior.

10. Consider the set of points $P(x, y)$ whose coordinates satisfy $y^2 = 12x$.
    a. What is the name of this curve?
    b. What are the coordinates of its focus?
    c. What are the coordinates of its vertex?
    d. Write an equation of its directrix.

11. *Given:* triangle ABC; D and E are midpoints of $\overline{AC}$ and $\overline{BC}$ respectively; $\overline{DF}$, $\overline{CH}$, and $\overline{EG}$ are each perpendicular to $\overline{AB}$; F, H, and G belong to $\overline{AB}$. Use coordinate geometry to *prove* that $DF + EG = CH$.

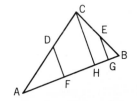

CHAPTER TEST

1. What are the coordinates of the projection of $A(-5, -3)$ into the y-axis?

2. To which quadrant does $C(-.04, 7.6)$ belong?

3. What are the slopes of the diagonals of each square which has one side contained in the y-axis?

4. Given triangle ABC with $A(-7, 5)$; $B(3, -1)$; $C(5, 3)$. Determine the distance between the midpoint of $\overline{AB}$ and the midpoint of $\overline{AC}$.

5. Determine t so that $\overleftrightarrow{AB}$ with $A(2, 3)$; $B(6, 5)$, is parallel to $\overleftrightarrow{CD}$, with $C(6, -1)$; $D(5, t)$.

6. Determine t so that $\overleftrightarrow{AB}$ with $A(2, 3)$; $B(6, 5)$, is perpendicular to $\overleftrightarrow{CD}$, with $C(6, -1)$; $D(5,t)$.

7. Determine the slope of the line of points $P(x, y)$ selected by the equation $3x + 4y = 12$.

8. Write an equation in x and y of the circle with center $A(2, -6)$ and radius 4.

9. Write a "simple" equation in x and y of the line of points $P(x, y)$ such that
   a. the line passes through $A(5, 4)$ and $B(2, -2)$.
   b. the line passes through $T(-4, 7)$ with slope of $\frac{3}{4}$.
   c. each point $P(x, y)$ is equidistant from $A(5, 4)$ and $B(2, -2)$.
   d. the line is vertical and passes through $M(2, -17)$.
   e. the line is horizontal and passes through $M(2, -17)$.
   f. the line passes through $D(76, 33)$ and the origin.

10. True or false?
   a. $\forall_t \ |t - 7| = |7 - t|$
   b. $\forall_t \ \sqrt{4t^2 + 9} = 2t + 3$
   c. The number 10^7 is closer to 10^8 than to 10^4.
   d. $B(3, -4)$ is midway between $A(1, 2)$ and $C(6, -13)$.
   e. $B(3, -4)$ is between $A(1, 2)$ and $C(6, -13)$.
   f. $\forall_t \ AB = 2t$, with $A(7, 5t)$; $B(7, 3t)$.

11. Given $A(5, -4)$, $B(7, 6)$, $C(7, -4)$, $D(5, 6)$
   a. determine AB.   **d.** determine the slope of $\overline{AB}$.
   b. determine AC.   **e.** determine the slope of $\overline{AC}$.
   c. determine AD.   **f.** determine the slope of $\overline{AD}$.

   g. determine the coordinates of the midpoint of $\overline{AB}$.
   h. determine the coordinates of the midpoint of $\overline{AC}$.
   i. determine the coordinates of the midpoint of $\overline{AD}$.
   j. write an equation of the circle, one of whose diameters is $\overline{AB}$.

12. Given the set of points $P(x, y)$ selected by $y^2 = 20x$
   a. what are the coordinates of the focus?
   b. what are the coordinates of the vertex?
   c. write an equation of the directrix.
   d. graph this parabola, its focus, its directrix and its axis.

13. Given the equation $3x + 4y = 12$
   a. write an equivalent equation in slope-intercept form.
   b. what is the slope of the graph of this equation?
   c. what is the y-intercept of this graph?
   d. draw the graph of this equation.

14. Use coordinate geometry to prove that for each quadrilateral the two segments whose endpoints are midpoints of opposite sides of the quadrilateral bisect each other. Copy the figure below to begin your proof.

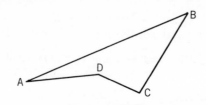

BIBLIOGRAPHY

Allendoerfer, C. B. and Oakley, C. O. *Fundamentals of Freshman Mathematics.* New York: McGraw-Hill Book Co., Inc., 1959. pp. 229-304, 311-314, 318-329.

Bell, E. T. *Mathematics, Queen and Servant of Science.* New York: McGraw-Hill Book Co., Inc., 1951. pp. 121-140.

Bell, E. T. *Men of Mathematics.* New York: Simon and Schuster, Inc., 1937. Chapter 3.

Kasner, E. and Newman, J. *Mathematics and the Imagination.* New York: Simon and Schuster, Inc., 1940. pp. 95-99.

Moore, J. T. *Fundamental Principles of Mathematics.* New York: Holt, Rinehart and Winston, Inc., 1960. pp. 143-151.

Sanford, V. *A Short History of Mathematics.* New York: Houghton Mifflin Co., 1930. pp. 43-44.

School Mathematics Study Group. *Geometry.* New Haven: Yale University Press, 1961. pp. 567-629.

School Mathematics Study Group. *Intermediate Mathematics, Part I.* New Haven: Yale University Press, 1961. pp. 119-164, 303, 359.

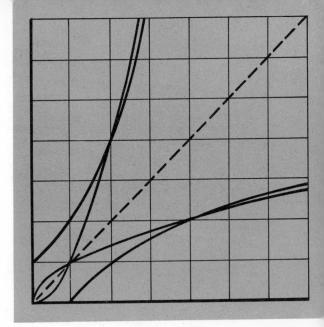

CHAPTER 6

Relations, Functions, and Inequalities

PRODUCT SETS

We shall now consider sets whose members are *ordered pairs*. Recall that a pair of things in a specified order is called an *ordered pair*, and the symbol "(c, d)" is used for the ordered pair which has c for its first component and d for its second component.

From the set $A = \{1, 2, 3\}$, we can form the set

$$\{(1, 1),\ (1, 2),\ (1, 3),\ (2, 1),\ (2, 2),\ (2, 3),\ (3, 1),\ (3, 2),\ (3, 3)\}$$

This set consists of *all* possible ordered pairs whose components belong to the set A.

This set is called the *product set* of A and A. It is denoted by the symbol "$A \times A$" (read: A cross A).

The product set $A \times A$, where $A = \{1, 2, 3\}$, may be represented graphically as a *lattice* of points. The graph of these nine points is shown in figure 1.

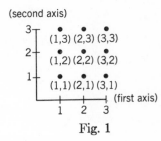

Fig. 1

155

As a second example, consider the two different sets

$$B = \{0, 1, 2\} \text{ and } C = \{3, 4\}$$

The product set $B \times C$ (read: B cross C) consists of all possible ordered pairs whose first components are elements of B and whose second components are elements of C; thus $B \times C = \{(0, 3), (0, 4), (1, 3), (1, 4), (2, 3), (2, 4)\}$. The graph of this set is shown in figure 2.

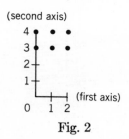

Fig. 2

Describe a way of choosing the ordered pair of numbers associated with a particular point of the graph.

We formally define *product set* as follows:

■ *Definition of Product Set* For each pair of sets A and B, the *product set* $A \times B$ is the set of all ordered pairs (a, b) such that $a \in A$ and $b \in B$.

Study the following examples.

Examples: *i.*   Graph $I \times I$ if I is the set of all integers.

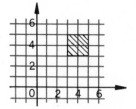

INCOMPLETE GRAPH OF $I \times I$

Why is it not possible to show the complete graph of $I \times I$?

ii.   Graph $B \times B$ if $B = \{m \mid m \text{ is a } real \text{ number and } 3 \leq m \leq 5\}$.

iii.   Graph $A \times B$ if $A = \{-3, -1, 4\}$ and $B = \{-2, 1, 4\}$.

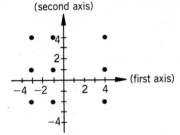

iv.   Graph $C \times D$ if

$C = \{a \mid a$ is a real number and $1 \le a \le 2\}$ and

$D = \{b \mid b$ is a real number and $-3 \le b \le 4\}$

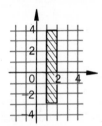

v.   Graph $R \times R$ if R is the set of all real numbers.

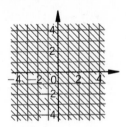

INCOMPLETE GRAPH OF $R \times R$

Is the complete graph of $R \times R$ the entire plane?

EXERCISES

1. True or false?

a. If I is the set of all integers and R is the set of all real numbers, then $I \times I$ is a proper subset of $R \times R$.

b. If $A = \{0, 5\}$, then $A \times A = \{(0,0), (0,5), (5,0), (5,5)\}$.

c. If $C = \{-1, 1\}$ and $D = \{2, 3\}$, then
$D \times C = \{(-1, 2), (-1, 3), (1, 2), (1, 3)\}$.

d. If $A = \{0, 3\}$ and $B = \{2, 4\}$, then $A \times B = \{0, 2, 3, 4\}$.

e. If $A = \{1, 5\}$ and $B = \{0\}$, then $A \times B = \{(1, 0), (5, 0)\}$.

f. If $A = \{1, 5\}$ and $B = \{0\}$, then $A \times B = B \times A$.

g. If $A = \{1, 2\}$ and $B = \{2, 1\}$, then $A \times B = B \times A$.

h. For all sets A and B, if $A \neq B$, then $A \times B = B \times A$.

i. If R is the set of real numbers, then $R \times R$ is the set of all ordered pairs of real numbers.

j. For every set A, $A \times \phi = \phi \times A = \phi$.

2. List the members of the product set $T \times T$, where $T = \{3, -3\}$.

3. List the members of the product set $A \times A$, where $A = \{a_1, a_2, a_3\}$.

4. List the members of $E \times F$, where $E = \{-1, 0, 1\}$ and $F = \{-2\}$.

5. List the members of $C \times D$, where $C = \{c\}$ and $D = \{-3, -2, -1\}$.

6. Tell how many members the product set $B \times B$ has, if

   a. $B = \{b_1\}$

   b. $B = \{b_1, b_2\}$

   c. $B = \{b_1, b_2, b_3\}$

   d. $B = \{b_1, b_2, b_3, \ldots, b_n\}$

7. Graph the product set $Q \times Q$, where $Q = \{-4, -3, -2\}$.

8. Graph the set $S \times S$, where $S = \{-1, 0, 1, 2\}$.

9. Graph $A \times B$, where $A = \{-1, 5\}$ and $B = \{1, -5\}$.

10. Graph the product set $H \times I$, where $H = \{2\}$ and I is the set of all integers.

11. Graph $R \times A$, where $A = \{-3\}$ and R is the set of all real numbers.

12. Graph $B \times C$, where $B = \{-4, -2, 2, 4\}$ and $C = \{m \mid m$ is a real number and $1 \leq m \leq 3\}$.

13. Graph $D \times E$, where $D = \{r \mid r$ is a real number and $-1 \leq r \leq 1\}$ and $E = \{t \mid t$ is a real number and $-2 \leq t \leq 4\}$.

14. Graph $F \times R$, where $F = \{x \mid x$ is a real number and $2 < x < 3\}$ and R is the set of all real numbers.

15. Graph $N \times N$, where N is the set of all natural numbers.

16. Graph $I \times N$, where I is the set of all integers and N is the set of all natural numbers.

RELATIONS

Every set of ordered pairs is a *relation*. Since a relation is a *set*, we shall, in every discussion, specify a *universal* set, that is, a set from which subsets will be formed.

We define a relation as follows:

■ *Definition of Relation.* For all sets A and B, each subset of ordered pairs in $A \times B$ is called a *relation* in $A \times B$.

Therefore, every relation is a relation in some product set, say $A \times B$, where $A \times B$ is the universe of discussion. For example, suppose we let

$$A = \{\text{Alabama, Alaska}, \ldots, \text{Wyoming}\},$$

the set of the fifty states of the United States of America, and

$$B = \{\text{Montgomery, Juneau}, \ldots, \text{Cheyenne}\},$$

the set of the fifty state capitals. Let $A \times B$ be the universe of discussion. How many elements does the set $A \times B$ contain? Notice that the set of fifty ordered pairs consisting of the states of the United States and their respective capitals, namely

$$\{(\text{Alabama, Montgomery}), \ldots, (\text{Wyoming, Cheyenne})\}$$

is a subset of $A \times B$ and, hence, is a relation in $A \times B$. Is (Florida, Tallahassee) an element of this relation? How about (Pennsylvania, Juneau)? Notice that, although Austin is the capital of Texas, the ordered pair (Austin, Texas) is *not* an element of this relation in $A \times B$. Why not?

The set of *first* components of the ordered pairs which comprise a relation is called the *domain* of the relation. Thus, the domain of the relation given above is the set of the fifty states, namely

$$\{\text{Alabama, Alaska}, \ldots, \text{Wyoming}\}.$$

The set of *second* components of the ordered pairs which comprise a relation is called the *range* of the relation. Hence, the range of the relation given above is the set of fifty state capitals, namely

$$\{\text{Montgomery, Juneau}, \ldots, \text{Cheyenne}\}.$$

Examples: i. Let $A = \{0, 1, 2\}$ and $B = \{3, 4\}$. Then $A \times B = \{(0, 3),$ $(0, 4), (1, 3), (1, 4), (2, 3), (2, 4)\}$. Thus, since $F = \{(0, 3),$ $(2, 4)\}$ is a subset of $A \times$ B, F is a relation in $A \times$ B. Notice that the domain of F is $\{0, 2\}$ and its range is $\{3, 4\}$. Is $\{(1, 4),$ $(0, 4)\}$ a relation in $A \times B$? Is $\{(1, 3)\}$? Is $\{(3, 1)\}$?

ii. Let $S = \{1, 2, 3\}$. Then $S \times S = \{(1, 1), (1, 2), (1, 3), (2, 1)$ $(2, 2), (2, 3), (3, 1), (3, 2), (3, 3)\}$. Let $T = \{(1, 2), (2, 1),$ $(3, 2)\}$. T is a subset of $S \times S$ and, therefore T is a relation in $S \times S$; the domain of T is $\{1, 2, 3\}$ and the range of T is $\{1, 2\}$. Both $S \times S$ and T are shown on the diagram below. The graph of $S \times S$ is shown by the lattice of nine points. The three points of the lattice which are black is the graph of the relation T.

Recall that we associate the first components of the ordered pairs with the horizontal axis and the second components with the vertical axis.

In this course we shall usually study relations which are ordered pairs of real numbers, that is, relations in $R \times R$ where $R = \{x | x$ is a real number$\}$. Therefore, unless stated otherwise, when we speak of a relation, it will be understood that we are speaking of a relation in $R \times R$.

EXERCISES

1. True or false? (In these problems, N is the set of natural numbers, I is the set of integers, and R is the set of real numbers.)

   a. For every set A, $A \subseteq A$.

   b. For every set A, $\phi \subseteq A$.

   c. If $A = \{(1, 2), (2, 0), (3, 8)\}$, then A is a relation in $N \times N$.

   d. If $B = \{(-2, 0), (3, 5), (\frac{1}{2}, 1)\}$, then B is a relation in $I \times I$.

   e. If $T = \{(-3, -2), (-2, 1), (0, 0), (\frac{1}{2}, -2)\}$, then T is a relation in $R \times R$.

   f. ϕ is a relation in $R \times R$.

   g. $R \times R$ is a relation in $R \times R$.

   h. $I \times I$ is a relation in $R \times R$.

   i. The domain of the relation $\{(-1, 0), (2, -2), (4, 1)\}$ is $\{0, -2, 1\}$.

   j. The range of the relation $\{(-2, 3), (3, 4)\}$ is $\{3, 4\}$.

2. Specify the *domain* and the *range* of each of the following relations. The universal set in each of these problems is $R \times R$.

   a. $\{(-3, 1), (-1, 1), (1, 0), (3, 0)\}$

   b. $\{(2, -2), (2, -1), (2, 0), (2, 1), (2, 2)\}$

   c. $\{(-2, 0), (-1, 0), (0, 0), (1, 0), (2, 0)\}$

   d. $\{(-2, -2), (-1, -1), (0, 0), (1, 1), (2, 2)\}$

   e. $\{(-2, 2), (-1, 1), (0, 0), (1, -1), (2, -2)\}$

   f. $\{(0, 0)\}$

   g. $\{(-\pi, \pi), (-\pi, -\pi), (\pi, \pi), (\pi, -\pi)\}$

   h. $\{\ldots, (-2, 2), (-1, 2), (0, 2), (1, 2), (2, 2), \ldots\}$

   i. $\{\ldots, (-3, -2), (-1, 0), (1, 2), (3, 4), \ldots\}$

   j. $\{(1, 1), (\frac{1}{2}, \frac{1}{2}), (\frac{1}{3}, \frac{1}{4}), (\frac{1}{4}, \frac{1}{8}), (\frac{1}{5}, \frac{1}{16}), \ldots\}$

Specifying relations

Relations are usually designated in one of three ways. One way is simply to list the ordered pairs which belong to the relation. This method is called the *roster* method. Here are two examples of relations which are specified by the roster method.

Examples: i. $\{(-1, 2), (0, 4), (1, -3)\}$

         ii. $\{\ldots, (-1, -1), (0, 0), (1, 1), \ldots\}$

Another way to designate a relation is to display the *graph* of the relation. Here are the graphs of the relations specified in the examples above.

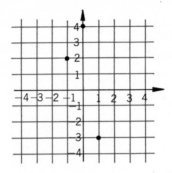 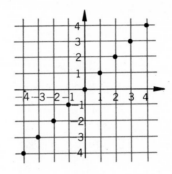

Consider the relation specified by the following graph.

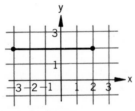

Fig. 3

Does the ordered pair $(\frac{1}{2}, 2)$ belong to this relation? Does $(-3, 2)$? Does $(2, -2)$? Notice that the domain of this relation is $\{x \mid -3 \leq x \leq 2\}$ and the range is $\{2\}$. Observe that it would be impossible to designate this relation by the roster method. Why? Thus, we see that the graphic method of specifying relations has advantages in certain instances.

A third method of designating a relation is by means of the solution set of an *open* sentence in two variables. For example, consider the open sentence $y = x$. Notice that the solution set of this equation, namely $\{(x, y) \mid y = x\}$, is a set of ordered pairs and, hence, a relation. The solution set of every open sentence in two variables is a set of ordered pairs and, therefore, a relation.

Examples: i.   Graph the relation $\{(x, y) \mid x = 2\}$.

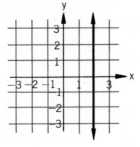

ii.   Graph the relation $\{(x, y) \mid y = 3\}$.

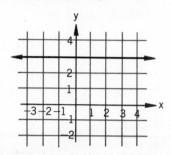

iii.   Designate the relation $\{(x, y) \mid x^2 + y^2 = 0\}$ by the roster method *and* by the graphic method.

Roster: $\{(0, 0)\}$
Graph:

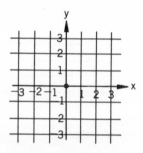

iv.   A relation is designated by the graph below. Specify this relation as the solution set of an open sentence.

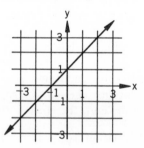

Solution: $\{(x, y) \mid y = x + 1\}$.

Suppose a relation is specified by a graph as in figure 4 on page 163. If we project each point of the graph into the first axis, we determine the set of first components of the ordered pairs in the relation, that is, the domain of the relation. Similarly, by projecting each point of the graph into the second axis, we determine the range of the relation. For example, in the case of the relation specified below, the domain and the range are $\{x \mid -2 \le x \le 6\}$ and $\{y \mid -2 \le y \le 3\}$, respectively.

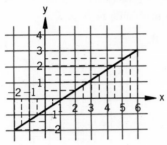

Fig. 4

1. Graph each of the following relations.
    a. $\{(-5, 4), (-5, -1), (-2, 2), (1, -3)\}$
    b. $\{(x, y)\,|\,y = x\}$
    c. $\{(x, y)\,|\,y = -x\}$
    d. $\{(x, y)\,|\,x^2 + y^2 = -1\}$
    e. $\{(x, y)\,|\,y = 2x - 1\}$
    f. $\{(x, y)\,|\,y = -2x + 3\}$
    g. $\{(x, y)\,|\,x = 0\}$
    h. $\{(x, y)\,|\,2x - 3y = 1\}$
    i. $\{(x, y)\,|\,y = 0\}$
    j. $\{(x, y)\,|\,y = |x|\}$

2. Specify each of the following relations by either the roster method or an open sentence, whichever is appropriate.

a.

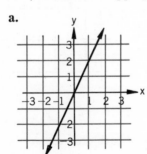

c.

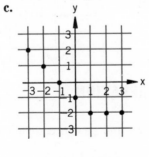

e.

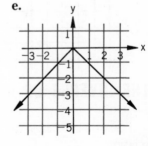

b.

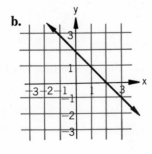

d.

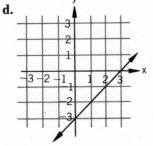

f.

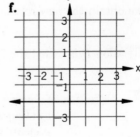

3. State the domain and the range of each of the following relations. The universal set in each of these problems is $R \times R$.

a. **d.** **g.**

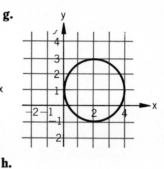

b. **e.** **h.**

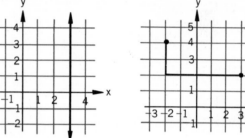

c. **f.** **i.**

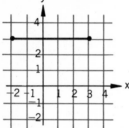

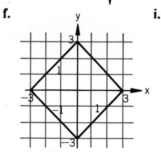

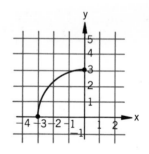

THE INVERSE OF A RELATION

If we *interchange* the first and second components of each ordered pair in the relation

$$A = \{(1, 2), (3, 4), (5, 6), (7, 8)\}$$

we obtain the new relation

$$B = \{(2, 1), (4, 3), (6, 5), (8, 7)\}$$

Relation B is called the *inverse* of relation A. In general, the inverse of a relation is defined as follows:

■ *Definition of Inverse Relation* For each relation A, the *inverse* of A is the relation A' (read: A inverse) obtained by interchanging the components of each of the ordered pairs in A.

The inverse of a relation specified by the roster method is easy to obtain. For example, the inverse of

$$T = \{(1, -1), (3, -3), (5, -5), (7, -7)\}$$

is

$$T' = \{(-1, 1), (-3, 3), (-5, 5), (-7, 7)\}.$$

It should be recognized that *the domain of T' is the range of T* and that *the range of T' is the domain of T*. Every relation A and its inverse A' exhibit this relationship; that is, for each relation A, the range of A is the domain of A' and the domain of A is the range of A'. For instance, suppose that the domain of a relation A is $\{2, 4, 6, 8\}$. Then we know that the range of the relation A' is $\{2, 4, 6, 8\}$. Similarly, if the range of a relation C is $\{-1, 0, 1\}$, then the domain of the relation C' is $\{-1, 0, 1\}$.

Now we shall seek a way of specifying the inverses of relations which are designated by open sentences. For example, consider the equation

$$y = x + 2$$

This equation defines a relation, namely the set of all ordered pairs (x, y) which satisfy the equation. Therefore, if (a, b) is an element of the relation defined by the equation $y = x + 2$, then we know that $b = a + 2$ is a *true* statement. Notice that since $(a, b) = (5, 7)$ is an element of the relation defined by $y = x + 2$, then $(b, a) = (7, 5)$ must be an element of the inverse relation. Similarly, if we interchange the variables x and y in the given open sentence, we obtain the new open sentence $x = y + 2$; it is easy to verify that (b, a) will satisfy this open sentence. (Remember, we know that $b = a + 2$.) Thus, we see that the inverse of the relation

$$\{(x, y) \mid y = x + 2\}$$

is

$$\{(x, y) \mid x = y + 2\}$$

The same argument applies in every case where we seek to specify the inverse of a relation defined by an open sentence: if a relation is defined by an open sentence, then an open sentence which defines the inverse relation can be obtained by simply interchanging the two variables present. Here are some examples.

Examples: i.   If $T = \{(x, y) \mid 2x - 3y = 4\}$,
then $T' = \{(x, y) \mid 2y - 3x = 4\}$.

    ii.   If $S = \{(x, y) \mid y > x\}$,
then $S' = \{(x, y) \mid x > y\}$.

   iii.   If $A = \{(x, y) \mid y \neq x + 1\}$,
then $A' = \{(x, y) \mid x \neq y + 1\}$.

Now we shall consider a way of designating the inverse of a relation which is defined by a graph. The basic ideas are presented by means of examples. Consider the relations K and K' in figure 5.

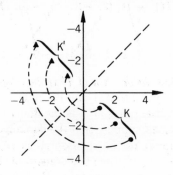

Fig. 5

$K = \{(1, -1), (2, -2), (3, -3)\}$ and $K' = \{(-1, 1), (-2, 2), (-3, 3)\}$. Do you notice the *symmetry* between the graphs of K and K' (round dots and triangular dots respectively)?

Notice the symmetry between the graphs of H and H' in figure 6a below, where

$$H = \{(-4, -1), (-3, 0), (-2, 1), (-1, 2), (0, 3), (1, 4)\}$$
$$\text{and } H' = \{(-1, -4), (0, -3), (1, -2), (2, -1), (3, 0), (4, 1)\}$$

Do the same for G and G' in figure 6b where

$$G = \{(1, -3), (2, -2), (3, -1), (3, -3), (4, -4)\}$$
$$\text{and } G' = \{(-3, 1), (-2, 2), (-1, 3), (-3, 3), (-4, 4)\}$$

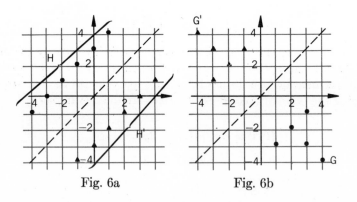

Fig. 6a   Fig. 6b

In each case, the broken line has been introduced to reveal the symmetry shown by the graph of a relation and its inverse. Notice that in each instance the graphs of a relation and its inverse are "mirror reflections" through the broken line whose equation is $y = x$. Here are more examples which illustrate this.

Examples: In each case determine the graph of the inverse of the relation whose graph is given.

i.   Graph of Relation *A*   Graph of Relation *A'*

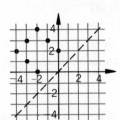   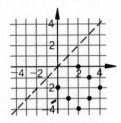

ii.   Graph of Relation *B*   Graph of Relation *B'*

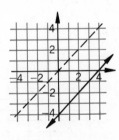   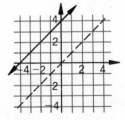

iii.   Graph of Relation *C*   Graph of Relation *C'*

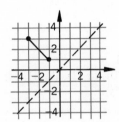   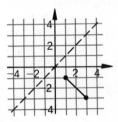

iv.   Graph of Relation *D*   Graph of Relation *D'*

   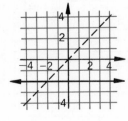

EXERCISES

1.   True or false?
   a.   For every relation T, $(T')' = T$.
   b.   For all relations A and B, if B is the inverse of A, then A is the inverse of B.
   c.   If $K = \{(x, y)\,|\,x^2 + y^2 = 1\}$, then $K' = \{(x, y)\,|\,x^2 + y^2 = 1\}$.
   d.   If $H = \{(x, y)\,|\,y = -x\}$, then $H' = \{(x, y)\,|\,y = -x\}$.
   e.   If $G = \{(a_1, b_1),\ (a_2, b_2),\ (a_3, b_3)\}$, then the domain of G' is $\{a_1, a_2, a_3\}$.
   f.   If $B' = \{(x_1, y_1),\ (x_2, y_2),\ (x_3, y_3)\}$, then the range of B is $\{x_1, x_2, x_3\}$.
   g.   If $S = \{(x, y)\,|\,2x - y = 2\}$, then $(0, 1)\ \epsilon\ S$.
   h.   If $T = \{(x, y)\,|\,y > x\}$, then $(1, 2)\ \epsilon\ T'$.
   i. $\{\ldots, (-1, -1),\ (0, 0),\ (1, 1),\ \ldots\}$ and $\{(x, y)\,|\,y = x\}$ are two designations of the same relation in $R \times R$.
   j. $(2, 3)\ \epsilon\ A'$ if and only if $(3, 2)\ \epsilon\ A$.

2.   Using either the roster method or the open sentence method, specify the inverse of each of the following relations:
   a. $\{(4, -3),\ (-1, -3),\ (\frac{1}{2}, 0),\ (2, -2)\}$
   b. $\{(1, 1),\ (1, 2),\ (1, 4),\ (1, 6),\ (1, 7)\}$
   c. $\{\ldots, (-2, -1),\ (-1, 0),\ (0, 1),\ (1, 2),\ \ldots\}$
   d. $\{\ldots, (-3, -6),\ (-2, -4),\ (-1, -2),\ (0, 0),\ (1, 2),\ (2, 4),\ (3, 6),\ \ldots\}$
   e. $\{(x, y)\,|\,x + y = 4\}$
   f. $\{(x, y)\,|\,x - y = 2\}$
   g. $\{(r, d)\,|\,2d = r + 3\}$
   h. $\{(t, c)\,|\,t - 3c + 7 = 0\}$
   i. $\{(x, y)\,|\,y \geq x - 2\}$
   j. $\{(x, y)\,|\,3x - 2y < 1\}$

3.   Graph the inverse of each of the following relations.

a.
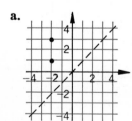

b.
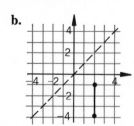

c.
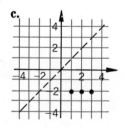

d.
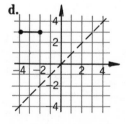

e.
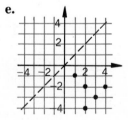

f.
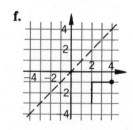

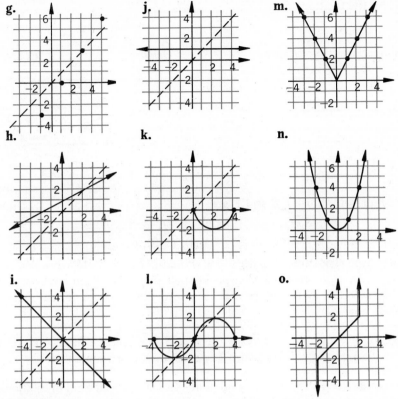

FUNCTIONS

It is interesting and profitable to regard a relation as a "matching" or "pairing-off" operation,* in which one or more elements of the range are "matched" or "paired" with some element or elements of the domain. For example, consider the relation

$$N = \{(1, 0), (2, 5), (2, 6), (3, 4), (1, 5)\}$$

Notice that the relation N assigns 0 and 5 to 1, 5 and 6 to 2, and 4 to 3. The "pairing" operation N may be visualized in this way

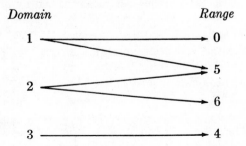

* When relations are interpreted in this way, they are frequently called *mappings*.

Consider the relations S and T:

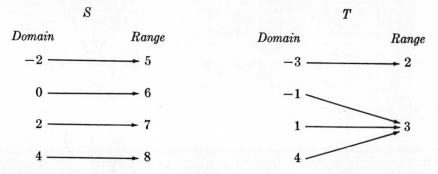

The roster-representations of S and T are

$$S = \{(-2, 5), (0, 6), (2, 7), (4, 8)\}$$
$$\text{and} \quad T = \{(-3, 2), (-1, 3), (1, 3), (4, 3)\}$$

Notice that, unlike relation N, both S and T match one and only one element of their ranges with any particular element of their domains. Such relations are of special importance in mathematics and are called *functions*. A formal definition of function is now stated.

■   *Definition of Function*   A *function* in $A \times B$ is a relation in $A \times B$, no two ordered pairs of which have the same first component.

Thus, we see that every function is a relation — a very special kind of relation.

It is important to be able to determine whether a relation — regardless of how it is specified — is a function. If a relation is designated by the roster method, the decision is easy. For instance,

$$H = \{(1, 3), (2, 4), (3, 5), (1, 6)\}$$

is not a function since two of its ordered pairs, namely (1, 3) and (1, 6), have the same first component. On the other hand,

$$K = \{(-2, 0), (-1, 3), (1, 5), (2, 2)\}$$

is a function since no two ordered pairs of K have the same first component.

Also, it is easy to decide whether relations specified by graphs are functions.

Observe, as illustrated in figure 7, that if any vertical line intersects the graph of a relation in more than one point, then the relation contains two or more ordered pairs with the same first component.

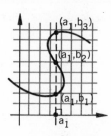

Thus, we conclude that a relation is a function if and only if no vertical line intersects the graph of the relation in more than one point. We will refer to this principle as the *vertical line* test.

Examine the following relations: G, H, K, and M

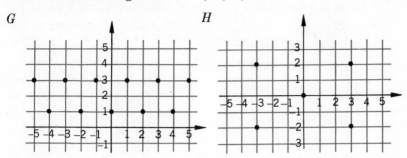

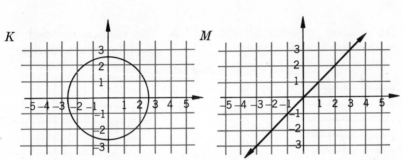

Notice that no two ordered pairs of G or M have the same first component; hence both G and M are functions. On the other hand, neither H nor K is a function since both of these relations fail the vertical line test.

Now let us consider the case where a relation is defined by an open sentence, say in the variables x and y. If, for any replacement of x, there are two or more values of y which satisfy the open sentence, then the open sentence *does not* define a function. Here are two examples which illustrate the basic idea.

Examples: *i.*   Is $\{(x, y) \mid y = x + 1\}$ a function?

Yes, since for any particular replacement of x, only one value of y will satisfy the equation $y = x + 1$.

ii.   Is $\{(x, y) \mid y^2 = x\}$ a function?

No, since for some replacements of x there are two values of y which satisfy $y^2 = x$. For instance, both $(4, 2)$ and $(4, -2)$ satisfy the equation.

EXERCISES

1. True or false?

 a. $A_1 = \{(-3, 1), (-1, 1), (1, 0), (3, 0)\}$ is a function.

 b. $A_2 = \{(2, -2), (2, -1), (2, 0), (2, 1), (2, 2)\}$ is a function.

 c. $A_3 = \{(1, 1)\}$ is a function.

 d. $A_4 = \{(1, 0), (2, 0), (3, 0), (4, 0)\}$ is a function.

e. The relation specified by the graph below is a function.

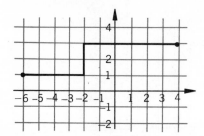

f. The relation specified by the graph below is a function.

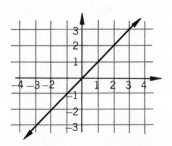

g. The relation specified by the graph below is a function.

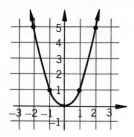

h. The relation specified by the graph below is a function.

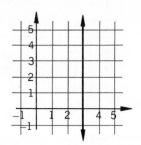

i. $\{(x, y) \mid y = x\}$ is a function.

j. $\{(x, y) \mid y^2 = \frac{1}{2}x\}$ is a function.

k. $\{(x, y) \mid y = |x|\}$ is a function.

l. $\{(x, y) \mid y = x^2\}$ is a function.

m. The domain of the function $f = \{(1, 3), (2, 3), (3, 3)\}$ is $\{1, 2, 3\}$ and the range of f is $\{3\}$.

n. If $F = \{(2, 2), (4, 2), (6, 2)\}$, then $F' = \{(2, 2), (2, 4), (2, 6)\}$.

o. If $G = \{(x, y) \mid y = x + 3\}$, then $G' = \{(x, y) \mid y = x - 3\}$.

2. Use the vertical line test to determine whether the following graphs specify functions.

a.

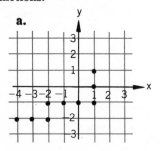

b.

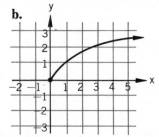

c.

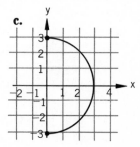

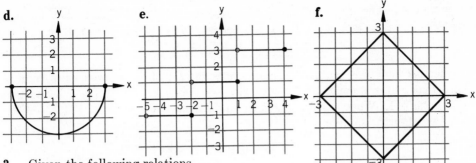

d. **e.** **f.**

3. Given the following relations

$$H = \{(-2, 1), (-2, 2), (-2, 3), (-2, 4)\}$$
$$K = \{(0, -4), (2, -2), (4, 0)\}$$
$$S = \left\{(x, y) \,\middle|\, y = \frac{1}{2}x\right\}$$
$$T = \{(x, y) \,|\, y = 2\}$$

a. Graph each relation. Which relations are functions?

b. Graph the inverse of each relation. Which inverses are functions?

c. What is the domain of each relation? range of each relation?

d. What is the domain of each inverse? range of each inverse?

4. Write an open sentence which specifies the relation which is graphed in **2c**.

5. Write an open sentence which specifies the relation which is graphed in **2d**.

6. Write an open sentence which specifies the relation which is graphed in **2f**.

(HINT: What is the graph of the solution set of $|x| + |y| = 2$?)

Functional Notation

As we learned in the previous section, a function is a relation, no two ordered pairs of which have the same first component. In other words, a matching operation which determines a function associates with each element of the domain of the function *exactly one* element of its range. When considering a particular function, say f, we use the symbol $f(x)$ to denote the second component of the ordered pair whose first component is x. For example, if

$$f = \{(-3, 2), (-1, -3), (0, 2), (2, -2), (5, 1)\}$$

then $f(0) = 2$. What is $f(2)$? $f(-1)$? $f(-3)$? The symbol $f(x)$ is read "f at x" and is often called the *value* of the function f at x. Thus, the value of the function f at 2 is -2. What is the value of f at 5?

As a second example, suppose that

$$r = \left\{\left(-2, \frac{1}{2}\right), (1, 3), \left(\frac{3}{2}, 0\right), (0, 4)\right\}$$

Notice that $r(0) = 4$. What is $r(-2)$? $r(1)$? $r(\frac{3}{2})$? The value of r at 1 is 3. What is the value of r at 0? At -2?

Now consider the function $g = \{(x, y) \,|\, y = 2x + 1\}$. Notice that for any replacement of x, $y = g(x)$. Thus, another way of specifying g is to write

$$g = \{(x, g(x)) \,|\, g(x) = 2x + 1\}$$

Remember that this sentence is read: "g is the set of all ordered pairs $(x, g(x))$ such that g at x is equal to $2x + 1$." We see that $g(1) = 2 \cdot 1 + 1 = 3$ and that $g(a) = 2a + 1$. What is $g(0)$? $g(2)$? $g(-1)$? What is the value of g at 3? At $3h$?

As a fourth example, suppose that

$$F = \{(x, y) \,|\, y = x^2 - 1\}$$

Since for every replacement of x, $y = F(x)$, another way of symbolizing F is to write

$$F = \{(x, F(x)) \,|\, F(x) = x^2 - 1\}$$

Observe that $F(0) = 0^2 - 1 = -1$ and that $F(b) = b^2 - 1$. What is $F(-1)$? $F(2)$? $F(-2c)$?

This notation can be used to discuss more complicated situations. For example, suppose that

$$S = \{(-2, 4), (-1, 2), (0, 0), (1, -2), (2, -4)\}$$

$$\text{and} \quad T = \{(1, -2), (2, -1), (3, 0), (4, 1), (5, 2), (6, 3)\}$$

Notice that, since $T(4) = 1$, $S(T(4)) = S(1) = -2$. Similarly, $S(T(1)) = S(-2) = 4$. What is $S(T(3))$? $T(S(-1))$? $S(S(1))$? $T(T(5))$? Now consider the expression $S(T(6))$; since $T(6) = 3$, we have $S(T(6)) = S(3)$; but 3 is *not* an element of the domain of S. Thus the expression $S(3)$ is *undefined*. What is true about $T(T(3))$? About $T(S(1))$?

As another example, suppose that

$$h = \left\{(x, h(x)) \,\Big|\, h(x) = \frac{1}{x}\right\}$$

$$\text{and} \quad p = \{(x, p(x)) \,|\, p(x) = x - 1\}$$

Verify that each of the following statements is true

$$p(h(1)) = p(1) = 0 \qquad\qquad p\left(h\left(\frac{1}{2}\right)\right) = p(2) = 1$$

$$p(h(2)) = p\left(\frac{1}{2}\right) = -\frac{1}{2}$$

$$p(h(a)) = p\left(\frac{1}{a}\right) = \frac{1}{a} - 1$$

$$p(h(-1)) = p(-1) = -2$$

These examples suggest that $p(h(x))$ means the result obtained by substituting $h(x)$ for x in $p(x)$. That is

$$p(h(x)) = p\left(\frac{1}{x}\right) = \frac{1}{x} - 1$$

Similarly, $h(p(x)) = h(x - 1) = \dfrac{1}{x - 1}$. Notice that while both $h(1)$ and $p(1)$ are defined, $h(p(1))$ is not! The value of $p(h(1))$ is 0. What is the value of $p(h(-1))$? What is the value of $h(p(0))$?

EXERCISES

Each of the problems **1-3** refers to one of these six functions

$A = \{(-4,2), (-2,1), (2,-1), (4,-2)\}$ $f = \{(x, f(x)) \mid f(x) = |x|\}$

$B = \{(2,-4), (1,-2), (-1,2), (-2,4)\}$ $g = \{(x, g(x)) \mid g(x) = x^2\}$

m 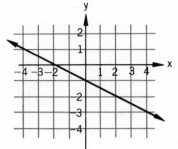 h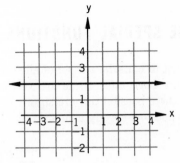

1. True or false?

   a. $A(2) = -1$

   b. $B(-1) = -2$

   c. $f(2) = 2$

   d. $f(-2) = 2$

   e. $g(3) = 6$

   f. $g(-2) = -4$

   g. $m(-2) = 0$

   h. $m(4) = 3$

   i. $h(0) = 0$

   j. $h(4) = 2$

   k. $m(h(-2)) = 0$

   l. $B = A'$

   m. $A(B(-1)) = -1$

   n. $f(g(2)) = 4$

   o. $g(f(-2)) = -4$

   p. $B(m(4)) = 2$

   q. $f(h(-3)) = 2$

   r. $f(g(x)) = |x^2|$

   s. $g(f(x)) = |x|^2$

   t. $h' = \{(x, y) \mid x = 2\}$

   u. $A(g(2)) = B(f(-1))$

2. Find the value of each of the following:

   a. $A(B(2))$

   b. $m(h(-4))$

   c. $f(g(-2))$

   d. $f(a)$

   e. $f(x + a)$

   f. $g(x + a) - g(a)$

   g. $m(-4) \cdot m(-2)$

   h. $[g(3)]^2$

   i. $B(1) + B(2)$

   j. $g(a) \div B(-1)$

   k. $g(\sqrt{7})$

   l. $g(-\sqrt{3})$

3. Determine the domain and the range of each of the functions $A, B, f, g, m,$ and h.

4. Suppose that $s = \{(x, s(x)) \mid s(x) = 2 - x\}$ and $t = \{(x, t(x)) \mid t(x) = -x - 2\}$.

   a. Find $s(3)$ and find $s(h)$.

   b. Find $s(3) + s(h)$.

   c. Find $s(3 + h)$.

   d. Does $s(3 + h) = s(3) + s(h)$, for all h?

   e. Find $s(t(x))$.

   f. Find $t(s(x))$.

   g. Does $s(t(x)) = t(s(x))$, for all x?

5. Suppose that $f = \left\{(x, f(x)) \mid f(x) = \dfrac{1}{2} - x^2\right\}$ and $g = \{(x, g(x)) \mid g(x) = \sqrt{x}\}$.

   a. Find $g(9) \cdot g(h)$.

   b. Find $g(9h)$.

   c. Does $g(9h) = g(9) \cdot g(h)$, for all h?

   d. Find $f(g(x))$.

   e. Find $g(f(x))$.

   f. Does $f(g(x)) = g(f(x))$, for all x?

   g. Find $2 \cdot f(h)$.

   h. Find $f(2h)$.

   i. True or false? $\bigvee_h f(2h) = 2 \cdot f(h)$

6. Suppose that $r = \{(x, r(x)) \mid r(x) = x^2 + 1\}$ and $n = \{(x, n(x)) \mid n(x) = 2x\}$.

    a. Find $r(4) - r(h)$.   **d.** Find $r(n(x))$.

    b. Find $r(4 - h)$.   **e.** Find $n(r(x))$.

    c. Does $r(4 - h) = r(4) - r(h)$, for all h?   **f.** Does $r(n(x)) = n(r(x))$, for all x?

SOME SPECIAL FUNCTIONS

Let us consider the set of all straight lines in a coordinate plane. Some of these lines are horizontal, some are vertical, and all others are oblique. Examples of these three possibilities are shown in figure 8. Which one of the four lines in this figure does *not* specify a function?

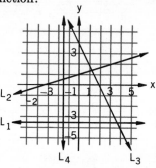

Fig. 8

Notice that the horizontal line L_1 specifies a function, each ordered pair of which has the same second component, namely $-3\frac{1}{2}$. In other words, this function assigns the number $-3\frac{1}{2}$ to each element of its domain. Functions of this type are called *constant* functions.

■   *Definition of Constant Function* A function K is a *constant function* if and only if each element (ordered pair) of K has the same second component.

Observe that every equation of the form $y = c$, c a real number, defines a constant function, namely the set of all ordered pairs in $R \times R$ which satisfy the equation $y = c$.

Here are four examples of constant functions and their graphs.

$\{(1, 3), (2, 3), (3, 3), (4, 3)\}$ $\{(x, y) \mid y = 1\}$

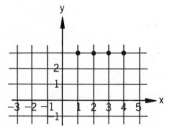   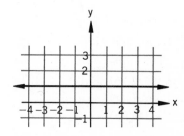

$\{(x, f(x)) | f(x) = -2\}$

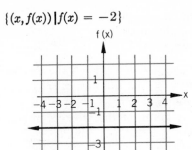

$\{(x, 3)\}$

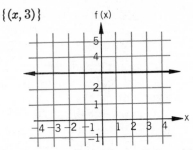

Notice the use of the new symbolism in the last example. The notation $\{(x, 3)\}$ is read: "The set of all ordered pairs $(x, 3)$." It will be understood that, in the absence of restrictions to the contrary, the replacement set for x is the set of real numbers, that is, $\{(x, 3)\}$ is an abbreviation of $\{(x, y) | x$ is a real number and $y = 3\}$.

Now let us turn our attention to the set of all *oblique* lines in a coordinate plane. Every oblique line specifies a function which is called a *linear function*. Since every oblique line can be defined by an equation of the form $y = mx + b$, and conversely, we formally define a linear function as follows:

■   *Definition of Linear Function*   A function f in $R \times R$ is a *linear function* if and only if $f = \{(x, y) | y = mx + b\}$ where m is a non-zero real number and b is a real number.

Notice that we have specified that m be non-zero. What type of function is $f = \{(x, y) | y = mx + b\}$ if $m = 0$ and b is a real number?

Here are four examples of linear functions and their graphs.

$\{(x, y) | y = 2x + 1\}$

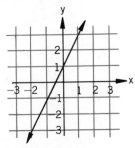

$\{(x, 3x - 2)\}$

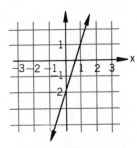

$\{(x, y) | \frac{1}{2}x + \frac{1}{3}y = 1\}$

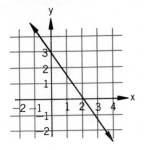

$\{(x, g(x)) | g(x) = -x\}$

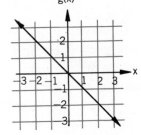

Is $\{(x, y)\,|\,y = x^2 + 1\}$ a linear function? Why or why not?
Is $\{(x, y)\,|\,y = -4\}$ a linear function? Why or why not?
Is $\{(x, y)\,|\,x = 3\}$ a linear function? Why or why not?

Another interesting and very useful function in $R \times R$ is called the *greatest integer function* and is denoted by $\{(x, [x])\}$. For any real number x, $[x]$ is the greatest integer not greater than x. For example, $[4.2] = 4$; $[\frac{5}{2}] = 2$; and $[2] = 2$. What does $[-\frac{1}{2}]$ equal? $[-2]$? $[0]$? The graph of the greatest integer function (figure 9) reveals its basic characteristics.

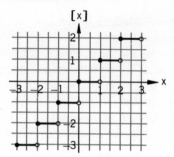

INCOMPLETE GRAPH OF THE GREATEST INTEGER FUNCTION

Fig. 9

The greatest integer function is sometimes called the *unit step function*. Do you see why?

EXERCISES

1. True or false?
   a. $\{(x, y)\,|\,x = -2\}$ is a *constant* function.
   b. $\{(x, f(x))\,|\,f(x) = 2\}$ is a constant function.
   c. If $K = \{(x, y)\,|\,y = 5\}$, then $K' = \{(x, y)\,|\,x = 5\}$.
   d. $\{(x, 2)\}$ is a constant function.
   e. $\{(x, x)\}$ is a *linear* function.
   f. $\{(x, y)\,|\,y = 2x - 5\}$ is a linear function.
   g. $\{(x, y)\,|\,x = y + 2\}$ is a linear function.
   h. $\{(x, y)\,|\,y = [x]\}$ is the greatest integer function.
   i. The range of the greatest integer function is the set of real numbers.
   j. $[2.9] - 2 = 1$
2. Graph the linear function $\{(x, x - 1)\}$.
3. Graph the linear function $\{(x, \frac{1}{2}x + 2)\}$.
4. Graph the constant function $\{(x, -5)\}$.
5. Graph the linear function $\{(x, y)\,|\,y = -x\}$.
6. Graph the linear function $\{(x, h(x))\,|\,h(x) = x\}$.
7. If $f(x) = [x]$, find $f(-\frac{5}{2})$; $f(-1)$; $f(-\frac{1}{4})$; $f(.25)$; $f(.99\overline{9})$.

8. A function which assigns each member of its domain to itself is called an *identity function*. For example, $E = \{(x, y) \,|\, y = x\}$ is an identity function. Graph E. Is $E' = E$?

9. Prove that the inverse of every linear function is a linear function.

10. Prove that every linear function F sets up a one-to-one correspondence between the set of real numbers and the set of real numbers. (Hint: The proof must consist of two parts: first, show that for each real number t, F assigns the real number $F(t)$ to t; second, show that for each real number c, there is a real number d such that $c = F(d)$.)

11. Prove that if $g = \{(x, g(x)) \,|\, g(x) = mx + b\}$ and r and s are real numbers, $r \neq s$, then $\dfrac{g(r) - g(s)}{r - s} = m$.

DIRECT PROPORTION

Let us consider a simple example to introduce the idea of *direct proportion*. The cent-value of 4 three-cent stamps is 12; of 7 three-cent stamps is 21; of 100 three-cent stamps is 300; and of no three-cent stamps is zero. We may display such pairs in the following way:

$$A = \{(0, 0), (1, 3), (2, 6), (3, 9), (4, 12), \ldots\}$$

Each element of A is of the form (n, t) where t is the cent-value of n stamps. Does the domain of A contain $2\frac{1}{2}$? -1? -4? Why or why not? Describe the domain of A; the range of A.

We may also specify the function A using the open sentence method

$$A = \{(n, t) \; \epsilon \; W \times W \,|\, t = 3n\}$$

where W is the set of whole numbers: 0, 1, 2, 3, 4, 5, $\ldots$.

The graph of A is shown in figure 10.

Observe that $A = \{(n, t) \; \epsilon \; W \times W \,|\, t = 3n\}$ is a subset of $B = \{(n, t) \; \epsilon \; R \times R \,|\, t = 3n\}$.

Notice that $(-2, -6)$ belongs to B but not to A. The same is true of $(2\frac{1}{3}, 7)$. Explain why this is so. In both cases we say that t is *directly proportional* to n or that t *varies directly as* n.

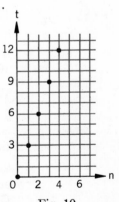

Fig. 10

To say that y is directly proportional to x, or y varies directly as x, is to claim that there exists a non-zero real number, say c, such that for every value of x under consideration, the value of y is given by $c \cdot x$. To be more specific, we shall define a *direct proportion* as follows:

■   *Definition of Direct Proportion Function*   Let the replacement set for x be
denoted by X and the replacement set for y be denoted by Y.
Then for every $c \neq 0$, $\{(x, y) \in X \times Y \mid y = c \cdot x\}$. is a *direct pro-*
portion function.

Figure 11 shows the graphs of several direct proportions in $R \times R$.

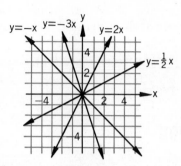

Fig. 11

Notice that each of the four direct proportions which is graphed in figure 11 is also
a linear function. Notice also that the real number c is what distinguishes one direct
proportion from another; c is called the *constant of proportionality* or *constant of
variation.*

Your experience with direct proportion is quite extensive as the following
examples will illustrate.

Examples: i.   The distance, d, you travel at a rate of 20 mph is directly proportional to t, the time you travel. What is the direct proportion
for this example?

$\{(t, d) \mid d = 20t\}$ where t and d are non-negative real numbers.

ii.   The price, p, you pay for gasoline at the rate of 31 cents a gallon
is directly proportional to n, the number of gallons you purchase.
What is the direct proportion for this example?

$\{(n, p) \mid p = 31n\}$ where n is a whole number.

iii. y is directly proportional to x and y is 4 when x is 7. Find the
constant of proportionality. What is the direct proportion for
this example?

Since y varies directly as x, the direct proportion is defined by
an equation of the form $y = cx$. We know that the ordered pair
$(7, 4)$ must satisfy the defining equation; therefore, $4 = 7c$.
Thus, c, the constant of proportionality, is $\frac{4}{7}$. Hence the direct
proportion is $\{(x, y) \mid y = \frac{4}{7}x\}$.

iv.   Suppose that $(2, 5)$ and $(4, h)$ are elements of the same direct
proportion. What is the value of h?

Since $(2, 5)$ and $(4, h)$ are elements of the same direct proportion, there exists a real number c such that $5 = 2c$ and $h = 4c$. Why? Therefore

(*) $$\frac{5}{2} = \frac{h}{4} \qquad \text{Why?}$$

$$2h = 20$$
$$h = 10$$

Hence the value of h is 10. [NOTE: Equations like (*), that is, equations which pattern in the form $\frac{a}{b} = \frac{c}{d}$, are often called *proportions*.]

v. The voltage, y, in a given circuit varies directly as the current, x. If $y = 200$ volts when $x = 15$ amperes, what is y when $x = 27$ amperes?

The direct proportion is of the form $\{(x, y) \mid y = cx\}$. Since $(15, 200)$ must satisfy the equation $y = cx$, we know that $200 = 15c$ or that $c = \frac{40}{3}$. We now conclude that the direct proportion under consideration is $\{(x, y) \mid y = \frac{40}{3}x\}$. Thus, if $x = 27$ amperes, then $y = \frac{40}{3} \cdot 27$ or 360 volts.

EXERCISES

1. True or false?

   a. $\left\{(x, y) \mid y = \frac{1}{2}x\right\}$ is a direct proportion.

   b. $\{(x, y) \mid 3y = 2x\}$ is a direct proportion.

   c. $\{(x, y) \mid 2x - y = 0\}$ is a direct proportion.

   d. $\left\{(x, y) \mid y = \frac{3}{x}\right\}$ is a direct proportion.

   e. $\left\{(x, y) \mid \frac{y}{x} = 1\right\}$ is a direct proportion.

   f. Every linear function is a direct proportion.

   g. The constant of variation for the direct proportion $\left\{(x, y) \mid \frac{y}{2} = 3x\right\}$ is 3.

   h. The constant of variation for the direct proportion $\{(x, y) \mid 2y - x = 0\}$ is $\frac{1}{2}$.

   i. If $(1, 3)$ is a member of the direct proportion $\{(x, y) \mid y = cx\}$, then $c = \frac{1}{3}$.

   j. If $(2, 5)$ is a member of the direct proportion $\{(x, y) \mid y = cx\}$, then $c = \frac{5}{2}$.

   k. If $(5, 3)$ and $(7, k)$ are elements of the same direct proportion, then $\frac{3}{5} = \frac{k}{7}$.

   l. If $(t, 4)$ and $(6, 8)$ are elements of the same direct proportion, then $\frac{t}{4} = \frac{8}{6}$.

2.   Graph each of the following direct proportions.

   a. $\left\{(x, y) \in R \times R \mid y = \frac{1}{4}x\right\}$ **d.** $\{(x, y) \in R \times R \mid y = -2x\}$

   b. $\{(x, y) \in R \times R \mid y = 3x\}$ **e.** $\{(x, y) \in R \times R \mid x + y = 0\}$

   c. $\left\{(x, y) \in R \times R \mid y = -\frac{1}{2}x\right\}$ **f.** $\{(x, y) \in R \times R \mid 3y = 2x\}$

3.   The amount, y, of money you earn varies directly as the number, x, of hours you work. If you earn \$4.55 for 7 hours work, then

   a. Find the direct proportion under consideration. [CAUTION: state any necessary restrictions on values of x and y.]

   b. Find the number of hours you must work in order to earn \$7.93.

   c. Graph the direct proportion under consideration.

4.   The elongation, E, of a spring balance varies directly as the applied weight, W. If E is 5 inches when W is 15 pounds, find the weight necessary to produce an elongation of $7\frac{1}{2}$ inches.

5.   In a vacuum the distance, d, through which a body falls starting from a position of rest varies directly as the *square* of the time, t, that it takes to fall. If a body falls 64 feet in 2 seconds, then how far will it fall in $5\frac{1}{2}$ seconds? (Hint: the direct proportion is defined by an equation of the form $d = c \cdot t^2$.)

6.   Prove:

   a. $\forall_a \forall_{b \neq 0} \forall_c \forall_{d \neq 0}$, if $\dfrac{a}{b} = \dfrac{c}{d}$, then $ad = bc$

   b. $\forall_{a \neq 0} \forall_{b \neq 0} \forall_{c \neq 0} \forall_{d \neq 0}$, if $\dfrac{a}{b} = \dfrac{c}{d}$, then $\dfrac{b}{a} = \dfrac{d}{c}$

   c. $\forall_a \forall_{b \neq 0} \forall_{c \neq 0} \forall_{d \neq 0}$, if $\dfrac{a}{b} = \dfrac{c}{d}$, then $\dfrac{a}{c} = \dfrac{b}{d}$

   d. $\forall_a \forall_{b \neq 0} \forall_c \forall_{d \neq 0}$, if $\dfrac{a}{b} = \dfrac{c}{d}$, then $\dfrac{a+b}{b} = \dfrac{c+d}{d}$

   e. $\forall_{a \neq 0} \forall_{b \neq 0} \forall_{c \neq 0} \forall_{d \neq 0}$, if $\dfrac{a}{b} = \dfrac{c}{d}$, then $\dfrac{a+b}{a} = \dfrac{c+d}{c}$

INVERSE PROPORTION

   In the previous section we defined direct proportion. We shall now consider a different kind of proportion.

   To say that y is *inversely proportional* to x or that y varies inversely as x is to claim that there exists a non-zero real number, say c, such that for every value of x under consideration, the value of y is given by $c \cdot \dfrac{1}{x}$. The concept of *inverse proportion function* is formally defined as follows:

■ *Definition of Inverse Proportion Function*   Let the replacement set for x be denoted by X and the replacement set for y be denoted by Y. Then for every $c \neq 0$, $\left\{(x,y) \, \epsilon \, X \times Y \,\middle|\, y = c \cdot \dfrac{1}{x}\right\}$ is an *inverse proportion function*.

As in the case of direct proportions, the constant c is called the *constant of proportionality*.

Notice that every equation of the form $y = c \cdot \dfrac{1}{x}$ defines an inverse proportion; we shall examine the graphs of a few such equations. To begin, let us graph $y = 2 \cdot \dfrac{1}{x}$; in the following table are listed some of the ordered pairs (x,y) which satisfy this equation.

x	-8	-4	-2	$-\frac{1}{2}$	$-\frac{1}{4}$	$\frac{1}{4}$	$\frac{1}{2}$	2	4	8
y	$-\frac{1}{4}$	$-\frac{1}{2}$	-1	-4	-8	8	4	1	$\frac{1}{2}$	$\frac{1}{4}$

The graph of these ordered pairs is shown in figure 12.

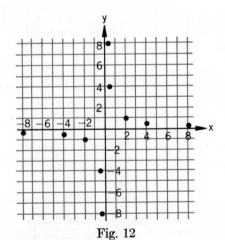

Fig. 12

In order to complete the graph, there are several questions we should answer.

1. Does the graph of $y = 2 \cdot \dfrac{1}{x}$ contain a point whose first coordinate is zero? Why or why not?

2. Replace x in $y = 2 \cdot \dfrac{1}{x}$ successively by 10, 100, 1000 and by 10,000, and observe the pattern of corresponding y-values; describe this pattern.

3. Replace x in $y = 2 \cdot \dfrac{1}{x}$ successively by $\dfrac{1}{10}, \dfrac{1}{100}, \dfrac{1}{1000}$, and by $\dfrac{1}{10,000}$, and observe the corresponding y-values; describe this pattern.

4. Replace x in $y = 2 \cdot \dfrac{1}{x}$ by $-\dfrac{1}{10}$, $-\dfrac{1}{100}$, $-\dfrac{1}{1000}$, and by $-\dfrac{1}{10,000}$, and observe the pattern of corresponding y-values; describe this pattern.

5. Replace x in $y = 2 \cdot \dfrac{1}{x}$ successively by -10, -100, -1000, and by $-10,000$, and observe the pattern of corresponding y-values; describe this pattern.

Finally, let us assume that if we draw a smooth curve through the points we have plotted, each point so introduced will belong to the graph of $y = 2 \cdot \dfrac{1}{x}$.[*] Reproduce the graph in figure 12, and connect the points with a smooth curve. You now have the graph of the inverse proportion $\left\{ (x, y) \in R \times R \,\middle|\, y = 2 \cdot \dfrac{1}{x} \right\}$. Notice that the graph consists of two disjoint curves, one in the first quadrant and the other in the third quadrant.

Now let us consider another inverse proportion, namely $H = \left\{ (x, y) \,\middle|\, y = -2 \cdot \dfrac{1}{x} \right\}$. Notice that in this example the constant of proportionality is negative. Here is a list of some of the ordered pairs (x, y) belonging to H.

x	-8	-4	-2	$-\frac{1}{2}$	$-\frac{1}{4}$	$\frac{1}{4}$	$\frac{1}{2}$	2	4	8
y	$\frac{1}{4}$	$\frac{1}{2}$	1	4	8	-8	-4	-1	$-\frac{1}{2}$	$-\frac{1}{4}$

Plotting these points and then arguing as we did in the previous example we obtain the graph of H (figure 13).

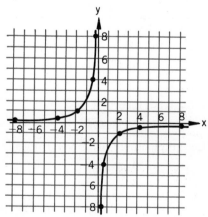

Fig. 13

How do the graphs of $\left\{(x, y) \mid y = 2 \cdot \dfrac{1}{x}\right\}$ and $\left\{(x, y) \mid y = -2 \cdot \dfrac{1}{x}\right\}$ differ? In view of what you learned in the above examples, describe the character of the graph of any inverse proportion $\left\{(x, y) \in R \times R \mid y = c \cdot \dfrac{1}{x}\right\}$ when $c > 0$; when $c < 0$. Study the following examples.

Examples: i. y is inversely proportional to x and y is 2 when x is 3. Find the constant of proportionality. What is the inverse proportion for this example?

Since y varies inversely as x, the inverse proportion is defined by an equation of the form $y = c \cdot \dfrac{1}{x}$. The ordered pair $(3, 2)$ satisfies this equation; hence, $2 = c \cdot \frac{1}{3}$. Thus, c, the constant of proportionality, is 6 and the inverse proportion is

$$\left\{(x, y) \mid y = \frac{6}{x}\right\}$$

ii.   In a simple electric circuit, the current, i, varies inversely as the resistance, r. Given that i is 10 amperes when r is 5 ohms, find the inverse proportion for this situation and find i when r is 20 ohms.

The inverse proportion under consideration is defined by an equation of the form $i = c \cdot \dfrac{1}{r}$. Since $(5, 10)$ belongs to this proportion, we know that $10 = c \cdot \frac{1}{5}$. Thus, c, the constant of proportionality, is 50, and so the inverse proportion is

$$\left\{(r, i) \mid i = \frac{50}{r}\right\}$$

Replacing r in $i = \dfrac{50}{r}$ by 20, we find that the corresponding value of i is $2\frac{1}{2}$.

EXERCISES

1.   True or false?

a. $\{(x, y) \mid y = 3x\}$ is an inverse proportion.

b. $\left\{(x, y) \mid y = \dfrac{2}{x}\right\}$ is an inverse proportion.

c. $\{(x, y) \mid xy = 1\}$ is an inverse proportion.

d. $\left\{(x, y) \mid 2y = \dfrac{1}{x}\right\}$ is an inverse proportion.

e.   Some inverse proportions are linear functions.

f.   The constant of proportionality for the inverse proportion $\{(x, y) \mid 2xy = 1\}$ is $\frac{1}{2}$.

g. The constant of proportionality for the inverse proportion $\left\{(x, y) \mid \dfrac{y}{3} = \dfrac{1}{x}\right\}$ is $\frac{1}{3}$.

h. No inverse proportion contains an ordered pair whose first component is 0.

i. The graph of $\{(x, y) \in R \times R \mid xy = 4\}$ consists of the union of two disjoint sets of points, one being a subset of the set of points in quadrant III.

j. The graph of $\{(x, y) \in R \times R \mid xy = -4\}$ consists of the union of two disjoint sets of points, one being a subset of the set of points in quadrant I and the other being a subset of the set of points in quadrant III.

2. Graph each of the following inverse proportions.

a. $\left\{(x, y) \in R \times R \mid y = \dfrac{1}{x}\right\}$
d. $\left\{(x, y) \in R \times R \mid xy = -\dfrac{1}{2}\right\}$

b. $\left\{(x, y) \in R \times R \mid y = -\dfrac{1}{x}\right\}$
e. $\{(x, y) \in R \times R \mid 2xy = 3\}$

c. $\left\{(x, y) \in R \times R \mid xy = \dfrac{1}{2}\right\}$
f. $\left\{(x, y) \in R \times R \mid xy = -\dfrac{3}{2}\right\}$

3. Boyle's law states that the pressure, p, of a gas at constant temperature varies inversely as the volume, v. If $v = 450$ cubic inches when $p = 40$ pounds per square inch, then find p when $v = 675$ cubic inches.

4. The weight, w, of an object varies inversely as the *square* of its distance, d, from the center of the earth. Assuming the earth to be a sphere of radius 4000 miles, approximately how much will a 50 lb. object at the earth's surface weigh if it were taken 500 miles above the earth's surface? (Hint: The inverse proportion is defined by an equation of the form $w = c \cdot \dfrac{1}{d^2}$.)

5. The illumination, y, received on an object from a given source of light varies inversely as the square of its distance, x, from the source. If the measure of the illumination on a book is 8 foot-candles (a measure of the intensity of light) when the book is 3 feet from a particular source of light, find

i. the inverse proportion under consideration.

ii. the measure of illumination in foot-candles when the book is 4 feet from the source of light; 5 feet from the source of light; 8 feet from the source of light.

DESCRIBING SUBSETS OF A PLANE BY INEQUALITIES

Recall that the graph of every first degree equation in two variables is a straight line; and, conversely, every straight line in a coordinate plane is the graph of some first degree equation in two variables. In this section we shall examine some *first degree inequalities in two variables* and shall determine their graphs. Here are three first degree inequalities in two variables.

$$y > x \qquad\qquad 2x + y < 0 \qquad\qquad \frac{1}{2}x < y$$

Examples: *i.*   Graph the solution set of $y > x$.

To determine whether any given ordered pair (x, y) satisfies the inequality $y > x$, we replace x by the first component of the ordered pair and y by the second component; if the resulting statement is true, then the ordered pair is a solution of the inequality. Thus, any ordered pair (x, y) whose second component is greater than its first component will be a solution of $y > x$. Does the ordered pair $(2, 3)$ belong to the solution set of $y > x$? $(2, 4)$? $(2, 5)$? $(2, 2)$? $(2, 2\frac{1}{2})$? $(2, -3)$? Now we shall construct the graph of the solution set of $y > x$. See figure 14.

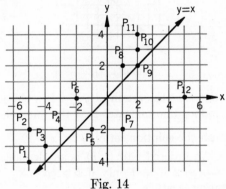

Fig. 14

Observe that every point of the line corresponds to a solution of the equation $y = x$. Which of the points P_1 through P_{12} correspond to solutions of $y > x$? Describe the graph of the solution set of $y > x$. Notice that the line in figure 14 — like every line in a coordinate plane — separates the points of the plane which are not on the line into two disjoint sets of points: the two sets of points on either side of the line, each of which is called an *open half-plane*. (Whenever we say "half-plane" we mean "open half-plane".) The union of any line with one of the half-planes it determines is called a *closed half-plane*. Thus, we may describe the graph of $y > x$ as the half-plane "above" the line which is the graph of $y = x$. The graph of $y > x$ is shown in figure 15. The purpose of the *broken* line is to indicate that the boundary points of the half-plane are *not* part of the graph.

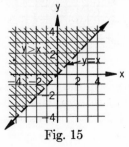

Fig. 15

Knowing that the graph of $y > x$ is the half-plane "above" the broken line, describe the graph of $y < x$.

ii. Graph the solution set of $y \leq x$.

Since the solution set for $y \leq x$ is the union of the solution sets for $y = x$ and for $y < x$, we see that the graph of $y \leq x$ is shown in figure 16 below.

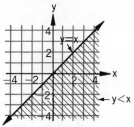

Fig. 16

Notice that the graph of $y \leq x$ is a closed half-plane; the *solid* boundary line indicates that the line belongs to the set.

iii Graph the solution set of $y > \frac{1}{2}x - 2$.

An ordered pair (a, b) is an element of the solution set of $y > \frac{1}{2}x - 2$ if and only if $b > \frac{1}{2}a - 2$. Hence, (a, b) is *not* a solution if either

$$b = \frac{1}{2}a - 2$$

or

$$b < \frac{1}{2}a - 2$$

Which of the ordered pairs $(4, 5)$, $(6, 1)$, $(-2, 4)$, $(-2, -4)$ are solutions of $y > \frac{1}{2}x - 2$? The graph of $y > \frac{1}{2}x - 2$ is a half-plane. Is the graph of the half-plane "above" or "below" the line graph of $y = \frac{1}{2}x - 2$? See figure 17.

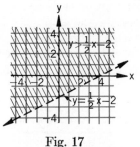

Fig. 17

As you have probably surmised, the graph of every open sentence of the form $Ax + By > C$, A and B not both zero, is a half-plane whose boundary is the line graph of the equation $Ax + By = C$. Thus, in order to obtain the graph of any instance of $Ax + By > C$, we first find the line graph of $Ax + By = C$. The only remaining problem is selecting the correct half-plane. This can be done by writing the inequality $Ax + By > C$ in an equivalent form, called the y-form of the inequality, where y "stands alone" in one member of the inequality. For example, suppose we wish to obtain the graph of the inequality $2x + y > 1$. The y-form of this inequality is $y > -2x + 1$. It is now readily seen that the desired graph is the half-plane "above" the line graph of $y = -2x + 1$.

The following example illustrates another way to describe a subset of the plane by an inequality.

Example: Find the solution set of $x^2 + y^2 \leq 25$.

The solution set for $x^2 + y^2 \leq 25$ is the union of the solution sets for $x^2 + y^2 = 25$ and for $x^2 + y^2 < 25$. The graph of $x^2 + y^2 = 25$ is a circle whose center has coordinates $(0, 0)$ and whose radius is 5. Moreover, by the Pythagorean relation, $x^2 + y^2$ represents the square of the distance from the origin to any point with coordinates (x, y); thus, a point belongs to the graph of $x^2 + y^2 < 25$ if and only if it lies *inside* the circle graph of $x^2 + y^2 = 25$. We conclude that the graph of the solution set of $x^2 + y^2 \leq 25$ is given by the shaded region of figure 18, boundary included.

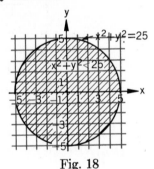

Fig. 18

EXERCISES

1. True or false?

    a. The graph of the solution set of $y > x - 3$ is a closed half-plane.

    b. The graph of the solution set of $y \leq x + 2$ is a half-plane.

    c. The inequality $y > x - 3$ defines a relation.

    d. The inequality $y < x + 2$ defines a function.

    e. The y-form of $x + y < 3$ is $y < 3 - x$.

    f. The y-form of $2x - y < 1$ is $y > 2x - 1$.

    g. The graph of the solution set of $y \geq \frac{1}{2}x - 5$ is the intersection of the graphs of the solution sets of $y = \frac{1}{2}x - 5$ and of $y > \frac{1}{2}x - 5$.

    h. The intersection of the graphs of $y > x$ and of $y < x$ is the empty set.

i. The union of the graphs of $y > x$ and of $y < x$ is the entire plane.

j. The graph of $y > 3x - 2$ is the half-plane "below" the line graph of $y = 3x - 2$.

k. The graph of $y > 2x + 3$ consists of each point of the plane whose second coordinate is three more than twice its first coordinate.

l. The graph of $Ax + By < C$ may be obtained by graphing $Ax + By = C$, a straight line which determines two half-planes, and then deciding which of the two is the correct half-plane.

m. If the open sentence $y < 3$ is understood to be a first degree inequality in two variables x and y, then an equivalent form of the open sentence is $y + 0 \cdot x < 3$.

n. If the open sentence $x \geq -2$ is understood to be a first degree inequality in two variables x and y, then an equivalent form of the open sentence is $0 \cdot y + x \geq -2$.

2. Graph the solution set for each of the following open sentences in two variables, x and y.

a. $y > x + 1$

b. $y \leq -x + 2$

c. $-y > 2x + 2$

d. $3x + 2y < 2$

e. $y \geq 2$

f. $y < -1$

g. $x > 0$

h. $3x - 2y < 2$

i. $\dfrac{x - 4}{4} > \dfrac{y - 3}{2}$

j. $x^2 + y^2 \leq 16$

k. $x^2 + y^2 \geq 16$

l. $x^2 + y^2 < 9$

m. $2x + 2y < 9$

n. $x^2 + y^2 \geq 0$

VOCABULARY

Use each of the following correctly in a sentence. Numerals in parentheses refer to pages where these words were used. If you are not sure of the meaning of any word, turn to the indicated pages.

closed half-plane (187)
component (155)
constant function (176)
constant of proportionality (180)
direct proportion (179)
domain of a relation (159)
function (170)
functional notation (173)
greatest integer function (178)
half-plane (187)
identity function (179)
inverse of a relation (164)

inverse proportion (182)
lattice (155)
linear function (177)
open half-plane (187)
product set (156)
proportion (181)
range of a relation (159)
relation (158)
unit step function (178)
value of a function (173)
vertical line test (170)

REVIEW EXERCISES

The following eight relations, F_1, F_2, F_3, ..., F_8, are referred to in problems **1–5.**

$$F_1 = \{(4, 0), (-4, 0), (0, 4), (0, -4)\}$$
$$F_2 = \{(1, 5), (-3, 2), (4, -7), (0, 5)\}$$
$$F_3 = \{\ldots, (-2, 0), (-1, 0), (0, 0), (1, 0), (2, 0), \ldots\}$$
$$F_4 = \left\{(x, y)\,|\,y = \tfrac{1}{3}x + 1\right\}$$
$$F_5 = \{(x, y)\,|\,y = -|x| - 1\}$$
$$F_6 = \{(x, y)\,|\,x^2 + y^2 = 4\}$$

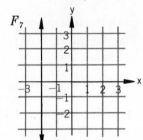

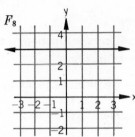

1. Which of the relations F_1 through F_8 are functions? Which are linear functions? Which are constant functions?

2. Classify each of the relations F_1 through F_8 as being either finite or infinite.

3. Find the domain and the range of each of the relations F_1 through F_8.

4. Specify in some appropriate way the inverse of each of the relations F_1 through F_8.

5. Which of the relations $F_1{}'$ through $F_8{}'$ are functions?

The following four functions, f, g, y, and k, are referred to in problems **6–10**
$$f = \{(-3, 4), (-2, -4), (0, 0), (2, 4), (3, -4), (4, 3)\}$$
$$g = \{(x, g(x))\,|\,g(x) = x^2\}$$

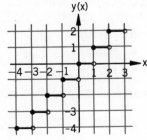

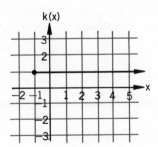

6. Find:

a. $f(-2)$ **b.** $f(3)$ **c.** $f(0)$ **d.** $f(f(2))$

7. Find:

   a. $g(-4)$ **c.** $g(\sqrt{7})$ **e.** $g(r)$

   b. $g(4)$ **d.** $g(g(3))$ **f.** $g(t+1)$

8. Find:

   a. $y(-2)$ **c.** $y(34)$ **e.** $y(6.72)$

   b. $y\left(\dfrac{1}{2}\right)$ **d.** $y(a)$ **f.** $y(-6.72)$

9. Find:

   a. $k(0)$ **b.** $k\left(-\dfrac{1}{2}\right)$ **c.** $k(7)$ **d.** $k(7.34)$

10. True or false?

   a. f' is a function.   **d.** g is a linear function.

   b. y is the greatest integer function.   **e.** The domain of k is $\{x \mid x \geq 1\}$.

   c. k is a constant function.   **f.** The range of f is $\{-3, -2, 0, 2, 3, 4\}$.

The following four functions p_1, p_2, p_3, and p_4 are referred to in problems **11–17.**

$$p_1 = \left\{(x, y) \mid y = \frac{x}{3}\right\} \qquad p_3 = \{(x, y) \mid y = x - 1\}$$

$$p_2 = \left\{(x, y) \mid y = \frac{3}{x}\right\} \qquad p_4 = \left\{(x, y) \mid x = \frac{1}{y}\right\}$$

11. Which of the functions p_1 through p_4 are linear functions?

12. Which of the functions p_1 through p_4 are direct proportions?

13. Which of the functions p_1 through p_4 are inverse proportions?

14. Graph p_1.

15. Graph p_2.

16. Graph p_3 and p_3' on the same coordinate system.

17. Graph p_4.

18. Use the roster method to specify $A \times B$ if $A = \{2, 4, 6\}$ and $B = \{0, 4\}$. Graph $A \times B$.

19. Given the functions f and g such that $f(x) = 2x - 1$ and $g(x) = 3x + 2$ for all real numbers x; determine

   a. $g(f(x))$ **d.** $g(f(10))$

   b. $f(g(x))$ **e.** $f(g(10))$

   c. $f(f(x))$ **f.** $f(f(10))$

20. The measure, y, of a diagonal of a square varies directly as the measure, x, of a side. Find:

   a. the constant of proportionality.

   b. the direct proportion under consideration.

   c. the measure of a side of a square whose diagonal has a measure of $\frac{9}{2}$ inches.

21. At a constant temperature, the volume, y, of an enclosed gas varies inversely as the pressure, x. If 6 cubic feet of gas is under a pressure of 21 pounds per square inch, and the pressure is increased to 30 pounds per square inch, what is the new volume of the gas?

22. Graph the solution set for each of the following open sentences

a. $x + 2y - 4 \geq 0$ **c.** $\dfrac{x}{3} < \dfrac{y}{3}$ **e.** $x^2 + y^2 \geq 5$

b. $x - 2y - 4 > 0$ **d.** $y > -3$ **f.** $x \leq 2$

23. Use the open-sentence method to specify k' if $k = \{(x, y) \,|\, y = 3x^2 + 4\}$.

CHAPTER TEST

Each of the problems **1–22** refers to one or more of the nine sets below.

$$A = \{-2, -1, 0, 1, 2\}$$
$$B = \{-1, 0, 1\}$$
$$f = \{(x, y) \,|\, y = 2x\}$$
$$g = \{(x, y) \,|\, x^2 + y^2 \leq 9\}$$
$$h = \{(4, 5), (5, 5), (6, 5), (7, 5)\}$$

$$k = \{(x, 4)\}$$
$$r = \{(x_1, r_1), (x_1, r_2), (x_1, r_3)\}$$
$$y = \{(x, y(x)) \,|\, y(x) = [x] + 1\}$$
$$z = \left\{(x, y) \,\Big|\, y = \frac{7}{x}\right\}$$

1. Which, if any, of the above sets are *not* relations?

2. Which, if any, of the above sets *are* functions?

3. How many elements does the product set $A \times B$ contain?

4. Is $A \times B = B \times A$?

5. Which, if any, of the above sets are constant functions?

6. Which, if any, of the above sets are linear functions?

7. Which, if any, of the above sets are direct proportions?

8. Which, if any, of the above sets are inverse proportions?

9. What is the value of h at 5?

10. Graph $A \times B$.

11. Graph f.

12. Graph g.

13. Graph k.

14. Graph y.

15. Graph f'.

16. What are the domain and range of g?

17. What are the domain and range of k?

18. What are the domain and range of y?

19. What are the domain and range of z?

20. Specify f'.

21. Specify h'.

22. Specify z'.

23. Graph the solution set of the open sentence $x - y < 2$.

24. Neglecting air resistance, the distance, y, through which a body falls from a position of rest varies directly as the *square* of the time, x, that it falls. If a body falls 64 feet in 2 seconds, how far will it fall in 3 seconds?

25. The frequency, y, of a radio wave is inversely proportional to the length, x, of the wave. If a wave 300 meters long has a frequency of 800 kilocycles per second, what is the length of a wave with a frequency of 900 kilocycles per second?

26. Given the functions f and g such that $f(x) = 3x + 1$ and $g(x) = x^2$ for all real numbers x, determine

    a. $f(-2)$ **e.** $f(g(x))$

    b. $g(.03)$ **f.** $g(f(x))$

    c. $f(a + b)$ **g.** $f(f(x))$

    d. $g(2t - 3)$ **h.** $g(g(x))$

27. Describe the vertical line test and its purpose.

BIBLIOGRAPHY

Allendoerfer, C. B. and Oakley, C. O. *Principles of Mathematics.* Second Edition. New York: McGraw-Hill Book Co., Inc., 1963. Chapter 6.

Evenson, A. B. *Modern Mathematics.* Chicago: Scott, Foresman and Co., 1962. Chapters 5 and 6.

Heimer, R., Kocher, F. and Lottes, J. *A Program in Contemporary Algebra.* New York: Holt, Rinehart and Winston, Inc., 1963. Book 4, Unit VI.

Rose, I. H. *A Modern Introduction to College Mathematics.* New York: John Wiley & Sons, Inc., 1959. pp. 18–37.

School Mathematics Study Group. *Mathematics For High School: Intermediate Mathematics, Part I.* New Haven: Yale University Press, 1961. Chapter 3.

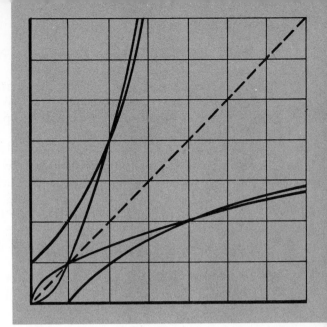

CHAPTER 7

Quadratic Functions

WHAT IS A QUADRATIC FUNCTION?

We have already learned that for all real numbers m and b, the polynomial $mx + b$ defines either a linear function, $\{(x, mx + b)\}$, or a constant function, $\{(x, b)\}$, depending on whether or not m is zero. Another important type of function is a function whose values are specified by a quadratic polynomial, $ax^2 + bx + c$. Such a function is called a *quadratic function*.

■ *Definition of Quadratic Function* $\forall_{a \epsilon R,\, a \neq 0} \forall_{b \epsilon R} \forall_{c \epsilon R}$ Q is a *quadratic function* if and only if $Q = \{(x, ax^2 + bx + c)\}$.

Here are six examples of quadratic functions.

$\{(x, y) \,|\, y = 2x^2 + x + 1\}$ $\qquad\qquad$ $\{(x, y) \,|\, y = x^2\}$

$\{(x, y) \,|\, y = 3x^2 - 1\}$ $\qquad\qquad$ $\left\{\left(x, \dfrac{1}{2}x^2 + 2\right)\right\}$

$\{(x, y) \,|\, y = -x^2 + x\}$ $\qquad\qquad$ $\{(x, f(x)) \,|\, f(x) = 7 - x^2\}$

For each of the six examples above, determine a, b, and c according to the definition of quadratic function.

Is $\{(x, y)\,|\,3x^2 = y\}$ a quadratic function? Is $\{(x, y)\,|\,x^2 + \frac{1}{2}y = 2\}$ a quadratic function? $\{(x, 2x + 5)\}$? $\{(x, y)\,|\,y^2 = x\}$? Why or why not in each case?

Let us now turn our attention to the problem of graphing certain quadratic functions. As a first example, let us seek the graph of the quadratic function $F = \{(x, y)\,|\,y = x^2\}$. We, of course, are seeking the set of all points $P(x, y)$ in the coordinate plane whose coordinates satisfy the equation $y = x^2$. The following table lists a few of the ordered pairs (x, y) which satisfy the equation $y = x^2$.

x	-3	-2	-1	0	1	2	3
y	9	4	1	0	1	4	9

Notice that $F(2) = F(-2) = 4$; $F(3) = F(-3) = 9$; $F(-5) = F(5) = 25$; $F(\sqrt{3}) = F(-\sqrt{3}) = 3$. From this, we observe two things

$$\forall_x \; F(x) \geq 0 \quad \text{and} \quad \forall_x \; F(x) = F(-x)$$

We are now prepared to obtain the graph of F. We begin by plotting the seven ordered pairs of F that are tabulated above; if we draw a smooth curve through these points, we have the graph of F. See figure 1. Notice that if (b, t) belongs to F, then $(-b, t)$ also belongs to F. The graph of any function which has this property is said to be *symmetric with respect to the vertical coordinate axis*. The graph of F is called a *parabola*. You will discover that the graph of every quadratic function is a parabola.

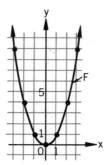

Fig. 1

There are two important characteristics which all parabolas have in common. First, every parabola is symmetric with respect to some line called the *axis of symmetry* of the parabola; second, the parabola intersects its axis of symmetry at a point called the *vertex* of the parabola. What is an equation of the axis of symmetry of the parabola F above? What are the coordinates of its vertex? What is the smallest member of the range of F? Does the range of F have a greatest member?

Let us now consider the relationship between the graphs of the quadratic functions F, G, and K if $F = \{(x, y)\,|\,y = x^2\}$, $G = \{(x, y)\,|\,y = 2x^2\}$ and $K = \{(x, y)\,|\,y = \frac{1}{2}x^2\}$. Examine the following lists of ordered pairs which belong to G, F, and K respectively

G: $(-3, 18)$, $(-2, 8)$, $(-1, 2)$, $(0, 0)$, $(1, 2)$, $(2, 8)$, $(3, 18)$

↑   ↑   ↑   ↑   ↑   ↑   ↑

F: $(-3, 9)$, $(-2, 4)$, $(-1, 1)$, $(0, 0)$, $(1, 1)$, $(2, 4)$, $(3, 9)$

↓   ↓   ↓   ↓   ↓   ↓   ↓

K: $(-3, \frac{9}{2})$, $(-2, 2)$, $(-1, \frac{1}{2})$, $(0, 0)$, $(1, \frac{1}{2})$, $(2, 2)$, $(3, \frac{9}{2})$

If we focus our attention on the ordered pairs of G, F, and K which have the same first component, we see that in each case the second component of the ordered pair in G is twice the second component of the corresponding ordered pair in F; and, the second component of the ordered pair in K is half the second component of the corresponding ordered pair in F.

It is instructive to observe the relationship among the graphs of F, G, and K. See figure 2.

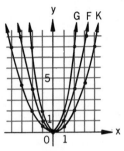

Fig. 2

Notice that each of the parabolas above is symmetric with respect to the y-axis and that each has the same vertex, namely the origin. The basic distinction between the graphs of F and G is the fact that the graph of $G = \{(x, y) \mid y = 2x^2\}$ is a "narrower" parabola than the graph of $F = \{(x, y) \mid y = x^2\}$. On the other hand, we see that the graph of $K = \{(x, y) \mid y = \frac{1}{2}x^2\}$ is a "wider" parabola than the graph of F. On the basis of the preceding discussion, how would you describe the graph of the quadratic function $\{(x, y) \mid y = 3x^2\}$ in relation to the graph of F? The graph of $\{(x, y) \mid y = \frac{1}{3}x^2\}$ in relation to the graph of F?

Examples: i.   Graph the quadratic function $M = \{(x, y) \mid y = -x^2\}$. Recall that $-x^2$ means $-(x^2)$.

Notice that $\bigvee_x x^2 + (-x^2) = 0$. Thus, since $(-x^2)$ is the additive inverse of x^2 for all replacements of x, the graph of $M = \{(x, y) \mid y = -x^2\}$ is the "mirror reflection" in the x-axis of the graph of $F = \{(x, y) \mid y = x^2\}$.

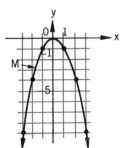

Observe that this graph opens "downward". What is the greatest member of the range of this function? Does the range have a smallest member?

ii. What are the domain and the range of the quadratic function $M = \{(x, y) \mid y = -x^2\}$ whose graph is shown in the first example? Domain: $\{x \mid x$ is a real number$\}$. Range: $\{y \mid y \leq 0\}$.

iii. Determine the *maximum* value of the quadratic function $f = \{(x, f(x)) \mid f(x) = -\frac{1}{2}x^2\}$; that is, determine the *greatest* member of the range of f.

We begin by constructing the graph of f. Some of the ordered pairs belonging to f are given in the following table. Verify that each is correct.

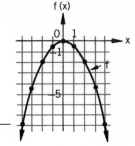

f (x)

x	± 4	± 3	± 2	± 1	0
$f(x)$	-8	$-4\frac{1}{2}$	-2	$-\frac{1}{2}$	0

Recall that $f(x)$ is the value of the function f at x. In other words, if the ordered pair (a, b) belongs to f, then b is the value of f at a. The set of all second components of the ordered pairs belonging to f is the set of values of f.

By studying the graph of f we see that the highest point of the parabola, namely the vertex, has zero for its second coordinate. Thus the maximum value of f is zero. Notice that f has *no* minimum value! Explain.

iv. Determine the *minimum* value of the quadratic function $g = \{(x, g(x)) \mid g(x) = 3x^2\}$; that is, determine the *smallest* member of the range of g.

We begin by constructing the graph of g. Some of the ordered pairs belonging to g are given in the following table. Verify that each is correct.

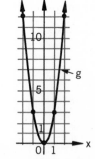

g (x)

x	± 2	± 1	0
$g(x)$	12	3	0

Notice that the second component of every ordered pair belonging to g is greater than or equal to zero, and the lowest point of the parabola, namely the vertex, has zero for its second coordinate. Thus, the minimum value of g is zero. Observe that g has no maximum value! Explain.

v. The graph of a quadratic function h is given. Determine the graph of h'. (Recall the definition of inverse function from Chapter 6.) Is h' a function?

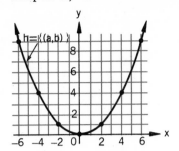 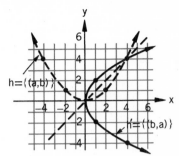

The graph of h' fails the "vertical line" test, and so h' is *not* a function. Notice, however, that the graph of h' *is* a parabola.

EXERCISES

1. True or false?

   a. $\{(x, y) \mid x^2 + y = 1\}$ is a quadratic function.

   b. $t = \{(x, t(x)) \mid t(x) = 1 - x\}$ is a quadratic function.

   c. $x^2 + x$ is a quadratic polynomial.

   d. $\{(x, 4x^2)\}$ is a quadratic polynomial.

   e. If $q = \{(x, q(x)) \mid q(x) = 2x^2\}$, then $\forall_x \; q(x) = q(-x)$.

   f. The graph of $r = \{(x, r(x)) \mid r(x) = x^2 + 1\}$ is symmetric with respect to the second coordinate axis.

   g. The coordinates of the vertex of the parabola pictured at the right are $(1, 2)$.

   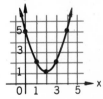

   h. An equation of the axis of symmetry of the parabola pictured at the right is $y = 2$.

   i. The graphs of the quadratic functions $A = \{(x, y) \mid y = x^2\}$ and $B = \{(x, y) \mid y = \frac{1}{4}x^2\}$ are parabolas which have the same vertex and the same axis of symmetry, but the graph of B is a "wider" parabola than the graph of A.

   j. The graph of $C = \{(x, y) \mid y = 5x^2\}$ is a parabola which is "narrower" than the parabola which is the graph of $A = \{(x, y) \mid y = x^2\}$.

   k. The graph of the quadratic function $\{(x, y) \mid y = \frac{1}{2}x^2\}$ is a parabola which opens "downward".

   l. The graph of $\{(x, y) \mid y = -2x^2\}$ is a parabola which opens "downward"

m. The maximum value of the function pictured at the right is 4.

n. The minimum value of the function pictured at the right is 0.

o. The inverse of the function pictured at the right is a function.

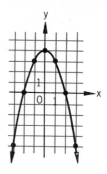

2. Graph the following quadratic functions. Determine the axis of symmetry and the coordinates of the vertex of each parabola. Also, indicate whether the function has a maximum or a minimum value and what it is.

a. $f_1 = \{(x, y) \mid y = 4x^2\}$

b. $f_2 = \left\{(x, y) \mid y = \frac{1}{4}x^2\right\}$

c. $f_3 = \{(x, y) \mid y = -4x^2\}$

d. $f_4 = \left\{(x, y) \mid y = -\frac{1}{4}x^2\right\}$

e. $f_5 = \{(x, y) \mid y = x^2 + 1\}$

f. $f_6 = \{(x, y) \mid y = x^2 - 1\}$

g. $f_7 = \{(x, y) \mid y = -x^2 + 1\}$

h. $f_8 = \{(x, y) \mid y = -x^2 - 1\}$

3. Graph each of the following relations.

a. f_1'. (See problem **2a.**)

b. f_4'. (See problem **2d.**)

QUADRATIC FUNCTIONS OF THE TYPE $\{(x, y) \mid y = ax^2 + p\}$

Thus far, our discussion of quadratic functions has been limited almost entirely to those definable by equations of the type $y = ax^2$. We have learned that the graph of a quadratic function of the type

$$\{(x, y) \mid y = ax^2\}$$

is a parabola

i. whose axis of symmetry is the y-axis and whose vertex is the origin

ii. which opens "upward" or "downward" depending on whether $a > 0$ or $a < 0$

Also we learned that the larger the value of $|a|$, the "narrower" the parabola; and, the smaller the value of $|a|$, the "wider" the parabola.

We shall now broaden our scope by examining the graphs of a more general type of quadratic function, namely $\{(x, y) \mid y = ax^2 + p\}$. Our problem is basically one of determining the effect of the addition of a real number p to ax^2 in the defining equation of the type $y = ax^2$, which we considered previously. Observation of the graphs of several instances will be instructive. Let

$$F_1 = \{(x, y) \,|\, y = x^2\}$$
$$F_2 = \{(x, y) \,|\, y = x^2 + 2\}$$
$$F_3 = \{(x, y) \,|\, y = x^2 - 3\}$$

Some of the ordered pairs belonging to F_1, F_2, and F_3, respectively, are given in the following tables. Verify that each ordered pair is a member of the given function.

F_1:

x	-2	-1	0	1	2
y	4	1	0	1	4

F_2:

x	-2	-1	0	1	2
y	6	3	2	3	6

F_3:

x	-2	-1	0	1	2
y	1	-2	-3	-2	1

In figure 3, the graphs of F_2 and F_3 are contrasted with the graph of F_1.

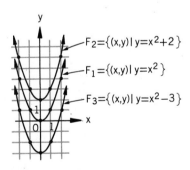

Fig. 3

Notice that each point of the graph of $F_2 = \{(x, y) \,|\, y = x^2 + 2\}$ is two units above some point of the graph of $F_1 = \{(x, y) \,|\, y = x^2\}$; on the other hand, each point of the graph of $F_3 = \{(x, y) \,|\, y = x^2 - 3\}$ is three units below some point of $F_1 = \{(x, y) \,|\, y = x^2\}$. In other words, if the graph of $F_1 = \{(x, y) \,|\, y = x^2\}$ is shifted up two units, you obtain the graph of $F_2 = \{(x, y) \,|\, y = x^2 + 2\}$. If the graph of $F_1 = \{(x, y) \,|\, y = x^2\}$ is shifted down three units, you obtain the graph of $F_3 = \{(x, y) \,|\, y = x^2 - 3\}$.

Now let us contrast the graphs of $\{(x, y) | y = -x^2 + 2\}$ and $\{(x, y) | y = -x^2 - 1\}$ with the graph of $\{(x, y) | y = -x^2\}$.

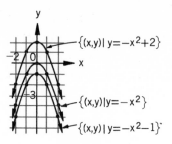

Fig. 4

Describe, in a way similar to that above, the graphs of $\{(x, y) | y = -x^2 + 2\}$ and $\{(x, y) | y = -x^2 - 1\}$ in relation to the graph of $\{(x, y) | y = -x^2\}$.

After you study the above examples and graph a few more instances of $y = ax^2 + p$, you should conclude that, for real number replacements of a and p, the graph of $\{(x, y) | y = ax^2 + p\}$ is the graph of $\{(x, y) | y = ax^2\}$ shifted $|p|$ units vertically. If $p > 0$, the parabola is shifted upward; if $p < 0$, the parabola is shifted downward. What can you say about the axis of symmetry of each parabola which is a graph of a quadratic function of the type $\{(x, y) | y = ax^2 + p\}$? About the vertex?

EXERCISES

1. True or false?
   a. The vertex of the parabola which is the graph of $\{(x, y) | y = 2x^2\}$ is the origin.
   b. The pair of coordinates of the vertex of the graph of $\{(x, y) | y = 2x^2 + 2\}$ is $(2, 0)$.
   c. The pair of coordinates of the vertex of the graph of $\{(x, y) | y = \frac{1}{2}x^2 - 2\}$ is $(0, -2)$.
   d. The pair of coordinates of the vertex of the graph of $\{(x, f(x)) | f(x) = -2x^2 + 3\}$ is $(0, 3)$.
   e. The pair of coordinates of the vertex of the graph of $\{(x, y) | y + 4 = -x^2\}$ is $(0, 4)$.
   f. An equation of the axis of the graph of $\{(x, y) | y = x^2 - 1\}$ is $x = 1$.
   g. The graph of $\{(x, y) | y = x^2 + 1\}$ opens upward.
   h. The graph of $\{(x, y) | y = x^2 - 1\}$ opens downward.
   i. The graph of $\{(x, y) | y = -x^2 + 2\}$ opens upward.
   j. The graph of $\{(x, y) | y = -x^2 - 2\}$ opens downward.

2. Graph each of the following quadratic functions. In each instance, determine whether the function has a minimum value or a maximum value and what that value is. Also, give the coordinates of the vertex and an equation of the axis of symmetry of each parabola.

$$3 + -2 = 1$$

$$-3 + -2 = -5$$

$$\frac{h}{h} \cdot \frac{h}{h} \cdot \frac{1}{1}$$

$$= \frac{h}{s} - \frac{h}{h} + \frac{h}{1} = \frac{1}{h}$$

$$= \frac{1}{1} + \frac{h}{1} - \frac{e}{1} \cdot \frac{e}{1}$$

$f(-3)$ $4 \cdot (-3) - 1 = -13$ ✓

(-1) $4(-1) - 1 = -5$ ✓

(-2) $4(-2) - 1 = -9$ ✓ $\boxed{x \leq}$

(1) $4(1) - 1 = 3$ ✗

(3) $4(3) - 1 = 11$ ✗

(-3) $3(-3) + 2 = -7$ ✗

(-1) $3(-1) + 2 = -1$

(-2) $3(-2) + 2 = -4$

(1) $3(1) + 2 = 5$

(3) $3(3) + 2 = 11$

$\boxed{x > -2}$

a. $\{(x, y) \mid y = 2x^2 + 1\}$

b. $\left\{(x, y) \mid y = \dfrac{1}{2}x^2 - 1\right\}$

c. $g = \{(x, g(x)) \mid g(x) = -2x^2 + 3\}$

d. $\{(x, x^2 - 4)\}$

e. $\{(x, y) \mid 4y + x^2 = 2\}$

3. Determine the domain and the range of the quadratic functions specified in

    a. Problem **2a.**   **c.** Problem **2c.**   **e.** Problem **2e.**

    b. Problem **2b.**   **d.** Problem **2d.**

4. Graph.

    a. $\{(x, y) \mid y = (x - 1)^2\}$ **c.** $\{(x, y) \mid y = -(x - 3)^2\}$

    b. $\{(x, y) \mid y = (x + 1)^2\}$ **d.** $\{(x, y) \mid y = (x + 3)^2\}$

5. If $y(x) = 2(x - 1)^2 + 1$, find

    a. $y(1)$ **h.** $y(4)$

    b. $y(-1)$ **i.** $y(2)$

    c. $y(0)$ **j.** $y(4) + y(2)$

    d. $y(3)$ **k.** $y(4 + 2)$

    e. $y(-3)$ **l.** $\dfrac{y(5) - y(2)}{(5) - (2)}$

    f. $y(3a)$ **m.** $\dfrac{y(t + 3) - y(t)}{(t + 3) - (t)}$

    g. $y(t + 3)$ **n.** $\dfrac{y(t + 11) - y(t)}{(t + 11) - (t)}$

QUADRATIC FUNCTIONS OF THE TYPE $\{(x, y) \mid y = a(x - k)^2\}$

Another special class of quadratic functions is one whose members are defined by equations of the form $y = a(x^2 - 2kx + k^2)$ or, more simply, $y = a(x - k)^2$, $a \neq 0$. For example, each of the equations

$$y = x^2 - 8x + 16 = (x - 4)^2$$
$$y = 2x^2 + 4x + 2 = 2(x + 1)^2 = 2[x - (-1)]^2$$
$$y = \tfrac{1}{2}x^2 - 2x + 2 = \tfrac{1}{2}(x - 2)^2$$

defines a quadratic function of this type.

Our study of quadratic functions of the type $\{(x, y) \mid y = a(x - k)^2\}$ will consist of two basic investigations: first, we seek a relationship among the graphs of members of this class whose defining equations differ only in the value of k; and second, we shall look for a relationship among the graphs of the members of this class which differ only in the value of a. Pursuing our first objective, let us graph three examples of $\{(x, y) \mid y = a(x - k)^2\}$ all of which have a common value of a, namely 1. Let

$$G_1 = \{(x, y) \mid y = (x - 3)^2\}$$
$$G_2 = \{(x, y) \mid y = (x - 8)^2\}$$
$$G_3 = \{(x, y) \mid y = (x + 6)^2\}$$

Some of the ordered pairs belonging to G_1, G_2, and G_3, respectively, are tabulated below. Check to see that each ordered pair belongs to the specified function.

G_1:

x	1	2	3	4	5
y	4	1	0	1	4

G_2:

x	6	7	8	9	10
y	4	1	0	1	4

G_3:

x	-8	-7	-6	-5	-4
y	4	1	0	1	4

The graphs of G_1, G_2, and G_3 are displayed in figure 5.

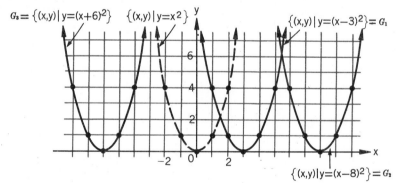

Fig. 5

For purposes of comparison, the familiar graph of $y = x^2$ is included (dashed marking) in figure 5. Notice that each point of the graph of $\{(x, y) \mid y = (x - 3)^2\}$ is precisely *three* units to the *right* of a point of the graph of $\{(x, y) \mid y = x^2\}$; that each point of the graph of $\{(x, y) \mid y = (x - 8)^2\}$ is precisely *eight* units to the *right* of a point of the graph of $\{(x, y) \mid y = x^2\}$; and that each point of the graph of $\{(x, y) \mid y = (x + 6)^2\}$ is precisely *six* units to the *left* of a point of the graph of $\{(x, y) \mid y = x^2\}$. In other words, you can visualize the graph of $\{(x, y) \mid y = (x - 3)^2\}$ as being the graph of $\{(x, y) \mid y = x^2\}$ shifted *three* units to the *right;* the graph of $\{(x, y) \mid y = (x - 8)^2\}$ as being the graph of $\{(x, y) \mid y = x^2\}$ shifted *eight* units to the *right;* and the graph of $\{(x, y) \mid y = (x + 6)^2\}$ as the graph of $\{(x, y) \mid y = x^2\}$ shifted *six* units to the *left.*

On the basis of the above observations, describe the graph of $\{(x, y) \mid y = (x - 1)^2\}$ in relation to the graph of $\{(x, y) \mid y = x^2\}$. Graph $\{(x, y) \mid y = (x - 1)^2\}$ and make sure that your description was correct. Similarly describe the graph of

$\{(x, y) \mid y = (x + 2)^2\}$ in relation to the graph of $\{(x, y) \mid y = x^2\}$. Verify your description by graphing $\{(x, y) \mid y = (x + 2)^2\}$.

Pursuing our second objective, the graphs of three instances of $\{(x, y) \mid y = a(x - k)^2\}$ all of which have the same value of k, namely 5, are displayed in figure 6 below.

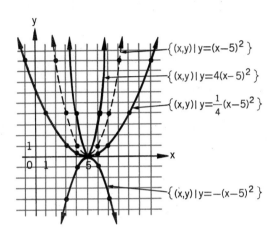

Fig. 6

The dashed marking pictures the graph of $\{(x, y) \mid y = (x - 5)^2\}$, and is included for purposes of comparison. What do you notice about the axes of symmetry of the graphs of $\{(x, y) \mid y = 4(x - 5)^2\}$, $\{(x, y) \mid y = \frac{1}{4}(x - 5)^2\}$ and $\{(x, y) \mid y = -(x - 5)^2\}$? What do you observe about the vertices of these graphs? Notice also that the graph of:

$\{(x, y) \mid y = 4(x - 5)^2\}$ is "narrower" than that of $\{(x, y) \mid y = (x - 5)^2\}$;

$\{(x, y) \mid y = \frac{1}{4}(x - 5)^2\}$ is "wider" than that of $\{(x, y) \mid y = (x - 5)^2\}$;

$\{(x, y) \mid y = -(x - 5)^2\}$ is the "mirror reflection" in the x-axis of the graph of $\{(x, y) \mid y = (x - 5)^2\}$.

On the basis of the above observations, describe the graph of $\{(x, y) \mid y = 3(x - 5)^2\}$ in relation to the graph of $\{(x, y) \mid y = (x - 5)^2\}$. Do the same for $\{(x, y) \mid y = \frac{1}{3}(x - 5)^2\}$. Verify each description by graphing the function.

If you study the above examples and graph more instances of $\{(x, y) \mid y = a(x - k)^2\}$, you should arrive at these conclusions.

    i. The graph of $\{(x, y) \mid y = a(x - k)^2\}$ is the graph $\{(x, y) \mid y = ax^2\}$ shifted $|k|$ units to the right or left, depending on whether $k > 0$ or $k < 0$, respectively.

    ii. The vertex of the graph of $\{(x, y) \mid y = a(x - k)^2\}$ has the coordinates $(k, 0)$.

    iii. If $a > 0$, the graph opens upward; if $a < 0$, the graph opens downward.

EXERCISES

1. True or false?

    a. The vertex of the graph of $\{(x, y) \mid y = (x - 1)^2\}$ is the point whose coordinates are $(1, 0)$.

    b. The pair of coordinates of the vertex of the graph of $\{(x, y) \mid y = 2(x - 1)^2\}$ is $(2, 0)$.

    c. The pair of coordinates of the vertex of the graph of $\{(x, y) \mid y = 3(x + 2)^2\}$ is $(-2, 0)$.

    d. The pair of coordinates of the vertex of the graph of $\{(x, y) \mid y = -2(x + 3)^2\}$ is $(3, 0)$.

    e. An equation of the axis of symmetry of the graph of $\{(x, y) \mid y = \frac{1}{2}(x - 3)^2\}$ is $x = \frac{1}{2}$.

    f. An equation of the axis of symmetry of the graph of $\{(x, y) \mid y = -\frac{1}{2}(x + 3)^2\}$ is $y = -3$.

    g. The graph of $\{(x, y) \mid y = -2(x - 4)^2\}$ is the mirror reflection in the x-axis of the graph of $\{(x, y) \mid y = 2(x - 4)^2\}$.

    h. The graph of $\{(x, y) \mid y = -\frac{1}{4}(x + 4)^2\}$ opens downward.

    i. The graph of $\{(x, y) \mid y = \frac{1}{2}(x + 1)^2\}$ opens upward and has the same axis of symmetry and the same vertex as the graph of $\{(x, y) \mid y = (x + 1)^2\}$, but is a wider parabola.

    j. The quadratic function $\{(x, y) \mid y = \frac{1}{3}(x - 2)^2\}$ has zero for its minimum value.

2. Graph each of the following quadratic functions. In each instance, determine whether the function has a minimum value or a maximum value and what that value is. Also, give the coordinates of the vertex and an equation of the axis of symmetry of each parabola. In each problem, plot at least five points before drawing the graph.

    a. $\left\{(x, y) \mid y = \dfrac{1}{2}(x - 4)^2\right\}$ **f.** $\left\{(x, y) \mid \dfrac{1}{3}y = (x - 5)^2\right\}$

    b. $\{(x, y) \mid y = -2(x - 1)^2\}$ **g.** $\{(x, (x - 7)^2)\}$

    c. $\{(x, y) \mid y = 2(x + 1)^2\}$ **h.** $\{(x, -(x + 2)^2)\}$

    d. $\left\{(x, y) \mid y = \dfrac{1}{4}(x + 4)^2\right\}$ **i.** $\{(x, y) \mid y = x^2 + 12x + 36\}$

    e. $\left\{(x, y) \mid y = -\dfrac{1}{3}(x + 2)^2\right\}$ **j.** $f = \left\{(x, f(x)) \mid f(x) = -x^2 + x - \dfrac{1}{4}\right\}$

3. Graph $\{(x, y) \mid y = (x - 4)^2\}$ and then graph each of the following quadratic functions on the same set of axes.

    a. $\{(x, y) \mid y = (x - 4)^2 + 1\}$ **c.** $\{(x, y) \mid y = (x - 4)^2 + 4\}$

    b. $\{(x, y) \mid y = (x - 4)^2 - 1\}$ **d.** $\{(x, y) \mid y = (x - 4)^2 - 4\}$

4. Graph $\{(x, y) \mid y = (x + 2)^2\}$ and then graph each of the following quadratic functions on the same set of axes.

    a. $\{(x, y) \mid y = (x + 2)^2 + 2\}$ **b.** $\{(x, y) \mid y = (x + 2)^2 - 2\}$

THE GENERAL CASE

We have learned, in the preceding sections, that for specified values of a, p, and k,

i. the graph of $\{(x,y)\,|\,y = ax^2 + p\}$ may be visualized as the graph of $\{(x,y)\,|\,y = ax^2\}$ shifted $|p|$ units up or down, according to whether $p > 0$ or $p < 0$, respectively;

ii. the graph of $\{(x,y)\,|\,y = a(x-k)^2\}$ may be visualized as the graph of $\{(x,y)\,|\,y = ax^2\}$ shifted $|k|$ units to the right or left, according to whether $k > 0$ or $k < 0$, respectively.

We shall now attempt to graph quadratic functions of the more general type $\{(x,y)\,|\,y = a(x-k)^2 + p,\ a \neq 0\}$. To begin, let us examine one instance, say $A = \{(x,y)\,|\,y = \frac{1}{2}(x-3)^2 + 1\}$, and compare this function with the function $B = \{(x,y)\,|\,y = \frac{1}{2}(x-3)^2\}$. Some of the ordered pairs belonging to functions A and B, respectively, are given in the following tables.

A:

x	1	2	3	4	5
y	3	$1\frac{1}{2}$	1	$1\frac{1}{2}$	3

B:

x	1	2	3	4	5
y	2	$\frac{1}{2}$	0	$\frac{1}{2}$	2

If we focus our attention on the second components of two ordered pairs, one from A and one from B, which have the same first component, we observe that in every case the second component of the ordered pair in A is precisely *one* greater than that in B. This means that the graph of $A = \{(x,y)\,|\,y = \frac{1}{2}(x-3)^2 + 1\}$ can be visualized (see figure 7) as the graph of $B = \{(x,y)\,|\,y = \frac{1}{2}(x-3)^2\}$ shifted up one unit. Similarly, the graph of $\{(x,y)\,|\,y = \frac{1}{2}(x-3)^2 + 4\}$ can be visualized as the graph of $\{(x,y)\,|\,y = \frac{1}{2}(x-3)^2\}$ shifted up four units; and the graph of $\{(x,y)\,|\,y = \frac{1}{2}(x-3)^2 - 5\}$ might be visualized as the graph of $\{(x,y)\,|\,y = \frac{1}{2}(x-3)^2\}$ shifted down five units. Study figure 7.

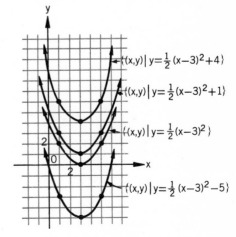

Fig. 7

Graph more instances of $\{(x, y)\,|\,y = a(x - k)^2 + p\}$. You should conclude that for specified values of a and k, the graph of $\{(x, y)\,|\,y = a(x - k)^2 + p\}$ may be visualized as the graph of $\{(x, y)\,|\,y = a(x - k)^2\}$ shifted $|p|$ units up or down depending on whether $p > 0$ or $p < 0$, respectively.

Examples: i. Graph each of the following quadratic functions on the same coordinate system.

$$A_1 = \{(x, y)\,|\,y = x^2\}$$
$$A_2 = \{(x, y)\,|\,y = (x - 2)^2\}$$
$$A_3 = \{(x, y)\,|\,y = (x - 2)^2 - 1\}$$

We begin by obtaining some of the ordered pairs belonging to A_1, A_2, and A_3, respectively.

A_1:

x	-2	-1	0	1	2
y	4	1	0	1	4

A_2:

x	0	1	2	3	4
y	4	1	0	1	4

A_3:

x	0	1	2	3	4
y	3	0	-1	0	3

The graphs of A_1, A_2, and A_3 are now easy to obtain.

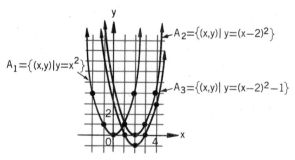

Notice that the graph of A_2 may be visualized as the graph of A_1 shifted two units to the right; and the graph of A_3 may be visualized as the graph of A_2 shifted one unit down.

ii. Graph each of the following quadratic functions on the same coordinate system.

$$B_1 = \{(x, y) \mid y = 2x^2\}$$
$$B_2 = \{(x, y) \mid y = 2(x + 1)^2\}$$
$$B_3 = \{(x, y) \mid y = 2(x + 1)^2 + 3\}$$

Some of the ordered pairs belonging to B_1, B_2, and B_3, respectively, are tabulated below.

B_1:

x	-2	-1	0	1	2
y	8	2	0	2	8

B_2:

x	-3	-2	-1	0	1
y	8	2	0	2	8

B_3:

x	-3	-2	-1	0	1
y	11	5	3	5	11

The graphs of B_1, B_2, and B_3 are as follows:

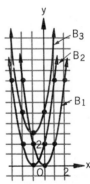

Notice that the graph of B_2 may be visualized as the graph of B_1 shifted one unit to the left; and the graph of B_3 may be visualized as the graph of B_2 shifted three units up.

iii. Graph each of the following quadratic functions on the same coordinate system.

$$K_1 = \left\{(x, y) \mid y = -\frac{1}{2}x^2\right\}$$
$$K_2 = \left\{(x, y) \mid y = -\frac{1}{2}(x + 3)^2\right\}$$
$$K_3 = \left\{(x, y) \mid y = -\frac{1}{2}(x + 3)^2 + 4\right\}$$

The following are some of the ordered pairs belonging to K_1, K_2, and K_3, respectively

K_1:

x	-2	-1	0	1	2
y	-2	$-\frac{1}{2}$	0	$-\frac{1}{2}$	-2

K_2:

x	-5	-4	-3	-2	-1
y	-2	$-\frac{1}{2}$	0	$-\frac{1}{2}$	-2

K_3:

x	-5	-4	-3	-2	-1
y	2	$3\frac{1}{2}$	4	$3\frac{1}{2}$	2

The graphs of K_1, K_2, and K_3 are as follows:

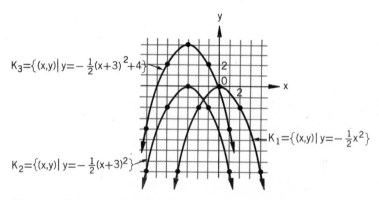

$K_3 = \{(x,y) \mid y = -\frac{1}{2}(x+3)^2 + 4\}$

$K_1 = \{(x,y) \mid y = -\frac{1}{2}x^2\}$

$K_2 = \{(x,y) \mid y = -\frac{1}{2}(x+3)^2\}$

Observe that the graph of K_2 may be visualized as the graph of K_1 shifted three units to the left; and the graph of K_3 may be visualized as the graph of K_2 shifted four units up.

EXERCISES

1. True or false?

   a. The vertex of the parabola, which is the graph of $\{(x, y) \mid y = (x - 4)^2 + 2\}$, is $(-4, 2)$.

   b. The vertex of the parabola, which is the graph of $\{(x, y) \mid y = 3(x - 5)^2 - 2\}$, is $(5, 2)$.

   c. The vertex of the parabola, which is the graph of $\{(x, y) \mid y = 2x^2 + 7\}$, is $(2, 7)$.

   d. The vertex of the parabola, which is the graph of $\{(x, y) \mid y = -3x^2 + 4\}$, is $(0, 4)$.

e. The vertex of the parabola, which is the graph of $\{(x, y) \,|\, y = -2(x - 3)^2\}$, is $(-2, 3)$.

f. An equation of the axis of symmetry of the parabola, which is the graph of $\{(x, y) \,|\, y = -3(x - 6)^2 + 1\}$, is $x = 1$.

g. An equation of the axis of symmetry of the parabola, which is the graph of $\{(x, y) \,|\, y = 3(x - \frac{1}{2})^2 + 4\}$, is $x = \frac{1}{2}$.

h. An equation of the axis of symmetry of the parabola, which is the graph of $\{(x, y) \,|\, y = -(x + 2)^2 + 1\}$, is $x = -2$.

i. The graph of $\{(x, y) \,|\, y = (x - 3)^2 - 1\}$ opens down.

j. The graph of $\{(x, y) \,|\, y = 4(x + 2)^2 - 3\}$ opens up.

2. Graph each of the following quadratic functions. Then, in each case, give

     i. the domain and range of the function

     ii. the coordinates of the vertex of the parabola

     iii. an equation of the axis of symmetry of the parabola

a. $\{(x, y) \,|\, y = (x - 2)^2 + 3\}$

b. $\{(x, y) \,|\, y = -(x + 3)^2 - 2\}$

c. $\{(x, y) \,|\, y = \frac{1}{2}(x + 5)^2 + 4\}$

d. $\{(x, y) \,|\, y = -2(x - 1)^2 - 3\}$

e. $\{(x, -(x + \frac{1}{2})^2 + 2)\}$

f. $\{(x, y) \,|\, y = 2(x + 4)^2 - 2\}$

g. $\{(x, y) \,|\, y = -\frac{1}{2}(x - 4)^2 + 3\}$

h. $\{(x, y) \,|\, y = 3(x + 3)^2 + 1\}$

i. $\{(x, y) \,|\, y = -3(x - 2)^2 - 1\}$

j. $\{(x, y) \,|\, y = \frac{1}{2}[(x + 1)^2 + 4]\}$

3. Graph the *inverse* of each of the following quadratic functions.

a. $f = \{(x, y) \,|\, y = (x + 2)^2 + 2\}$

b. $g = \{(x, g(x)) \,|\, g(x) = 2(x - 1)^2 - 4\}$

c. $F = \{(x, F(x)) \,|\, F(x) = -(x - 4)^2 - 2\}$

d. $G = \{(x, y) \,|\, y = -\frac{1}{2}(x + 2)^2 + 2\}$

4. If $(1, \frac{3}{2})$ is an element of the quadratic function $\{(x, y) \,|\, y = (x - 2)^2 + p\}$, then what is the value of p?

COMPLETING THE SQUARE

We are now ready to take the final step toward obtaining, in a quick way, the graph of any quadratic function. Recall that a function Q is a quadratic function if and only if Q is specified by an equation of the form $y = ax^2 + bx + c$, $a \neq 0$. Every equation of the form $y = ax^2 + bx + c$ can be expressed in an equivalent form $y = a(x - k)^2 + p$, a fact that we shall prove later in this section. Meanwhile, to obtain some insight, let us examine a few special instances. As a first example, consider the function $F = \{(x, y) \,|\, y = x^2 - 8x + 16\}$.

Since $\forall_x \; x^2 - 8x + 16 = (x - 4)^2$, it follows that

$$F = \{(x, y) \,|\, y = (x - 4)^2\}$$

Notice that $y = (x - 4)^2$ is an instance of the set of equations of the type $y = a(x - k)^2 + p$, where $a = 1$, $k = 4$ and $p = 0$.

As a second example, consider the function $f = \{(x, y) \,|\, y = 2x^2 + 8x + 8\}$. Since $\forall_x \; 2x^2 + 8x + 8 = 2(x^2 + 4x + 4) = 2(x + 2)^2$, it follows that

$$f = \{(x, y) \,|\, y = 2(x + 2)^2\}$$

Is the equation $y = 2(x + 2)^2$ an instance of the set of equations of the type $y = a(x - k)^2 + p$? If so, what are the values of a, k, and p?

Now let us turn our attention to a more complicated example, say $g = \{(x, y) \,|\, y = x^2 - 6x + 7\}$. We can determine the desired equivalent form of the defining equation $y = x^2 - 6x + 7$ by using the procedure called *completing the square*. In the case of $y = x^2 - 6x + 7$, it is done as follows:

$$
\begin{aligned}
y &= x^2 - 6x + 7 \\
&= (x^2 - 6x \quad\;) + 7 \\
&= (x^2 - 6x + 9) + 7 - 9 \\
&= (x - 3)^2 - 2
\end{aligned}
$$

Notice that in the first step we simply separated the term "7" from the terms involving "x." Then we determined what must be added to $x^2 - 6x$ to produce a perfect square trinomial in x, the answer being 9. Adding and subtracting 9, as indicated in the second step, produced an equivalent expression which, in turn, gave the desired form. Thus, we see that

$$\{(x, y) \,|\, y = x^2 - 6x + 7\} = \{(x, y) \,|\, y = (x - 3)^2 - 2\}$$

As a fourth example, consider $\{(x, y) \,|\, y = 3x^2 + 12x + 16\}$. The steps in obtaining the desired equivalent form of the defining equation $y = 3x^2 + 12x + 16$ are these.

$$
\begin{aligned}
y &= 3x^2 + 12x + 16 \\
&= (3x^2 + 12x \quad\;) + 16 \\
&= 3(x^2 + 4x \quad\;) + 16 \\
&= 3(x^2 + 4x + 4) + 16 - 12 \\
&= 3(x + 2)^2 + 4
\end{aligned}
$$

Notice that adding 4 to $x^2 + 4x$ was equivalent to adding 12 to the right-hand member of the equation which accounts for the subtraction of 12. Explain why this is so. We conclude that

$$\{(x, y) \,|\, y = 3x^2 + 12x + 16\} = \{(x, y) \,|\, y = 3(x + 2)^2 + 4\}$$

In each of the above examples we considered a quadratic function defined by an equation of the form $y = ax^2 + bx + c$, and derived an equivalent equation of the form $y = a(x - k)^2 + p$; that this can always be done is shown in the proof of the following theorem.

Theorem   For all real numbers a, b, c, and x $(a \neq 0)$,
$$ax^2 + bx + c = a(x - k)^2 + p \quad \text{where}$$
$$k = -\frac{b}{2a} \text{ and } p = \frac{4ac - b^2}{4a}$$

Proof (Justify each step of the proof.)

$$ax^2 + bx + c = (ax^2 + bx \qquad) + c$$

$$= a\left(x^2 + \frac{b}{a}x \qquad\right) + c$$

$$= a\left(x^2 + \frac{b}{a}x + \frac{b^2}{4a^2}\right) + c - \frac{b^2}{4a}$$

$$= a\left(x + \frac{b}{2a}\right)^2 + \left(c - \frac{b^2}{4a}\right)$$

$$= a\left[x - \left(-\frac{b}{2a}\right)\right]^2 + \left(\frac{4ac - b^2}{4a}\right)$$

$$= a(x - k)^2 + p$$

As a result of this theorem we conclude that every quadratic function $\{(x, y)\,|\,y = ax^2 + bx + c\} = \{(x, y)\,|\,y = a(x - k)^2 + p\}$ where $k = -\dfrac{b}{2a}$ and $p = \dfrac{4ac - b^2}{4a}$. We also conclude that, for all real numbers a, b, and c, $a \neq 0$, the graph of $\{(x, y)\,|\,y = ax^2 + bx + c\}$ is a parabola.

EXERCISES

1. True or false?

a. The vertex of the parabola, which is the graph of
$$\left\{(x, y)\,|\,y = (x - 3)^2 + \frac{1}{2}\right\}, \text{ is } \left(3, \frac{1}{2}\right).$$

b. The vertex of the parabola, which is the graph of $\{(x, y)\,|\,y = 2(x + 3)^2 + 4\}$, is $(-3, 4)$.

c. The vertex of the parabola, which is the graph of
$$\left\{(x, y)\,|\,y = \frac{1}{2}(x + 5)^2\right\}, \text{ is } (0, -5).$$

d. The parabola, described by $\{(x, y)\,|\,y = -\frac{1}{2}(x - 1)^2 + 1\}$, opens down.

e. The equation $y = 2x^2 - 4x + 5$ is equivalent to the equation $y = 2(x^2 - 2x + 1) + 5$.

f. $\{(x, y)\,|\,y = x^2 - 6x + 10\} = \{(x, y)\,|\,y = (x - 3)^2 + 1\}$.

g. $\{(x, y)\,|\,y = 2(x - 1)^2 - 3\} = \{(x, y)\,|\,y = 2x^2 - 2x - 3\}$.

h. $\left\{\left(x, x^2 - x + \frac{1}{4}\right)\right\} = \left\{\left(x, \left(x - \frac{1}{2}\right)^2\right)\right\}$.

i. The quadratic function $\{(x, y)\,|\,y = -(x - 4)^2 + 3\}$ has a minimum value.

j. The maximum value of the quadratic function $\{(x, y)\,|\,y = -2(x + 4)^2 + 3\}$ is 3.

2. Use the "completing the square" method of the present section to write an equivalent equation of the form $y = a(x \pm r)^2 + t$, for some real numbers a, r, and t.

a. $y = x^2 + 2x + 3$

e. $y = -x^2 + 6x$

b. $y = x^2 + 3x + 1$

f. $y = 4 - x - \dfrac{1}{2}x^2$

c. $y = 2x^2 + 4x - 5$

g. $y = -4x - x^2$

d. $y = 3x^2 - 3x - 3$

h. $y = \dfrac{x^2}{4} - \dfrac{x}{2} + 1$

3. Graph each of the following quadratic functions. In each case, give

  i. the domain and range of the function

  ii. the coordinates of the vertex of the parabola

  iii. an equation of the axis of symmetry of the parabola

a. $\{(x, y) | y = x^2 - 2x + 1\}$

e. $\{(x, y) | y = 2x^2 - 12x + 19\}$

b. $\left\{\left(x, \dfrac{1}{2}x^2 + 2x + 4\right)\right\}$

f. $\{(x, x - x^2)\}$

c. $\{(x, y) | y + 2x^2 + 8 = 8x\}$

g. $\{(x, y) | y = -(2x^2 + 16x + 33)\}$

d. $\{(x, y) | y = -x^2 - 4x - 7\}$

h. $\{(x, 2x^2 - 2x + 1)\}$

4. Solve the following "challenge" problems.

  a. If the ordered pairs $(2, -7)$ and $(-1, 2)$ belong to the quadratic function $\{(x, y) | y = -x^2 + bx + c\}$, then what are the values of b and c?

  b. Determine whether the quadratic function $\{(x, y) | 4y + x^2 - 12x + 45 = 0\}$ has a maximum value or a minimum value, and what that value is.

  c. Write an equation which defines the quadratic function Q that meets both of the following conditions.

  i. the vertex of the parabola, which is the graph of Q, is the point whose coordinates are $(2, 8)$.

  ii. the ordered pair $(0, 0)$ belongs to Q.

APPLICATIONS OF QUADRATIC FUNCTIONS

Quadratic functions describe many situations in the world around us. Let us consider several sample problems which may be solved by using quadratic functions. Consider the following problem.

If an object is thrown vertically into the air, its distance d above the ground at any moment depends, among other things, on the elapsed time t. Let us suppose that, in a particular case, a ball is thrown into the air in such a way that its distance d (in feet) above the ground at any time t (in seconds) is given by the equation $d = 80t - 16t^2$. Notice that this equation defines a quadratic function, namely $D = \{(t, 80t - 16t^2)\}$. Some of the ordered pairs belonging to D are tabulated.

t	0	1	2	3	4	5
d	0	64	96	96	64	0

Plotting these points and drawing a smooth curve through them we obtain the graph of D.

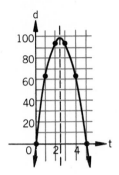

Observe that none of the tabulated points is the vertex of the parabola. By symmetry, however, we see that the first coordinate of the vertex must be $2\frac{1}{2}$, and hence the second coordinate is $80 \cdot \frac{5}{2} - 16 \cdot (\frac{5}{2})^2 = 100$. We conclude that the maximum height (above the ground) attained by the ball is 100 feet; the time required for the ball to reach its maximum height is $2\frac{1}{2}$ seconds; and the ball remains in the air for a total of 5 seconds. Notice that the "realistic" domain of the above function is $\{t | 0 \leq t \leq 5\}$ rather than the set of all real numbers. Similarly, the "realistic" range of the function is $\{d | 0 \leq d \leq 100\}$.

This problem illustrates a situation that occurs frequently in applications of mathematics, namely that the domain and range of a function used as a mathematical model of a *physical* situation are often proper subsets of what they would be in a purely mathematical discussion.

The following problem also involves finding a maximum value.

A rectangular field beside a river is to be fenced in. No fence is needed along the river bank. What are the dimensions of the field of greatest area which can be fenced in using 80 feet of fencing?

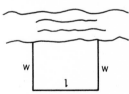

When solving this problem consider the picture adjoining. The conditions of the problem require that $l + 2w = 80$. In the table on the right we list some of the infinitely many possible dimensions along with the corresponding area-measures A.

l	w	$A = l \cdot w$
64	8	512
60	10	600
50	15	750
32	24	768
28	26	728

Evidently there are values of l and w which correspond to a maximum value of A. Our problem is to find these values of l and w. To begin, we know that $l + 2w = 80$ and $A = l \cdot w$. Furthermore, $l + 2w = 80$ is equivalent to $l = 80 - 2w$. Substituting $80 - 2w$ for l in $A = l \cdot w$, we get $A = (80 - 2w)w$, or

$$A = -2w^2 + 80w$$

Notice that this equation defines a quadratic function, namely $Q = \{(w, A) \mid A = -2w^2 + 80w\}$. It will help to obtain the graph of Q. We begin by completing the square in the defining equation.

$$
\begin{aligned}
A &= -2(w^2 - 40w \qquad) \\
&= -2(w^2 - 40w + 400) + 800 \\
&= -2(w - 20)^2 + 800
\end{aligned}
$$

We are now able to obtain the graph of Q.

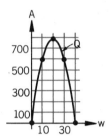

An examination of the graph of Q reveals that the maximum area, which is 800 square feet, is obtained when the width of the field is 20, and hence the length is 40.

Here is another problem which involves a parabola.

An orange grove now has 20 trees per acre, and the average yield is 300 oranges per tree. It is estimated that for each additional tree planted per acre, the average yield per tree will be reduced by 10 oranges. How many trees per acre will give the largest yield of oranges?

In solving this problem, let x be the number of new trees planted per acre; then there are $(20 + x)$ trees per acre having an average yield of $(300 - 10x)$ oranges per tree.

Now if we let y be the total yield of oranges per acre, then we can conclude that for every $x \geq 0$,

$$
\begin{aligned}
y &= (20 + x)(300 - 10x) \\
&= 6000 + 100x - 10x^2
\end{aligned}
$$

We shall now graph the quadratic function

$$S = \{(x, y) \mid y = 6000 + 100x - 10x^2\}$$

To begin, we complete the square in the defining equation.

$$
\begin{aligned}
y &= 6000 + 100x - 10x^2 \\
&= -10(x^2 - 10x \qquad) + 6000 \\
&= -10(x^2 - 10x + 25) + 6000 + 250 \\
&= -10(x - 5)^2 + 6250
\end{aligned}
$$

We are now able to obtain the graph of S.

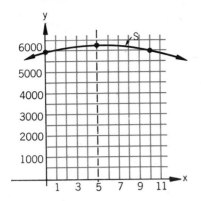

An examination of the graph of S reveals that the maximum yield of 6250 oranges per acre is obtained if the original number of trees per acre, namely 20, is increased by 5; that is, 25 trees per acre will produce the maximum yield of oranges.

EXERCISES

1.   A man has 120 feet of chicken wire and with it he desires to construct a rectangular chicken pen, making use of an existing wall as one side of the pen. Find the dimensions of the pen so that it will have maximum area.

2.   An object is thrown into the air in such a way that its distance d (in feet) above the ground at any time t (in seconds) is given by the equation $d = 64t - 16t^2$.

   a.   Sketch the portion of the graph of the function $\{(t, d)\,|\,d = 64t - 16t^2\}$ that pertains to the given situation.

   b.   From the graph, tell the greatest height attained by the object.

   c.   How many seconds are required for the object to reach its greatest height?

   d.   For how long a period of time is the object in the air?

3.   A farmer estimates that if he harvests his potatoes now, he will have 180 bushels worth \$1.00 per bushel; but if he waits, the crop will increase 30 bushels per week while the price will drop 10 cents per bushel per week. When should he harvest the potatoes in order to obtain the maximum cash return?

4.   A restaurant chain, in planning a new cafeteria, knows from experience that with a seating capacity of 100 or less they can expect a monthly profit of approximately \$20.00 per seat. Within reasonable limits on size, they also know that if the seating capacity grows beyond 100, the monthly profit per seat decreases by 10 cents for each added seat. What seating capacity will give the maximum profit?

5.   A steamboat with capacity of 200 passengers is to be chartered for an excursion. The price of one ticket is to be \$30.00 if 100 people or less buy tickets, but the steamship company agrees to reduce the price of every ticket by 20 cents for each ticket sold in excess of 100. What number of passengers will produce the largest income?

6. Among all the pairs of real numbers whose *sum* is 60, there is a pair whose *product* is greater than the product of every other such pair. Find that pair of real numbers.

7. **a.** Among all the pairs of real numbers whose difference is 10, there is a pair whose product is less than the product of every other such pair. Find that pair of real numbers.

b. Show that there is no pair of numbers with difference of 10 for which the product is the greatest.

VOCABULARY

Use each of the following correctly in a sentence. Numerals in parentheses refer to pages where these words were used. If you are not sure of the meaning of any word, turn to the indicated page.

axis of symmetry (196)   parabola (196)
maximum value (198)   quadratic function (195)
minimum value (198)   vertex (196)

REVIEW EXERCISES

1. True or false?

a. $\{(x, 3x^2)\}$ is a quadratic function.

b. $3x^2 + 1$ is a quadratic polynomial.

c. The graph of $\{(x, y) \mid y = 2x^2 - 1\}$ is symmetric with respect to the x-axis.

d. The graphs of the quadratic functions $A = \{(x, \frac{1}{2}x^2 + 3)\}$ and $B = \{(x, x^2 + 3)\}$ are parabolas which have the same vertex and the same axis of symmetry, but the graph of A is a narrower parabola than the graph of B.

e. The pair of coordinates of the vertex of the graph of $\{(x, y) \mid y = 2(x + 3)^2 + 2\}$ is $(3, 2)$.

f. An equation of the axis of symmetry of the graph of $\{(x, (x - \frac{1}{2})^2 + 1)\}$ is $x = \frac{1}{2}$.

g. The graph of $\{(x, 4 - (x + 2)^2)\}$ opens down.

h. The quadratic function $\{(x, y) \mid y = -(x + 4)^2 + 5\}$ has a maximum value of 5.

i. The quadratic function $\{(x, y) \mid y = \frac{1}{2}(x - 4)^2\}$ has no minimum value.

j. $\{(x, x^2 + \frac{2}{3}x + \frac{1}{9})\} = \{(x, (x + \frac{1}{3})^2)\}$.

2. For each quadratic function specified below, determine

i. the coordinates of the vertex of its graph

ii. an equation of the axis of symmetry of its graph

iii. whether its graph opens upward or downward

iv. whether it has a maximum or a minimum value and

v. the maximum or minimum value

a. $\{(x, y)\,|\,y = 2(x - 1)^2 - 1\}$

b. $\left\{(x, y)\,|\,y = \frac{1}{3}(x + 2)^2 + 4\right\}$

c. $\{(x, -5(x - 7)^2 - 2)\}$

d. $\{(x, 6(x + 3)^2 + 4)\}$

e. $\{(x, y)\,|\,(x + 7)^2 = 2y + 3\}$

f. $\left\{(x, y)\,|\,y = -\left(x + \frac{1}{2}\right)^2 + \frac{1}{2}\right\}$

3. Use the "completing the square" method to express each of the following equations in the form $y = a(x \pm r)^2 \pm t$ for some real numbers a, r, and t.

a. $y = \frac{1}{2}x^2 + 2x - 4$

b. $2 + x^2 = y + 4x$

c. $2x^2 + y = x + \frac{7}{8}$

d. $y = 5x^2 - 5x + \frac{5}{4}$

e. $4y = x^2 - 4x - 8$

f. $x - y = x^2$

4. Graph each of the following quadratic functions. Select an appropriate scale for each axis.

a. $\left\{(x, y)\,|\,y = \frac{1}{2}(x + 2)^2 - 6\right\}$

b. $\left\{(x, y)\,|\,y = 5\left(x - \frac{1}{2}\right)^2\right\}$

c. $\left\{(x, y)\,|\,y = -2\left(x - \frac{1}{4}\right)^2 + 1\right\}$

d. $\{(x, (x - 2)^2 - 2)\}$

e. $\{(x, y)\,|\,y = 4x^2 + 20x + 24\}$

f. $\left\{(x, y)\,|\,y = -\left(x + \frac{1}{3}\right)^2 + 3\right\}$

CHAPTER TEST

1. Define *quadratic function* T as a set of ordered pairs (x, y).

2. A parabola is drawn at the right.

   a. Which point is its vertex: A, B, C, or D?

   b. Which line is its axis of symmetry: L_1, L_2, or the y-axis?

3. Draw the parabola defined by $y = \frac{1}{2}(x - 2)^2 - 3$.

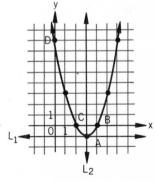

4. True or false?

   a. Every parabola passes the vertical line test for a function.

   b. If $M = \{(x, y)\,|\,y = (x - 2)^2\}$, then for each t in the domain of M, $M(t) = M(-t)$.

   c. The graph of $\{(x, -2x^2)\}$ has the same size and shape as the graph of $\{(x, y)\,|\,y = 2(x - 3)^2 + 5\}$.

d. The maximum value of each quadratic function is the greatest member of its domain provided such a number exists.

e. The minimum value of each quadratic function is the least member of its range provided such a number exists.

f. If $K = \{(x, y) | y = x^2 - 2\}$, then for each r in the domain of K, $K(r) = K(-r)$.

5. Nine relations are described below. Which of them are quadratic functions?

$A = \{(x, y) | y = 3(x + 4)^2 + 6\}$

$B = \{(x, y) | y = [x]^2 + 2\}$ [Recall that $[x]$ means the greatest integer less than or equal to x]

$C = \{(x, y) | 3y = 2x + x^2\}$

$D = \{(x, y) | xy = 4\}$

$E = \{(x, y) | y = 3x - 4\}$

$F = \{(x, y) | y = 3x^2 - 4\}$

$G = \{(x, y) | y = 3(x - 4)^2\}$

$H = \{(x, y) | x^2 + y^2 = 7\}$

$I = \{(x, y) | x^2 + y = 7\}$

6. For each quadratic function specified below, determine *i.* the coordinates of the vertex of the parabola which is its graph; *ii.* whether its graph opens upward or downward; *iii.* whether it has a maximum or a minimum value; and *iv.* what that value is.

a. $\{(x, y) | y = 2(x + 5)^2 + 9\}$

b. $\{(x, y) | 2y = 3x + x^2\}$

c. $\{(x, y) | y = -4x^2 + 6\}$

d. $\{(x, y) | x^2 + y + 8 = 0\}$

7. Express each of the following equations in the form $y = a(x \pm r)^2 \pm t$ for some real numbers a, r, and t.

a. $y = x^2 + 4x + 3$

b. $y = 3x^2 - 5x$

c. $2 + 10x + y = 5x^2$

d. $y = -2x^2 + 6x - 7$

8. Given a function f such that $f(x) = 2x^2 + 3$, compute each of the following. Express your answer in the *simplest* way.

a. $f(5)$

b. $f(-5)$

c. $f(3)$

d. $f(4)$

e. $f(4) - f(3)$

f. $f(4 - 3)$

g. $\dfrac{f(7) - f(2)}{7 - 2}$

h. $\dfrac{f(a + 4) - f(a)}{(a + 4) - a}$

9. A manufacturing concern finds that it makes a profit of $20.00 on each article if 600 or fewer are made each week. The profit decreases by 2 cents per article over 600. How many articles should be produced per week in order to realize maximum profit?

BIBLIOGRAPHY

Heimer, R. T., Kocher, F. and Lottes, J. J. *A Program in Contemporary Algebra.* New York: Holt, Rinehart and Winston, Inc., 1963, Book 4, Unit VII.

School Mathematics Study Group. *Intermediate Mathematics, Part I.* New Haven: Yale University Press, 1961. pp. 203-221.

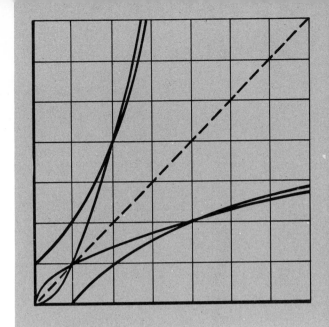

CHAPTER 8

Quadratic Equations and Inequalities

QUADRATIC EQUATIONS

Every equation which patterns in the form

$$ax^2 + bx + c = 0$$

where a, b, and c are real numbers and $a \neq 0$, is called a *quadratic equation.* Each of the following is equivalent to a quadratic equation.

$2x^2 - 3x + 1 = 0$ $\dfrac{x^2}{3} = \dfrac{1}{9}$ $x^2 = 0$

$7 - x^2 = 5x$ $4 - \dfrac{1}{2}x^2 = 0$ $2x^2 - 6 = 0$

$x^2 + 3x = 0$ $7x^2 - 14x = 0$ $x^2 = 6x$

In solving equations such as those above it is often helpful to begin by finding an equivalent equation of the form $ax^2 + bx + c = 0$. Write each of the nine equations above in this form and determine the values of a, b, and c.

To find the solution sets for quadratic equations we shall consider three cases.

221

CASE I: $b = 0$; that is, equations such as $3x^2 - 12 = 0$ and $x^2 + 16 = 0$

CASE II: $c = 0$; that is, equations such as $2x^2 - 5x = 0$ and $-\frac{1}{2}x^2 + 7x = 0$

CASE III: $b \neq 0$ and $c \neq 0$; that is, equations such as $x^2 - 7x + 12 = 0$ and $2x^2 - 5x + 6 = 0$

Do cases I, II, and III cover all possible types of quadratic equations?

In solving quadratic equations for which $b = 0$ (case I), we shall be considering equations which are equivalent to some instance of the equation $x^2 = k$, k a real number. In solving such equations, we make use of the following two theorems.

Theorem 1 $\forall_x\ x^2 \geq 0$

Theorem 2 $\forall_x \forall_{k \geq 0}\ x^2 = k$ if and only if $x = \sqrt{k}$ or $x = -\sqrt{k}$

Examples: i.   Solve $3x^2 + 12 = 0$.

$$3x^2 + 12 = 0$$
$$3x^2 = -12$$
$$x^2 = -4$$

From theorem 1 above, there is no real number x for which $x^2 = -4$. Therefore, the real number solution set of $3x^2 + 12 = 0$ is ϕ.

ii.   Solve $5x^2 - 10 = 0$

$$5x^2 - 10 = 0$$
$$5x^2 = 10$$
$$x^2 = 2$$

From theorem 2 above, $x = \sqrt{2}$ or $x = -\sqrt{2}$. Therefore, the real number solution set of $5x^2 - 10 = 0$ is $\{\sqrt{2}, -\sqrt{2}\}$. Check to see that $\sqrt{2}$ and $-\sqrt{2}$ are solutions of $5x^2 - 10 = 0$.

In solving quadratic equations for which $c = 0$ (case II), we shall be considering equations which are equivalent to some instance of the equation $x^2 + dx = 0$, d a real number. In solving such equations we make use of the following theorem.

Theorem 3 $\forall_a \forall_b\ a \cdot b = 0$ if and only if $a = 0$ or $b = 0$

Example: Solve $3x^2 = 7x$.

$$3x^2 = 7x$$
$$3x^2 - 7x = 0$$
$$x^2 - \frac{7}{3}x = 0$$
$$x\left(x - \frac{7}{3}\right) = 0$$

From theorem 3 above, $x = 0$ or $x - \frac{7}{3} = 0$. Therefore, the real number solution set of $3x^2 = 7x$ is $\{0, \frac{7}{3}\}$.

In solving quadratic equations for which $b \neq 0$ and $c \neq 0$ (case III), we shall be considering equations of the form $ax^2 + bx + c = 0$ where a, b, and c are all non-zero real numbers. For some of these, the left member, $ax^2 + bx + c$, is readily factorable as the product of two binomials in x; others may not be easily factored. If the left member is readily factorable, we again make use of theorem 3.

Examples: i.   Solve $x^2 + 6 = 5x$.

$$x^2 + 6 = 5x$$
$$x^2 - 5x + 6 = 0$$
$$(x - 2)(x - 3) = 0$$

From theorem 3, $x - 2 = 0$ or $x - 3 = 0$. Therefore, the real number solution set of $x^2 + 6 = 5x$ is $\{2, 3\}$.

ii.   Solve $3x^2 + 4x = 4$.

$$3x^2 + 4x = 4$$
$$3x^2 + 4x - 4 = 0$$
$$(3x - 2)(x + 2) = 0$$

From theorem 3 above, $3x - 2 = 0$ or $x + 2 = 0$. Therefore, the real number solution set of $3x^2 + 4x = 4$ is $\{\frac{2}{3}, -2\}$.

iii.   Solve $x^2 + 4 = 4x$.

$$x^2 + 4 = 4x$$
$$x^2 - 4x + 4 = 0$$
$$(x - 2)(x - 2) = 0$$

From theorem 3, $x - 2 = 0$ or $x - 2 = 0$. Therefore, the real number solution set of $x^2 + 4 = 4x$ is $\{2\}$.

Notice that in the examples on pages 222-223 we have found that the real number solution set has been either the empty set, a one-member set, or a two-member set.

EXERCISES

1.   True or false?

  a. The real number solution set of $x^2 + 9 = 0$ is $\{-3, 3\}$.

  b. The real number solution set of $3x^2 - 12 = 0$ is $\{2\}$.

  c. $\forall_x$, if $x^2 - 3 = 0$, then $x = \sqrt{3}$ or $x = -\sqrt{3}$.

  d. $\{r \mid (r + 2)^2 = 0\} = \{-2\}$.

  e. The real number solution set of $x^2 = x$ is $\{1\}$.

  f. $\{x \mid (2x - 1)(x + 2) = 0\} = \{\frac{1}{2}, -2\}$.

  g. $\{x \mid 3x^2 - 2x - 1 = 0\} = \{x \mid (3x - 1)(x + 1) = 0\}$.

  h. If $\{x \mid 2x^2 + x - 6 = 0\} = \{x \mid x^2 + bx - 3 = 0\}$, then $b = \frac{1}{2}$.

  i. If $\{x \mid (x - 4)(x + a) = 0\} = \{4, 2\}$, then $a = 2$.

  j. $\forall_x$, if $(x + 2)^2 = 12$, then $x + 2 = \sqrt{12}$ or $x + 2 = -\sqrt{12}$.

2. Find the real number solution set for each of the following equations.

a. $x^2 - 20 = 0$

b. $24 - 2y^2 = 0$

c. $4x^2 = 49$

d. $2x^2 + 9 = 0$

e. $3t = t^2$

f. $2x^2 = 5x$

g. $3x - 2x^2 = 0$

h. $0 = 4y^2 - \dfrac{1}{4}$

i. $y^2 + 9 = 6y$

j. $6x^2 + 7x - 5 = 0$

k. $-10x + 2x^2 - 28 = 0$

l. $x^2 - \dfrac{5}{3}x - 4 = 0$

[HINT: Use the mult. prop. with 3.]

m. $y^2 + \dfrac{2}{3}y = \dfrac{5}{4}$

n. $x^3 - 9x = 0$

o. $x^3 - 3x^2 - 28x = 0$

THE QUADRATIC FORMULA

Since every quadratic equation is an instance of

$$ax^2 + bx + c = 0 \quad (a \neq 0)$$

we conclude that the solution set of a quadratic equation depends upon the values of a, b, and c. It seems likely, therefore, that the solutions of $ax^2 + bx + c = 0$ may be expressed in terms of a, b, and c. The development of these expressions is our next objective. You should be able to justify each step in the following development.

Proof   For any real numbers a, b, c, and x $(a \neq 0)$

if $ax^2 + bx + c = 0$

then $ax^2 + bx = -c$

$$x^2 + \frac{b}{a}x = -\frac{c}{a}$$

$$x^2 + \frac{b}{a}x + \frac{b^2}{4a^2} = \frac{b^2}{4a^2} - \frac{c}{a}$$

(*) $$\left(x + \frac{b}{2a}\right)^2 = \frac{b^2 - 4ac}{4a^2}$$

Now, if we assume that $\dfrac{b^2 - 4ac}{4a^2} \geq 0$, then we can conclude that

$$x + \frac{b}{2a} = \sqrt{\frac{b^2 - 4ac}{4a^2}} \quad \text{or} \quad x + \frac{b}{2a} = -\sqrt{\frac{b^2 - 4ac}{4a^2}}$$

and therefore

$$x = \frac{-b}{2a} + \frac{\sqrt{b^2 - 4ac}}{|2a|} \quad \text{or} \quad x = \frac{-b}{2a} - \frac{\sqrt{b^2 - 4ac}}{|2a|}$$

Since $|2a| = 2a$ for $a > 0$ and $|2a| = -2a$ for $a < 0$, the solution set is

$$\left\{ \frac{-b}{2a} + \frac{\sqrt{b^2 - 4ac}}{2a}, \ \frac{-b}{2a} - \frac{\sqrt{b^2 - 4ac}}{2a} \right\} \quad \text{for} \quad a > 0$$

and

$$\left\{ \frac{-b}{2a} + \frac{\sqrt{b^2 - 4ac}}{-2a}, \ \frac{-b}{2a} - \frac{\sqrt{b^2 - 4ac}}{-2a} \right\} \quad \text{for} \quad a < 0$$

Show that in either case, $a > 0$ or $a < 0$, the solution set is

$$\left\{ \frac{-b + \sqrt{b^2 - 4ac}}{2a}, \ \frac{-b - \sqrt{b^2 - 4ac}}{2a} \right\}$$

Thus, we have proved that $\forall_{a \neq 0} \forall_b \forall_c$, if $b^2 - 4ac \geq 0$, then

$$\{x \mid ax^2 + bx + c = 0\} = \left\{ \frac{-b + \sqrt{b^2 - 4ac}}{2a}, \ \frac{-b - \sqrt{b^2 - 4ac}}{2a} \right\}$$

Observe that if $b^2 - 4ac = 0$, then $\sqrt{b^2 - 4ac} = 0$, and hence under this condition

$$\{x \mid ax^2 + bx + c = 0\} = \left\{ -\frac{b}{2a} \right\}$$

Now, let us go back and examine equation (*) under the assumption that $b^2 - 4ac < 0$. Notice that

$$\forall_{a \neq 0} \forall_b \forall_x \left(x + \frac{b}{2a} \right)^2 \geq 0$$

and thus the real number solution set of (*) is empty if $b^2 - 4ac < 0$.

These results are summarized in the following theorem.

Theorem 4 (Quadratic Formula Theorem) $\forall_{a \neq 0} \forall_b \forall_c$, if $b^2 - 4ac > 0$, then

$$\{x \mid ax^2 + bx + c = 0\} = \left\{ \frac{-b + \sqrt{b^2 - 4ac}}{2a}, \ \frac{-b - \sqrt{b^2 - 4ac}}{2a} \right\};$$

if $b^2 - 4ac = 0$, then $\{x \mid ax^2 + bx + c = 0\} = \left\{ -\frac{b}{2a} \right\}$; and

if $b^2 - 4ac < 0$, then $\{x \mid ax^2 + bx + c = 0\} = \phi$.

Notice that the value of $b^2 - 4ac$ determines whether the real number solution set of a quadratic equation $ax^2 + bx + c = 0$ has no elements, one element, or two elements; accordingly, $b^2 - 4ac$ is called the *discriminant* of the quadratic equation $ax^2 + bx + c = 0$. In this context, the discriminant $b^2 - 4ac$ is often denoted by the symbol Δ, read "delta".

The following examples illustrate the procedures for applying theorem 4.

Example: *i.*   Solve $2x^2 - x - 5 = 0$.

We see that $2x^2 - x - 5 = 0$ patterns in the desired form, and that $a = 2$, $b = (-1)$ and $c = (-5)$. Hence

$$\Delta = b^2 - 4ac$$
$$= (-1)^2 - 4(2)(-5)$$
$$= 1 + 40 = 41$$

Hence, the solution set for $2x^2 - x - 5 = 0$ is given by

$$\left\{ \frac{-b + \sqrt{b^2 - 4ac}}{2a}, \ \frac{-b - \sqrt{b^2 - 4ac}}{2a} \right\}$$

which is equal to

$$\left\{ \frac{1 + \sqrt{41}}{4}, \ \frac{1 - \sqrt{41}}{4} \right\}$$

Example: *ii.*   Solve $9x^2 + 25 = 30x$.

We begin by writing the equivalent equation $9x^2 - 30x + 25 = 0$ and note that $a = 9$, $b = (-30)$, and $c = 25$.

Hence $\Delta = b^2 - 4ac$
$$= (-30)^2 - 4(9)(25)$$
$$= 900 - 900$$
$$= 0$$

Thus, since the discriminant of $9x^2 + 25 = 30x$ is zero, its solution set is $\{-\frac{30}{2(9)}\} = \{\frac{30}{18}\} = \{\frac{5}{3}\}$.

Example: *iii.*   Solve $3x^2 + 2x + 1 = 0$.

We first observe that $3x^2 + 2x + 1 = 0$ patterns in the form $ax^2 + bx + c = 0$, and that $a = 3$, $b = 2$, and $c = 1$.

Hence $\Delta = b^2 - 4ac$
$$= 2^2 - 4(3)(1)$$
$$= 4 - 12 = -8$$

Since the discriminant of $3x^2 + 2x + 1 = 0$ is less than zero, we conclude that the real number solution set of this equation is ϕ.

You should observe that, while theorem 4 may be employed to solve any quadratic equation, it is often easier to employ the methods of the previous section, when applicable, to find the solution set of a quadratic equation. To be more specific, theorem 4 is most useful in solving instances of

$$ax^2 + bx + c = 0 \quad (a \neq 0)$$

where the polynomial $ax^2 + bx + c$ is not readily factorable.

EXERCISES

1. True or false?

a. For each quadratic equation $ax^2 + bx + c = 0$, if $b^2 - 4ac < 0$, then the equation has no real number solutions.

b. For each quadratic equation $ax^2 + bx + c = 0$, if $b^2 - 4ac = 0$, then the equation has exactly one real root.

c. For each quadratic equation $ax^2 + bx + c = 0$, if $b^2 - 4ac > 0$, then the equation has two real roots.

d. The discriminant of the quadratic equation $x^2 + 3x + 2 = 0$ is $3^2 + 4(2)$.

e. The discriminant of $x^2 + 4x + 3 = 0$ is 4.

f. The discriminant of $x^2 - x = 1$ is -3.

g. The equation $4x^2 + 4x + 1 = 0$ has two real roots.

h. The solution set of the equation $(x - 2)(x + 3) = 0$ is $\{2, -3\}$.

i. $\{x | x^2 - 15 = 0\} = \{\sqrt{15}\}$

j. $\forall_{r \neq 0} \forall_s \forall_t$, if $s^2 - 4rt \geq 0$, then $\{x | rx^2 + sx + t = 0\} = $
$$\left\{ \frac{-s + \sqrt{s^2 - 4rt}}{2r}, \ \frac{-s - \sqrt{s^2 - 4rt}}{2r} \right\}.$$

2. Find the real number solution set for each of the following equations.

a. $2x^2 + 9x - 18 = 0$

b. $x^2 + \frac{1}{2}x - 3 = 0$

c. $3x^2 - 8x - 3 = 0$

d. $x^2 + 2x + 5 = 0$

e. $x^2 - 6x + 4 = 0$

f. $5x - 1 = 4x^2$

g. $x^2 = \frac{1}{2}x$

h. $x^2 - 2x - \frac{5}{4} = 0$

i. $x^2 - 6x = 0$

j. $x^2 - 6 = 0$

k. $2x^2 - 3x + 4 = 0$

l. $4x^2 = 5x + 6$

m. $5x = 4x^2$

n. $4x^2 - 1 = 0$

o. $\frac{1}{2}x^2 + 3x = -\frac{1}{2}$

p. $\frac{1}{9}x^2 = 4$

q. $\frac{1}{2}x^2 - x + 4 = 0$

r. $x^2 = 7x$

s. $x^2 = 7$

t. $x^2 + 1 = 0$

3. For what values of k will the equation $2x^2 + 4x + (2 - k - k^2) = 0$ have exactly one root?

4. Two-inch squares are cut from each corner of a rectangular piece of cardboard which is twice as long as it is wide, and the ends are turned up to form an open box. If the volume of the box is 896 cubic inches, then what were the dimensions of the original piece of cardboard?

5. Find two consecutive positive integers whose product is 756.

6. If an object is shot vertically from the surface of the earth with an initial velocity of v feet per second, and if air resistance and other disturbing factors are neglected, it is proved in physics that $S = vt - 16t^2$, where S feet is the height of the object above the surface at the end of t seconds. How many seconds are required for an object to reach a height of 5000 feet if it is shot vertically from the surface of the earth with an initial velocity of 600 feet per second?

7. The sum of the numbers named by the digits of a two-digit numeral is 9. The number named by the tens digit is three more than the square of the number named by the units digit. Find the original number.

8. The measure of one leg of a right triangle is 7 feet greater than the measure of the other leg. The measure of the hypotenuse is 17 feet. Find the measure of each leg of the triangle. (HINT: use the Pythagorean Relation.)

9. The sum S of the first k natural numbers is given by the formula $S = \dfrac{k(k+1)}{2}$. Beginning with 1, how many consecutive natural numbers must be added to obtain a sum of 300?

10. The sum of the first k positive odd integers is given by the formula $S = k^2$. (This formula is presented as a theorem to be proved as a problem in Chapter 15.) Find the value of n for which $1 + 3 + 5 + 7 + \ldots + n = 361$.

11. The sum of the first k positive even integers is given by the formula $S = k(k + 1)$. (This formula is presented as a theorem to be proved as a problem in Chapter 15.) Beginning with 2, how many consecutive positive even integers must be added to obtain a sum of 240?

12. Find the measure of the side of a square if the measure of a diagonal is 5 feet greater than the measure of a side.

Some properties of the roots of quadratic equations

The roots of a quadratic equation have some interesting properties which are worth mentioning. Two of these properties are stated in the following theorem.

Theorem 5 If the solution set of the quadratic equation $ax^2 + bx + c = 0$ is $\{r, s\}$, then $r + s = -\dfrac{b}{a}$ and $r \cdot s = \dfrac{c}{a}$.

Proof   Let $r = \dfrac{-b + \sqrt{b^2 - 4ac}}{2a}$ and $s = \dfrac{-b - \sqrt{b^2 - 4ac}}{2a}$

Then

$$r + s = \dfrac{-b + \sqrt{b^2 - 4ac}}{2a} + \dfrac{-b - \sqrt{b^2 - 4ac}}{2a}$$

$$= \dfrac{-b + \sqrt{b^2 - 4ac} - b - \sqrt{b^2 - 4ac}}{2a}$$

$$= \dfrac{-2b}{2a} = -\dfrac{b}{a}$$

and

$$r \cdot s = \dfrac{-b + \sqrt{b^2 - 4ac}}{2a} \cdot \dfrac{-b - \sqrt{b^2 - 4ac}}{2a}$$

$$= \dfrac{b^2 - (b^2 - 4ac)}{4a^2} = \dfrac{4ac}{4a^2} = \dfrac{c}{a}$$

Corollary   If the solution set of the quadratic equation $ax^2 + bx + c = 0$

is $\{r\}$, that is, if $b^2 - 4ac = 0$, then $2r = -\dfrac{b}{a}$ and $r^2 = \dfrac{c}{a}$.

The proof of this corollary is left to the student.

Examples: *i.*   Without solving the equation $3x^2 - 5x = 7$, find the sum and the product of the roots.

$3x^2 - 5x = 7$ is equivalent to $3x^2 - 5x - 7 = 0$; hence, the value of a is 3, the value of b is -5, and the value of c is -7.

Therefore, the sum of the roots is $-\dfrac{b}{a} = -\dfrac{-5}{3} = \dfrac{5}{3}$ and the

product of the roots is $\dfrac{c}{a} = -\dfrac{7}{3}$.

ii.   Write an equation whose solution set is $\left\{\dfrac{2}{3}, \dfrac{1}{5}\right\}$.

The sum of the roots is $\dfrac{2}{3} + \dfrac{1}{5} = \dfrac{13}{15}$ and the product of the

roots is $\left(\dfrac{2}{3}\right)\left(\dfrac{1}{5}\right) = \dfrac{2}{15}$. Hence, $-\dfrac{b}{a} = \dfrac{13}{15}$ and $\dfrac{c}{a} = \dfrac{2}{15}$. Since

$ax^2 + bx + c = 0 \ (a \neq 0)$ is equivalent to $x^2 + \dfrac{b}{a}x + \dfrac{c}{a} = 0$,

$x^2 - \dfrac{13}{15}x + \dfrac{2}{15} = 0$ is an equation whose solution set is

$\left\{\dfrac{2}{3}, \dfrac{1}{5}\right\}$. Is $15x^2 - 13x + 2 = 0$ another such equation?

EXERCISES

1. True or false?
   a. The sum of the roots of $2x^2 - 9x - 5 = 0$ is $\frac{9}{2}$.
   b. The sum of the roots of $\frac{1}{2}x^2 - 8 = 0$ is 2.
   c. The sum of the roots of $3x^2 = \frac{1}{3}x$ is -1.
   d. The product of the roots of $2x^2 - 9x - 5 = 0$ is $\frac{5}{2}$.
   e. The product of the roots of $\frac{1}{2}x^2 - 8 = 0$ is 16.
   f. The product of the roots of $3x^2 = \frac{1}{3}x$ is 0.
   g. If the sum of the roots of $ax^2 - 4x - 21 = 0$ is 4, then $a = -1$.
   h. If the product of the roots of $x^2 - 4x + b = 0$ is -5, then $b = -5$.
   i. If the product of the roots of $ax^2 + 2x + b = 0$ is 1, then $a = -b$.
   j. If the sum of the roots of $ax^2 + bx - 3 = 0$ is -1, then $a = b$.

2. Find *i.* the sum and *ii.* the product of the real roots, if any, of each of the following equations.

   a. $x^2 - x - 6 = 0$ **c.** $x^2 + \dfrac{1}{4} = x$

   b. $4x^2 + 5x - 21 = 0$ **d.** $6x^2 + 5x = 6$

e. $2x^2 - 23x + 56 = 0$ **h.** $2x^2 + 9x - 5 = 0$

f. $2x^2 = 5x$ **i.** $x^2 - \frac{1}{3}x - \frac{2}{9} = 0$

g. $\frac{1}{4} - 9x^2 = 0$ **j.** $x^2 - \frac{5}{6}x + \frac{1}{6} = 0$

3.   Write a quadratic equation in x whose real number solution set is given below. Write the equation in the form $ax^2 \pm bx \pm c = 0$ for some integers a, b, and c.

a. $\{2, 5\}$ **f.** $\{\sqrt{6}, -\sqrt{6}\}$

b. $\{-3, 4\}$ **g.** $\{1 + \sqrt{2}, 1 - \sqrt{2}\}$

h. ϕ

c. $\{7, -2\}$

i. $\left\{\frac{1}{2}, \frac{1}{3}\right\}$

d. $\{-6, -3\}$

e. $\{6\}$ **j.** $\left\{-\frac{3}{7}, \frac{2}{5}\right\}$

4.   For what values of k will the sum of the roots of the following equation be 8?

$$x^2 - (k^2 - 2k)x + 3 = 0$$

5.   For what values of k will the product of the roots of the following be zero?

$$2x^2 + x + (4k^2 - 4k - 3) = 0$$

6.   Prove: if the quadratic equation $ax^2 + bx + c = 0$ has roots r and s, then $ax^2 + bx + c = a(x - r)(x - s)$.

7. For each quadratic equation $ax^2 + bx + c = 0$ with a, b, and c odd integers, prove that there are no integer solutions. [HINT: First prove that there are no even integer solutions and then prove that there are no odd integer solutions.]

8. Solve: $\sqrt{2}x^2 - \sqrt{7}x - \sqrt{8} = 0$.

FRACTIONAL EQUATIONS

By a *fractional equation*, we will mean any equation which contains a non-polynomial rational expression in one or both of its members. The following equations are examples of fractional equations.

$$x = \frac{-2}{x - 3} \qquad \frac{2x - 9}{x - 7} + \frac{x}{2} = \frac{5}{x - 7} \qquad \frac{2x^2}{x - 3} - 1 = \frac{4x + 6}{x - 3}$$

We now wish to learn to solve fractional equations. Our discussion will consist of finding the solution sets of the above equations. In examining the first equation

$$x = \frac{-2}{x - 3}$$

observe that 3 is *not* a permissible replacement for x. Why not? *It follows that 3 cannot be a solution of this equation.* In attempting to solve this equation, our objective, as you might expect, is to find an equivalent equation whose solution set is easy to obtain. Applying the multiplication property ($\forall_a \forall_b \forall_c$, if $a = b$, then $ac = bc$) with $x - 3$, we obtain a new equation which contains no fractions. This procedure is appropriate since, under the above-stated restriction on the replacements for x, x may not be replaced by 3 and hence $x - 3$ cannot be zero.

Thus, in solving this equation, we proceed in the following manner (remember that for each equation, $x \neq 3$).

$$x = \frac{-2}{x - 3}$$

$$x \cdot (x - 3) = (x - 3) \cdot \frac{-2}{x - 3}$$

$$x^2 - 3x = -2$$

$$x^2 - 3x + 2 = 0$$

$$(x - 2)(x - 1) = 0$$

$$x - 2 = 0 \text{ or } x - 1 = 0$$

Hence, the real number solution set of $x = \dfrac{-2}{x - 3}$ is $\{2, 1\}$.

Now let us solve the second equation

$$\frac{2x - 9}{x - 7} + \frac{x}{2} = \frac{5}{x - 7}$$

Notice that in this equation 7 is not a permissible replacement for x and hence 7 must be excluded from consideration as a root. This time, in order to obtain a new equation which is "free" of fractions, we shall use the multiplication property with $2(x - 7)$; this expression, under the above-stated restriction on the replacements for x, cannot have the value zero. Multiplying each member of the equation by $2(x - 7)$, we obtain the new equivalent equation

$$2(x - 7) \cdot \left[\frac{2x - 9}{x - 7} + \frac{x}{2} \right] = 2(x - 7) \cdot \left[\frac{5}{x - 7} \right], \quad (x \neq 7)$$

which, in turn, may be simplified as indicated by the following steps (for each equation, $x \neq 7$).

$$2(2x - 9) + x(x - 7) = 2(5)$$

$$4x - 18 + x^2 - 7x = 10$$

$$x^2 - 3x - 28 = 0$$

$$(x - 7)(x + 4) = 0$$

Since x may not be replaced by 7, we find that the desired solution set is $\{-4\}$.

Finally, let us consider the third equation

$$\frac{2x^2}{x - 3} - 1 = \frac{4x + 6}{x - 3}$$

In this case, 3 is not a permissible replacement for x and thus 3 must be eliminated from consideration as a solution; with this thought in mind we use the multiplication property with $x - 3$ and proceed through the following sequence of equivalent equations. (You supply the justification for each step; keep in mind that for each equation, $x \neq 3$.)

$$(x - 3) \cdot \left[\frac{2x^2}{x - 3} - 1\right] = (x - 3) \cdot \left[\frac{4x + 6}{x - 3}\right]$$

$$2x^2 - (x - 3) = 4x + 6$$
$$2x^2 - x + 3 = 4x + 6$$
$$2x^2 - 5x - 3 = 0$$
$$(2x + 1)(x - 3) = 0$$

Solving this last equation, we find that the desired solution set is $\{-\frac{1}{2}\}$. Why is $\{-\frac{1}{2}, 3\}$ *not* the solution set?

EXERCISES

1. True or false?

a. $\forall_{x \neq 0} \; x\left(\dfrac{1}{x^2}\right) = \dfrac{1}{x}$

b. $\forall_x \; x\left(\dfrac{4 - x}{x}\right) = 4 - x$

c. For every replacement of x, except 0 and 2

$$x(x - 2) \cdot \left[\frac{1}{x} + \frac{1}{x - 2}\right] = 2(x - 1)$$

d. For every replacement of x, except 2 and -1

$$(x + 1)(x - 2) \cdot \left[\frac{x}{(x + 1)(x - 2)} + 2\right] = x + 2$$

e. For each $x \neq 0$, the equations $x - \dfrac{1}{x} = 0$ and $x^2 - 1 = 0$ are equivalent.

f. For each $x \neq 4$, the equations $x = \dfrac{5}{x - 4}$ and $x^2 - 4x = 5$ are equivalent.

g. For each $x \neq 3$, the equations $\dfrac{x^2}{x - 3} + 3x + 2 = 0$ and $x^2 + 3x + 2 = 0$ are equivalent.

h. For each $x \neq -2$, the equations $x + \dfrac{1}{x + 2} = 1$ and $x^2 + 2x + 1 = 1$ are equivalent.

i. $\forall_a \forall_b \forall_c$, if $a = b$, then $ac = bc$.

j. $\forall_a \forall_b \forall_c$, if $ac = bc$, then $a = b$.

2. Find the solution set for each of the following equations.

a. $x - 4 = \dfrac{-1}{x}$

b. $\dfrac{1}{x} + \dfrac{x - 1}{x(x + 2)} = \dfrac{-x}{x + 2}$

c. $\dfrac{3x^2}{3x + 1} - 2 = \dfrac{2x + 1}{3x + 1}$

d. $\dfrac{x^2 + 12}{x - 3} = \dfrac{7x}{x - 3}$

e. $\dfrac{1 + x}{1 - x} = \dfrac{x - 1}{x + 1}$

f. $\dfrac{2x}{x - 3} + \dfrac{1}{2x + 3} + \dfrac{3x + 9}{2x^2 - 3x - 9} = 0$

g. $\dfrac{4x^2}{x+2} - \dfrac{10}{x+2} + 4 = 0$

i. $12x^{-2} - x^{-1} = 1$

[HINT: Use the mult. prop with x^2.]

h. $\dfrac{x}{x+1} + \dfrac{x}{x-1} = 0$

j. $5\left(\dfrac{x}{x-1}\right)^2 + \dfrac{14x}{x-1} - 3 = 0$

3. If the sum of the roots of the quadratic equation $kx^2 - (k^2 + 2)x + 2 = 0$ is equal to 3, then what is the value of k?

4. If the product of the roots of the quadratic equation $k^2x^2 + 3x + (k+4) = 0$ is equal to 3, then what is the value of k?

5. The sum of a number and its reciprocal is 4, and the number is greater than 2. Find the number.

6. Together, two water pipes of different diameters can fill a pool in 4 minutes. Separately, the smaller pipe requires 6 more minutes to fill the pool than the larger pipe. How many minutes does it take for each pipe alone to fill the pool?

RADICAL EQUATIONS

Many *radical* equations in one variable may be solved by resorting to quadratic equations. By a radical equation in one variable we shall mean equations like

$$2 - x = \sqrt{x} \qquad x + 2 = \sqrt{2x + 7} \qquad \sqrt{2x - 3} = 1 + \sqrt{x + 3}$$

where the variable appears under a radical sign. To solve radical equations like these, we square each member of the equation, thus obtaining a new equation which contains fewer radicals. But will the process of squaring each member of an equation always yield an equivalent equation? To answer this question, let us determine what happens in the case of the first equation.

$$2 - x = \sqrt{x}$$

Squaring, we get the new equation

$$(2 - x)^2 = (\sqrt{x})^2$$

which, in turn, is equivalent to

$$x^2 - 5x + 4 = 0$$

The solution set for this last equation is $\{1, 4\}$. Upon checking to see if 1 and 4 are roots of this equation, we find that 1 *is* a solution and 4 is *not*. Why not? This example illustrates that *the process of squaring each member of an equation does not necessarily yield an equivalent equation.*

Let us explore the reasons why the squaring of each member of an equation cannot be depended upon to yield an equivalent equation. To begin, we know that, $\forall_a \forall_b$, if $a = b$, then $a^2 = b^2$. Why? We must decide whether the converse of this is true; that is, is it true that $\forall_a \forall_b$, if $a^2 = b^2$, then $a = b$? The answer is "no"; this is easy to prove by producing a counterexample; for instance, $3^2 = (-3)^2$, but $3 \neq -3$.

Another way of looking at this is by examining equivalent forms of the equation $a^2 = b^2$.

$$a^2 - b^2 = 0$$
$$(a - b)(a + b) = 0$$
$$a - b = 0 \text{ or } a + b = 0$$
$$a = b \text{ or } a = -b$$

Thus we see that the sentence "$a^2 = b^2$" is equivalent to the compound sentence "$a = b$ or $a = -b$". Now let us relate these findings to what occurred above in the attempted solution of $2 - x = \sqrt{x}$. We began by squaring each member of the equation, thus obtaining the new equation $(2 - x)^2 = (\sqrt{x})^2$. We now know that this "squared" equation is equivalent to the disjunction

$$(2 - x) = \sqrt{x} \quad \text{or} \quad (2 - x) = -\sqrt{x}$$

Since the solution set of this disjunction is the *union* of the solution sets of "$2 - x = \sqrt{x}$" and of "$2 - x = -\sqrt{x}$", that is $\{x | 2 - x = \sqrt{x}\} \cup \{x | 2 - x = -\sqrt{x}\}$, we see that the solution set of the given equation is a *subset* of the solution set of the "squared" equation.

We conclude that although squaring both members of an equation does not always produce an equivalent equation, the solution set of the given equation is always a subset of the solution set of the "squared" equation. This fact can be put to good advantage in solving any radical equation which involves only square root radicals. Study the following examples.

Example: i.   Find the solution set for $x + 2 = \sqrt{2x + 7}$.

Squaring each member of this equation we have

$$(x + 2)^2 = (\sqrt{2x + 7})^2$$
$$x^2 + 4x + 4 = 2x + 7$$
$$x^2 + 2x - 3 = 0$$
$$(x + 3)(x - 1) = 0$$

The solution set for this last equation is $\{-3, 1\}$. We know that the solution set of the given equation is a subset of $\{-3, 1\}$. Checking, we find that 1 satisfies the equation $x + 2 = \sqrt{2x + 7}$ since $1 + 2 = \sqrt{2 + 7}$. On the other hand, -3 does *not* satisfy the equation $x + 2 = \sqrt{2x + 7}$ since $(-3) + 2 \neq \sqrt{2(-3) + 7}$. Notice that -3 *does* satisfy the equation $x + 2 = -\sqrt{2x + 7}$.

Example: ii.   Solve the equation $x = 2 - \sqrt{2x - 5}$.

Squaring each member of this equation, we have

$$x^2 = (2 - \sqrt{2x - 5})^2$$
$$x^2 = 4 - 4\sqrt{2x - 5} + (2x - 5)$$

Notice that this squared equation still contains the radical $\sqrt{2x - 5}$ and is more complicated than the original one. To avoid this complication, let us write the original equation

$x = 2 - \sqrt{2x - 5}$ in the equivalent form $\sqrt{2x - 5} = 2 - x$ before squaring each member. Then we obtain

$$(\sqrt{2x - 5})^2 = (2 - x)^2$$
$$2x - 5 = 4 - 4x + x^2$$
$$x^2 - 6x + 9 = 0$$
$$(x - 3)(x - 3) = 0$$

The solution set for this last equation is $\{3\}$. However, replacing x in the given equation by 3, we obtain the statement "$3 = 2 - \sqrt{1}$", which is false. Thus, we conclude that the solution set of $x = 2 - \sqrt{2x - 5}$ is ϕ.

Example: *iii.*   Solve the equation $\sqrt{2x + 3} - \sqrt{x + 1} = 1$.

Let us first write this equation in the equivalent form

$$\sqrt{2x + 3} = 1 + \sqrt{x + 1}$$

Squaring each member of this last equation we obtain

$$(\sqrt{2x + 3})^2 = (1 + \sqrt{x + 1})^2$$
$$2x + 3 = 1 + 2\sqrt{x + 1} + x + 1$$
$$x + 1 = 2\sqrt{x + 1}$$

Since this last equation contains a radical, we square each of its members and obtain the quadratic equation

$$x^2 - 2x - 3 = 0$$

The roots of this quadratic equation are 3 and -1. Checking, we find that both 3 and -1 satisfy the original equation; hence, its solution set is $\{3, -1\}$.

EXERCISES

1. True or false?
   a. $\forall_x \sqrt{x}$ is a real number if and only if $x \geq 0$.
   b. $\forall_x \sqrt{x - 2}$ is a real number if and only if $x \geq 0$.
   c. $\forall_{x \geq 0} \sqrt{x} \geq 0$
   d. $\forall_{x \geq 2} \sqrt{x - 2} \geq 0$
   e. $\forall_x \sqrt{x^2} = x$
   f. The real number solution set for $\sqrt{x} = -1$ is $\{1\}$.
   g. The real number solution set for $\sqrt{x^2} = -2$ is $\{2, -2\}$.
   h. The real number solution set of the inequality $\sqrt{x} < 0$ is ϕ.
   i. The real number solution set of the inequality $\sqrt{x - 3} \leq 0$ is ϕ.
   j. The equation "$(x - 3)^2 = (\sqrt{2x - 3})^2$" is equivalent to the compound open sentence "$(x - 3) = \sqrt{2x - 3}$ or $(x - 3) = -\sqrt{2x - 3}$".
   k. The real number solution set of the equation $(x - 3)^2 = (\sqrt{2x - 3})^2$ is a subset of the real number solution set of the equation $x - 3 = \sqrt{2x - 3}$.

l. If some real number m is a root of the equation $(x - 3)^2 = (\sqrt{2x - 3})^2$ and m does not satisfy the equation $x - 3 = \sqrt{2x - 3}$, then m is a solution of the equation $x - 3 = -\sqrt{2x - 3}$.

m. $\forall_x \forall_{k \geq 0}$, if $x^2 = k$, then $x = \sqrt{k}$.

n. $\forall_x \forall_{k \geq 0}$, if $x^2 = k$, then $x = -\sqrt{k}$.

o. $\forall_x \forall_{k \geq 0}$, if $x^2 = k$, then $x = \sqrt{k}$ or $x = -\sqrt{k}$.

2. Find the real number solution set for each of the following equations.

a. $x - 3 = \sqrt{2x - 3}$

b. $\sqrt{x^2 - 3} + 1 = 0$

c. $\sqrt{2x^2 - x + 10} - x = 2$

d. $x = \sqrt{3x - 2} + 2$

e. $\sqrt{2x^2} = \sqrt{-15x - 25}$

f. $\sqrt{x + 2} + \sqrt{3 - x} = 3$

g. $\sqrt{\sqrt{x^2 + 6x}} = 2$

h. $\sqrt{3x + 1} + 1 = \sqrt{x}$

i. $\sqrt{2 - 8x} = 2 - 2\sqrt{1 - 6x}$

j. $\sqrt{3x + 2} = 3\sqrt{x} - \sqrt{2}$

Other equations with the quadratic pattern

There are many other equations which are not quadratic, but which are equivalent to an equation having the pattern

$$a \cdot \boxed{}^2 + b \cdot \boxed{} + c = 0, \quad (a \neq 0)$$

Because of the similarity between this pattern and the pattern of a quadratic equation, namely

$$ax^2 + bx + c = 0, \quad (a \neq 0)$$

any non-quadratic equation which has the above-stated form is said to "pattern like a quadratic equation" or "have quadratic form".

The equation $2x^4 - 5x^2 + 2 = 0$, for example, has quadratic form since it may be written in the equivalent form

$$i. \quad 2[x^2]^2 - 5[x^2] + 2 = 0$$

which has the stipulated pattern. To solve this equation, we shall give x^2 a temporary name, say y; that is, let $y = x^2$, thus obtaining the quadratic equation

$$ii. \quad 2y^2 - 5y + 2 = 0$$

The solution set for equation *ii.* is $\{\frac{1}{2}, 2\}$. Notice that by finding the replacements for y, namely $\frac{1}{2}$ and 2, which satisfy equation *ii.*, we have found the real number values of x^2 which satisfy equation *i*. The final step, therefore, in finding the solution set for equation *i*. is to solve the equations "$x^2 = 2$" and "$x^2 = \frac{1}{2}$". Hence, the solution set for equation *i*. is

$$\left\{ x \mid x^2 = 2 \text{ or } x^2 = \frac{1}{2} \right\} = \left\{ \sqrt{2}, \ -\sqrt{2}, \ \frac{1}{\sqrt{2}}, \ -\frac{1}{\sqrt{2}} \right\}$$

We conclude that the solution set for $2x^4 - 5x^2 + 2 = 0$ is

$$\left\{ \sqrt{2}, \ -\sqrt{2}, \ \frac{\sqrt{2}}{2}, \ -\frac{\sqrt{2}}{2} \right\}$$

Study the following examples; they will give you some idea of the various types of equations which may have quadratic form, and which you may solve by the technique presented above.

Example: *i.*   Find the solution set of the equation $2x - 7\sqrt{x} - 4 = 0$.

The equation $2x - 7\sqrt{x} - 4 = 0$ is equivalent to

$$2(\sqrt{x})^2 - 7(\sqrt{x}) - 4 = 0 \text{ [since } \forall_{x\geq0} (\sqrt{x})^2 = x]$$

Replacing $\sqrt{x}$ by y, we obtain $2y^2 - 7y - 4 = 0$ which is equivalent to $(y - 4)(2y + 1) = 0$. Hence

$$\{y | 2y^2 - 7y - 4 = 0\} = \{y | y = 4 \text{ or } y = -\tfrac{1}{2}\}$$

As we replaced $\sqrt{x}$ by y above, we now replace y by $\sqrt{x}$, and obtain

$$\{x | 2x - 7\sqrt{x} - 4 = 0\} = \{x | \sqrt{x} = 4 \text{ or } \sqrt{x} = -\tfrac{1}{2}\} = \{16\}$$

Remember that there is no real number x such that $\sqrt{x} = -\tfrac{1}{2}$. Why not?

Example: *ii.*   Find the solution set of $(x^2 - 6x)^2 - 5(x^2 - 6x) + 6 = 0$.

The equation $(x^2 - 6x)^2 - 5(x^2 - 6x) + 6 = 0$ patterns like a quadratic equation. Replacing $(x^2 - 6x)$ by y we obtain $y^2 - 5y + 6 = 0$ which is equivalent to $(y - 3)(y - 2) = 0$.

Hence

$$\{y | y^2 - 5y + 6 = 0\} = \{y | y = 3 \text{ or } y = 2\}$$

As we replaced $(x^2 - 6x)$ by y above, we now replace y by $(x^2 - 6x)$, and obtain

$$\{x | (x^2 - 6x)^2 - 5(x^2 - 6x) + 6 = 0\}$$
$$= \{x | x^2 - 6x = 3 \text{ or } x^2 - 6x = 2\}$$

Using theorem 4 (the Quadratic Formula), we find that

$$\{x | x^2 - 6x = 3\} = \{3 + 2\sqrt{3}, \ 3 - 2\sqrt{3}\}$$

and that

$$\{x | x^2 - 6x = 2\} = \{3 + \sqrt{11}, \ 3 - \sqrt{11}\}$$

Therefore, the desired solution set is

$$\{3 + 2\sqrt{3}, \ 3 - 2\sqrt{3}, \ 3 + \sqrt{11}, \ 3 - \sqrt{11}\}$$

Example: *iii.*   Find the solution set of the equation $2x^{-2} + 5x^{-1} - 3 = 0$.

The equation $2x^{-2} + 5x^{-1} - 3 = 0$ is equivalent to

$$2 \cdot \frac{1}{x^2} + 5 \cdot \frac{1}{x} - 3 = 0 \ \left[\text{since } \forall_{x\neq0} \forall_c \ x^{-c} = \frac{1}{x^c} \right]$$

which, in turn, is equivalent to $2\left(\dfrac{1}{x}\right)^2 + 5\left(\dfrac{1}{x}\right) - 3 = 0$.

Replacing $\frac{1}{x}$ by y, we obtain $2y^2 + 5y - 3 = 0$ which is equivalent to $(2y - 1)(y + 3) = 0$. Hence

$$\{y \mid 2y^2 + 5y - 3 = 0\} = \{y \mid y = \tfrac{1}{2} \text{ or } y = -3\}$$

As we replaced $\frac{1}{x}$ by y, we now replace y by $\frac{1}{x}$, and obtain

$$\{x \mid 2x^{-2} + 5x^{-1} - 3 = 0\} = \left\{x \middle| \frac{1}{x} = \frac{1}{2} \text{ or } \frac{1}{x} = -3\right\} = \left\{2, \ -\frac{1}{3}\right\}$$

EXERCISES

1. Write an equivalent equation in the pattern $a \cdot \boxed{}^2 + b \cdot \boxed{} + c = 0$ for some real numbers a, b, and c and for some expression $\boxed{}$ involving a variable.

    a. $3(x + 4) + 2(x + 4)^2 + 6 = 0$

    b. $5t^4 - 3t^2 - 7 = 0$

    e. $5\left(\dfrac{1}{9x^2}\right) + 4\left(\dfrac{1}{3x}\right) + 2 = 0$

    c. $3x + 2\sqrt{3x - 5} = 5$

    d. $x^6 - x^3 - 1 = 0$.

    f. $2\sqrt{x} - 7x + 8 = 0$

    g. $3(x^2 - 1) + 4 - 5(x^2 - 1)^2 = 0$

2. True or false?

    a. The equation $2x + \sqrt{2x - 5} - 5 = 0$ has an equivalent equation having the pattern $a \cdot \boxed{}^2 + b \cdot \boxed{} + c = 0$.

    b. The first step in one technique of solving the equation $(x + 1)^2 + 4(x + 1) - 5 = 0$ consists of finding the solution set of an equation like $z^2 + 4z - 5 = 0$.

    c. The equation $x^4 + 3x - 4 = 0$ has "quadratic form".

    d. The equation $(x^2 - 1)^2 + 8 = 6x^2 - 6$ is equivalent to *some* equation having "quadratic form".

    e. The equation $2\left(\dfrac{1}{x^2}\right) + 3\left(\dfrac{1}{x}\right) - 7 = 0$ is equivalent to *some* equation having "quadratic form".

    f. The equation $7x^{\frac{1}{2}} + x = 3$ is equivalent to *some* equation having "quadratic form".

    g. The equation $x^6 + 3x^3 + 2 = 0$ is equivalent to *some* equation having "quadratic form".

    h. The equation $2x^4 - 5 = 3x^8$ is equivalent to *some* equation having "quadratic form".

    i. The equation $\dfrac{2}{x^4} - x^{-2} + 3 = 0$ is equivalent to *some* equation having "quadratic form".

    j. The equation $\left(\dfrac{x}{x + 1}\right)^2 - \dfrac{1}{2} = \dfrac{x}{x + 1}$ is equivalent to *some* equation having "quadratic form".

3. Find the real number solution set for each of the following equations.

a. $x^4 - 13x^2 + 36 = 0$

b. $x - 2\sqrt{x} = 15$

c. $(x^2 + 2x)^2 - 2(x^2 + 2x) - 3 = 0$

d. $(x^2 - x)^2 + 12 = 8(x^2 - x)$

e. $2(2x^2 + x)^2 + 7(2x^2 + x) + 3 = 0$

f. $3x + \sqrt{3x - 2} = 2$

g. $\dfrac{1}{x^4} - \dfrac{6}{x^2} + 8 = 0$

h. $x = 6\sqrt{x} - 2$

i. $2x^{-2} + 4x^{-1} + 3 = 0$

j. $\dfrac{1}{(x - 4)^2} + \dfrac{5}{(x - 4)} - 36 = 0$

[HINT: Replace $\dfrac{1}{x - 4}$ by y.]

k. $\left(\dfrac{x - 1}{x}\right)^2 - 3\left(\dfrac{x - 1}{x}\right) + 2 = 0$

QUADRATIC INEQUALITIES

The graph of the quadratic function

$$F = \{(x, y) \mid y = \tfrac{1}{4}x^2 - x - 3\}$$
$$= \{(x, y) \mid y = \tfrac{1}{4}(x - 2)^2 - 4\}$$

is given in figure 1. Observe that the parabola which is the graph of F intersects the x-axis at two points, $(-2, 0)$ and $(6, 0)$. Note that

$$x_1 < -2 \text{ and } F(x_1) > 0$$
$$x_2 > 6 \text{ and } F(x_2) > 0$$
$$-2 < x_3 < 6 \text{ and } F(x_3) < 0$$

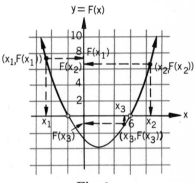

Fig. 1

Answer the following questions by examining figure 1. Is $F(3)$ positive or negative? Is $F(8)$ positive or negative? Is $F(-6)$ positive or negative?

You have probably discovered that we may consider the graph of $F = \{(x, \tfrac{1}{4}x^2 - x - 3)\}$ as the union of three disjoint sets of points

i. the two points of F which coincide with the x-axis (observe that these points have zero for their second coordinates)

ii. the points of F below the x-axis (observe that these points have negative second coordinates)

iii. the points of F above the x-axis (observe that these points have positive second coordinates)

Thus, we see that $\{x \mid \tfrac{1}{4}x^2 - x - 3 = 0\} = \{-2, 6\}$ and $\{x \mid \tfrac{1}{4}x^2 - x - 3 < 0\} = \{x \mid -2 < x < 6\}$. By observing the graph of F, you should be able to determine the solution set for the open sentence $\tfrac{1}{4}x^2 - x - 3 > 0$. What is this solution set?

Notice that we used a graphic approach to determine the solution sets of the inequalities "$\tfrac{1}{4}x^2 - x - 3 < 0$" and "$\tfrac{1}{4}x^2 - x - 3 > 0$". These are but two examples of some open sentences that we shall now learn to solve by algebraic techniques.

■ *Definition of Quadratic Inequality* Every inequality which patterns in either of the forms

$$ax^2 + bx + c > 0$$

or

$$ax^2 + bx + c < 0$$

where a, b, and c are real numbers, $a \neq 0$, is called a *quadratic inequality.*

Each of the following is equivalent to a quadratic inequality.

$2x^2 + x - 3 > 0$	$x - x^2 < 0$	$16 - 9x^2 < 0$
$4x^2 > 9$	$-3x^2 - x + 10 > 0$	$x^2 < 7x$

In order to find the solution set of a quadratic inequality we shall first determine an equivalent inequality of the form $(x + p)^2 > k$ or of the form $(x + p)^2 < k$. Inequalities of the form $(x + p)^2 > k$ or of the form $(x + p)^2 < k$ are easily solved as you will see when you study the following examples.

Example: i. Solve $(t + 3)^2 > 0$.

Each real number except -3 is a solution of $(t + 3)^2 > 0$ since $\forall_{x \neq 0} \ x^2 > 0$. Verify that -3 is *not* a solution of $(t + 3)^2 > 0$; that -10 is a solution; that 6 is a solution.

ii. Solve $(t + 3)^2 < 0$.

There are no real number solutions of $(t + 3)^2 < 0$ since $\forall_x \ x^2 \geq 0$. Verify that -10 is not a solution of $(t + 3)^2 < 0$; that -3 is not a solution; that 7 is not a solution.

iii. Solve $(t + 3)^2 < 5$.

Using the theorem* which states that

$$\forall_x \forall_{k \geq 0} \ x^2 < k \text{ if and only if } -\sqrt{k} < x < \sqrt{k}$$

we have

$$(t + 3)^2 < 5$$
$$-\sqrt{5} < t + 3 < \sqrt{5}$$
$$-3 - \sqrt{5} < t < -3 + \sqrt{5}$$

Thus, the solution set of $(t + 3)^2 < 5$ is

$$\{t \mid -3 - \sqrt{5} < t < -3 + \sqrt{5}\}$$

iv. Solve $(t + 3)^2 > 5$.

Using the theorem* which states that

$$\forall_x \forall_{k \geq 0} \ x^2 > k \text{ if and only if } x > \sqrt{k} \text{ or } x < -\sqrt{k}$$

* The proof of this theorem is taken up in exercise 5 on page 244.

we have

$$(t+3)^2 > 5$$

$$t+3 > \sqrt{5} \quad \text{or} \quad t+3 < -\sqrt{5}$$

$$t > -3 + \sqrt{5} \quad \text{or} \quad t < -3 - \sqrt{5}$$

Thus, the solution set of $(t+3)^2 > 5$ is

$$\{t \mid t > -3 + \sqrt{5} \text{ or } t < -3 - \sqrt{5}\}$$

We will now demonstrate that each quadratic inequality $ax^2 + bx + c > 0$ for which $a > 0$ is equivalent to a quadratic inequality of the form $(x + p)^2 > k$. Justify each step.

$$ax^2 + bx + c > 0$$

$$x^2 + \frac{b}{a}x + \frac{c}{a} > 0$$

$$x^2 + \frac{b}{a}x > \frac{-c}{a}$$

$$x^2 + \frac{b}{a}x + \frac{b^2}{4a^2} > \frac{b^2}{4a^2} - \frac{c}{a}$$

$$\left(x + \frac{b}{2a}\right)^2 > \frac{b^2 - 4ac}{4a^2}$$

The last inequality is of the form

$$(x + p)^2 > k$$

if $\dfrac{b}{2a}$ is replaced by p and $\dfrac{b^2 - 4ac}{4a^2}$ is replaced by k.

Study the use of this technique in solving the following inequalities.

Example: i. Solve $3t^2 - 5t + 7 > 0$.

Justify each step.

$$3t^2 - 5t + 7 > 0$$

$$3t^2 - 5t > -7$$

$$t^2 - \frac{5}{3}t > \frac{-7}{3}$$

$$t^2 - \frac{5}{3}t + \frac{25}{36} > -\frac{7}{3} + \frac{25}{36}$$

$$\left(t - \frac{5}{6}\right)^2 > \frac{-84 + 25}{36}$$

$$\left(t - \frac{5}{6}\right)^2 > -\frac{59}{36}$$

Every real number is a solution of $(t - \frac{5}{6})^2 > -\frac{59}{36}$ since $\forall_t \ (t - \frac{5}{6})^2 \geq 0$.

Example: ii.   Solve $3t^2 - 5t + 7 < 0$.

Justify each step.

$$3t^2 - 5t + 7 < 0$$
$$3t^2 - 5t \quad\ < -7$$

$$t^2 - \frac{5}{3}t < -\frac{7}{3}$$

$$t^2 - \frac{5}{3}t + \frac{25}{36} < -\frac{7}{3} + \frac{25}{36}$$

$$\left(t - \frac{5}{6}\right)^2 < \frac{-59}{36}$$

No real number is a solution of $(t - \frac{5}{6})^2 < \frac{-59}{36}$ since $\forall_t \ (t - \frac{5}{6})^2 \geq 0$.

Example: iii.   Solve $3t^2 - 5t - 4 > 0$.

Justify each step.

$$3t^2 - 5t - 4 > 0$$
$$3t^2 - 5t \quad\ > 4$$

$$t^2 - \frac{5}{3}t > \frac{4}{3}$$

$$t^2 - \frac{5}{3}t + \frac{25}{36} > \frac{4}{3} + \frac{25}{36}$$

$$\left(t - \frac{5}{6}\right)^2 > \frac{73}{36}$$

$$t - \frac{5}{6} > \frac{\sqrt{73}}{6} \quad \text{or} \quad t - \frac{5}{6} < \frac{-\sqrt{73}}{6}$$

$$t > \frac{5 + \sqrt{73}}{6} \quad \text{or} \quad t < \frac{5 - \sqrt{73}}{6}$$

Thus, the solution set for $3t^2 - 5t - 4 > 0$ is

$$\left\{ t \mid t > \frac{5 + \sqrt{73}}{6} \quad \text{or} \quad t < \frac{5 - \sqrt{73}}{6} \right\}$$

Example: iv.   Solve $3t^2 - 5t - 4 < 0$.

Justify each step.

$$3t^2 - 5t - 4 < 0$$
$$3t^2 - 5t \quad\ < 4$$

$$t^2 - \frac{5}{3}t < \frac{4}{3}$$

$$t^2 - \frac{5}{3}t + \frac{25}{36} < \frac{4}{3} + \frac{25}{36}$$

$$\left(t - \frac{5}{6}\right)^2 < \frac{73}{36}$$

$$\frac{-\sqrt{73}}{6} < t - \frac{5}{6} < \frac{\sqrt{73}}{6}$$

$$\frac{5 - \sqrt{73}}{6} < t < \frac{5 + \sqrt{73}}{6}$$

Thus, the solution set for $3t^2 - 5t - 4 < 0$ is

$$\left\{ t \,\middle|\, \frac{5 - \sqrt{73}}{6} < t < \frac{5 + \sqrt{73}}{6} \right\}$$

Example: v.   Solve $-3t^2 + 5t + 4 > 0$.

Justify each step.

$$-3t^2 + 5t + 4 > 0.$$
$$3t^2 - 5t - 4 < 0$$

and this is the inequality of the previous example. What is the solution set of $-3t^2 + 5t + 4 > 0$?

EXERCISES

1. True or false?

   a. The open sentence "$2x - 1 > 0$" is a quadratic inequality.

   b. The open sentence "$x - x^2 \leq 0$" is equivalent to the compound open sentence "$x - x^2 < 0$ and $x - x^2 = 0$."

   c. $\forall_x$, if $x^2 > 0$, then $x > 0$.

   d. $\forall_x \forall_{k \geq 0}$ $x^2 > k$ if and only if $-\sqrt{k} < x < \sqrt{k}$.

   e. $\forall_x \forall_{k \geq 0}$ $x^2 < k$ if and only if $x > \sqrt{k}$ or $x < -\sqrt{k}$.

   f. $\{y \,|\, y^2 - 4y + 6 < 0\} = \{y \,|\, (y - 2)^2 < -2\}$.

   g. If the graph of a quadratic function $F_1 = \{(x, ax^2 + bx + c)\}$ appears as shown, then the real number solution set of $ax^2 + bx + c > 0$ is empty.

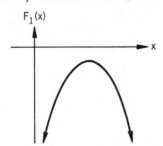

$F_1(x)$

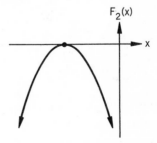

$F_2(x)$

   h. If the graph of a quadratic function $F_2 = \{(x, ax^2 + bx + c)\}$ appears as shown, then the solution set of $ax^2 + bx + c \leq 0$ is the set of all real numbers.

i. If the graph of a quadratic function $F_3 = \{(x, ax^2 + bx + c)\}$ appears as shown, then the solution set of $ax^2 + bx + c = 0$ is $\{r\}$.

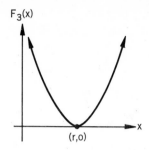

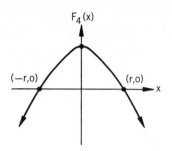

j. If the graph of a quadratic function $F_4 = \{(x, ax^2 + bx + c)\}$ appears as shown, then the solution set of $ax^2 + bx + c < 0$ is $\{x \mid -r < x < r\}$.

k. The real number solution set for $(x - 2)^2 > -2$ is ϕ.

l. The real number solution set for $(x - 2)^2 > 4$ is $\{x \mid x > 4 \text{ or } x < 0\}$.

m. The real number solution set for $(x - 2)^2 < 4$ is $\{x \mid x < 2 \text{ and } x > -2\}$.

n. Every real number satisfies the inequality $(x + 1)^2 > -1$.

2. Find the solution set for each of the following open sentences.

a. $-x^2 - 6x + 5 > 0$

b. $x^2 - 10x + 16 < 0$

c. $4x^2 > 9$

d. $x^2 - 8x + 15 > 0$

e. $\frac{1}{2}x^2 - 2x \leq 0$

f. $x - x^2 < 0$

g. $2x^2 - 4x + 5 > 0$

h. $\frac{1}{2}x^2 + 4x + 10 > 0$

i. $16 - 9x^2 > 0$

j. $-x^2 + 6x - 9 \geq 0$

k. $18x^2 - 24x - 1 > 0$

l. $12x^2 + 12x - 5 < 0$

m. $18x^2 - 12x + 11 < 0$

n. $18t^2 - 60t + 35 > 0$

o. $50y^2 + 80y > 13$

p. $15x^2 + 7x > 2$

3. Graph the quadratic function

$$Q = \left\{(x, y) \mid y = -\left(x + \frac{3}{2}\right)^2 + \frac{25}{4}\right\}$$

and, by observing the graph of Q, determine the solution set for

a. $-\left(x + \frac{3}{2}\right)^2 + \frac{25}{4} > 0$

b. $-\left(x + \frac{3}{2}\right)^2 + \frac{25}{4} \leq 0$

4. Prove that $\forall_{a>0} \forall_{b>0} (a > b) \rightarrow (a^2 > b^2)$.

5. The theorems

  i. $\forall_x \forall_{k \geq 0} (x^2 < k) \leftrightarrow (-\sqrt{k} < x < \sqrt{k})$

  ii. $\forall_x \forall_{k \geq 0} (x^2 > k) \leftrightarrow (x > \sqrt{k} \text{ or } x < -\sqrt{k})$

were stated and used without proof in the present section (see examples, page 240).

a. Graph the solution sets of the open sentences "$-\sqrt{k} < x < \sqrt{k}$" and "$|x| < \sqrt{k}$" to demonstrate that they are equivalent.

b. The proof of theorem i. follows. Notice that the proof consists of two parts. Justify each step in each part of the proof.

PART I
$$\forall_x \forall_{k \geq 0} \ (x^2 < k) \rightarrow (-\sqrt{k} < x < \sqrt{k})$$
$$x^2 < k$$
$$x^2 - k < 0$$
$$x^2 - (\sqrt{k})^2 < 0$$
$$(x - \sqrt{k})(x + \sqrt{k}) < 0$$
$$(x - \sqrt{k} > 0 \text{ and } x + \sqrt{k} < 0) \text{ or } (x - \sqrt{k} < 0 \text{ and } x + \sqrt{k} > 0)$$
$$(x > \sqrt{k} \text{ and } x < -\sqrt{k}) \text{ or } (x < \sqrt{k} \text{ and } x > -\sqrt{k})$$
$$(\sqrt{k} < x < -\sqrt{k}) \text{ or } (-\sqrt{k} < x < \sqrt{k})$$

Now, since the solution set for $\sqrt{k} < x < -\sqrt{k}$ is ϕ, it follows that $x^2 < k$ is equivalent to $-\sqrt{k} < x < \sqrt{k}$.

PART II
$$\forall_x \forall_{k \geq 0} \ (-\sqrt{k} < x < \sqrt{k}) \rightarrow (x^2 < k)$$
$$-\sqrt{k} < x < \sqrt{k}$$
$$|x| < \sqrt{k} \quad \text{(see part a)}$$
$$|x|^2 < (\sqrt{k})^2$$
$$x^2 < k$$

c. Prove theorem ii. (NOTE: the proof consists of two parts.)

VOCABULARY

Use each of the following correctly in a sentence. Numerals in parentheses refer to pages where these words were used. If you are not sure of the meaning of any word, turn to the indicated pages.

discriminant (225)
fractional equation (230)
quadratic inequality (239)

quadratic equation (221)
quadratic formula (224)
radical equation (233)

REVIEW EXERCISES

1. True or false?

a. The discriminant of the quadratic equation $2x^2 + 4x + 5 = 0$ is equal to -4.

b. The quadratic equation $2x^2 + bx + 5 = 0$ will have *one* root if and only if $b^2 = 40$.

c. $\forall_{a \neq 0}$ the sum of the roots of the quadratic equation $ax^2 + 2x + 3 = 0$ is $\dfrac{3}{a}$.

d. The product of the roots of the quadratic equation $\frac{1}{2}x^2 - x + 2 = 0$ is 4.

e. $\forall_x \ \sqrt{x + 3}$ is a real number if and only if $x > -3$.

f. The equation "$x^2 = y^2$" is equivalent to the equation "$x = y$".

g. If r is a root of $(x - a)^2 = (\sqrt{bx + c})^2$ and r does not satisfy the equation $x - a = \sqrt{bx + c}$, then r is a solution of the equation $x - a = -\sqrt{bx + c}$.

h. The equation $2x + 3 + (2x + 3)^{\frac{1}{2}} - 2 = 0$ is equivalent to *some* equation having "quadratic form".

i. The open sentence "$x = y$ or $x = -y$" is equivalent to the open sentence "$x^2 = y^2$".

j. $x^4 + 4x^2 - 1 = 0$ patterns in the form $y^2 + 4y - 1 = 0$ where x^4 has been replaced by y.

2. Find the real number solution set for each of the following open sentences.

a. $4x^2 - 4x + 1 = 0$

b. $12x^2 - x - 1 = 0$

c. $3x^2 + 4x + 5 = 0$

d. $x^2 - 5x - 6 = 18$

e. $\dfrac{4}{x + 1} - \dfrac{x}{x - 2} = -2$

f. $\dfrac{3x}{x + 2} - \dfrac{x}{x + 1} = 2$

g. $\dfrac{5}{x + 3} + \dfrac{2}{x} = \dfrac{6}{x + 1}$

h. $\sqrt{x^2} = -6$

i. $\sqrt{x^2 + 1} + \sqrt{2x} = 0$

j. $4x^4 - 7x^2 - 2 = 0$

k. $6x^{-2} + x^{-1} - 1 = 0$

l. $x^2 + 8x + 12 > 0$

m. $49t^2 + 70t + 9 < 0$

n. $\dfrac{x}{7} = \dfrac{7}{x}$

o. $x - 5 = \dfrac{14}{x}$

3. If the sum of the roots of the quadratic equation $ax^2 + 2x - 4 = 0$ is -8, then what is the product of its roots?

4. If the discriminant of the quadratic equation $3x^2 - x + c = 0$ is 25, then what is the value of c?

5. If the price of oranges rises 10 cents per dozen, a person will be able to buy two dozen fewer oranges with $6.00 than was possible at the original price. What was the original price?

6. How wide a uniform border should be left on a page 7 inches by 11 inches to have an area of 45 square inches available for printed matter?

CHAPTER TEST

1. Find the real number solution set for each of the following open sentences.

a. $x^2 - 2x = 4$

b. $\dfrac{1}{x - 1} - \dfrac{1}{x + 1} = \dfrac{x}{x + 1}$

c. $x = 3 + \sqrt{14 - 2x}$

d. $16x^4 - 40x^2 + 9 = 0$

e. $16x^2 - 8x + 15 > 0$

f. $3x^2 + 7x > 6$

2. How many real number solutions does a quadratic equation have if its discriminant is equal to the following?

a. 73

b. (-5)

3. If the discriminant of $3x^2 + bx = 1$ is 48 and $b < 0$, then what is the value of b?

4. What are the sum and product of the roots of $2x^2 = 4x + 5$?

5. Write an equation in x whose solution set is $\{\frac{3}{2}, -\frac{2}{3}\}$. The equation should be in the form $ax^2 \pm bx \pm c = 0$ for some *integers* a, b, and c.

6. If an object is shot vertically upward with an initial velocity of v feet per second, its height, S, above the starting level, measured in feet, after t seconds, is given approximately by the formula $S = vt - 16t^2$. How many seconds are required for an object to reach a height of 192 feet if it is shot vertically upward with an initial velocity of 128 feet per second?

CUMULATIVE REVIEW

The following exercises cover the material in chapters 5 through 8.

1. Using the data contained in the graph below, make the necessary computations and answer the following questions.

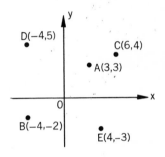

a. Is A between B and C?

b. What are the coordinates of the midpoint of $\overline{DE}$?

c. What is the slope of $\overleftrightarrow{AE}$?

d. $BD = ?$

e. $AB = ?$

f. Is $\overleftrightarrow{AC}$ perpendicular to $\overleftrightarrow{AE}$?

g. Write a "simple" equation in x and y of the line passing through points E and C.

h. Write an equation in x and y of all points $P(x, y)$ which are two units from point D.

2. Write a "simple" equation in x and y of the line whose slope is $\frac{3}{4}$ and whose y-intercept is 0.

3. Write a "simple" equation in x and y of the line which passes through the point $P(5, -3)$ and which has a slope of $\frac{4}{3}$.

4. Use coordinate geometry to prove the following theorem.

> The midpoint of the hypotenuse of a right triangle is equidistant from the three vertices of the triangle.

5. Let $A = \{m \mid m$ is a real number and $-1 \le m \le 3\}$ and $B = \{-2, 3, 5\}$.

    a. Graph $A \times B$.   **b.** Graph $B \times A$.

6. True or false?

    a. If $A = \{2, 4, 6, 8\}$ and $B = \{1, 3, 5, 9\}$, then $\{(1, 2), (3, 4), (5, 6), (9, 8)\}$ is a relation in $A \times B$.

    b. The domain of the relation $\{(-3, 5), (0, 5), (4, 1)\}$ is $\{-3, 0, 4\}$.

c. The range of the relation $\{\ldots, (-2,1), (-1,1), (0,1), (1,1), (2,1), \ldots\}$ is $\{\ldots, -2, -1, 0, 1, 2, \ldots\}$.

d. If $f = \{(x,y)\,|\,x^2 + y^2 = 0\}$, then f is a function.

e. If $g = \{(x,y)\,|\,y = [x]\}$, then $g' = \{(x,y)\,|\,x = [y]\}$.

f. $\{(x, -3)\}$ is a constant function.

g. $\{(x,y)\,|\,y = -2\}$ is a linear function.

h. The inverse of every linear function is a linear function.

i. $[3] - [2.9] = 1$

j. $\{(x,y)\,|\,x - 2y = 0\}$ is a direct proportion.

k. The constant of variation for the direct proportion $\left\{(x,y)\,\left|\,\dfrac{y}{3} = 2x\right.\right\}$ is 2.

l. $\left\{(x,y)\,\left|\,\dfrac{y}{2} = \dfrac{3}{x}\right.\right\}$ is an inverse proportion.

m. No inverse proportion contains an ordered pair whose second component is 0.

n. The graph of the solution set of $2y + x > 3$ is a closed half-plane.

o. The graph of the solution set of $y \geq 2x - 7$ is the union of the graphs of $y = 2x - 7$ and of $y > 2x - 7$.

7. Suppose that

$$f = \{(x,y)\,|\,x^2 + y^2 + 2 = 0\}$$
$$g = \{(x,y)\,|\,y = -\tfrac{1}{2}x + 2\}$$
$$h = \{(x,y)\,|\,x = 3\}$$
$$r = \{(x,y)\,|\,y = -2\}$$
$$t = \{(x,y)\,|\,y = -|x| + 1\}$$

a. Describe the graph of relation f.

b. Graph g. Is g a function?

c. Graph g'. Is g' a function?

d. Graph h. Is h a function?

e. Graph h'. Is h' a function?

f. Graph r. Is r a function?

g. Graph r'. Is r' a function?

h. Graph t. Is t a function?

i. Graph t'. Is t' a function?

8. Specify each of the following relations by either the roster method or an open sentence, whichever is appropriate.

a.

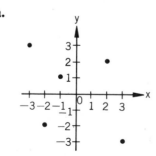

b.

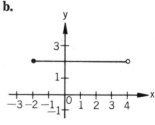

c.

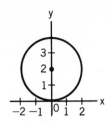

d.

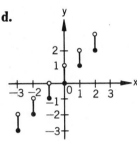

(incomplete graph)

e.

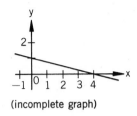

(incomplete graph)

9. Let $g(x) = (x + 1)$ and $f(x) = x^2$.

a. Find $g(2) \cdot g(h)$.

b. Find $g(2h)$.

c. True or false?
   $\forall_h \ g(2h) = g(2) \cdot g(h)$

d. Find $g(f(x))$.

e. Find $f(g(x))$.

f. True or false?
   $\forall_x \ g(f(x)) = f(g(x))$

g. Find $f(2) - f(h)$.

h. Find $f(2 - h)$.

i. True or false?
   $\forall_h \ f(2 - h) = f(2) - f(h)$

10. True or false?

a. $\{(x, y) \mid 2x^2 - y + 3 = 0\}$ is a quadratic function.

b. The graph of $\{(x, y) \mid y = -3x^2 + x - 2\}$ is the "mirror reflection" in the x-axis of the graph of $\{(x, y) \mid y = 3x^2 - x + 2\}$.

c. The quadratic function $\{(x, y) \mid y = \frac{1}{4}(x + 3)^2\}$ has zero for its minimum value.

d. The vertex of the parabola which is the graph of $\{(x, y) \mid y = 2(x - 3)^2 + 8\}$ is $(8, 3)$.

e. The parabola which is the graph of $\{(x, y) \mid y + (x + 2)^2 = 3\}$ opens upward.

f. $\{t \mid (t - 2)^2 = 1\} = \{3\}$

g. $\{x \mid 2x^2 - 3 = 0\} = \left\{\sqrt{\dfrac{3}{2}}\right\}$

h. The discriminant of the quadratic equation $7x - 5 = 3x^2$ is 109.

i. $\forall_{h \neq 0} \forall_k \forall_c$, if $k^2 - 4hc \geq 0$, then

$$\{x \mid hx^2 + kx + c = 0\} = \left\{\dfrac{-k + \sqrt{k^2 + 4hc}}{2h}, \ \dfrac{-k - \sqrt{k^2 + 4hc}}{2h}\right\}$$

j. The sum of the roots of $y^2 + \frac{1}{4} = y$ is -1.

k. The product of the roots of $2x^2 + 9x = 5$ is $\frac{5}{2}$.

l. $\forall_{x \neq 3}\ x(x - 3) \cdot \left[\dfrac{1}{x} - \dfrac{2}{x - 3}\right] = -x - 3$

m. $\forall_r \forall_s$, if $r = s$, then $r^2 = s^2$

n. $\forall_r \forall_s$, if $r^2 = s^2$, then $r = s$

o. The real number solution set of the equation $x^4 + x^2 + 1 = 0$ is ϕ.

p. The open sentence $(x + 2)^2 < 5$ is equivalent to the open sentence $(x + 2 < \sqrt{5}$ and $x + 2 > -\sqrt{5})$.

11. Graph each of the following quadratic functions. Select an appropriate scale for each axis.

a. $\left\{(x, y) \mid y = \dfrac{1}{3}(x - 3)^2 + 3\right\}$ **b.** $\{(x, y) \mid y = -x^2 + 5x - 12\}$

12. Express each of the following equations in the form $y = a(x \pm k)^2 \pm p$ for some real numbers a, k, and p.

a. $4x^2 - y = 3x + 2$ **b.** $\dfrac{x}{3} - x^2 + y = 1$

13. Find the real number solution set for each of the following open sentences

a. $x^2 - \dfrac{1}{3}x - \dfrac{5}{12} = 0$ **d.** $\dfrac{x^2 + 3}{x^2 - 2x - 3} = \dfrac{3}{x - 3}$

b. $\dfrac{1}{5}x^2 - 2x + 5 = 0$ **e.** $(x - 4)^4 + 18 = 11(x - 4)^2$

f. $\sqrt{3 - 2x} - \sqrt{2x + 2} = 3$

c. $3x^2 + \dfrac{1}{4} = \dfrac{1}{2}x$ **g.** $3x^2 - 4x - 2 < 0$

14. There are two positive numbers for each of which the following is true: adding 2 to the number and squaring the sum results in the same number as multiplying the original number by 12 and adding $\frac{1}{4}$ to the product. Determine the two numbers.

BIBLIOGRAPHY

Allendoerfer, C. B. and Oakley, C. O. *Fundamentals of Freshman Mathematics.* New York: McGraw-Hill Book Co., Inc., 1959. pp. 156–159.

Heimer, R. T., Kocher, F. and Lottes, J. J. *A Program in Contemporary Algebra.* New York: Holt, Rinehart and Winston, Inc., 1963, Book 4, Units IV and V.

Nichols, Eugene D. *Modern Elementary Algebra.* New York: Holt, Rinehart and Winston, Inc., 1965. Chapter 12.

Sanford, V. *A Short History of Mathematics.* New York: Houghton Mifflin Co., 1930. pp. 165–168.

School Mathematics Study Group. *Mathematics, Part I.* New Haven: Yale University Press, 1961. pp. 222–246.

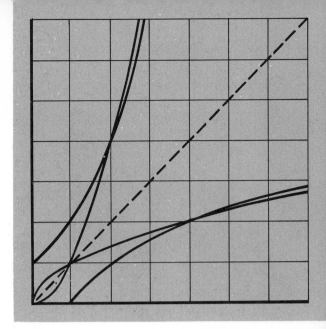

CHAPTER 9

Complex Numbers

ANOTHER KIND OF NUMBER

In this chapter we shall "extend" the system of real numbers; that is, we will present another number system, but a portion of the new system will "behave exactly like" the real number system. This richer system permits us to do more things with numbers *and* provides a very useful tool for some scientists and engineers.

Although this number system will probably be new to you, it has been known for more than one hundred years. If was formulated by Karl Friedrich Gauss (1777-1855) in 1797 but he did not publish his writing until 1835. You may wish to learn more about this famous mathematician. If you do, read about him in books such as *Men of Mathematics* by E. T. Bell or *Mathematics and the Imagination* by E. Kasner and J. R. Newman.·

Earlier in this book, we established a one-to-one correspondence between all the points of a plane and all ordered pairs of real numbers. This correspondence is suggested in figure 1.

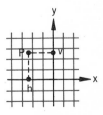

Fig. 1

251

Describe, once again, this one-to-one correspondence which pairs each point P of the plane and each ordered pair of real numbers (h, v).

Each such ordered pair of real numbers is called a *complex number*. Eight complex numbers are listed below.

$(5, -3)$ $\qquad$ $\left(\dfrac{1}{2}, \sqrt{6}\right)$ $\qquad$ $(\pi, -4.27)$ $\qquad$ $(0, 1)$

$(8, 8)$ $\qquad$ $(1, 0)$ $\qquad$ $(-2.5, -3.68)$ $\qquad$ $\left(\dfrac{1}{5}, \dfrac{-2}{5}\right)$

■ *Definition of Complex Number*   For all real numbers a and b, each ordered pair of real numbers (a, b) is a *complex number z;* and each complex number z is an ordered pair of real numbers (a, b).

We shall designate the set of all complex numbers by the letter C. List five more members of C, the set of complex numbers.

Equality of complex numbers

The definition of equality for ordered pairs of real numbers suggests the following definition of equality of complex numbers.

■ *Definition of Equality of Complex Numbers*   For all complex numbers z_1 and z_2, if $z_1 = (a, b)$ and $z_2 = (c, d)$, then $z_1 = z_2$ if and only if $a = c$ and $b = d$.

Examples: $\quad$ *i.* $\quad$ $(2, 5) = (\sqrt{4}, 4 + 1)$ since $2 = \sqrt{4}$ and $5 = 4 + 1$.

$\qquad\qquad$ *ii.* $\quad$ $(2, 3) \neq (3, 2)$ since $2 \neq 3$.

EXERCISES

1. Determine m and n for each of the following according to the definition of equality of complex numbers.

a. $(m, -5) = (4, n)$

b. $(-m, 2) = (3, 4n)$

c. $(3m, 17) = \left(2, \dfrac{n}{3}\right)$

d. $(3 - m, n - 3) = (6, 6)$

e. $(4m + 3, 2) = (0, \sqrt{n})$

f. $\left(\dfrac{m}{5}, \dfrac{3n}{4}\right) = (.6, 7.5)$

g. $\left(3 + \dfrac{2}{m}, 5\right) = \left(7, \dfrac{n}{4} - 2\right)$

h. $(2mn, 4) = (40, m)$

i. $(m + n, m - n) = (2, -6)$

j. $(2m + 3n, m + 2n) = (4, -4)$

2. True or false?

a. $(2 - 3, 0 - 5) = (-1, 5)$

b. $\{6, 4\} = \{4, 6\}$

c. $(6, 4) = (4, 6)$

d. $(3, 4^2) = (\sqrt{9}, 16)$

e. For all real numbers a, b, c, d, e, and f

     i. $(a, b) = (a, b)$

    ii. $[(a, b) = (c, d)] \to [(c, d) = (a, b)]$

   iii. $[(a, b) = (c, d) \text{ and } (c, d) = (e, f)] \to (a, b) = (e, f)$

    iv. $[(a, b) = (c, d)] \to [(b, a) = (d, c)]$

     v. $[(a, b) = (c, d)] \to [(d, c) = (b, a)]$

    vi. $[(a, b) = (c, d)] \to [(c, d) = (b, a)]$

   vii. $[(a, b) = (b, a)] \to [a = b]$

f. $(\sqrt{2^2 + 3^2}, \ \sqrt{2^2} + \sqrt{3^2}) = (\sqrt{2^2} + \sqrt{3^2}, \ \sqrt{2^2 + 3^2})$

g. $(2.4\overline{9}, \ \sqrt{32}) = (2.5, \ 4\sqrt{2})$

ADDITION OF COMPLEX NUMBERS

We will now learn how to add, subtract, multiply, divide, and perform other operations with complex numbers. Addition for complex numbers is defined as follows:

■   *Definition of Addition of Complex Numbers* For all complex numbers z_1 and z_2, if $z_1 = (a, b)$ and $z_2 = (c, d)$, then $z_1 + z_2 = (a + c, b + d)$.

Note the use of the heavy mark (+) to indicate addition for complex numbers and the usual mark (+) to indicate addition for real numbers; notice also that addition for complex numbers is defined in terms of addition for *real* numbers.

Examples: *i.* $(3, 4) + (2, 7) = (3 + 2, 4 + 7) = (5, 11)$

           ii. $(-5, 6) + (8, -4) = (-5 + 8, 6 + (-4)) = (3, 2)$

          iii. $\left(\sqrt{2}, \frac{1}{2}\right) + \left(\sqrt{3}, \frac{1}{3}\right) = \left(\sqrt{2} + \sqrt{3}, \frac{5}{6}\right)$

EXERCISES

Compute.

1. $(8, -3) + (2, 7)$

2. $\left(\frac{2}{3}, \frac{1}{4}\right) + \left(\frac{3}{7}, \frac{3}{4}\right)$

3. $(-9, 4.6) + (6.47, -5.3)$

4. $(\sqrt{2}, \ \sqrt{3}) + (\sqrt{5}, \ \sqrt{6})$

5. $(10, 7) + (10, -7)$

6. $(-4, -3) + (-4, 3)$

7. $(121, -9.47) + (121, 9.47)$

8. $(a, b) + (a, -b)$

9. $\left(\frac{7}{8}, -\frac{5}{7}\right) + (0, 0)$

10. $(\pi, -\sqrt{6}) + (0, 0)$

11. $(3.17, -3.17) + (0, 0)$

12. $(c, d) + (0, 0)$

13. $(5, 6) + (-5, -6)$

14. $(-4, 9) + (4, -9)$

15. $(3, -2) + (-3, 2)$

16. $(e, f) + (-e, -f)$

17. $(8, 3) + (2, -4)$

18. $(2, -4) + (8, 3)$

19. $(8217, -6428) + (15, 6)$

20. $(15, 6) + (8217, -6428)$

21. $(a, b) + (c, d)$

22. $(c, d) + (a, b)$

23. $(8, 0) + (7, 0)$

24. $\left(\frac{1}{2}, 0\right) + \left(\frac{1}{3}, 0\right)$

25. $(-6, 0) + (2, 0)$

26. $(a, 0) + (b, 0)$

CLOSURE, COMMUTATIVITY, AND ASSOCIATIVITY OF COMPLEX NUMBERS UNDER ADDITION

Verify the following three statements by computing.

$$(-5, 2) + (4, 1.3) = (-1, 3.3)$$
$$(-6, -\pi) + (-2, 3\pi) = (-8, 2\pi)$$
$$(612, -722) + \left(\frac{1}{2}, \frac{1}{3}\right) = \left(612\frac{1}{2}, -721\frac{2}{3}\right)$$

Is each of the three sums a complex number?

These statements suggest the following theorem which states that C, the set of all complex numbers, is *closed* under addition $(+)$.

Theorem 1 $\forall_{z_1 \epsilon C} \forall_{z_2 \epsilon C}$ $z_1 + z_2$ is a complex number.

Proof   Suppose $z_1 = (a, b)$ and $z_2 = (c, d)$

Then $z_1 + z_2$

$$= (a, b) + (c, d) \qquad \text{Why?}$$
$$= (a + c, b + d) \qquad \text{Why?}$$

and $(a + c, b + d)$ is a complex number   Why?

Now, verify the following three equations by computing.

$$(-5, 2) + (4, 1.3) = (4, 1.3) + (-5, 2)$$
$$(-6, -\pi) + (-2, 3\pi) = (-2, 3\pi) + (-6, -\pi)$$
$$(612, -722) + \left(\frac{1}{2}, \frac{1}{3}\right) = \left(\frac{1}{2}, \frac{1}{3}\right) + (612, -722)$$

These statements suggest the following theorem which states that addition of complex numbers is *commutative*.

Theorem 2 $\forall_{z_1 \epsilon C} \forall_{z_2 \epsilon C}$ $z_1 + z_2 = z_2 + z_1$

Proof   Suppose $z_1 = (a, b)$ and $z_2 = (c, d)$

Then $z_1 + z_2$

$$= (a, b) + (c, d) \qquad \text{Why?}$$
$$= (a + c, b + d) \qquad \text{Why?}$$
$$= (c + a, d + b) \qquad \text{Why?}$$
$$= (c, d) + (a, b) \qquad \text{Why?}$$
$$= z_2 + z_1 \qquad \text{Why?}$$

EXERCISES

1. Verify the following equation by computing.

$$[(2, -6) + (3, -4)] + (-9, 12) = (2, -6) + [(3, -4) + (-9, 12)]$$

2. Write three more equations involving ordered pairs of real numbers that pattern in the form seen in problem 1. Verify each of the three by computing.

3. Prove that addition of complex numbers is *associative;* that is, prove
$$\forall_{z_1 \epsilon C} \forall_{z_2 \epsilon C} \forall_{z_3 \epsilon C} \ (z_1 + z_2) + z_3 = z_1 + (z_2 + z_3) \qquad [\text{HINT}: \text{ Review the proof of}$$
Theorem 2]

4. True or false? For all real numbers c and d

  a. $(c, 0) + (d, 0) = (c + d, 0)$
  b. $(c, d) + (c, -d) = (2c, 0)$
  c. $(c, d) = (c, 0) + (0, d)$

THE ADDITIVE IDENTITY AND ADDITIVE INVERSES FOR COMPLEX NUMBERS

Verify the following three equations by computing.

$$(8, -6) + (0, 0) = (8, -6)$$
$$\left(\sqrt{7}, \frac{2}{3}\right) + (0, 0) = \left(\sqrt{7}, \frac{2}{3}\right)$$
$$(42.6, -17.39) + (0, 0) = (42.6, -17.39)$$

The statements above suggest that there is a complex number z, namely $(0, 0)$, that is the *additive identity* in C. The existence of this number and its property is established by the following theorem.

Theorem 3 There exists a unique complex number z_1, namely $(0, 0)$, such that
$$\forall_{z_2 \epsilon C} \ z_2 + z_1 = z_2.$$

Proof Suppose $z_2 = (a, b)$, $z_1 = (x, y)$, and $z_2 + z_1 = z_2$.

Thus, if $z_2 + z_1 = z_2$

then $(a, b) + (x, y) = (a, b)$	Why?
$(a + x, b + y) = (a, b)$	Why?
$a + x = a$ and $b + y = b$	Why?
$x = 0$ and $y = 0$	Why?

and $(x, y) = (0, 0) = z_1$

Now, verify the following three equations by computing.

$$(6, -2) + (-6, 2) = (0, 0)$$
$$\left(\frac{1}{2}, \frac{2}{3}\right) + \left(-\frac{1}{2}, -\frac{2}{3}\right) = (0, 0)$$
$$(-42, 16) + (42, -16) = (0, 0)$$

These statements suggest that for each complex number z there exists a complex number, called the *additive inverse* of z, whose behavior is stated by the following theorem.

Theorem 4 $\forall_{z \epsilon C}$, there exists a unique complex number (called the additive inverse of z and denoted by $-z$) such that $z + (-z) = (0,0)$; and, if $z = (a, b)$, then $-z = (-a, -b)$.

Proof Suppose $z = (a, b)$, $-z = (x, y)$, and $z + (-z) = (0,0)$.

Thus, if $z + (-z) = (0,0)$

then $(a, b) + (x, y) = (0,0)$	Why?
$(a+x, b+y) = (0,0)$	Why?
$a + x = 0$ and $b + y = 0$	Why?
$x = -a$ and $y = -b.$	Why?

Hence $(x, y) = (-a, -b) = -z$ for $z = (a, b)$ and $z + (-z) = (0,0)$.

What is the additive inverse of $(7, -6)$? $(-3, 0)$? $\left(0, \dfrac{1}{2}\right)$?

EXERCISES

1. For each complex number, list its additive inverse.

   a. $(2, 5)$
   b. $(2, -5)$
   c. $(-3, 6)$
   d. $(-8, -10)$
   e. $(7, 7)$

   f. $(1, 0)$

   g. $(0, 1)$
   h. $(0, 0)$
   i. $(-2, -2)$
   j. $(\sqrt{5}, -\sqrt{6})$
   k. $(x - y, x + y)$

   l. $\left(\dfrac{-5}{6}, \dfrac{3-t}{4}\right)$

2. True or false? For *all* complex numbers z_1, z_2, and z_3

   a. $z_1 + z_2 = (0, 0)$
   b. $(z_1 + z_2) \epsilon C$
   c. $z_2 + z_3 = z_3 + z_2$
   d. $z_1 + (0, 0) = z_1$
   e. $(0, 0) + z_1 = (0, 0)$

   f. $-z_1 + z_1 = (0, 0)$
   g. $z_1 + (z_2 + z_3) = (z_1 + z_2) + z_3$
   h. $-z_3 \epsilon C$
   i. $(0, 0) + z_1 = z_1$
   j. $z_2 + (-z_2) = (0, 0)$

3. True or false?

   a. The additive inverse of the additive identity is the additive identity.

   b. $-\left(5 - \sqrt{6}, -\dfrac{1}{2}\right) = \left(5 + \sqrt{6}, \dfrac{1}{2}\right)$

   c. $-(-5, 7) = (|-5|, -7)$

   d. $-(9, |-8 + 6|) = (-9, |8 - 6|)$

Subtraction of complex numbers

In the set of *natural* numbers, $a - b$ is called the difference of a and b and is defined to be the natural number c (if it exists) for which $b + c = a$. For example

$$8 - 6 = 2 \text{ since } 6 + 2 = 8$$
$$19 - 7 = 12 \text{ since } 7 + 12 = 19$$
$$4 - 17 \text{ does not exist (is not a natural number) since}$$
there is no natural number n for which $17 + n = 4$

In the set of *real* numbers, $r_1 - r_2$ is called the difference of r_1 and r_2 and is defined in a similar way; that is, $r_1 - r_2$ is the real number r_3 for which $r_2 + r_3 = r_1$. For example

$$4.27 - 1.13 = 3.14 \text{ since } 1.13 + 3.14 = 4.27$$
$$3.27 - 5.69 = -2.42 \text{ since } 5.69 + (-2.42) = 3.27$$
$$\frac{1}{2} - \frac{1}{3} = \frac{1}{6} \text{ since } \frac{1}{3} + \frac{1}{6} = \frac{1}{2}$$

Likewise, in the set of *complex* numbers, $z_1 - z_2$ is called the difference of z_1 and z_2 and is defined as the complex number z_3 for which $z_2 + z_3 = z_1$. Using this definition, we shall prove that z_3 is the complex number $z_1 + (-z_2)$.

Theorem 5 $\forall_{z_1 \epsilon C} \forall_{z_2 \epsilon C} \ z_1 - z_2 = z_1 + (-z_2)$

Proof   Suppose $z_1 = (a, b)$, $z_2 = (c, d)$, and $z_3 = (x, y)$ for $z_1 - z_2 = z_3$; that is, for $z_2 + z_3 = z_1$.

Thus, if $z_2 + z_3 = z_1$

then $(c, d) + (x, y) = (a, b)$	Why?
$(c + x, d + y) = (a, b)$	Why?
$c + x = a$ and $d + y = b$	Why?
$x = a - c$ and $y = b - d$	Why?
$x = a + (-c)$ and $y = b + (-d)$	Why?

and $z_3 = (x, y) = (a + (-c), b + (-d))$	
$= (a, b) + (-c, -d)$	Why?
$= (a, b) + (-(c, d))$	Why?
$= z_1 + (-z_2)$.	Why?

And since $z_3 = z_1 + (-z_2)$, it follows from the definition that

$$z_1 - z_2 = z_1 + (-z_2)$$

Examples: i. $(4, 7) - (5, 3) = (4, 7) + (-(5, 3))$
$$= (4, 7) + (-5, -3)$$
$$= (-1, 4)$$

ii. $(3, -6) - (-5, 9) = (3, -6) + (-(-5, 9))$
$$= (3, -6) + (5, -9)$$
$$= (8, -15)$$

Note the use of the heavy mark $(-)$ to indicate subtraction for complex numbers.

EXERCISES

1. Prove that C is closed with respect to subtraction; that is, prove that for all complex numbers z_1 and z_2, $z_1 - z_2$ is a complex number. [HINT: Review the proof of Theorem 1.]

2. Prove that $(a, b) - (c, d) = (a - c, b - d)$, for all real numbers a, b, c, and d.

3. Compute.

a. $(3, -4) - (7, 6)$

b. $(4.4, 2.9) - (3.3, 1.5)$

c. $(-7, -2) - (5, -3)$

d. $\left(\frac{1}{4}, -\frac{1}{4}\right) - \left(\frac{1}{3}, \frac{1}{3}\right)$

e. $(-\pi, 7) - (-3\pi, -2)$

f. $(1, 0) - (0, 1)$

g. $(12, 0) - (4, 0)$

h. $(3, 0) - (7, 0)$

i. $(-2, 0) - (-6, 0)$

j. $\left(\frac{1}{3}, 0\right) - \left(\frac{1}{4}, 0\right)$

k. $(-8, 0) - (-3, 0)$

l. $(a, 0) - (b, 0)$

m. $(-7, 6) - (0, 0)$

n. $(5, -32) - (0, 0)$

o. $(a, b) - (0, 0)$

p. $(0, 0) - (-7, 6)$

q. $(0, 0) - (5, -32)$

r. $(0, 0) - (a, b)$

4. True or false? For all complex numbers z_1, z_2, and z_3

a. $z_1 - z_2 = z_2 - z_1$

b. $z_1 - z_3 \in C$

c. $(0, 0) - z_1 = -z_1$

d. $z_2 - (0, 0) = (0, 0)$

e. $z_3 - z_3 = (0, 0)$

f. $z_2 - z_3 = -z_3 + z_2$

g. $z_1 - (0, 0) = z_1$

h. $(z_1 - z_2) - z_3 = z_1 - (z_2 - z_3)$

MULTIPLICATION OF COMPLEX NUMBERS

The definition of the product of a pair of complex numbers may seem complicated to you at this time. Later, you will see that it provides us with a way of determining a number whose square corresponds to a negative real number. Is there a *real* number whose *square* is a *negative real* number?

■ *Definition of Multiplication of Complex Numbers* $\forall_{z_1 \in C} \forall_{z_2 \in C}$, if $z_1 = (a, b)$ and $z_2 = (c, d)$, then $z_1 \cdot z_2 = (ac - bd, ad + bc)$.

Note the use of the heavy dot ($\cdot$) to indicate multiplication for complex numbers; also notice that multiplication for complex numbers is defined in terms of three operations for *real* numbers. Which three?

Examples:

i. $(2, 6) \cdot (3, 4) = (2 \cdot 3 - 6 \cdot 4, \ 2 \cdot 4 + 6 \cdot 3)$
$$= (6 - 24, \ 8 + 18) = (-18, \ 26)$$

ii. $(-5, 2) \cdot (6, -3) = (-5 \cdot 6 - 2(-3), \ -5(-3) + 2 \cdot 6)$
$$= (-30 + 6, \ 15 + 12) = (-24, \ 27)$$

EXERCISES

1. Compute.

a. $(3, 5) \cdot (2, 4)$

b. $(2, 4) \cdot (3, 5)$

c. $(-2, 6) \cdot (5, -1)$

d. $\left(\frac{1}{2}, \frac{1}{3}\right) \cdot (6, 12)$

e. $(-10, 7) \cdot (1, 1)$

f. $(-10, 7) \cdot (1, -1)$

g. $(-10, 7) \cdot (0, 1)$

h. $(-10, 7) \cdot (0, 0)$

i. $(-10, 7) \cdot (1, 0)$

j. $\left(\frac{2}{3}, -\frac{7}{12}\right) \cdot (1, 0)$

k. $(a, b) \cdot (1, 0)$

l. $(2, -6) \cdot (2, 6)$

m. $(3, 7) \cdot (3, -7)$

n. $(-5, 2) \cdot (-5, -2)$

o. $(a, b) \cdot (a, -b)$

p. $(-3k, 2t) \cdot (-3k, -2t)$

q. $(4, 0) \cdot (0, 1)$

r. $(-3, 0) \cdot (0, 1)$

s. $\left(\frac{7}{16}, 0\right) \cdot (0, 1)$

t. $(a, 0) \cdot (0, 1)$

u. $(6, 0) \cdot (5, 0)$

v. $(-2, 0) \cdot (-3, 0)$

w. $(14, 0) \cdot (-5, 0)$

x. $(-10, 0) \cdot (8, 0)$

y. $(a, 0) \cdot (b, 0)$

z. $\left(\frac{1}{2}, 0\right) \cdot \left(-\frac{1}{3}, 0\right)$

a′. $\left(-\frac{2}{3}, 0\right) \cdot \left(-\frac{5}{7}, 0\right)$

b′. $(3, 4) \cdot \left(\frac{3}{25}, \frac{-4}{25}\right)$

c′. $(2, 5) \cdot \left(\frac{2}{29}, \frac{-5}{29}\right)$

d′. $(-4, 3) \cdot \left(\frac{-4}{25}, \frac{-3}{25}\right)$

e′. $(-2, -7) \cdot \left(\frac{-2}{53}, \frac{7}{53}\right)$

f′. $(a, b) \cdot \left(\frac{a}{a^2 + b^2}, \frac{-b}{a^2 + b^2}\right)$, $[a^2 + b^2 \neq 0]$

2. Compute the following *powers* of $(0, 1)$.

a. the second power of $(0, 1)$; that is, $(0, 1) \cdot (0, 1)$

b. the third power of $(0, 1)$; that is, $(0, 1) \cdot (0, 1) \cdot (0, 1)$

c. the fourth power of $(0, 1)$

d. the fifth power of $(0, 1)$

e. the sixth power of $(0, 1)$

f. the seventh power of $(0, 1)$

g. the eighth power of $(0, 1)$

h. the ninth power of $(0, 1)$

i. the twelfth power of $(0, 1)$

j. the thirteenth power of $(0, 1)$

k. the fourteenth power of $(0, 1)$

l. the fifteenth power of $(0, 1)$

CLOSURE, COMMUTATIVITY, AND ASSOCIATIVITY OF COMPLEX NUMBERS UNDER MULTIPLICATION

Verify the following three statements by computing.

$$(3, 5) \cdot (2, 4) = (-14, 22)$$
$$(-2, 6) \cdot (5, -1) = (-4, 32)$$
$$\left(\frac{1}{2}, \frac{1}{3}\right) \cdot (-6, -12) = (1, -8)$$

Is each of the three products a complex number?

These statements suggest the following theorem which states that C is *closed* with respect to multiplication.

Theorem 6 $\forall_{z_1 \epsilon C} \forall_{z_2 \epsilon C} \; z_1 \cdot z_2$ is a complex number.

Proof   Suppose $z_1 = (a, b)$ and $z_2 = (c, d)$

Then $z_1 \cdot z_2$

$= (a, b) \cdot (c, d)$	Why?
$= (ac - bd, ad + bc)$	Why?

and $(ac - bd, ad + bc)$ is a complex number   Why?

Now, verify the following three equations by computing.

$$(2, 4) \cdot (-3, 5) = (-3, 5) \cdot (2, 4)$$
$$(100, 5) \cdot (1, 6) = (1, 6) \cdot (100, 5)$$
$$(-2, -3) \cdot (5, -7) = (5, -7) \cdot (-2, -3)$$

These statements suggest the following theorem which states that multiplication of complex numbers is *commutative*.

Theorem 7 $\forall_{z_1 \epsilon C} \forall_{z_2 \epsilon C} \; z_1 \cdot z_2 = z_2 \cdot z_1$

Proof   Suppose $z_1 = (a, b)$ and $z_2 = (c, d)$.

Then $z_1 \cdot z_2$

$= (a, b) \cdot (c, d)$	Why?
$= (ac - bd, ad + bc)$	Why?
$= (ca - db, cb + da)$	Why?
$= (c, d) \cdot (a, b)$	Why?
$= z_2 \cdot z_1$	Why?

EXERCISES

1.   Verify the following equation by computing.

$$[(2, 5) \cdot (-4, 3)] \cdot (-2, -7) = (2, 5) \cdot [(-4, 3) \cdot (-2, -7)]$$

2.   Write three more equations involving ordered pairs of real numbers that pattern in the form seen in problem **1.** Verify each of the three by computing.

3.   Prove that multiplication of complex numbers is *associative*; that is, prove

$$\forall_{z_1 \in C} \forall_{z_2 \in C} \forall_{z_3 \in C} \; (z_1 \cdot z_2) \cdot z_3 = z_1 \cdot (z_2 \cdot z_3)$$

[HINT: Review the proof of Theorem 7.]

4.   True or false? For all real numbers c and d

a. $(c, 0) \cdot (d, 0) = (cd, 0)$ **c.** $(c, 0) \cdot (0, 1) = (0, c)$

b. $(c, d) \cdot (c, -d) = (c^2 + d^2, 0)$

5.   Prove that multiplication is *distributive* over addition in the set of complex numbers; that is, prove

$$\forall_{z_1 \in C} \forall_{z_2 \in C} \forall_{z_3 \in C} \; z_1 \cdot (z_2 + z_3) = (z_1 \cdot z_2) + (z_1 \cdot z_3)$$

6.   Write three instances of the theorem proved in problem **5.** Verify each by computing.

THE MULTIPLICATIVE IDENTITY AND MULTIPLICATIVE INVERSES FOR COMPLEX NUMBERS

Verify the following three equations by computing.

$$(8, -6) \cdot (1, 0) = (8, -6)$$

$$\left(\sqrt{7}, \frac{2}{3}\right) \cdot (1, 0) = \left(\sqrt{7}, \frac{2}{3}\right)$$

$$(42.6, -17.39) \cdot (1, 0) = (42.6, -17.39)$$

The statements above suggest that there is a complex number z, namely $(1, 0)$, that is the *multiplicative identity* in C. The existence of this number and its property is established by the following theorem.

Theorem 8   There exists a unique complex number z_1, namely $(1, 0)$, such that $\forall_{z_2 \in C} \; z_2 \cdot z_1 = z_2$.

Proof   Suppose $z_2 = (a, b)$, $z_1 = (x, y)$, and $z_2 \cdot z_1 = z_2$.

Thus, if $z_2 \cdot z_1 = z_2$

then $(a, b) \cdot (x, y) = (a, b)$	Why?
$(ax - by, ay + bx) = (a, b)$	Why?
$ax - by = a$ and $ay + bx = b$	Why?

We must now solve the conjunction

$$(ax - by = a) \text{ and } (ay + bx = b)$$

Now, if (x_1, y_1) satisfies this conjunction, then we know that

$$(ax_1 - by_1 = a) \text{ and } (ay_1 + bx_1 = b)$$

Applying the multiplication property with $(-b)$ for the first equation and with a for the second equation, we obtain

$$(-abx_1 + b^2y_1 = -ab) \text{ and } (a^2y_1 + abx_1 = ab)$$

Applying the addition property

$$\forall_{r \in R} \forall_{s \in R} \forall_{t \in R} \forall_{u \in R}, \text{ if } r = s \text{ and } t = u, \text{ then } r + t = s + u$$

to the above conjunction, we obtain

$$a^2 y_1 + b^2 y_1 = 0$$

Therefore

$$y_1(a^2 + b^2) = 0$$

Hence

$$y_1 = 0 \text{ or } a^2 + b^2 = 0$$

[NOTE: $a^2 + b^2 = 0$ if and only if a and b are both zero; that is, $(a, b) = (0, 0)$.]

Now, if $y_1 = 0$ and $ax_1 - by_1 = a$ we may replace y_1 by 0 and obtain

$$ax_1 - b \cdot 0 = a$$
$$ax_1 = a$$
$$x_1 = 1, \ (a \neq 0)$$

Thus, $(x, y) = (1, 0) = z_1$ such that for each complex number z_2

$$z_2 \cdot z_1 = z_2$$

Compute

$$(-3, 7) \cdot (1, 0) \qquad \left(\frac{2}{3}, -4.6\right) \cdot (1, 0) \qquad (0, 0) \cdot (1, 0)$$

Now, compute to verify that each of the following three equations is true.

$$(3, 4) \cdot \left(\frac{3}{25}, \frac{-4}{25}\right) = (1, 0)$$

$$(2, -7) \cdot \left(\frac{2}{53}, \frac{7}{53}\right) = (1, 0)$$

$$(-5, 2) \cdot \left(\frac{-5}{29}, \frac{-2}{29}\right) = (1, 0)$$

The truth of these statements suggests that for each complex number z (except $(0, 0)$, as you will soon see), there exists a complex number, called the *multiplicative inverse* of z, whose behavior is stated by the following theorem.

Theorem 9 $\forall_{z \in C}$ except $(0, 0)$, there exists a unique complex number

$$\left(\text{called the multiplicative inverse of } z \text{ and denoted by } \frac{1}{z}\right)$$

such that

$$z \cdot \frac{1}{z} = (1, 0)$$

and if $z = (a, b)$, then

$$\frac{1}{z} = \left(\frac{a}{a^2 + b^2}, \frac{-b}{a^2 + b^2}\right)$$

Proof   Suppose $z = (a, b)$, $\dfrac{1}{z} = (x, y)$, and $z \cdot \dfrac{1}{z} = (1, 0)$.

Thus if $z \cdot \dfrac{1}{z} = (1, 0)$

then $\qquad (a, b) \cdot (x, y) = (1, 0) \qquad$ Why?

$\qquad\qquad (ax - by, ay + bx) = (1, 0) \qquad$ Why?

$\qquad\qquad ax - by = 1 \text{ and } ay + bx = 0 \qquad$ Why?

We must now solve the conjunction

$$(ax - by = 1) \text{ and } (ay + bx = 0)$$

Now, if (x_1, y_1) satisfies this conjunction, then we know that

$$(ax_1 - by_1 = 1) \text{ and } (ay_1 + bx_1 = 0)$$

Using the multiplication property with a for the first equation and with b for the second equation

$$(a^2 x_1 - aby_1 = a) \text{ and } (aby_1 + b^2 x_1 = 0)$$

Using the addition property

$$a^2 x_1 + b^2 x_1 = a$$
$$(a^2 + b^2)x_1 = a$$
$$x_1 = \frac{a}{a^2 + b^2}, \qquad (a^2 + b^2 \neq 0 \text{ and therefore } (a, b) \neq (0, 0))$$

Hence $x_1 = \dfrac{a}{a^2 + b^2}$ and $ay_1 + bx_1 = 0$.

Replacing x_1 by $\dfrac{a}{a^2 + b^2}$, we obtain

$$ay_1 + b\left(\frac{a}{a^2 + b^2}\right) = 0$$
$$ay_1 + \frac{ab}{a^2 + b^2} = 0$$
$$ay_1 = \frac{-ab}{a^2 + b^2}$$
$$y_1 = \frac{-b}{a^2 + b^2}, \qquad (a \neq 0)$$

Thus, $(x, y) = \left(\dfrac{a}{a^2 + b^2}, \dfrac{-b}{a^2 + b^2}\right) = \dfrac{1}{z}$ for which $z = (a, b) \neq (0, 0)$

and $z \cdot \dfrac{1}{z} = (1, 0)$.

The multiplicative inverse of $(3, 7)$ is $(\frac{3}{58}, \frac{-7}{58})$. What is $\dfrac{1}{z}$ if z is $(2, 5)$? $(2, -5)$? $(-2, -5)$? $(1, 0)$? $(0, 1)$? $(\frac{7}{3}, 0)$?

EXERCISES

1. For each complex number, determine its multiplicative inverse.

   a. $(3, 5)$ $\qquad$ e. $(5, 0)$ $\qquad\qquad$ h. $(t, 0), \ (t \neq 0)$

   b. $(-3, -5)$ $\qquad$ f. $\left(\dfrac{1}{3}, 0\right)$ $\qquad$ i. $(0.1, 0.2)$

   c. $(3, -5)$ $\qquad\qquad\qquad\qquad\quad$ j. $(5, 3m)$

   d. $(-3, 5)$ $\qquad$ g. $\left(\dfrac{-8}{7}, 0\right)$ $\qquad$ k. $(\sqrt{2}, \sqrt{3})$

l. $(-\sqrt{7}, \sqrt{5})$

m. $(-1, 0)$

q. $\left(0, -\frac{1}{3}\right)$

n. $(0, 1)$

r. $(0, b)$, $(b \neq 0)$

o. $(0, -1)$

s. $(-2t, -3w)$, $((t, w) \neq (0, 0))$

p. $(0, -3)$

t. $(t + 2, 5)$

2. True or false? For all complex numbers z_1, z_2, and z_3,

a. $z_1 \cdot z_2 = (1, 0)$

f. if $z_1 \neq (0,0)$, then $\dfrac{1}{z_1} \cdot z_1 = (1, 0)$

b. $(z_1 \cdot z_2) \in C$

g. $z_1 \cdot (z_2 \cdot z_3) = (z_1 \cdot z_2) \cdot z_3$

c. $z_1 \cdot z_2 = z_2 \cdot z_1$

h. if $z_3 \neq (0,0)$, then $\dfrac{1}{z_3}$ belongs to C

d. $z_1 \cdot (1, 0) = z_1$

i. $(1, 0) \cdot z_2 = z_2$

e. $(1, 0) \cdot z_1 = (1, 0)$

j. if $z_2 \neq (0,0)$, then $z_2 \cdot \dfrac{1}{z_2} = (1, 0)$

Division of complex numbers

In the set of *natural* numbers, $a \div b$ is defined to be the natural number c (if it exists) for which $b \cdot c = a$. For example

$$8 \div 2 = 4 \text{ since } 2 \cdot 4 = 8$$
$$51 \div 17 = 3 \text{ since } 17 \cdot 3 = 51$$
6 ÷ 4 does not exist (is not a natural number) since there is no natural number n for which $4 \cdot n = 6$

In the set of *real* numbers, $r_1 \div r_2$, $(r_2 \neq 0)$, is defined in a similar way to be the real number r_3 for which $r_2 \cdot r_3 = r_1$. For example

$$6.25 \div 1.25 = 5 \text{ since } 1.25(5) = 6.25$$
$$8 \div \sqrt{2} = 4\sqrt{2} \text{ since } \sqrt{2}(4\sqrt{2}) = 8$$
$$-30 \div \tfrac{1}{3} = -90 \text{ since } \tfrac{1}{3}(-90) = -30$$

Likewise, in the set of *complex* numbers $z_1 \div z_2$, $(z_2 \neq (0, 0))$ is defined to be the complex number z_3 for which $z_2 \cdot z_3 = z_1$. Using this definition we shall prove that z_3 is the complex number $z_1 \cdot \dfrac{1}{z_2}$ for which $z_1 \div z_2 = z_3$, $(z_2 \neq (0, 0))$.

Theorem 10 $\forall_{z_1 \in C} \forall_{z_2 \in C,\ z_2 \neq (0,0)}$ $z_1 \div z_2 = z_1 \cdot \dfrac{1}{z_2}$

Proof   Suppose $z_1 = (a, b)$, $z_2 = (c, d)$ and $z_3 = (x, y)$ for which $z_1 \div z_2 = z_3$; that is, for which $z_2 \cdot z_3 = z_1$.

Thus, if $z_2 \cdot z_3 = z_1$

then $(c, d) \cdot (x, y) = (a, b)$ Why?

$(cx - dy, cy + dx) = (a, b)$ Why?

$cx - dy = a$ and $cy + dx = b$ Why?

We must now solve the conjunction

$$(cx - dy = a) \text{ and } (cy + dx = b)$$

Suppose that (x_1, y_1) satisfies this conjunction; then we know that

$$(cx_1 - dy_1 = a) \text{ and } (cy_1 + dx_1 = b)$$

Using the multiplication property with $(-d)$ for the first equation and c for the second equation

$$(-cdx_1 + d^2y_1 = -ad) \text{ and } (c^2y_1 + cdx_1 = bc)$$

Using the addition property

$$c^2y_1 + d^2y_1 = bc - ad$$
$$(c^2 + d^2)y_1 = bc - ad$$

Thus $\qquad\qquad y_1 = \dfrac{bc - ad}{c^2 + d^2}, \quad (c^2 + d^2 \neq 0 \text{ and therefore}$

$$(c, d) \neq (0, 0))$$

Hence $\quad y_1 = \dfrac{bc - ad}{c^2 + d^2} \text{ and } cx_1 - dy_1 = a.$

Replacing y_1 by $\dfrac{bc - ad}{c^2 + d^2}$, we obtain

$$cx_1 - d\left(\frac{bc - ad}{c^2 + d^2}\right) = a$$

$$cx_1 = a + \frac{d(bc - ad)}{c^2 + d^2}$$

$$cx_1 = \frac{ac^2 + ad^2 + bcd - ad^2}{c^2 + d^2}$$

$$cx_1 = \frac{ac^2 + bcd}{c^2 + d^2}$$

$$x_1 = \frac{ac + bd}{c^2 + d^2}, \quad (c \neq 0)$$

Thus $\quad z_3 = (x, y) = \left(\dfrac{ac + bd}{c^2 + d^2}, \dfrac{bc - ad}{c^2 + d^2}\right)$

$$= (a, b) \cdot \left(\frac{c}{c^2 + d^2}, \frac{-d}{c^2 + d^2}\right)$$

$$= (a, b) \cdot \frac{1}{(c, d)}$$

$$= z_1 \cdot \frac{1}{z_2}$$

And since $z_3 = z_1 \cdot \dfrac{1}{z_2}$, it follows from the definition that

$$z_1 \div z_2 = z_1 \cdot \frac{1}{z_2}$$

Examples: i. $(-2, 7) \div (3, 4) = (-2, 7) \cdot \dfrac{1}{(3, 4)}$

$$= (-2, 7) \cdot \left(\frac{3}{25}, \frac{-4}{25}\right)$$

$$= \left(\frac{-6}{25} - \frac{-28}{25}, \frac{8}{25} + \frac{21}{25}\right)$$

$$= \left(\frac{22}{25}, \frac{29}{25}\right)$$

ii. $(7, -10) \div (3, -5) = (7, -10) \cdot \dfrac{1}{(3, -5)}$

$$= (7, -10) \cdot \left(\frac{3}{34}, \frac{5}{34}\right)$$

$$= \left(\frac{21}{34} - \frac{-50}{34}, \frac{35}{34} + \frac{-30}{34}\right)$$

$$= \left(\frac{71}{34}, \frac{5}{34}\right)$$

Note the use of the heavy mark ($\div$) to indicate division for complex numbers.

EXERCISES

1.   Prove that C is closed with respect to division; that is, prove that for all complex numbers z_1 and z_2, $z_1 \div z_2$ is a complex number, provided that $z_2 \neq (0, 0)$.

2.   Compute.

   a. $(4, 3) \div (2, 5)$
   b. $(4, 3) \div (2, -5)$
   c. $(8, 0) \div (2, 0)$
   d. $(2, 0) \div (8, 0)$
   e. $(-10, 0) \div (2, 0)$
   f. $(6, 0) \div \left(\dfrac{1}{3}, 0\right)$
   g. $(a, 0) \div (b, 0)$, $(b \neq 0)$
   h. $(5, -4) \div (1, 0)$
   i. $(-10, -6) \div (1, 0)$
   j. $(83, -712) \div (1, 0)$
   k. $(a, b) \div (1, 0)$

   l. $(6, 9) \div (1, -2)$
   m. $(6, 9) \div (-1, 2)$
   n. $(10, 2) \div (2, 3)$
   o. $(10, 2) \div (-2, -3)$
   p. $(a, b) \div (c, d)$, $[(c, d) \neq (0, 0)]$
   q. $(a, b) \div (-c, -d)$, $[(c, d) \neq (0, 0)]$
   r. $(8, 9) \div (8, 9)$
   s. $(a, b) \div (a, b)$, $[(a, b) \neq (0, 0)]$
   t. $(1, 0) \div (3, 4)$
   u. $\dfrac{1}{(3, 4)}$, [the multiplicative inverse of $(3, 4)$]

3.   True or false? For all complex numbers z_1, z_2, and z_3

   a. $z_1 \div z_2 = z_2 \div z_1$, if neither z_1 nor z_2 is $(0, 0)$
   b. $z_2 \div z_3$ belongs to C, if $z_3 \neq (0, 0)$
   c. $(1, 0) \div z_2 = \dfrac{1}{z_2}$, if $z_2 \neq (0, 0)$
   d. $z_2 \div (1, 0) = (1, 0)$

e. $z_3 + z_3 = (1,0)$, if $z_3 \neq (0,0)$

f. $z_2 + z_3 = \dfrac{1}{z_3} \cdot z_2$, if $z_3 \neq (0,0)$

g. $z_3 + (1,0) = z_3$

h. $(0,0) + z_2 = (0,0)$, if $z_2 \neq (0,0)$

i. $z_1 + z_2 = -[z_1 + (-z_2)]$, if $z_2 \neq (0,0)$

j. $(z_1 + z_2) + z_3 = z_1 + (z_2 + z_3)$, if $z_2 \neq (0,0)$ and $z_3 \neq (0,0)$

4. Prove.

  a. $(m,n) + (m,n) = (1,0)$ for all real numbers m and n, $[(m,n) \neq (0,0)]$

  b. $(1,0) \div (r,s) = \dfrac{1}{(r,s)}$ for all real numbers r and s, $[(r,s) \neq (0,0)]$

  c. $(a,b) \div (c,d) = \left(\dfrac{ac+bd}{c^2+d^2}, \dfrac{bc-ad}{c^2+d^2} \right)$ for all real numbers a, b, c, and d, $[(c,d) \neq (0,0)]$

  d. $(a,b) \div (c,d) = [(a,b) \cdot (c,-d)] \div [(c,d) \cdot (c,-d)]$ for all real numbers a, b, c, and d, $[(c,d) \neq (0,0)]$

THE COMPLEX NUMBER SYSTEM AS A FIELD

You have now studied several number systems.

> the natural number system
> the integer number system
> the rational number system
> the real number system
> the complex number system

Any number system composed of a set (T) of elements and two operations $(+)$ and $(\cdot)$ for these elements is called a *field*, if for *all* elements a, b, and c belonging to T, the following eleven properties hold.

  i. $a + b$ belongs to T

  ii. $a \cdot b$ belongs to T

  iii. $a + b = b + a$

  iv. $a \cdot b = b \cdot a$

  v. $(a + b) + c = a + (b + c)$

  vi. $(a \cdot b) \cdot c = a \cdot (b \cdot c)$

  vii. $a \cdot (b + c) = (a \cdot b) + (a \cdot c)$

  viii. there exists an element d belonging to T for which $a + d = a$

  ix. there exists an element f belonging to T for which $a \cdot f = a$

  x. for each a, there exists an element g belonging to T for which $a + g = d$

  xi. for each a (except the element d), there exists an element h belonging to T for which $a \cdot h = f$

EXERCISES

Determine whether each number system listed below is a field. If it is not a field, then tell which of the eleven requirements of a field do not hold.

1. the natural number system
2. the integer number system
3. the rational number system

4. the real number system
5. the complex number system

Some complex numbers that "behave" like real numbers

You may have already noticed that some complex numbers "behave" like real numbers. For example

$$(2, 0) + (7, 0) = (9, 0)$$
and $\quad 2 + 7 = 9$

$$(-17.4, 0) + (3.1, 0) = (-14.3, 0)$$
and $\quad -17.4 + 3.1 = -14.3$

$$(6, 0) \cdot (-10, 0) = (-60, 0)$$
and $\quad 6 \cdot -10 = -60$

$$\left(\frac{1}{2}, 0\right) \cdot \left(\frac{3}{7}, 0\right) = \left(\frac{3}{14}, 0\right)$$
and $\quad \dfrac{1}{2} \cdot \dfrac{3}{7} = \dfrac{3}{14}$

In general, for all real numbers a and b, there is a one-to-one correspondence such that if $(a, 0)$ is paired with a and $(b, 0)$ is paired with b, then $(a, 0) + (b, 0)$ is paired with $a + b$ and $(a, 0) \cdot (b, 0)$ is paired with $a \cdot b$. For this reason, we say

> For each real number a, the complex number
> $(a, 0)$ *behaves like* the real number a.

And from this point on we will often speak of the complex number 3 when we mean $(3, 0)$; the complex number -2.7 when we mean $(-2.7, 0)$. By this agreement

$3 \cdot (2, 7)$ will mean $(3, 0) \cdot (2, 7)$ which is equal to $(6, 21)$
$-7 + (4, 12)$ will mean $(-7, 0) + (4, 12)$ which is equal to $(-3, 12)$
$(4, 0) + (-9, 0)$ is equal to $(-5, 0)$ and may be expressed simply as -5

EXERCISES

Compute. Express your answer with only a real number symbol if possible; otherwise, express it as an ordered pair of real numbers.

Examples:　　i.　$(2, 3) + (6, -3) = (8, 0) = 8$
　　　　　　　ii.　$4 \cdot (2, 3) = (4, 0) \cdot (2, 3) = (8, 12)$

1. $(3, 2) + (-8, -2)$
2. $(3, 2) + (-8, 2)$

3. $6 + (5, 0)$
4. $6 + (5, -9)$

5. $(4,0) \cdot \left(\frac{1}{2}, 0\right)$

6. $(3,6) \cdot 2$

7. $(17,6) - 4$

8. $4 - (17,6)$

9. $(10,5) \div 5$

10. $5 \div (10,5)$

11. $5 \cdot [(3,2) + (-1,4)]$

12. $[5 \cdot (3,2)] + [5 \cdot (-1,4)]$

13. $-(5,0)$

14. $-[(3,2) + (7,-2)]$

15. $\dfrac{1}{(3,4)}$

16. $\dfrac{1}{(5,0)}$

17. $(4,0) + [(3,0) \cdot (0,1)]$

18. $(-6,0) + [(7,0) \cdot (0,1)]$

19. $(72,0) + [(53,0) \cdot (0,1)]$

20. $4 + [3 \cdot (0,1)]$

21. $-6 + [7 \cdot (0,1)]$

22. $72 + [(53,0) \cdot (0,1)]$

23. $(a,0) + [(b,0) \cdot (0,1)]$

24. $a + [b \cdot (0,1)]$

Another notation for complex numbers—standard form

We have been using ordered pair notation (a,b) for complex numbers where a and b have been replaced by real number symbols. We also showed that in a special case we could use a for $(a,0)$ because the real number a and the complex number $(a,0)$ "behave" alike.

Now we will show that under these conditions, we could use the notation $a + [b \cdot (0,1)]$ for (a,b). Study the following and supply a reason for each step.

For all real numbers a and b

$$(a,b) = (a,0) + (0,b) \qquad \text{Why?}$$
$$= (a,0) + [(b,0) \cdot (0,1)] \qquad \text{Why?}$$
$$= \quad a \quad + [b \cdot (0,1)] \qquad \text{Why?}$$

We shall introduce what is called *standard form* by using

$$i \text{ for } (0,1)$$

in the preceding. Thus, for all real numbers a and b

$$(a,b) = a + [b \cdot (0,1)] \qquad \text{Proved above}$$
$$= a + [b \cdot i] \qquad \text{Replacing } (0,1) \text{ by } i$$
$$= a + bi \qquad bi \text{ means } b \cdot i$$

Thus, $(5,3)$ is $5 + 3i$; $(-2.4, 6.3)$ is $-2.4 + 6.3i$; $7 + 8i$ is $(7,8)$; and $-\frac{2}{3} + \frac{1}{2}i$ is $(-\frac{2}{3}, \frac{1}{2})$ and in general, we shall use (a,b) and $a + bi$ interchangeably and discontinue using heavy marks $(+, \cdot, -, \div)$ in favor of the customary marks $(+, \cdot, -, \div)$. Study *each* of the following examples.

Examples: *i.* $(-2,7)$ may be expressed as $-2 + 7i$

ii. $(3,0)$ may be expressed as $3 + 0i$ or more simply as 3

iii. $(0,5)$ may be expressed as $0 + 5i$ or more simply as $5i$

iv. $(2,-3)$ may be expressed as $2 + (-3)i$ or more simply as $2 - 3i$

   v.　Since $i = (0, 1)$ and $(0, 1) \cdot (0, 1) = (-1, 0) = -1$, it follows that $i \cdot i = i^2 = (-1, 0) = -1$.

  vi.　$(5i)(3i) = 15i^2 = 15(-1) = -15$

 vii.　Since $(0, -1) = -(0, 1) = -i$ and $(0, -1) \cdot (0, -1) = (-1, 0) = -1$, it follows that $(-i)(-i) = (-i)^2 = (-1, 0) = -1$. Notice also that $i^2 = (-i)^2$.

We shall now restate, in $a + bi$ notation, the portions of this chapter that are necessary for working with the standard form.

For all real numbers a, b, c, and d

$$a + bi \text{ is a complex number}$$
$$a + bi = c + di \text{ if and only if } a = c \text{ and } b = d$$
$$(a + bi) + (c + di) = (a + c) + (b + d)i$$
$$-(a + bi) = -a - bi$$
$$(a + bi) - (c + di) = (a - c) + (b - d)i$$
$$(a + bi) \cdot (c + di) = (ac - bd) + (ad + bc)i$$
$$\frac{1}{a + bi} = \left(\frac{a}{a^2 + b^2}\right) + \left(\frac{-b}{a^2 + b^2}\right)i, \ (a^2 + b^2 \neq 0)$$
$$(a + bi) \div (c + di) = (a + bi) \cdot \frac{1}{c + di}$$
$$= (a + bi) \cdot \left(\frac{c}{c^2 + d^2} + \frac{-d}{c^2 + d^2}i\right)$$
$$= \left(\frac{ac + bd}{c^2 + d^2}\right) + \left(\frac{bc - ad}{c^2 + d^2}\right)i, \ (c^2 + d^2 \neq 0)$$
$$(0, 1) = i \text{ and } i^2 = -1$$
$$(a, b) \text{ and } a + bi \text{ denote the same complex number}$$

EXERCISES

1.　Determine m and n for each of the following according to the definition: For all real numbers a, b, c, and d, $a + bi = c + di$ if and only if $a = c$ and $b = d$.

  a.　$m + 4i = 5 + ni$

  b.　$-m + 2i = 3 + 4ni$

  c.　$(4m + 3) + 5i = 0 + (\sqrt{n})i$

  d.　$2m - 5i = -6 + ni$

  e.　$m + ni = -4 - 4i$

  f.　$m - ni = -4 - 4i$

  g.　$(m + n) + (m - n)i = 2 - 6i$

  h.　$m + ni = 7$

  i.　$m + ni = -4$

  j.　$m + ni = 3i$

  k.　$m + ni = -7i$

  l.　$m + ni = 0$

2.　True or false? For all real numbers a and b

  a.　$(-b)i = -(bi)$

  b.　$a + (-b)i = a - bi$

  c.　if $bi = i$, then $b = 1$

  d.　if $bi = -i$, then $b = -1$

3. Compute and express your answer in one of the forms x, yi, $x + yi$, or $x - yi$ for real numbers x and y.

a. $(8 + 2i) + (6 + 4i)$

b. $(3 + 4i) - (5 + i)$

c. $-(7 - 6i)$

d. $-(5 + 3i)$

e. $(3\sqrt{2} + 5i) + (\sqrt{2} - 7i)$

f. $(4.39 - 7.68i) - (6.72 - 2.57i)$

g. $(23 + 7i) + (23 - 7i)$

h. $(-14 - 78i) + (-14 + 78i)$

i. $(-4 + 6i) + (4 + 9i)$

j. $(-5 - 3i) - (2 - 6i)$

4. Compute and express your answer in one of the forms x, yi, $x + yi$, or $x - yi$ for real numbers x and y.

Example: $(2 + 3i) \cdot (5 + 4i)$

Using the definition of multiplication for complex numbers

$$(2 + 3i)(5 + 4i) = [2(5) - 3(4)] + [2(4) + 3(5)]i$$
$$= [10 - 12] + [8 + 15]i$$
$$= -2 + 23i$$

a. $(3 + 5i) \cdot (2 + 4i)$

b. $(-2 + 6i) \cdot (5 + 3i)$

c. $(4 + 2i) \cdot (3 - 2i)$

d. $(2 - 3i) \cdot (4 - 5i)$

e. $(6 - 3i) \cdot (6 + 3i)$

f. $(7 + 2i) \cdot (7 - 2i)$

g. $(10 - 8i) \cdot (10 + 8i)$

h. $(5 + 7i) \cdot (5 - 7i)$

i. $(3 + 2i) \cdot (3 + 2i)$

j. $(3 - 2i) \cdot (3 - 2i)$

k. $(\sqrt{7} + 4i) \cdot (\sqrt{7} - 4i)$

l. $(\sqrt{5} - i) \cdot (\sqrt{5} + i)$

m. $(\sqrt{3} - \sqrt{2}\,i) \cdot (\sqrt{3} + \sqrt{2}\,i)$

n. $(\sqrt{3} + 5i) \cdot (\sqrt{2} + 6i)$

5. Compute and express your answer in the simplest way. Look for a pattern as you proceed.

a. i^2

b. i^3 [HINT: Consider $i^2 \cdot i$]

c. i^4 [HINT: Consider $i^2 \cdot i^2$]

d. i^5

e. i^6

f. i^7

g. i^8

h. i^{12}

i. i^{16}

j. i^{20}

k. i^{21}

l. i^{22}

m. i^{23}

6. Complete in the simplest way: For each natural number n,

a. $i^{4n} = $ _____?_____   b. $i^{4n+1} = $ ___?___   c. $i^{4n+2} = $ ___?___   d. $i^{4n+3} = $ ___?___

7. True or false?

a. $i^2 = -1$

b. $(-i)^2 = -1$

c. $(3i)(3i) = 9i^2 = -9$

d. $(-3i)(-3i) = 9i^2 = -9$

e. $i^2 = (-i)^2$

f. $i = -i$

g. $(3i)^2 = (-3i)^2$

h. $3i = -3i$

i. $i^{17} = i^{19}$

j. $i^{27} = i^{31}$

8. Compute.

a. the fourth power of $2i$

b. the fourth power of $-2i$

c. the fifth power of $3i$

d. the fifth power of $-3i$

e. the sixth power of $\dfrac{i}{2}$

f. the sixth power of $-\dfrac{i}{2}$

g. the seventh power of $10i$

h. the seventh power of $-10i$

9. Compute and express your answer in one of the forms x, yi, $x + yi$, or $x - yi$ for real numbers x and y.

Example: **i.** $(2 + 5i) \div (3 - 4i)$

$$(2 + 5i) \div (3 - 4i) = (2 + 5i) \cdot \left(\frac{1}{3 - 4i}\right)$$

$$= (2 + 5i) \cdot \left(\frac{3}{25} + \frac{4}{25}i\right)$$

$$= \left(\frac{6}{25} - \frac{20}{25}\right) + \left(\frac{8}{25} + \frac{15}{25}\right)i = \frac{-14}{25} + \frac{23}{25}i$$

Consider another method: $\forall_{a\epsilon R} \forall_{b\epsilon R} \forall_{c\epsilon R} \forall_{d\epsilon R} \ [(c, d) \neq (0, 0)]$

$$(a + bi) \div (c + di) = \frac{a + bi}{c + di}$$

$$= \frac{a + bi}{c + di} \cdot \frac{c - di}{c - di}$$

$$= \frac{(ac + bd) + (bc - ad)i}{c^2 + d^2}$$

$$= \left(\frac{ac + bd}{c^2 + d^2}\right) + \left(\frac{bc - ad}{c^2 + d^2}\right)i$$

Thus $(2 + 5i) \div (3 - 4i) = \dfrac{2 + 5i}{3 - 4i}$

$$= \frac{2 + 5i}{3 - 4i} \cdot \frac{3 + 4i}{3 + 4i}$$

$$= \frac{(6 - 20) + (8 + 15)i}{9 + 16}$$

$$= \frac{-14}{25} + \frac{23}{25}i$$

Example: **ii.** $(5 + 6i) \div (2 + 3i) = \dfrac{5 + 6i}{2 + 3i}$

$$= \frac{5 + 6i}{2 + 3i} \cdot \frac{2 - 3i}{2 - 3i}$$

$$= \frac{(10 + 18) + (-15 + 12)i}{4 + 9}$$

$$= \frac{28 - 3i}{13} = \frac{28}{13} - \frac{3}{13}i$$

a. $(4 + 3i) \div (2 + 5i)$

b. $(4 + 3i) \div (2 - 5i)$

c. $\dfrac{1}{7 + 2i}$

d. $\dfrac{6 - 3i}{2 + 5i}$

e. $\dfrac{7 + 7i}{7 + 7i}$

f. $\dfrac{3 - 4i}{3 + 4i}$

g. $(\sqrt{5} + 3i) \div (\sqrt{7} - 2i)$

h. $\dfrac{1}{i}$

i. $\dfrac{i}{1}$

j. $\dfrac{3i}{i}$

k. $\dfrac{-8}{2i}$

l. $\dfrac{8i}{-2}$

m. $\dfrac{2 + 3i}{5 + 4i}$

n. $\dfrac{2 + 3i}{5 - 4i}$

o. $\dfrac{i}{i}$

p. $\dfrac{i}{-i}$

THE ABSOLUTE VALUE OF A COMPLEX NUMBER

In the real number system we defined the absolute value of x for each real number x. Determine $|-5|$; $|7|$; $|0|$. Restate the definition of $|x|$ for each real number x. We now proceed to define the absolute value of z for each complex number z.

■ *Definition of Absolute Value of Complex Number* $\forall_{z \epsilon C}$, if $z = (a, b) = a + bi$, then the *absolute value* of z (denoted by $|z|$) is $\sqrt{a^2 + b^2}$.

Do you see that this definition includes the definition of absolute value for the real numbers; that is, $\forall_{a \epsilon R} \forall_{b \epsilon R}$ if $b = 0$, then $(a, 0)$ is the real number a and

$$|(a, b)| = |(a, 0)|$$
$$= \sqrt{a^2 + 0}$$
$$= \sqrt{a^2} = |a|$$

Examples: i. If $z = (2, 3)$, then $|z| = |(2, 3)| = \sqrt{4 + 9} = \sqrt{13}$.

ii. If $z = -6 + 8i$, then $|z| = |-6 + 8i| = \sqrt{36 + 64} = \sqrt{100} = 10$.

iii. If $z = 4 - 6i$, then $|z| = |4 - 6i| = \sqrt{16 + 36} = \sqrt{52} = 2\sqrt{13}$.

EXERCISES

1. Compute the absolute value of each complex number listed.

   a. $10 + 3i$

   b. $10 + 5i$

   c. $10 - 5i$

   d. $5 + 10i$

   e. $5 - 10i$

   f. $-10 + 5i$

   g. $-10 - 5i$

   h. $\sqrt{2} + \sqrt{7} i$

   i. $\sqrt{5} + 3i$

   j. $1 + i$

   k. -4

   l. 4

   m. $9i$

   n. $-9i$

   o. i

   p. $-i$

   q. $2 + 2i$

   r. $2 + i$

   s. $m + ni$

   t. $3v + 3wi$

   u. $5 - 12i$

2. Prove that for each complex number z and for all real numbers a and b

    a. $|z| = |-z|$ [HINT: Let $z =$ **d.** $|a + bi| = |a - bi|$
       (a, b) or let $z = a + bi$.]   **e.** if $a = 0$, then $|a + bi| = |b|$

    b. $|a| = |(a, 0)|$ **f.** if $b = 0$, then $|a + bi| = |a|$

    c. $|b| = |(0, b)|$

3. Compute

    a. $|2 + 3i| \cdot |5 + 4i|$

    b. $|(2 + 3i) \cdot (5 + 4i)|$ **e.** $\left| \dfrac{2 + 5i}{3 - 4i} \right|$

    c. $|3 - 4i| \cdot |1 + 2i|$ **f.** $\dfrac{|2 + 5i|}{|3 - 4i|}$

    d. $|(3 - 4i) \cdot (1 + 2i)|$

4. Prove that for all complex numbers z_1 and z_2

    a. $|z_1 \cdot z_2| = |z_1| \cdot |z_2|$ [HINT: Let $z_1 = a + bi$ and $z_2 = c + di$.]

    b. $\left| \dfrac{z_1}{z_2} \right| = \dfrac{|z_1|}{|z_2|}$, if $z_2 \neq 0 + 0i$

5. Can you find a counter-example to disprove the following statement?
For all complex numbers z_1 and z_2, $|z_1 + z_2| \le |z_1| + |z_2|$.

THE CONJUGATE OF A COMPLEX NUMBER

When simplifying expressions of the form $\dfrac{a + bi}{c + di}$ or $\dfrac{a + bi}{c - di}$ you found that it was helpful to make use of $c - di$ or $c + di$. Also, you have proved that $|m + ni| = |m - ni|$ for all real numbers m and n. The following definition gives us a name and notation for certain pairs of complex numbers.

■   *Definition of Conjugate of a Complex Number* $\forall_{z \in C}$, if $z = (x, y) = x + yi$, then the *conjugate* of z (denoted by $\bar{z}$) is $(x, -y)$ or $x - yi$.

Examples: *i.*   If $z = 2 + 3i$, then $\bar{z} = \overline{2 + 3i} = 2 - 3i$.

           ii.   If $z = (3, -7)$, then $\bar{z} = \overline{(3, -7)} = (3, 7)$.

           iii.   If $z = -6 + 2i$, then $\bar{z} = \overline{-6 + 2i} = -6 - 2i$.

EXERCISES

1. Compute. Express your answer in the simplest form.

    a. $\overline{4 + 3i}$ **f.** $\overline{0 + 12i}$

    b. $\overline{4 - 3i}$ **g.** $\overline{0 - 5i}$

    c. $\overline{-4 - 3i}$ **h.** $\overline{3 + 0i}$

    d. $\overline{-4 + 3i}$ **i.** $\overline{-7 + 0i}$

    e. $\overline{\overline{(12 + 7i)}}$ [READ: The conjugate of the conjugate of $12 + 7i$.]

2. Compute. Express your answer in the simplest form.

a. $(3 + 2i) \cdot \overline{(3 + 2i)}$

b. $(\sqrt{6} - \sqrt{2}\,i) \cdot \overline{(\sqrt{6} - \sqrt{2}\,i)}$

c. $(17 + 5i) + \overline{(17 + 5i)}$

d. $(-6 + 9i) + \overline{(-6 + 9i)}$

e. $|\,2 + 5i\,|$

f. $|\,\overline{2 + 5i}\,|$

g. $|\,\overline{-(2 + 5i)}\,|$

3. Prove that for each complex number z and for each real number c

a. $\overline{\left(\dfrac{-}{z}\right)} = z$ [HINT: Let $z = a + bi$.]

b. $z + \overline{z} = (x, 0)$, for some real number x

c. $z \cdot \overline{z} = (x, 0)$, for some real number x

d. $\overline{0 + ci} = -(0 + ci)$

e. $\overline{c + 0i} = c + 0i$

f. $|\overline{z}| = |z|$

g. $|\overline{z}| = |\overline{(-z)}|$

h. $|\overline{z}| = \left|-\left(\dfrac{-}{z}\right)\right|$

4. Compute.

a. $\overline{(2 + 3i) + (5 - 7i)}$

b. $\overline{(2 + 3i)} + \overline{(5 - 7i)}$

c. $\overline{(-6 + 4i) + (4 - 9i)}$

d. $\overline{(-6 + 4i)} + \overline{(4 - 9i)}$

e. $\overline{(3 + 2i) \cdot (4 - 3i)}$

f. $\overline{(3 + 2i)} \cdot \overline{(4 - 3i)}$

5. Prove that for all complex numbers z_1 and z_2

a. $\overline{z_1 + z_2} = \overline{z_1} + \overline{z_2}$ [HINT: Let $z_1 = a + bi$ and $z_2 = c + di$.]

b. $\overline{z_1 \cdot z_2} = \overline{z_1} \cdot \overline{z_2}$

A GEOMETRIC MODEL FOR C

We began this chapter by introducing complex numbers as ordered pairs of real numbers. You should recall the one-to-one correspondence between ordered pairs of real numbers and the points of a plane as suggested earlier in figure 1. Since complex numbers were defined as ordered pairs of real numbers, we shall use the points of a plane as a model to illustrate many of the things that we have learned about complex numbers.

Since each ordered pair of real numbers (a, b) corresponds to a unique point $P(a, b)$ in the coordinate plane, we shall say that the point $P(a, b)$ is the *graph* of the complex number $z = (a, b) = a + bi$. In figure 2 we have *plotted* eight complex numbers $x + yi$ by plotting (x, y).

$z_4 = 5 + 4i = (5, 4)$

$z_2 = -3 + 0i = -3 = (-3, 0)$

$z_5 = -4 - 4i = (-4, -4)$

$z_8 = 0 - 2i = -2i = (0, -2)$

Find the graphs of z_1, z_3, z_6, and z_7 in figure 2 and express the corresponding complex number in $a + bi$ notation.

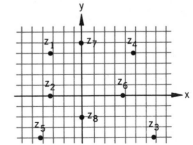

Fig. 2

EXERCISES

1. Establish a coordinate system in a plane (use graph paper) and plot each complex number listed below. Plot only four numbers on one set of axes.

a. $3 + 4i$ i. $2 + 6i$ q. 3

b. $-3 - 4i$ j. $-(2 + 6i)$ r. -4

c. $3 - 4i$ k. $5 - 7i$ s. $5i$

d. $-3 + 4i$ l. $-(5 - 7i)$ t. $-2i$

e. $2 + 0i$ m. $8 + 2i$ u. i

f. -6 n. $\overline{8 + 2i}$ v. $-i$

g. $0 - 5i$ o. $-5 + 4i$ w. i^2

h. $3i$ p. $\overline{-5 + 4i}$ x. $(-i)^2$

2. True or false?

a. There is a one-to-one correspondence between the complex numbers and the points in a plane.

b. For all real numbers x and y, the graph of $x + yi$ belongs to one of the axes.

c. The graphs of some complex numbers belong to the axes.

d. For each real number x, the graph of $x + 0i$ belongs to the y-axis.

e. For each real number y, the graph of $0 + yi$ belongs to the y-axis.

f. For each real number x, the graph of $x + 0i$ belongs to the x-axis.

Geometric interpretation of addition and subtraction for C

The addition of $z_1 = 2 + 3i$ and $z_2 = -4 + 2i$ is interpreted geometrically in the following manner. We know that $z_1 + z_2 = (2 + 3i) + (-4 + 2i) = -2 + 5i$. In figure 3, we have plotted z_1, z_2, and $z_1 + z_2$.

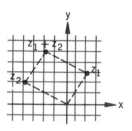

Fig. 3

Are the graphs of the origin, z_1, z_2, and $z_1 + z_2$ the vertices of a parallelogram? Of a rectangle? Compute the slopes of the segments indicated by the dash marks $\left(\text{recall that the slope of } \overline{PQ}, \text{ with } P(a, b) \text{ and } Q(c, d), \text{ is } \dfrac{d - b}{c - a}\right)$. Do opposite sides have the same slope? Is the quadrilateral a parallelogram? A rectangle? Recall that for two oblique segments, parallels have the same slope and perpendiculars have slopes whose product is negative one.

In general, if $\dfrac{b}{a} \neq \dfrac{d}{c}$, then for each complex number $z_1 = (a, b) = a + bi$ and each complex number $z_2 = (c, d) = c + di$, the sum $z_1 + z_2 = (a + c, b + d) = (a + c) + (b + d)i$ may be "constructed", using only straightedge and compass, by constructing the vertices of the parallelogram $ABCD$ with $A(0, 0)$; $B(a, b)$; $D(c, d)$; $C(a + c, b + d)$, as illustrated in figure 4.

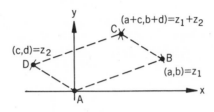

Fig. 4

Why did we eliminate the case where $\dfrac{b}{a} = \dfrac{d}{c}$?

To construct the difference, $z_1 - z_2$, of two complex numbers z_1 and z_2, we first construct $-z_2$ as shown in figure 5 and then construct $z_1 + (-z_2)$ as shown in figure 6. Does $z_1 + (-z_2) = z_1 - z_2$ for all complex numbers z_1 and z_2?

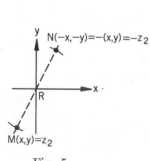

Fig. 5

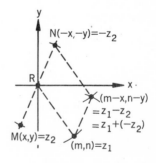

Fig. 6

In figure 5, are $M(x, y)$, $N(-x, -y)$, and $R(0, 0)$ collinear? Is the origin R the midpoint of segment $\overline{MN}$? Can you prove both of these facts?

EXERCISES

1. Prove that $ABCD$, with $A(0, 0)$, $B(a, b)$, $D(c, d)$, $C(a + c, b + d)$, is a parallelogram for all real numbers a, b, c, and d provided that $\dfrac{b}{a} \neq \dfrac{d}{c}$.

2. Prove that $R(0, 0)$ is the midpoint of $\overline{MN}$ with $M(x, y)$ and $N(-x, -y)$.

3. For each problem, plot z_1 and z_2. Then use only compass and straightedge to construct $z_1 + z_2$; $-z_2$; $z_1 - z_2$.

    a. $z_1 = (-2, 4)$ and $z_2 = (5, 2)$ **e.** $z_1 = 3 + 4i$ and $z_2 = -6 - 8i$

    b. $z_1 = -3 - 4i$ and $z_2 = 5 - 2i$ **f.** $z_1 = 5$ and $z_2 = -7$

    c. $z_1 = 6$ and $z_2 = 4i$ **g.** $z_1 = 6i$ and $z_2 = 4i$

    d. $z_1 = -2 + 6i$ and $z_2 = 4 - 2i$ **h.** $z_1 = 6i$ and $z_2 = -4i$

Geometric interpretation of absolute value for C

There is a geometric interpretation for the absolute value of a complex number. Recall that for each complex number $z = (a, b) = a + bi$, the absolute value of $z = |z| = \sqrt{a^2 + b^2}$. In figure 7, four complex numbers are plotted.

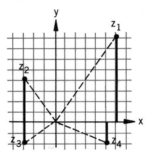

Fig. 7

First, observe that

$$z_1 = 6 + 8i \text{ and that } |z_1| = 10$$
$$z_2 = -3 + 4i \text{ and that } |z_2| = 5$$
$$z_3 = -3 - 2i \text{ and that } |z_3| = \sqrt{13}$$
$$z_4 = 5 - 2i \text{ and that } |z_4| = \sqrt{29}$$

Second, use the Pythagorean Relation (or the Distance Formula) to compute the distance between the origin and the graph of each complex number z_1, z_2, z_3, and z_4.

From the preceding, you should have observed that for each complex number $z = a + bi$ the distance between the origin and the graph of z is $\sqrt{a^2 + b^2}$, which is the absolute value of z.

EXERCISES

1. Plot each complex number and determine the distance between the origin and the graph of the complex number.

    a. $2 + 3i$ **e.** $\sqrt{2} + \sqrt{3}\, i$ **i.** -7

    b. $-2 - 3i$ **f.** i **j.** -6

    c. $2 - 3i$ **g.** 4 **k.** $5i$

    d. $-2 + 3i$ **h.** $-4i$ **l.** $-3i$

2. Plot each complex number z for which $|z| = 2$.

3. Plot each complex number z for which $|z| = 5$.

SQUARE ROOTS WHICH ARE COMPLEX NUMBERS

Verify each of the following by computing.

$$(5i)(5i) = 25i^2 = -25$$
$$(-5i)(-5i) = 25i^2 = -25$$
$$(\sqrt{7}\,i)(\sqrt{7}\,i) = 7i^2 = -7$$
$$(-\sqrt{7}\,i)(-\sqrt{7}\,i) = 7i^2 = -7$$

From the first equation above, it is evident that $5i$ is a square root of -25 since $(5i)(5i) = -25$. From the second equation, it is evident that $-5i$ is also a square root of -25. Why? From the last two equations, you should be able to tell two different square roots of -7. What are they? Thus it appears that

For each real number $a < 0$, $i\sqrt{-a}$ is a square root of a; also, $-i\sqrt{-a}$ is a square root of a.

Observe that, in this statement, $a < 0$ and therefore $-a > 0$ and $\sqrt{-a} > 0$. It also follows that $(i\sqrt{-a})^2 = a$ and that $(-i\sqrt{-a})^2 = a$. For $a < 0$, we do not call either $i\sqrt{-a}$ or $-i\sqrt{-a}$, the principal square root of a. We shall agree that the following holds.

AGREEMENT: For each $x > 0$, $\sqrt{-x} = i\sqrt{x}$ and $-\sqrt{-x} = -i\sqrt{x}$

Examples:

   i. $\sqrt{-4} = i\sqrt{4} = i \cdot 2 = 2i$

   ii. $-\sqrt{-9} = -i\sqrt{9} = -3i$

   iii. $\sqrt{-32} = i\sqrt{32} = i\sqrt{16} \cdot \sqrt{2} = 4i\sqrt{2}$

   iv. $\sqrt{-4} \cdot \sqrt{-9} = (2i)(3i) = 6i^2 = -6$

         Note that $\sqrt{-4} \cdot \sqrt{-9} \neq \sqrt{(-4)(-9)}$

         since $\sqrt{-4} \cdot \sqrt{-9} = -6$

         and $\sqrt{(-4)(-9)} = \sqrt{36} = 6$

   v. $\sqrt{-4} + \sqrt{-9} = 2i + 3i = (2 + 3)i = 5i$

   vi. $\sqrt{-200} = i\sqrt{200} = i\sqrt{100}\sqrt{2} = 10i\sqrt{2}$

   vii. $\sqrt{-6} \cdot \sqrt{7} = i\sqrt{6}\sqrt{7} = i\sqrt{42}$

   viii. $\sqrt{-27} + \sqrt{-12} = i\sqrt{27} + i\sqrt{12}$
$$= 3i\sqrt{3} + 2i\sqrt{3} = 5i\sqrt{3}$$

EXERCISES

1. Express in one of the forms $\sqrt{x}$, $-\sqrt{x}$, $i\sqrt{x}$, or $-i\sqrt{x}$ for a real number $x > 0$.

a. $\sqrt{-5}$

b. $-\sqrt{-5}$

c. $\sqrt{5}$

d. $-\sqrt{5}$

e. $\sqrt{-5} \cdot \sqrt{-7}$

f. $\sqrt{5} \cdot \sqrt{7}$

g. $\sqrt{-5} \cdot \sqrt{7}$

h. $\sqrt{5} \cdot \sqrt{-7}$

i. $(-\sqrt{5})(-\sqrt{7})$

j. $-2\sqrt{6}$

k. $2\sqrt{-6}$

l. $-2\sqrt{-6}$

2. Express in one of the forms $a\sqrt{x}$, $-a\sqrt{x}$, $ai\sqrt{x}$, or $-ai\sqrt{x}$ for positive real numbers a and x such that x does not have a perfect square factor.

a. $\sqrt{8}$

b. $\sqrt{27}$

c. $\sqrt{-8}$

d. $\sqrt{-27}$

e. $-\sqrt{8}$

f. $-\sqrt{27}$

g. $\sqrt{32}$

h. $-\sqrt{32}$

i. $\sqrt{-32}$

j. $-\sqrt{-32}$

k. $\sqrt{3} \cdot \sqrt{7}$

l. $\sqrt{-3} \cdot \sqrt{-7}$

m. $-\sqrt{-3} \cdot \sqrt{-7}$

n. $-\sqrt{-3} \cdot \sqrt{7}$

o. $\sqrt{-32} + \sqrt{-8}$

p. $-\sqrt{-32} + \sqrt{-8}$

q. $\sqrt{-32} - \sqrt{-8}$

r. $-\sqrt{-32} - \sqrt{-8}$

s. $\sqrt{-75} + \sqrt{-48}$

t. $\sqrt{-7} + \sqrt{-28} + \sqrt{-63}$

3. Supply the reasons in the proof of the following theorem.

Theorem $\forall_{a \in R, \ a < 0} \ (i\sqrt{-a})^2 = a$ and $(-i\sqrt{-a})^2 = a$; that is, $i\sqrt{-a}$ and $-i\sqrt{-a}$ are the square roots of a.

Proof For each real number $a < 0$ and for some complex numbers $x + yi$, if $x + yi$ is a square root of a

then $\qquad (x + yi)^2 = a$

$(x^2 - y^2) + (2xy)i = a + 0i$

$(x^2 - y^2 = a)$ and $(2xy = 0)$

$(2xy = 0) \rightarrow [(x = 0)$ or $(y = 0)]$

CASE I: $x = 0$ and $x^2 - y^2 = a$

$(x^2 - y^2 = a) \rightarrow (-y^2 = a)$

$(-y^2 = a) \rightarrow (y^2 = -a)$

$(y^2 = -a) \rightarrow (y = \sqrt{-a}$ or $y = -\sqrt{-a})$

Hence $x + yi = 0 + i\sqrt{-a} = i\sqrt{-a}$

or $x + yi = 0 - i\sqrt{-a} = -i\sqrt{-a}$

CASE II: $y = 0$ and $x^2 - y^2 = a$

$(x^2 - y^2 = a) \rightarrow (x^2 = a)$

There exists no real number x whose square is negative ($a < 0$).

4. Determine the two square roots of each of the following:

Example: $-5 + 12i$

Let a square root be $x + yi$ for some real numbers x and y.

Then $(x + yi)^2 = -5 + 12i$
$$(x^2 - y^2) + (2xy)i = -5 + 12i$$
$$(x^2 - y^2 = -5) \text{ and } (2xy = 12)$$
$$(x^2 - y^2 = -5) \text{ and } (xy = 6)$$
$$(x^2 - y^2 = -5) \text{ and } \left(y = \frac{6}{x}\right)$$
$$x^2 - \left(\frac{6}{x}\right)^2 = -5$$
$$x^2 - \frac{36}{x^2} = -5$$
$$x^4 - 36 = -5x^2$$
$$x^4 + 5x^2 - 36 = 0$$
$$(x^2 + 9)(x^2 - 4) = 0$$
$$(x^2 + 9 = 0) \text{ or } (x^2 - 4 = 0)$$
$$(x^2 = -9) \text{ or } (x^2 = 4)$$

There is no real number x for which $x^2 = -9$. However, if $x^2 = 4$, then ($x = 2$ or $x = -2$).

CASE I: $(x = 2)$ and $\left(y = \dfrac{6}{x}\right)$

$(x = 2)$ and $(y = 3)$

Hence, $x + yi = 2 + 3i$

CASE II: $(x = -2)$ and $\left(y = \dfrac{6}{x}\right)$

$(x = -2)$ and $(y = -3)$

Hence, $x + yi = -2 - 3i$

Therefore, the square roots of $-5 + 12i$ are $2 + 3i$ and $-2 - 3i$.

a. $-8 + 6i$ **c.** $-3 + 4i$ **e.** $8 + 6i$

b. $-21 + 20i$ **d.** $-12 + 16i$ **f.** $12 - 16i$

QUADRATIC EQUATIONS WITH COMPLEX SOLUTIONS

In Chapter 8 you studied about quadratic equations; that is, equations that pattern in the form $ax^2 + bx + c = 0$ for real numbers a, b, and c ($a \neq 0$). You also found that solution sets for such equations were given by the quadratic formula

$$\left\{ \frac{-b + \sqrt{b^2 - 4ac}}{2a} , \frac{-b - \sqrt{b^2 - 4ac}}{2a} \right\}$$

Recall that this set has

two *real* members if $b^2 - 4ac > 0$

one *real* member, $\dfrac{-b}{2a}$, if $b^2 - 4ac = 0$

no *real* members if $b^2 - 4ac < 0$

It has no real members if $b^2 - 4ac < 0$ since $\sqrt{b^2 - 4ac}$ is not a real number. But if $b^2 - 4ac < 0$, then $\sqrt{b^2 - 4ac}$ is a complex number and the solution set has *two complex* members, namely

$$\frac{-b + \sqrt{b^2 - 4ac}}{2a} \quad \text{and} \quad \frac{-b - \sqrt{b^2 - 4ac}}{2a}$$

Is one solution the conjugate of the other?

Example: i.   Solve $3x^2 + 2x + 1 = 0$ if the replacement set for x is C, the set of complex numbers.

Using the quadratic formula, the solution set of

$$3x^2 + 2x + 1 = 0$$

is

$$\left\{ \frac{-2 + \sqrt{2^2 - 4(3)(1)}}{2(3)}, \; \frac{-2 - \sqrt{2^2 - 4(3)(1)}}{2(3)} \right\}$$

$$= \left\{ \frac{-2 + \sqrt{-8}}{6}, \; \frac{-2 - \sqrt{-8}}{6} \right\}$$

$$= \left\{ \frac{-2 + 2i\sqrt{2}}{6}, \; \frac{-2 - 2i\sqrt{2}}{6} \right\}$$

$$= \left\{ \frac{-2}{6} + \frac{2i\sqrt{2}}{6}, \; \frac{-2}{6} - \frac{2i\sqrt{2}}{6} \right\}$$

$$= \left\{ -\frac{1}{3} + \frac{\sqrt{2}}{3}i, \; -\frac{1}{3} - \frac{\sqrt{2}}{3}i \right\}$$

Example: ii.   Solve $x^2 + 2 = 0$ if the replacement set for x is C.

Since $x^2 + 2 = 0$ is equivalent to $x^2 + 0 \cdot x + 2 = 0$, its solution set is

$$\left\{ \frac{0 + \sqrt{0 - 4(1)(2)}}{2(1)}, \; \frac{0 - \sqrt{0 - 4(1)(2)}}{2(1)} \right\}$$

$$= \left\{ \frac{\sqrt{-8}}{2}, \; \frac{-\sqrt{-8}}{2} \right\}$$

$$= \left\{ \frac{2i\sqrt{2}}{2}, \; \frac{-2i\sqrt{2}}{2} \right\}$$

$$= \{ i\sqrt{2}, \; -i\sqrt{2} \}$$

Consider another method by noting that $x^2 + 2 = 0$ is equivalent to $x^2 = -2$. Using the transformation principle

$$\forall_x \forall_k \; (x^2 = k) \text{ if and only if } (x = \sqrt{k} \text{ or } x = -\sqrt{k})$$

it follows that $(x^2 = -2)$ is equivalent to

$$(x = \sqrt{-2} \text{ or } x = -\sqrt{-2})$$

and the solutions of $(x = \sqrt{-2} \text{ or } x = -\sqrt{-2})$ are

$$i\sqrt{2} \text{ and } -i\sqrt{2}$$

Example: *iii.*   Solve $x^3 - 8 = 0$.

Recalling that $x^3 - 8$ can be factored as the difference of cubes

$$\forall_x \; x^3 - 8 = (x - 2)(x^2 + 2x + 4)$$

it follows that $x^3 - 8 = 0$ is equivalent to

$$(x - 2)(x^2 + 2x + 4) = 0$$

and is therefore equivalent to

$$x - 2 = 0 \text{ or } x^2 + 2x + 4 = 0 \qquad \text{Why?}$$

whose solution set is

$$\left\{ 2, \; \frac{-2 + \sqrt{2^2 - 4(1)(4)}}{2(1)}, \; \frac{-2 - \sqrt{2^2 - 4(1)(4)}}{2(1)} \right\}$$

$$= \left\{ 2, \; \frac{-2 + \sqrt{-12}}{2}, \; \frac{-2 - \sqrt{-12}}{2} \right\}$$

$$= \left\{ 2, \; \frac{-2 + 2i\sqrt{3}}{2}, \; \frac{-2 - 2i\sqrt{3}}{2} \right\}$$

$$= \{ 2, \; -1 + i\sqrt{3}, \; -1 - i\sqrt{3} \}$$

It is obvious that 2 is a solution since $2^3 = (2)(2)(2) = 8$ and $8 - 8 = 0$. We will demonstrate that $-1 + i\sqrt{3}$ is a solution.

$$(-1 + i\sqrt{3})^3 = [(-1 + i\sqrt{3}) \cdot (-1 + i\sqrt{3})] \cdot (-1 + i\sqrt{3})$$
$$= [(1 - 3) + (-\sqrt{3} - \sqrt{3})i] \cdot (-1 + i\sqrt{3})$$
$$= (-2 - 2\sqrt{3}\,i) \cdot (-1 + i\sqrt{3})$$
$$= (2 + 6) + (-2\sqrt{3} + 2\sqrt{3})i$$
$$= 8$$

and $8 - 8 = 0$. You should now demonstrate that $-1 - i\sqrt{3}$ is also a solution of $x^3 - 8 = 0$.

From the second example, we have seen that -2 has two square roots, namely $i\sqrt{2}$ and $-i\sqrt{2}$; and from the third example, we have seen that 8 has three cube roots, namely 2, $-1 + i\sqrt{3}$, and $-1 - i\sqrt{3}$. In further study of mathematics you will see that each number (real or complex) has n different nth roots among the complex numbers (for each natural number $n \geq 2$); for example, 27 has three different cube roots and $2\sqrt{3} + 2i$ has five different fifth roots.

EXERCISES

1. Determine all solutions among the complex numbers.

   a. $x^2 + x + 1 = 0$

   b. $x^2 - 4 = 0$

   c. $x^2 + 4 = 0$

   d. $2x^2 + 5x + 4 = 0$

   e. $x^3 - 27 = 0$ [There are three solutions!]

   f. $x^3 + 27 = 0$

   g. $-3x^2 + 2x - 1 = 0$

   h. $\frac{1}{2}x^2 + 10 = 4x$

   i. $5x^2 + 7 = 3x$

   j. $\sqrt{2}\,x^2 + \sqrt{3}\,x + \sqrt{5} = 0$

2. Recall that the *sum* of the solutions of $ax^2 + bx + c = 0$ is $-\frac{b}{a}$ and that the *product* of the solutions is $\frac{c}{a}$. Write a quadratic equation of the form

$$ax^2 + bx + c = 0$$

whose solution set is as given below.

Example: $\{3, 4\}$

$$3 + 4 = 7 = \frac{-b}{a} \quad \text{and} \quad 3(4) = 12 = \frac{c}{a}$$

Since $ax^2 + bx + c = 0$ is equivalent to $x^2 + \frac{b}{a}x + \frac{c}{a} = 0$, the answer is $x^2 - 7x + 12 = 0$.

   a. $\{\sqrt{2}, -\sqrt{2}\}$

   b. $\{2 - \sqrt{3}, 2 + \sqrt{3}\}$

   c. $\{i, -i\}$

   d. $\{3i, -3i\}$

   e. $\{i\sqrt{6}, -i\sqrt{6}\}$

   f. $\{-2 + i\sqrt{5}, -2 - i\sqrt{5}\}$

   g. $\{\sqrt{3} + i\sqrt{6}, \sqrt{3} - i\sqrt{6}\}$

   h. $\{3 + \sqrt{-5}, 3 - \sqrt{-5}\}$

VOCABULARY

Use each of the following correctly in a sentence. Numerals in parentheses refer to pages where these words were used. If you are not sure of the meaning of any word, turn to the indicated pages.

absolute value (273)
addition in C (253)
additive identity in C (255)
additive inverses in C (256)
associativity (255) and (261)
closure (254) and (260)
commutativity (254) and (260)
complex number (252)
conjugate (274)
distributivity (261)
division in C (264)

equality in C (252)
field (267)
Gauss (251)
graph of a complex number (275)
i (269)
multiplication in C (258)
multiplicative identity in C (261)
multiplicative inverses in C (262)
square root (279)
standard form (269)
subtraction in C (257)

REVIEW EXERCISES

1. Determine real numbers r and s that satisfy the following:

   a. $(3r, -10) = (-6, -5s)$ **d.** $3i = r + si$

   b. $r + si = 2 - 3i$ **e.** $3rs + 4si = 6 + 2i$

   c. $r + si = 6$ **f.** $(2r - 6s) + (3r + 4s)i = 2 + 7i$

2. Given the four complex numbers

$$z_1 = 3 + 5i \qquad z_2 = -6 \qquad z_3 = 2 - 7i \qquad z_4 = 2i$$

   determine the following and express your answer in one of the forms: x, yi, $x + yi$, $x - yi$ for real numbers x and y.

   a. $z_1 + z_3$

   b. $z_1 - z_3$

   c. $z_1 \cdot z_3$

   d. $z_1 \div z_3$

   e. the additive inverse of z_1; of z_2; of z_3; of z_4

   f. the multiplicative inverse of z_1; of z_4

   g. the conjugate of z_3

   h. the absolute value of z_1; of z_4

   i. the fifth power of z_4

   j. two square roots of z_2

   k. one of the four complex numbers listed above which behaves exactly like a real number

3. C, the set of complex numbers, is a field.

   a. What is the additive identity in C?

   b. What is the multiplicative identity in C?

   c. Write instances of

        i. the commutative and the associative properties of addition for complex numbers.

        ii. the commutative and the associative properties of multiplication for complex numbers.

        iii. the distributive property of multiplication over addition for complex numbers.

   d. For each complex number (a, b) in C determine the ordered pair of real numbers that is its

        i. additive inverse

        ii. multiplicative inverse (except for $(0, 0)$)

        iii. conjugate

4. Express each of the following in $a + bi$ notation.

   a. $(7, -6)$ **c.** i **e.** $6i$

   b. 9 **d.** $-i$ **f.** $\dfrac{1}{2 + 3i}$

5. Express each of the following in (a, b) notation.

   a. $-5 + 6i$ **c.** $-3i$ **e.** $-i$

   b. 9 **d.** i **f.** $-(5 - 7i)$

6. Determine the following powers.

   a. i^{22} **c.** i^{24} **e.** $(3i)^4$

   b. i^{23} **d.** i^{25} **f.** $(2i)^6$

7. Express in either the form a, or $a\sqrt{x}$, or $ai\sqrt{x}$ for some real number a and for some positive integer x which does not have a perfect square factor.

   a. $\sqrt{8} + \sqrt{18}$ **h.** $(\sqrt{-6})(\sqrt{-2})$

   b. $-\sqrt{18}$ **i.** $\sqrt{-5} \cdot \sqrt{-7} \cdot \sqrt{-5}$

   c. $\sqrt{-18}$ **j.** $\sqrt{-50} + \sqrt{-32}$

   d. $\sqrt{-8} + \sqrt{-18}$ **k.** $i\sqrt{3} + 2i\sqrt{3}$

   e. $\sqrt{6} \cdot \sqrt{2}$ **l.** $\sqrt{-9}$

   f. $\sqrt{-6} \cdot \sqrt{2}$ **m.** $-\sqrt{-9}$

   g. $(-\sqrt{6})(-\sqrt{2})$ **n.** $\sqrt{-4} \cdot \sqrt{-9}$

8. Solve. The replacement set for x is C, the set of complex numbers.

   a. $x^2 = -49$ **d.** $7x - x^2 = 4$

   b. $2x^2 + 8 = 0$ **e.** $2x^2 + 3 = 2x$

   c. $x^2 + x + 1 = 0$ **f.** $x^3 - 64 = 0$

9. Write a quadratic equation of the form $ax^2 + bx + c = 0$ with the given solution set.

   a. $\{2 + \sqrt{3}, 2 - \sqrt{3}\}$ **d.** $\{-2 + 3i, -2 - 3i\}$

   b. $\{3i, -3i\}$ **e.** $\{2 + \sqrt{-7}, 2 - \sqrt{-7}\}$

   c. $\{4 + i, 4 - i\}$ **f.** $\{i, -i\}$

10. Determine the two square roots of $-7 + 24i$. Express your answers in standard form, $a + bi$.

11. Consider $2 + 3i$ and $4 + 5i$ as polynomials in i. Multiply these two binomials, replace i^2 by -1, and simplify the result. Now, determine $(2 + 3i) \cdot (4 + 5i)$ by using the definition of product for complex numbers. Are the two results the same?

12. By the definition of product for complex numbers, $(a + bi) \cdot (c + di)$ is equal to $(ac - bd) + (ad + bc)i$. Show that the same result may be obtained by treating $a + bi$ and $c + di$ as polynomials in i, multiplying them, and replacing i^2 by -1.

CHAPTER TEST

1. Given the following four complex numbers

$$z_1 = 5 + 3i \qquad z_2 = 5 \qquad z_3 = 2 - 7i \qquad z_4 = 4i$$

express each answer below in one of the forms x, or yi, or $x + yi$, or $x - yi$ for some real numbers x and y.

a. $z_1 + z_3$

b. $z_1 - z_3$

c. $(z_1)(z_3)$

d. $z_1 \div z_3$

e. the multiplicative inverse of z_1

f. the additive inverse of z_3

g. the conjugate of z_1

h. the absolute value of z_3

i. the complex number listed among the four above which behaves exactly like a real number

j. the fourth power of z_4

k. $\left| \dfrac{z_2}{z_4} \right|$

2. Determine s and t such that $(3t + 2s, -6) = (5, 4s - t)$

3. Identify each of the following:

a. the additive identity in C

b. the multiplicative identity in C

c. the conjugate of (a, b), that is, $\overline{(a, b)}$

d. the absolute value of (a, b), that is, $|(a, b)|$

4. True or false? $\{i, -i, 1, -1\}$ is closed with respect to

a. addition

b. multiplication

c. subtraction

d. division

5. Write an *instance* of each of the following:

a. The commutative property of addition for complex numbers.

b. The associative property of multiplication for complex numbers.

c. The distributive property of multiplication over addition for complex numbers.

6. With reference to the figure below, which points correspond to the following complex numbers? Identify the point by the nearby letter.

a. $-5 - 3i$

b. $\overline{(-5 - 3i)}$

c. i^4

d. i

e. i^{23}

f. the opposite of the complex number plotted at J

g. the sum of the complex numbers plotted at E and at F

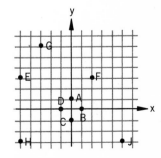

7. Determine all the square roots of negative one.

8. Determine the seventeenth power of i.

9. Express in one of the forms a, bi, $i\sqrt{c}$, $ai\sqrt{c}$, or $a + bi$ for some real numbers a, b, and c such that c is a positive integer with no perfect square factor.

   a. $\sqrt{-9}$
   b. $-\sqrt{-9}$
   c. $\sqrt{-8} + \sqrt{-32}$
   d. $(2 + \sqrt{-3})(2 + \sqrt{-3})$

   e. $(6 + \sqrt{-5})(6 - \sqrt{-5})$
   f. $(\sqrt{-7})(\sqrt{-2})$
   g. $(\sqrt{-7})(\sqrt{2})$
   h. $(-\sqrt{7})(-\sqrt{2})$

10. Solve. The replacement set for x is C, the set of complex numbers.

   a. $x^2 + 2x + 2 = 0$
   b. $2x^2 = -8$

   c. $2x^2 + 10 = 0$
   d. $x^3 - 27 = 0$

11. Write an equation of the form $ax^2 + bx + c = 0$ with the given solution set.

   a. $\{5i, -5i\}$
   b. $\{4 + 2i, 4 - 2i\}$

12. Which complex numbers behave exactly like real numbers?

13. Explain what is meant by "some complex numbers behave exactly like real numbers."

14. Determine the two square roots of $-5 - 12i$. Express your answers in standard form, $a + bi$.

BIBLIOGRAPHY

Allendoerfer, C. B. and Oakley, C. D. *Fundamentals of Freshman Mathematics.* New York: McGraw-Hill Book Co., Inc., 1959. pp. 48-53.

Kasner, E. and Newman, J. *Mathematics and the Imagination.* New York: Simon and Schuster, Inc., 1940. pp. 89-95, 99-104.

Moore, J. T. *Fundamental Principles of Mathematics.* New York: Holt, Rinehart and Winston, Inc., 1960. pp. 277-283.

School Mathematics Study Group. *Intermediate Mathematics, Part I.* New Haven: Yale University Press, 1961. pp. 298-302.

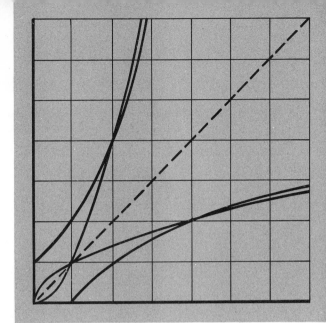

CHAPTER 10

Systems of Equations and Inequalities

EQUATIONS IN TWO VARIABLES

The following is an example of an equation in two variables, x and y.

$$2x + 3y - 2 = 0$$

We consider the solution set of this equation to be the set of all ordered pairs (x, y) of real numbers which satisfy the equation. For example, $(4, -2)$ belongs to the solution set of this equation because

$$2 \cdot (4) + 3 \cdot (-2) - 2 = 0$$

is true.

Verify that each of the ordered pairs

$$(1, 0) \qquad (\tfrac{1}{2}, \tfrac{1}{3}) \qquad (.7, .2) \qquad (\sqrt{2}, \tfrac{2}{3} - \tfrac{2}{3}\sqrt{2})$$

also satisfies the equation

$$2x + 3y - 2 = 0$$

You are, no doubt, aware that the solution set of this equation is an infinite set of ordered number pairs.

EXERCISES

For each equation, there are given four ordered real number pairs. Verify that three of these pairs satisfy the equation and one does not. [CAUTION: remember that x is the first member and y is the second member.]

1. $x - y = 3$; (x, y): $(-1, -4)$, $(0, -3)$, $(6, -3)$, $(6, 3)$

2. $5x + 2y - 1 = 0$; (x, y): $(-1, 3)$, $\left(0, \frac{1}{2}\right)$, $\left(\frac{1}{5}, 0\right)$, $\left(\frac{1}{5}, \frac{1}{2}\right)$

3. $\frac{1}{2}x - \frac{1}{3}y = 1$; (x, y): $(3, 2)$, $(2, 0)$, $\left(1, -1\frac{1}{2}\right)$, $(-4, -9)$

4. $.3y + .1x = .4$; (x, y): $(2, -2)$, $(-2, 2)$, $(4, 0)$, $(7, -1)$

5. $y = 3x - 1$; (x, y): $(2, 5)$, $(-1, 0)$, $(0, -1)$, $\left(\frac{1}{3}, 0\right)$

6. $\frac{1}{3}x = 1 + \frac{1}{2}y$; (x, y): $(0, -2)$, $(6, 2)$, $\left(1, -\frac{4}{3}\right)$, $(3, 2)$

7. $x = 2 - 3y$; (x, y): $\left(1, \frac{1}{3}\right)$, $\left(0, \frac{2}{3}\right)$, $(-4, 2)$, $(-3, 1)$

Independent, inconsistent, and dependent systems of equations

You learned earlier that an equation of the form

$$Ax + By + C = 0$$

where x and y are variables ranging over the real numbers and A, B, and C can be replaced by any (A and B not both 0) real number names, has a straight line for its graph. It is called a *linear equation.* When we graph two equations of this form

$$Ax + By + C = 0$$
$$Dx + Ey + F = 0$$

we obtain either two lines or one line. We shall be concerned with the problem of producing the set of all ordered pairs of real numbers, each pair satisfying *both* equations. A pair of such equations will be called a *system* of two linear equations in two variables. The process of determining all ordered pairs of numbers satisfying both equations will be referred to as *solving* the system.

■ *Definition of Solution Set of a System of Two Equations* The solution set of a system of two equations is the *intersection* of the solution sets of the respective equations.

To gain insight into the nature of the solution sets of systems of two linear equations, let us examine three graphs below. Each graph contains two lines, L_1 and L_2.

The first graph is the graph of the equations

$$L_1: \quad x - y - 1 = 0$$
$$L_2: \quad 2x + y + 4 = 0$$

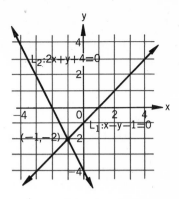

Of course, any other equations which are equivalent to the two given equations would have the same graphs. Note from this graph that the two lines have one point of intersection: $(-1, -2)$. Verify that the ordered pair $(-1, -2)$ satisfies each of the two equations given above. Thus, the solution set of the system above is $\{(-1, -2)\}$. We may show it as follows:

$$\{(x, y) \mid x - y - 1 = 0\} \cap \{(x, y) \mid 2x + y + 4 = 0\} = \{(-1, -2)\}$$

A system of two linear equations which has exactly one ordered pair of numbers for its solution set is called an *independent system*.

The second graph is the graph of the equations

$$L_1: \quad x - y - 1 = 0$$
$$L_2: \quad x - y + 2 = 0$$

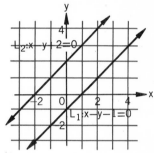

Here, also, any equations equivalent to the two given equations would have the same graphs. This graph shows that the two lines are parallel and, therefore, their intersection is the empty set. Thus, the solution set of this system is ϕ.

$$\{(x, y) \mid x - y - 1 = 0\} \cap \{(x, y) \mid x - y + 2 = 0\} = \phi$$

A system of two linear equations which has the empty set for its solution set is called an *inconsistent system*.

The third graph is the graph of the equations

$$L_1: \quad x - y + 1 = 0$$
$$L_2: \quad -2x + 2y - 2 = 0$$

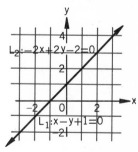

Note that, in this case, the two equations are equivalent and they have the same graph. This means that an infinite number of ordered number pairs satisfies both equations. For example, $(0, 1)$, $(-1, 0)$, and $(-\frac{1}{2}, \frac{1}{2})$ are three such pairs. Verify that each of these pairs satisfies each of the two equations in this system. We have

$$\{(x, y) \mid x - y + 1 = 0\} = \{(x, y) \mid -2x + 2y - 2 = 0\} = \{(x, x + 1)\}$$

Such a system is called a *dependent system*. Is every ordered number pair a solution of this system?

EXERCISES

1. **a.** Test whether $(-1, 2)$ is an element of the solution set of the system

$$2x = y - 4$$
$$\frac{y + 2}{2} = -2x$$

   b. Graph the two equations.
   c. Do the graphs intersect at the point $(-1, 2)$?
   d. How many points do the lines have in common?

2. **a.** Test whether $(0, 3)$ is an element of the solution set of the system

$$x + y - 3 = 0$$
$$2x = 3y - 1$$

   b. Graph the two equations.
   c. Do the graphs intersect at the point $(0, 3)$?
   d. How many points do the lines have in common?

3. **a.** Test whether $(-1, -1)$ is an element of the solution set of the system

$$x - y = 0$$
$$2x = 2y$$

   b. Graph the two equations.
   c. How many points do the graphs have in common?

4. **a.** Test whether $(1, 4)$ is an element of the solution set of the system

$$y = 3x + 1$$
$$2y - 6x - 3 = 0$$

   b. Graph the two equations.
   c. Do the graphs intersect at the point $(1, 4)$?
   d. How many points do the lines have in common?

5. Graph each equation and for each system tell whether it is independent, inconsistent, or dependent.

a.
$$x + y = 0$$
$$2x + 3y = 3$$

b.
$$2y = x + 1$$
$$2x + 2 = 4y$$

c.
$$x - 2y = 0$$
$$2y - x = 2$$

d.
$$3y = x - 4$$
$$2x - 1 = y + 7$$

e.
$$\frac{x + 2y}{2} = x$$
$$2y = x$$

f.
$$\frac{x - y}{2} = 1$$
$$3x = 6 + 3y$$

g.
$$2(x + y) = 3(x - y)$$
$$5y - x = 1$$

h.
$$x = y$$
$$x = 2y$$

SOLVING SYSTEMS OF EQUATIONS BY GRAPHING

Let us assemble some observations which you undoubtedly made and which are relevant to solving systems of equations.

   i. An equation of the form $Ax + By + C = 0$ has a line for its graph (A and B are not both 0).

   ii. Two linear equations in a system of equations have either two lines or one line for their graph.

   iii. Since two lines may intersect in one point, a system of two linear equations may have one ordered pair for its solution.

   iv. Since two lines may be parallel, a system of two linear equations may have the empty set for its solution set.

   v. Since two linear equations may be equivalent, a system of two linear equations may have an infinite set of ordered pairs for its solution set.

We can arrive at the solution set of some systems by graphing the equations. The three examples below illustrate this procedure.

Example: *i.* Solve by graphing.

$$x + 2y = 3$$
$$3y + 4x = 2$$

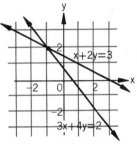

From the graph we see that the two lines intersect at $(-1, 2)$. We check to see whether this pair satisfies each equation.

CHECK:

$$x + 2y = 3$$
$$-1 + 2 \cdot 2 = 3$$
$$-1 + 4 = 3$$
$$3 = 3$$

$$3y + 4x = 2$$
$$3 \cdot 2 + 4(-1) = 2$$
$$6 - 4 = 2$$
$$2 = 2$$

Thus, $\{(x, y) \mid x + 2y = 3\} \cap \{(x, y) \mid 3y + 4x = 2\} = \{(-1, 2)\}$.

Is the system independent, dependent, or inconsistent?

Example: *ii.* Solve by graphing.

$$3x + y = 1$$
$$2y = 2 - 6x$$

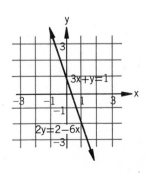

The two equations have the same graph. Thus, the solution set of the system consists of an infinite set of ordered number pairs. For example, $(0, 1)$, $(1, -2)$, and $(2, -5)$ are some elements of the solution set.

Thus, $\{(x, y)\,|\,3x + y = 1\} \cap \{(x, y)\,|\,2y = 2 - 6x\}$
$\qquad = \{(x, y)\,|\,y = -3x + 1\}$.

Is the system independent, dependent or inconsistent?

Example:　　*iii.* Solve by graphing.

$$2x - y = 2$$
$$y - 2x = 1$$

The graph of this system consists of two parallel lines. Therefore, the solution set of the system is the empty set.

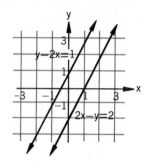

Thus, $\{(x, y)\,|\,2x - y = 2\} \cap \{(x, y)\,|\,y - 2x = 1\} = \phi$.

Tell whether the system is independent, dependent, or inconsistent.

EXERCISES

Solve each system by graphing and

  i. if the system is independent, check the number pair you obtain to verify that it is the solution

  ii. in case the system is either dependent or inconsistent, state which of the two it is

1. $2x + y = 3$
　　$y - x = -3$

2. $y = 2 - 3x$
　　$x = \dfrac{2}{3} - \dfrac{1}{3}y$

3. $3(x + y) = 1$
　　$3y = 2 - 3x$

4. $\dfrac{x}{2} = \dfrac{y}{3}$
　　$y - x = 1$

5. $4x - y + 3 = 0$
　　$x = y$

6. $3(x + 2y) = 4(y - x)$
　　$2y = 7x$

7. $\dfrac{x + y}{3} = \dfrac{2x - 1}{4}$
　　$4y = 2x + 3$

8. $x = 1$
　　$y = 2$

Equivalent systems of equations

The system

$$3x + y = 1$$
$$2y = 2 - 6x$$

which we graphed in Example *ii.* on page 293 is a dependent system. Applying the familiar equation properties, we can show that the equations are equivalent. We do this by deriving one equation from the other. Let us start with the second equation. Observe how each step is obtained.

$$2y = 2 - 6x$$
$$y = 1 - 3x$$
$$3x + y = 1$$

The last step yields the first equation in the system. This procedure is helpful in deciding whether or not *two systems* are equivalent. Consider the following two systems

SYSTEM 1 $$\begin{cases} 2(x - 4y) = 5(y - x) \\ \dfrac{x - 2}{3} = \dfrac{y + 1}{2} \end{cases}$$
SYSTEM 2 $$\begin{cases} 7x = 13y \\ \dfrac{x - 2}{3} = \dfrac{y + 1}{2} \end{cases}$$

Observe the following about these two systems.

The second equations are the same.

The first equations are equivalent; show that $2(x - 4y) = 5(y - x)$ and $7x = 13y$ are equivalent equations.

Now we must decide whether the two *systems* are equivalent. To do this, we use the following definition as a guide.

■ *Definition of Equivalent Systems* Two systems of open sentences are *equivalent* means that they have the same solution set.

Since equivalent equations have the same solution set, we know that the two systems above are equivalent. They have the same solution set.

We see then that if one (or both) equation(s) in an independent or dependent system is (are) replaced by an equivalent equation (or equivalent equations), the resulting system is equivalent to the original system.

EXERCISES

1. For each pair of systems of equations tell whether or not it is a pair of equivalent systems.

a.

SYSTEM 1 $$\begin{cases} 2(x - y) = 3(x + y) \\ 2x = y \end{cases}$$

SYSTEM 2 $$\begin{cases} x = -5y \\ 2x = y \end{cases}$$

b.

SYSTEM 1 $$\begin{cases} \dfrac{1}{2 + x} = \dfrac{2}{3 + y} \\ \dfrac{1}{x} = \dfrac{2}{y} \end{cases}$$

SYSTEM 2 $$\begin{cases} y = 2x \\ y - 2x - 1 = 0 \end{cases}$$

c.
SYSTEM 1 $\begin{cases} \dfrac{1}{x+1} = \dfrac{1}{y+2} \\ 3(x+1) = 2(y-1) \end{cases}$

SYSTEM 2 $\begin{cases} x - y = 1 \\ x + 1 = y - 1 \end{cases}$

d.
SYSTEM 1 $\begin{cases} \dfrac{1}{2(x-3y)} = \dfrac{2}{3(y-2x)} \\ 4(x+y+2) = 3(x-y-1) \end{cases}$

SYSTEM 2 $\begin{cases} 2x = 3y \\ x + 7y + 11 = 0 \end{cases}$

2.   For each system of equations, give an equivalent system in which each equation is of the form $Ax + By + C = 0$.

a.
$$\frac{1}{x+2} = \frac{2}{y+3}$$
$$5 + 2(x+1) = 1 - 3(y+4)$$

b.
$$\frac{3(x+3)}{4} = \frac{5(y-1)}{7}$$
$$2(2x-1) + 4 = 3(y-3)$$

c. $4(2x-3) = \frac{1}{3}(y+1)$
$$\frac{2x-3}{4} = \frac{9(y-1)}{5}$$

d. $2(3-2x) + 4(2-9y) = 0$
$$2(1-y) + 5(9-x) = 2$$

e.
$$\frac{1}{x} = \frac{2}{y}$$
$$\frac{1}{x-3} = \frac{3}{2y+5}$$

f.
$$\frac{2}{x+1} = \frac{3}{y+4}$$
$$\frac{1}{2x-1} = \frac{-4}{6-5y}$$

SOLVING SYSTEMS OF EQUATIONS BY COMPARISON

Perhaps you noticed that sometimes it is difficult to determine from a graph exactly what the coordinates of the point of intersection of two lines are. Or, it is not easy to tell from a graph whether or not two lines are parallel; that is, the graphical method of solving systems of equations has certain limitations.

We shall now resort to a method which does not have the limitations of the graphical method. This method is illustrated by an example. As you study it, note how the equation properties are used to arrive at equivalent equations.

Consider the system

$$7x - 3y = 2$$
$$7x + 9y = 6$$

To solve this system, we find an equivalent system of the form

$$Ax = My + N$$
$$Ax = Py + Q$$

$7x - 3y = 2$ gives us $7x = 3y + 2$

$7x + 9y = 6$ gives us $7x = -9y + 6$

If each of the equations: $7x = 3y + 2$ and $7x = -9y + 6$ is to be satisfied by the same pair of numbers, then the replacement for y must satisfy the following equation.

$$3y + 2 = -9y + 6$$

This last equation is a consequence of some known properties of equality. That is, if $3y + 2 = 7x$ and $7x = -9y + 6$, then $3y + 2 = -9y + 6$. Or, using the general form given above, we can show this as

If $My + N = Ax$ and $Ax = Py + Q$, then $My + N = Py + Q$.

What properties of equality are used in this derivation?

We now solve the derived equation: $3y + 2 = -9y + 6$.

$$3y + 2 = -9y + 6$$
$$12y = 4$$
$$y = \frac{1}{3}$$

Replacing y by $\frac{1}{3}$ in, say, the first of the two original equations and solving for x, we obtain

$$7x - 3y = 2$$
$$7x - 3\left(\frac{1}{3}\right) = 2$$
$$7x - 1 = 2$$
$$7x = 3$$
$$x = \frac{3}{7}$$

CHECK:

$7x - 3y = 2$	$7x + 9y = 6$
$7(\frac{3}{7}) - 3(\frac{1}{3}) = 2$	$7(\frac{3}{7}) + 9(\frac{1}{3}) = 6$
$3 - 1 = 2$	$3 + 3 = 6$
$2 = 2$	$6 = 6$

Thus, $\{(\frac{3}{7}, \frac{1}{3})\}$ is the solution set of the system

$$7x - 3y = 2$$
$$7x + 9y = 6$$

The method we used above is called the *comparison method*.

Do you think you would be able to read accurately the solution to this system from a graph? Why or why not?

EXERCISES

Using the comparison method, solve each of the following systems of equations.

1. $8x + 2y = 1$
   $8x + 3y = 2$

2. $3x + 9y = 1$
   $9y - 4x = 7$

3. $12x - 3y = 1$
   $6x + 2y = -4$
   [HINT: The second equation
   is equivalent to $12x + 4y = -8$.]

4. $4x + 7y = -1$
   $6x - 2y = -5$

5. $3y = 2x - 1$
   $6(x + y) = -2$

6. $3(x + y) = 1$
   $6x + 1 = 3y + 6$

7. $\dfrac{3x + y}{5} = y + 2$

   $\dfrac{-y + x}{4} = \dfrac{3y - 3x}{-9}$

8. $3(2x - 1) = 4(y + 2)$
   $5y = 2x + 1$

9. $x = y$

   $\dfrac{x + y}{2} = \dfrac{3(x - y)}{7}$

10. $7x - 3 = 2y$
    $6y + 9 = 21x$

11. $7x - 3 = 2y$
    $6y + 3 = 21x$

12. $x + 2y = 1$
    $2x - y = 1$

SOLVING SYSTEMS OF EQUATIONS BY SUBSTITUTION

We shall now illustrate another method of solving systems of equations. Consider the following system

$$4x + y = 1$$
$$2x - 3y = 4$$

First, we find an equation which is equivalent to the first equation and which is of the form $y = Mx + N$, called the *y-form* of an equation.

$$4x + y = 1$$
$$y = -4x + 1 \quad \text{[How was this y-form obtained?]}$$

Then replace y in the second equation by $-4x + 1$.

$$2x - 3y = 4$$
$$2x - 3(-4x + 1) = 4$$
$$2x + 12x - 3 = 4$$
$$14x = 7$$
$$x = \frac{1}{2}$$

Replacing x by $\frac{1}{2}$ in the second equation

$$2x - 3y = 4$$
$$2 \cdot \left(\frac{1}{2}\right) - 3y = 4$$
$$1 - 3y = 4$$
$$-3 = 3y$$
$$-1 = y$$

The pair $(\frac{1}{2}, -1)$ should satisfy each equation of the system.

CHECK:

$$4x + y = 1$$
$$4 \cdot \left(\frac{1}{2}\right) + (-1) = 1$$
$$2 - 1 = 1$$
$$1 = 1$$

$$2x - 3y = 4$$
$$2 \cdot \left(\frac{1}{2}\right) - 3(-1) = 4$$
$$1 + 3 = 4$$
$$4 = 4$$

Thus, $\{(\frac{1}{2}, -1)\}$ is the solution set of the system

$$4x + y = 1$$
$$2x - 3y = 4$$

This method is called *the substitution method*. Does the nature of the method justify its name? How?

We shall make a few observations about the substitution method which you will find helpful.

Note that we found the y-form of the first equation, because the coefficient of y was 1 and, therefore, this was a convenient thing to do. We could have found the "x-form" of the first equation instead and substituted what we obtained for x in the second equation. Or, we could have begun by finding either the y-form or the x-form of the second equation and made the appropriate substitution in the first equation.

After solving for x and obtaining $x = \frac{1}{2}$, we could have replaced x by $\frac{1}{2}$ in the first equation, $4x + y = 1$, instead of in the second equation, $2x - 3y = 4$. Do it to see whether you get the same solution for y.

Thus, when using the substitution method, you have some freedom in choosing what you will do. Be clever to choose the ways which will involve the simplest computing.

EXERCISES

Using the substitution method, solve each of the following systems of equations.

1. $2x + y = 3$
$2y - 3x = 6$

2. $2y - 5x = 1$
$x + y = -3$

3. $\dfrac{x + 2y}{2} = -\dfrac{1}{4}y$
$y - x = 7$

4. $\dfrac{x - 2y}{3} = x + y$
$2x - 4y = x - 3y$

5. $x + y = 0$
$\dfrac{2x + 4y}{5} = -\dfrac{1}{5}$

6. $\dfrac{1}{x + 4y} = \dfrac{1}{2}$
$8y - x = 7$

7. $4x + 3y = 0$
$y - x = -\dfrac{7}{12}$

8. $10x + 10y = -3$
$y - x = .5$

9. $\dfrac{1}{x - y} = -2$
$x + y = \dfrac{1}{4}$

10. $\dfrac{1}{x + y} = \dfrac{30}{11}$
$5x + 6y = 2$

11. $\dfrac{3}{2x + 1} = \dfrac{4}{y - 3}$
$8x = 3y + 10$

12. $\dfrac{x - 2}{2} = \dfrac{2y + 7}{3}$
$10 = 1.5x - 2y$

13. $\dfrac{5x + y}{y} = 3$
$\dfrac{2x + y}{3} = 1$

14. $\dfrac{3x + y}{3} = -1$
$\dfrac{x + 3}{y} = -1$

SOLVING SYSTEMS OF EQUATIONS BY ADDITION

Let us consider another way to solve systems of equations. Observe the procedure used in solving the following system

$$4x - y = -1$$
$$2y - 7x = 4$$

First, we find equations equivalent to the two given equations in which the coefficients of one variable (either x or y) are additive inverses. In this particular case, it is easier to do this for y. We obtain the equivalent system

$$-2y + 8x = -2$$
$$2y - 7x = 4$$

Show how this new equivalent system was obtained.
We use these two equations and add

$$-2y + 8x = -2$$
$$\underline{2y - 7x = 4}$$
$$x = 2$$

This step is based on the following property of addition.

$$\forall_a \forall_b \forall_c \forall_d, \text{ if } a = b \text{ and } c = d, \text{ then } a + c = b + d$$

Replacing x by 2 in the first equation

$$4x - y = -1$$
$$4 \cdot (2) - y = -1$$
$$8 - y = -1$$
$$-y = -9$$
$$y = 9$$

$(2, 9)$ should be the solution of this system.

CHECK:
$$4x - y = -1 \qquad\qquad 2y - 7x = 4$$
$$4 \cdot (2) - (9) = -1 \qquad 2 \cdot (9) - 7 \cdot (2) = 4$$
$$8 - 9 = -1 \qquad\qquad 18 - 14 = 4$$
$$-1 = -1 \qquad\qquad 4 = 4$$

Thus, $\{(2, 9)\}$ is the solution set of the given system.

This method of solving a system of equations is called the *addition method*. Does the nature of this method justify its name?

EXERCISES

1.   Using the addition method, solve each of the following systems of equations.

   a. $-x + y = -1$
   $x + y = 1$

   c. $3x - 2y = 10$
   $5x + 3y = -15$

   b. $2x + 3y = -14$
   $x - y = 3$

   d. $x + y = -3$
   $3x - 2y = -4$

e. $\dfrac{x-3}{2} = y + 3$

$\dfrac{y+6}{2} = 2x - 1$

f. $\dfrac{1}{2x} + \dfrac{2}{y} = -3$

$\dfrac{1}{x} + \dfrac{1}{y} = 0$

g. $2x - 3y = 1.3$

$y - x = -.5$

h. $x - y = .9$

$\dfrac{11}{2(x+y)} = 1$

i. $4x - 6y = 3.8$

$y - x = 1.3$

j. $7x + 9y = 3$

$9x - 7y = 2$

k. $\dfrac{2x+y}{3} = 2$

$y = 3 - 2x$

l. $\dfrac{4}{x-1} = \dfrac{2}{y+1}$

$2y = x - 3$

2. Solve each of the following systems of equations choosing the method you consider the most appropriate for the given system.

a. $x + 4y = 0$

$4x - y = 17$

b. $2x + 2y = 3$

$4y - 5x = 15$

c. $3y + 5x = 1$

$10x + 6y = 0$

d. $\dfrac{3x+2y}{3} = y$

$\dfrac{x-y}{2} = -x$

e. $\dfrac{2x+3y}{4} = \dfrac{x-y}{6}$

$\dfrac{x+7y}{5} = \dfrac{4x-y}{4}$

f. $\dfrac{1}{x} = \dfrac{2}{x+y}$

$x = 3y$

g. $2x - y = -1$

$3y - 5x = -1$

h. $\dfrac{3}{x+y} = \dfrac{7}{x+3y}$

$\dfrac{1}{y-x} = \dfrac{9}{4y+x}$

i. $-2(x - 3y) = 4(x + 6y)$

$7(x + y) = 2(3x + 2y)$

j. $\dfrac{1}{x+3} = \dfrac{2}{10-y}$

$\dfrac{3}{4x+3y} = \dfrac{1}{2x+2y}$

3. For each problem

    i. write the system of equations which fits the problem

    ii. solve the system using any method you wish

    iii. check the solution in the original problem

a. The sum of two numbers is 120. Their difference is 5. What are the two numbers?

b. If the order of the digits in a two-digit base-ten numeral is reversed, the resulting number is 4 less than twice the original number. The sum of the two numbers named by each of the digits is 13. What was the original number? [HINT: $53 = 5 \cdot 10 + 3$.]

c. A riverboat travels downstream 8 miles in 1 hour and returns the same distance in $1\frac{1}{2}$ hours. Find the rate of the boat in still water and the rate of the river's current.

d. X and Y are supplementary angles. The measure of X is $\frac{2}{5}$ of the measure of Y. What is the measure of each angle?

e. The length of each leg of an isosceles triangle is $1\frac{1}{2}$ times the length of the base. The perimeter of the triangle is 60 inches. Find the length of each side of the triangle.

f. Jane's father is 4 times as old as Jane is. Five years ago her father was 9 times as old as Jane was then. What are their present ages?

g. Three angles of a triangle are A, B, and C. The measure of angle B is 3 times the measure of angle A. Angles A and C are complementary. Find the measure of each angle.

h. Mr. Thrifty invests a total of $4500, one part of it earning simple interest at the rate of 5%, and the remainder at 6%. His total interest for one year is $250. How much money did he invest at 5% and how much at 6%?

i. A and B are complementary angles. If the measure of angle A is increased 9° and the measure of angle B is decreased 15°, then the measure of each of the two new angles will be the same. What are the measures of angles A and B?

j. The perimeter of a rectangle is 44 inches. If its length is decreased by the number of inches equal to the width, the new figure will be a square. What are the dimensions of the rectangle?

k. Adding 5 to the numerator and also to the denominator of a fraction gives a fraction equal to $\frac{1}{2}$. The numerator is 6 less than the denominator. What was the original fraction?

l. The perimeter of an isosceles triangle is 9 inches. Each leg is 13 times longer than the base. Find the measure of each side of the triangle.

GENERALIZATION OF METHODS OF SOLVING SYSTEMS OF EQUATIONS

We shall now consider a general form of a system of two linear equations and develop procedures which will serve as a model for any system. Let the system be given in this general form

$$a_1x + b_1y = c_1$$
$$a_2x + b_2y = c_2$$

ADDITION METHOD: As you study the procedure below, be prepared to explain each step.

$$a_1x + b_1y = c_1; \text{ multiplying by } -a_2: \quad -a_1a_2x - a_2b_1y = -a_2c_1$$
$$a_2x + b_2y = c_2; \text{ multiplying by } \quad a_1: \quad \underline{a_1a_2x + a_1b_2y = \quad a_1c_2}$$
$$\text{adding: } -a_2b_1y + a_1b_2y = -a_2c_1 + a_1c_2$$

Solving for y, we have

$$y(-a_2b_1 + a_1b_2) = -a_2c_1 + a_1c_2$$
$$y(a_2b_1 - a_1b_2) = a_2c_1 - a_1c_2$$
$$y = \frac{a_2c_1 - a_1c_2}{a_2b_1 - a_1b_2}$$

Returning to the original system and using the addition method again

$$a_1x + b_1y = c_1; \text{ multiplying by } -b_2: \quad -a_1b_2x - b_1b_2y = -b_2c_1$$
$$a_2x + b_2y = c_2; \text{ multiplying by } \quad b_1: \quad \underline{a_2b_1x + b_1b_2y = \quad b_1c_2}$$
$$\text{adding: } -a_1b_2x + a_2b_1x = -b_2c_1 + b_1c_2$$

Solving for x, we have

$$x(a_2b_1 - a_1b_2) = b_1c_2 - b_2c_1$$
$$x = \frac{b_1c_2 - b_2c_1}{a_2b_1 - a_1b_2}$$

We now check to verify that $\left(\dfrac{b_1c_2 - b_2c_1}{a_2b_1 - a_1b_2}, \dfrac{a_2c_1 - a_1c_2}{a_2b_1 - a_1b_2}\right)$ is indeed the solution of the system

$$a_1x + b_1y = c_1$$
$$a_2x + b_2y = c_2$$

CHECK:
$$a_1x + b_1y = a_1 \cdot \left(\frac{b_1c_2 - b_2c_1}{a_2b_1 - a_1b_2}\right) + b_1 \cdot \left(\frac{a_2c_1 - a_1c_2}{a_2b_1 - a_1b_2}\right)$$

$$= \frac{a_1b_1c_2 - a_1b_2c_1 + a_2b_1c_1 - a_1b_1c_2}{a_2b_1 - a_1b_2}$$

$$= \frac{a_2b_1c_1 - a_1b_2c_1}{a_2b_1 - a_1b_2}$$

$$= \frac{c_1(a_2b_1 - a_1b_2)}{a_2b_1 - a_1b_2}$$

$$= c_1$$

Thus, the ordered pair above satisfies the first equation.

$$a_2x + b_2y = a_2 \cdot \left(\frac{b_1c_2 - b_2c_1}{a_2b_1 - a_1b_2}\right) + b_2 \cdot \left(\frac{a_2c_1 - a_1c_2}{a_2b_1 - a_1b_2}\right)$$

$$= \frac{a_2b_1c_2 - a_2b_2c_1 + a_2b_2c_1 - a_1b_2c_2}{a_2b_1 - a_1b_2}$$

$$= \frac{a_2b_1c_2 - a_1b_2c_2}{a_2b_1 - a_1b_2}$$

$$= \frac{c_2(a_2b_1 - a_1b_2)}{a_2b_1 - a_1b_2}$$

$$= c_2$$

Thus, the ordered pair above satisfies the second equation.

Now given any system of equations of the form

$$a_1x + b_1y = c_1$$
$$a_2x + b_2y = c_2$$

we can make appropriate substitutions in

$$x = \frac{b_1c_2 - b_2c_1}{a_2b_1 - a_1b_2}$$

$$y = \frac{a_2c_1 - a_1c_2}{a_2b_1 - a_1b_2}$$

and immediately obtain the solution. Here is one example.

$$2x + y = 1$$
$$-x - 2y = 4$$

Here a_1 is replaced by 2, b_1 by 1, c_1 by 1, a_2 by -1, b_2 by -2, and c_2 by 4

$$x = \frac{b_1c_2 - b_2c_1}{a_2b_1 - a_1b_2} = \frac{(1)(4) - (-2)(1)}{(-1)(1) - (2)(-2)} = \frac{4+2}{-1+4} = \frac{6}{3} = 2$$

$$y = \frac{a_2c_1 - a_1c_2}{a_2b_1 - a_1b_2} = \frac{(-1)(1) - (2)(4)}{(-1)(1) - (2)(-2)} = \frac{-1-8}{-1+4} = \frac{-9}{3} = -3$$

Check to verify that $(2, -3)$ is the solution of the system.

SUBSTITUTION METHOD:

$$a_1x + b_1y = c_1$$
$$a_2x + b_2y = c_2$$

We find the x-form of the first equation.

$$a_1x + b_1y = c_1$$
$$a_1x = c_1 - b_1y$$
$$x = \frac{c_1 - b_1y}{a_1}$$

Now, replacing x by $\dfrac{c_1 - b_1y}{a_1}$ in the second equation

$$a_2x + b_2y = c_2$$

$$a_2 \cdot \left(\frac{c_1 - b_1y}{a_1}\right) + b_2y = c_2$$

$$\frac{a_2c_1 - a_2b_1y + a_1b_2y}{a_1} = c_2$$

$$a_2c_1 + (a_1b_2 - a_2b_1)y = a_1c_2$$
$$(a_1b_2 - a_2b_1)y = a_1c_2 - a_2c_1$$
$$y = \frac{a_1c_2 - a_2c_1}{a_1b_2 - a_2b_1}$$

Note that $\dfrac{a_1c_2 - a_2c_1}{a_1b_2 - a_2b_1}$ is equivalent to $\dfrac{a_2c_1 - a_1c_2}{a_2b_1 - a_1b_2}$, the value of y we obtained before. Explain why these two expressions are equivalent.

EXERCISES

1. Complete the generalization of the substitution method by substituting $\dfrac{a_1c_2 - a_2c_1}{a_1b_2 - a_2b_1}$ for y in the second equation, $a_2x + b_2y = c_2$, and solving for x.

2. Write the generalization of the comparison method, using as a system of equations

$$a_1x + b_1y = c_1$$
$$a_2x + b_2y = c_2$$

[HINT: an equivalent system is $\quad a_1a_2x + a_2b_1y = a_2c_1$
$$a_1a_2x + a_1b_2y = a_1c_2]$$

3. Solve each system by making appropriate substitutions in

$$x = \frac{b_1c_2 - b_2c_1}{a_2b_1 - a_1b_2}$$

$$y = \frac{a_2c_1 - a_1c_2}{a_2b_1 - a_1b_2}$$

a. $\quad 2x + y = 5$
$\quad\quad 4x - 3y = -15$

b. $\quad 2x + 5y = 2$
$\quad\quad 4x - 5y = 1$

c. $\quad 2x - 3y = 0$
$\quad\quad\quad x + y = -5$

d. $\quad\quad 4x + y = 0$
$\quad\quad -2x - y = -2$

DETERMINANTS

You found that the independent system of two linear equations in two variables

$$a_1x + b_1y = c_1$$
$$a_2x + b_2y = c_2$$

has the solution

$$\left(\frac{b_1c_2 - b_2c_1}{a_2b_1 - a_1b_2}, \frac{a_2c_1 - a_1c_2}{a_2b_1 - a_1b_2}\right)$$

Observe that this pair is the same as

$$\left(\frac{b_2c_1 - b_1c_2}{a_1b_2 - a_2b_1}, \frac{a_1c_2 - a_2c_1}{a_1b_2 - a_2b_1}\right)$$

Explain why this is so.

In the next section we are going to show how to arrive at this solution in a somewhat different way. First, we will introduce a new symbol called a *determinant*. Here is an example of such a symbol.

$$\begin{vmatrix} 4 & -3 \\ 2 & 1 \end{vmatrix}$$

Since this symbol has 2 rows and 2 columns we call it a 2 × 2 (READ: two by two) determinant.

We name the rows and columns as follows:

$$\begin{array}{cc} \text{first} & \text{second} \\ \text{column} & \text{column} \\ \downarrow & \downarrow \end{array}$$

$$\begin{array}{c} \text{first row} \to \\ \text{second row} \to \end{array} \begin{vmatrix} 4 & -3 \\ 2 & 1 \end{vmatrix}$$

The symbol

$$\begin{vmatrix} 4 & -3 \\ 2 & 1 \end{vmatrix}$$

names a number. To find this number, we do the following:

$$(4)(1) - (2)(-3) = 4 + 6 = 10$$

Generally

$$\forall_a \forall_b \forall_c \forall_d \ \begin{vmatrix} a & b \\ c & d \end{vmatrix} = ad - cb$$

EXERCISES

1. Find the number named by each of the following determinants.

a. $\begin{vmatrix} 1 & 2 \\ 3 & 9 \end{vmatrix}$

f. $\begin{vmatrix} 1 & 0 \\ 0 & 1 \end{vmatrix}$

b. $\begin{vmatrix} 5 & 0 \\ -2 & 3 \end{vmatrix}$

g. $\begin{vmatrix} \sqrt{2} & 5 \\ -2 & \sqrt{8} \end{vmatrix}$

c. $\begin{vmatrix} 9 & -7 \\ 0 & -3 \end{vmatrix}$

h. $\begin{vmatrix} -5i & -3 \\ 2 & 3i \end{vmatrix}$

d. $\begin{vmatrix} \dfrac{1}{3} & -1 \\ -5 & 9 \end{vmatrix}$

i. $\begin{vmatrix} i & -i \\ -i & 2i \end{vmatrix}$

j. $\begin{vmatrix} 0 & 7 \\ 0 & 9 \end{vmatrix}$

e. $\begin{vmatrix} \dfrac{2}{3} & \dfrac{1}{2} \\ 0 & \dfrac{3}{2} \end{vmatrix}$

2. Simplify each of the following:

Example: $\begin{vmatrix} 3a & 4a \\ a & 2a \end{vmatrix} = (3a)(2a) - (a)(4a) = 6a^2 - 4a^2 = 2a^2$

a. $\begin{vmatrix} a+b & a-b \\ 2 & 3 \end{vmatrix}$

b. $\begin{vmatrix} m+n & m+n \\ m+n & m-n \end{vmatrix}$

c. $\begin{vmatrix} a & \dfrac{1}{d} \\[2mm] -c & \dfrac{1}{b} \end{vmatrix}$

f. $\begin{vmatrix} \dfrac{1}{a-b} & a-b \\[3mm] a+b & \dfrac{1}{a+b} \end{vmatrix}$

d. $\begin{vmatrix} x+y & x+y \\ x & x \end{vmatrix}$

g. $\begin{vmatrix} m^2-n^2 & 1 \\[2mm] m+n & \dfrac{1}{m+n} \end{vmatrix}$

e. $\begin{vmatrix} p+r & -r \\ r & p-r \end{vmatrix}$

h. $\begin{vmatrix} a+b & 1 \\ a^3+b^3 & a^2-ab+b^2 \end{vmatrix}$

Using determinants in solving systems of equations

We are now ready to make use of determinants in solving systems of equations. We use our generalized form of a system of two linear equations in two variables.

$$a_1x + b_1y = c_1$$
$$a_2x + b_2y = c_2$$

To find the solution of this system, we do the following:

$$x = \frac{\begin{vmatrix} c_1 & b_1 \\ c_2 & b_2 \end{vmatrix}}{\begin{vmatrix} a_1 & b_1 \\ a_2 & b_2 \end{vmatrix}} = \frac{b_2c_1 - b_1c_2}{a_1b_2 - a_2b_1}$$

$$y = \frac{\begin{vmatrix} a_1 & c_1 \\ a_2 & c_2 \end{vmatrix}}{\begin{vmatrix} a_1 & b_1 \\ a_2 & b_2 \end{vmatrix}} = \frac{a_1c_2 - a_2c_1}{a_1b_2 - a_2b_1}$$

Note that this is the general solution we obtained earlier by other methods.

To discover how we obtained the determinants above, observe the pattern of coefficients in the system

$$a_1x + b_1y = c_1$$
$$a_2x + b_2y = c_2$$

and then answer each question below.

When solving for x, what is the first column of the determinant in the numerator? What is the second column of this determinant?

When solving for y, what is the first column of the determinant in the numerator? What is the second column of this determinant?

Is the determinant in the denominator, when solving for x and for y, the same? How is this determinant obtained?

The two examples below illustrate the use of determinants in arriving at the solutions of systems of equations.

Example: i. $2x + 3y = -2$
$$x + 5y = 3$$

$$x = \frac{\begin{vmatrix} -2 & 3 \\ 3 & 5 \end{vmatrix}}{\begin{vmatrix} 2 & 3 \\ 1 & 5 \end{vmatrix}} = \frac{-10 - 9}{10 - 3} = -\frac{19}{7}$$

$$y = \frac{\begin{vmatrix} 2 & -2 \\ 1 & 3 \end{vmatrix}}{7} = \frac{6 + 2}{7} = \frac{8}{7}$$

CHECK:

$$2x + 3y = -2$$

$$2\left(-\frac{19}{7}\right) + 3\left(\frac{8}{7}\right) = -2$$

$$-\frac{38}{7} + \frac{24}{7} = -2$$

$$-\frac{14}{7} = -2$$

$$-2 = -2$$

$$x + 5y = 3$$

$$\left(-\frac{19}{7}\right) + 5 \cdot \left(\frac{8}{7}\right) = 3$$

$$-\frac{19}{7} + \frac{40}{7} = 3$$

$$\frac{21}{7} = 3$$

$$3 = 3$$

Thus, $\left\{\left(-\frac{19}{7}, \frac{8}{7}\right)\right\}$ is the solution set of the given system.

Example: ii. $3x - y + 4 = 0$
$$\frac{x - 2y}{3} = 2$$

Before attempting to solve this system by the use of determinants, we find an equivalent system which is of the form

$$a_1x + b_1y = c_1$$
$$a_2x + b_2y = c_2$$

$3x - y + 4 = 0$	$\dfrac{x - 2y}{3} = 2$
$3x - y = -4$	$x - 2y = 6$
$3x + (-1)y = -4$	$x + (-2)y = 6$

Thus

$$3x + (-1)y = -4$$
$$x + (-2)y = 6$$

is such an equivalent system.

Now we are ready to use determinants.

$$x = \frac{\begin{vmatrix} -4 & -1 \\ 6 & -2 \end{vmatrix}}{\begin{vmatrix} 3 & -1 \\ 1 & -2 \end{vmatrix}} = \frac{8+6}{-6+1} = -\frac{14}{5}$$

$$y = \frac{\begin{vmatrix} 3 & -4 \\ 1 & 6 \end{vmatrix}}{-5} = \frac{18+4}{-5} = -\frac{22}{5}$$

CHECK:

$$3x - y + 4 = 0$$

$$3\left(-\frac{14}{5}\right) - \left(-\frac{22}{5}\right) + 4 = 0$$

$$-\frac{42}{5} + \frac{22}{5} + 4 = 0$$

$$-\frac{20}{5} + 4 = 0$$

$$-4 + 4 = 0$$

$$0 = 0$$

$$\frac{x - 2y}{3} = 2$$

$$\frac{\left(-\frac{14}{5}\right) - 2\left(-\frac{22}{5}\right)}{3} = 2$$

$$\frac{-\frac{14}{5} + \frac{44}{5}}{3} = 2$$

$$\frac{\frac{30}{5}}{3} = 2$$

$$\frac{6}{3} = 2$$

$$2 = 2$$

Thus, the solution set of the given system is $\left\{\left(-\frac{14}{5}, -\frac{22}{5}\right)\right\}$.

Why did we go back to the original system when checking whether the values we obtained for x and for y constitute the solution, rather than checking in the derived system?

EXERCISES

1.   Solve each system of equations using determinants. After obtaining values for x and y, check to verify that they *are* the solutions.

a. $2x + y = 4$
$x + 2y = 5$

b. $-x + y = 1$
$3x - 4y = -3$

c. $4x + y = 0$
$6x - y = 5$

d. $3x + 2y = 1$
$3x - 2y = -5$

e. $\dfrac{2x + y}{2} = x - 1$
$y - x = -3$

f. $2x - 3y = 2.5$
$-2y - x = .5$

g. $2(2x + y) = 3(x - 2y)$
$4(x - y) = x + y$

h. $\dfrac{x + 5y}{2} = 10y$
$5(x - 9y) = \dfrac{x}{2}$

i. $\dfrac{1}{2}x - \dfrac{1}{3}y = 5$
$\dfrac{1}{6}x - \dfrac{1}{6}y = 2$

j. $2(x + y) = 3y - 5x$
$y - x = 2(y - 5x) + 2$

2.   Using determinants, solve each system for x and for y. Give answers in the simplest form.

Example:
$$ay = x - 3$$
$$2y + bx - 1 = 0$$

First, we find an equivalent system of the form

$$a_1x + b_1y = c_1$$
$$a_2x + b_2y = c_2$$

$$ay = x - 3 \qquad\qquad 2y + bx - 1 = 0$$
$$x - ay - 3 = 0 \qquad\qquad bx + 2y = 1$$
$$x + (-a)y = 3$$

The equivalent system in the desired form is

$$x + (-a)y = 3$$
$$bx + 2y = 1$$

Now, we use determinants.

$$x = \frac{\begin{vmatrix} 3 & -a \\ 1 & 2 \end{vmatrix}}{\begin{vmatrix} 1 & -a \\ b & 2 \end{vmatrix}} = \frac{6 + a}{2 + ab}$$

$$y = \frac{\begin{vmatrix} 1 & 3 \\ b & 1 \end{vmatrix}}{2 + ab} = \frac{1 - 3b}{2 + ab}$$

CHECK: $\qquad ay = x - 3$

$$a \cdot \left(\frac{1 - 3b}{2 + ab}\right) = \frac{6 + a}{2 + ab} - 3$$

$$\frac{a - 3ab}{2 + ab} = \frac{6 + a - 6 - 3ab}{2 + ab}$$

$$\frac{a - 3ab}{2 + ab} = \frac{a - 3ab}{2 + ab}$$

$$2y + bx - 1 = 0$$

$$2 \cdot \left(\frac{1 - 3b}{2 + ab}\right) + b \cdot \left(\frac{6 + a}{2 + ab}\right) - 1 = 0$$

$$\frac{2 - 6b}{2 + ab} + \frac{6b + ab}{2 + ab} - \frac{2 + ab}{2 + ab} = 0$$

$$\frac{2 - 6b + 6b + ab - 2 - ab}{2 + ab} = 0$$

$$\frac{0}{2 + ab} = 0$$

$$0 = 0$$

a. $ax + 2y = 3$
$\quad ax + 3y = 1$

b. $mx = 2y + 1$
$\quad nx = -y - 4$

c. $mx = ty - 3$
$\quad 3x = ny$

d. $by = x - 1$
$\quad cy = 2x + 3$

e. $px + qy = 1$
$\quad rx + sy = -1$

f. $ax + by + 5 = 0$
$\quad bx + ay - 3 = 0$

g. $dx + my = t$
$\quad ex + sy = a$

h. $(a + b)x + 2y = 4$
$\quad (c + d)x - 3y = -5$

i. $\dfrac{1}{a}x + \dfrac{2}{b}y = \dfrac{1}{c}$

$\quad \dfrac{3}{a}x - \dfrac{4}{b}y = \dfrac{3}{c}$

j. $\dfrac{a + b}{x} = \dfrac{c + d}{y}$

$\quad \dfrac{m}{x} = \dfrac{n}{y}$

k. $\dfrac{a}{b}x + y = 2$

$\quad \dfrac{c}{d}x - y = 1$

l. $\quad \dfrac{x}{a + k} = \dfrac{y}{b + k}$

$\quad x(b + m) = y(a + m)$

m. $3(x + y) = 4y + 6x$
$\quad y - x = 4$

n. $2(2x + y) = x + 4$
$\quad 3x + 1 = -y$

o. $\quad \dfrac{1}{x - 1} = \dfrac{2}{y - 3}$

$\quad \dfrac{y}{4} = x - 1$

SYSTEMS OF ONE LINEAR AND ONE SECOND-DEGREE EQUATION

You have seen that the graph of a linear equation is a *line*, and in later study of mathematics you will learn that the graph of a second-degree equation in two variables is a *conic*. [What is a second-degree equation?]

■   *Definition of Conic*   A *conic* is the intersection of a plane with a right circular cone or a right circular cylinder.

The figures below show you how the various conics are formed. You see that a conic may be a circle, an ellipse, a straight line, two intersecting straight lines, two parallel straight lines, a parabola, a hyperbola (note the two branches) or a point. Remember that a cone really continues on and on just as a line continues on and on, and so the conics which are straight lines, parabolas, and hyperbolas also continue on and on. Parabolas and hyperbolas are treated further on page 322.

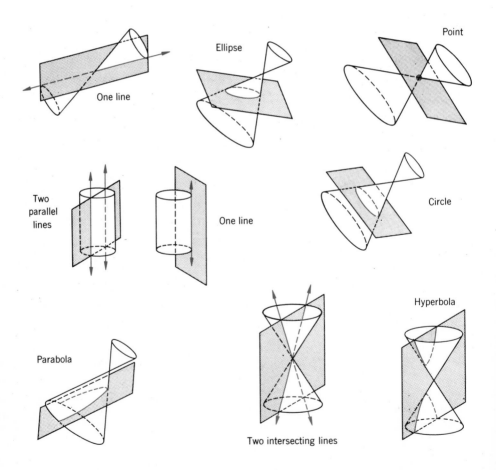

To get some insight into the nature of the solution sets of systems consisting of one linear and one second-degree equation, we shall examine some graphs consisting of a line and a conic. REMEMBER: The line we speak of here is the graph of a first-degree equation. The conic we talk about is the graph of a second-degree equation.

Take another look at the conics pictured on page 312 and note that a conic may also be a single line but realize that this line is a graph of a second-degree equation. Now consider the following systems and their solution sets.

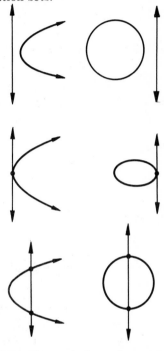

The line and the conic (a parabola in one case and a circle in the second case) do not intersect. Hence the solution set of each system is the *empty set*.

The line and the conic (which ones are used here?) intersect in one point. Hence the solution set of each system consists of *one ordered pair of numbers*.

The line and the conic intersect in two points. The solution set of the system consists of *two ordered pairs of numbers*.

Next we give three examples of systems in which the conic in each system is made up of lines or a line. The picture on the left shows a conic which is two intersecting lines. The line (from the first-degree equation) is exactly one branch of the conic and so the line is a subset of the conic. The solution set of the system is *an infinite set of ordered number pairs*.

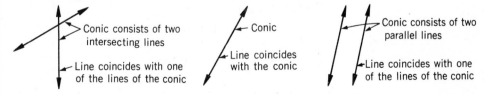

Conic consists of two intersecting lines

Line coincides with one of the lines of the conic

Conic

Line coincides with the conic

Conic consists of two parallel lines

Line coincides with one of the lines of the conic

The line is a subset of the conic. The solution set is an infinite set of ordered number pairs. Do you see that the line in each of the other two cases is also a subset of the conic and that the solution set of the system is therefore *an infinite set of ordered number pairs*?

EXERCISES

For each system below, graph the conic and the line. Then, from the graph, tell whether the system's solution set is the empty set or it consists of one ordered number pair, two ordered number pairs, or an infinite number of ordered number pairs.

1.	$y = x^2$	**4.**	$x^2 - y^2 = 0$
	$x + y = -4$		$x + y = 0$
2.	$x^2 + y^2 = 9$	**5.**	$(x + y - 1)(x + y + 1) = 0$
	$x = -3$		$x + y + 1 = 0$
3.	$x^2 + y^2 = 4$	**6.**	$(x + y)^2 = 0$
	$x = y$		$x + y = 0$

Each system that you graphed in exercises **1-6** above will now be considered algebraically. This will provide us with algebraic methods of obtaining the solution sets of some systems of one linear equation and one second-degree equation.

Example: i. $y = x^2$
$x + y = -4$

We find the x-form of the linear equation $x + y = -4$ which is $x = -4 - y$. Substituting in the equation of the conic

$$y = (-4 - y)^2$$
$$y = 16 + 8y + y^2$$
$$y^2 + 7y + 16 = 0$$

We examine the discriminant $b^2 - 4ac$ for this equation

$$b^2 - 4ac = 49 - 4 \cdot 16 = 49 - 64 = -15$$

Since the discriminant is negative, the equation has no real numbers for its solution. Therefore, the system has no real number pairs for its solution. Did you find previously (problem **1** of the exercises) that the graphs of the line and the conic did not intersect?

Example: ii. $x^2 + y^2 = 9$
$x = -3$

Since -3 for x must satisfy each equation, we substitute -3 for x in the first equation.

$$(-3)^2 + y^2 = 9$$
$$9 + y^2 = 9$$
$$y^2 = 0$$
$$y = 0$$

Check to verify that the pair $(-3, 0)$ satisfies each of the two equations. Since it does, the system has a solution set consisting of one ordered number pair. In your graph (problem **2** of the exercises) did you find that the graphs of the line and the conic intersect in one point?

Example: iii. $x^2 + y^2 = 4$
$$x = y$$

Since the second equation is $x = y$, we may replace x by y in the first equation.
$$y^2 + y^2 = 4$$
$$2y^2 = 4$$
$$y^2 = 2$$
$$y = \sqrt{2} \text{ or } y = -\sqrt{2}$$

Since $x = y$, the pairs $(\sqrt{2}, \sqrt{2})$ and $(-\sqrt{2}, -\sqrt{2})$ should satisfy each equation. Check to verify that it is so. Since each pair satisfies both equations, the solution set of the system is
$$\{(\sqrt{2}, \sqrt{2}), (-\sqrt{2}, -\sqrt{2})\}$$

It consists of two ordered number pairs. Did you find previously (problem **3** of exercises) that the graphs of the line and the conic intersect in two points?

Example: iv. $x^2 - y^2 = 0$
$$x + y = 0$$

The first equation is equivalent to each of the following
$$(x - y)(x + y) = 0$$
$$x - y = 0 \text{ or } x + y = 0$$
$$x = y \text{ or } \qquad x = -y$$

Thus, the solution set of the first equation is
$$A = \{(x, y) \,|\, x = y\} \cup \{(x, y) \,|\, x = -y\}$$

The solution set of the second equation, $x + y = 0$, is
$$B = \{(x, y) \,|\, x = -y\}$$

The intersection of these two sets is
$$A \cap B = \{(x, y) \,|\, x = -y\}$$

which is the solution set of the system.

Thus, the solution set of the system consists of an infinite number of ordered number pairs. Did your graph show this to be true?

Example: v. $(x + y - 1)(x + y + 1) = 0$
$$x + y + 1 = 0$$

The first equation is equivalent to
$$x + y - 1 = 0 \text{ or } x + y + 1 = 0$$

Its solution set is
$$C = \{(x, y) \,|\, x + y - 1 = 0\} \cup \{(x, y) \,|\, x + y + 1 = 0\}$$

The solution set of the second equation is
$$D = \{(x, y) \,|\, x + y + 1 = 0\}$$

The intersection of the two sets is
$$C \cap D = \{(x, y) \mid x + y + 1 = 0\}$$
Thus, the solution set of the system consists of an infinite number of ordered number pairs. Check back to see whether this agrees with your graph.

Example: vi. $(x + y)^2 = 0$
          $x + y = 0$

The first equation is equivalent to each of the following
$$(x + y)(x + y) = 0$$
$$x + y = 0 \text{ or } x + y = 0$$

Its solution set is
$$E = \{(x, y) \mid x + y = 0\} \cup \{(x, y) \mid x + y = 0\}$$
$$= \{(x, y) \mid x + y = 0\}$$
This is also the solution set of the second equation. Thus, the solution set of the system is
$$\{(x, y) \mid x + y = 0\}$$
which is the same as the solution set of each equation. Did your graph show this?

EXERCISES

1. Find the solution set of each system using $R \times R$ as the universal set.

a. $x^2 = y$
   $y = -2$

b. $y = x^2$
   $y - 2x = 3$

c. $x^2 + y^2 = 25$
   $7y - x = 25$

d. $x^2 + y^2 = 8$
   $x + y = 0$

e. $2x^2 + y^2 = 1$
   $2x + y - 3 = 0$

f. $\dfrac{x^2}{4} + \dfrac{y^2}{9} = 1$
   $2y - 2 = x$

g. $x^2 - 2y^2 = 7$
   $2y - x = 1$

h. $(2x + y + 3)(2x + y - 3) = 0$
   $2x + y - 3 = 0$

i. $(2x - y)^2 = 0$
   $2x - y = 0$

j. $x^2 + 8xy = 4$
   $x = y$

k. $3x^2 + 5y^2 - xy = 1$
   $x = -y$

l. $x^2 - y^2 = 0$
   $x - y = 0$

m. $x^2 - y^2 = 0$
   $7x = 13y - 10$

n. $x^2 + y^2 = 16$
   $2y = x - 10$

o. $5x^2 - y^2 + 3 = 0$
   $x + y = 4$

p. $\dfrac{1}{2}x^2 - \dfrac{1}{3}y^2 = \dfrac{1}{4}$
   $2x - y + 1 = 0$

2. For each problem

    i. write the system of equations which fits the problem

    ii. solve the system

    iii. check the solution in the original problem

a. The perimeter of a rectangle is 26 inches. Its area is 12 square inches. Find the dimensions of the rectangle.

b. The sum of two numbers is 27. Their product is 126. What are the two numbers?

c. The sum of two numbers is 3. The sum of the squares of these numbers is 17. What are the two numbers?

d. The square of one number is equal to a second number. The sum of the two numbers is 2. What are the two numbers? [Is there more than one pair of such numbers?]

e. The areas of two circles differ by 5 square inches. Measures of their radii differ by 1 inch. Find the measure of a radius of each of the circles.

f. The areas of two squares differ by 81 square inches. The square with the greater area has a perimeter 28 inches greater than the square with the lesser area. Find the lengths of the sides of each square.

g. The sum of two numbers is $1\frac{7}{15}$. The product of the reciprocals of these numbers is $1\frac{7}{8}$. Find the two numbers.

h. The product of the two numbers named by the digits of a two-digit numeral is 45 and their difference is 4. What is the two-digit numeral?

i. The sum of the areas of two circles is 89π square inches. The measures of their radii differ by 3 inches. What are the measures of the radii of the two circles?

SYSTEMS OF TWO SECOND-DEGREE EQUATIONS

Solving systems of two second-degree equations frequently becomes quite involved. We shall illustrate by examples some methods of handling such systems. Generally, the object is to find a simpler equivalent system.

Example: *i.* Find the solution set of the system

$$3x^2 + y^2 + 12 = 0$$
$$x^2 - 2y^2 - 31 = 0$$

We form a new equation equivalent to the first equation

$$6x^2 + 2y^2 + 24 = 0$$

[Look at the second equation in the system and explain why we chose 2 as a multiplier in forming this new equation.]

Now we use the new equivalent system

$$6x^2 + 2y^2 + 24 = 0$$
$$x^2 - 2y^2 - 31 = 0$$

By the addition property $7x^2 - 7 = 0$
$$7x^2 = 7$$
$$x^2 = 1$$
$$x = 1 \text{ or } x = -1$$

Substituting 1 for x in the equation $3x^2 + y^2 + 12 = 0$

$$3 \cdot (1)^2 + y^2 + 12 = 0$$
$$y^2 + 15 = 0$$
$$y^2 = -15$$

No real number is a solution of the equation $y^2 = -15$.

Explain why substituting -1 for x would lead to the same equation in y.

Thus, the system has no real number pair solutions.

We could have predicted that there were no real solutions in the above case by examining the first equation of this system, $3x^2 + y^2 + 12 = 0$, which is equivalent to $3x^2 + y^2 = -12$. Observe that $\forall_{x \in R} \forall_{y \in R} (3x^2 + y^2)$ is a non-negative number. Explain why. Therefore, there are no real numbers x and y for which $3x^2 + y^2 = -12$. Since no pair of real numbers satisfies one of the equations, it follows that no pair satisfies the system.

Example: *ii.*   Find the solution set of the system

$$6x^2 - 5y^2 + 39 = 0$$
$$x^2 + y^2 - 10 = 0$$

We form a new equation equivalent to the second equation: $5x^2 + 5y^2 - 50 = 0$. [Look at the first equation and explain why we chose 5 as a multiplier in forming this new equation.]

Now we use the new equivalent system

$$6x^2 - 5y^2 + 39 = 0$$
$$5x^2 + 5y^2 - 50 = 0$$

By the addition property $11x^2 - 11 = 0$
$$11x^2 = 11$$
$$x^2 = 1$$
$$x = 1 \text{ or } x = -1$$

Substituting 1 for x in the equation $6x^2 - 5y^2 + 39 = 0$

$$6 \cdot (1)^2 - 5y^2 + 39 = 0$$
$$-5y^2 + 45 = 0$$
$$5y^2 = 45$$
$$y^2 = 9$$
$$y = 3 \text{ or } y = -3$$

Thus, we have found at least two pairs for solutions: $(1, 3)$ and $(1, -3)$. Explain why substituting -1 for x in the first equation would produce the same equation in y. Thus, $(-1, 3)$ and $(-1, -3)$ are two more solutions.

CHECK: $(1, 3)$ in the first equation
$$6x^2 - 5y^2 + 39 = 0$$
$$6 \cdot (1)^2 - 5 \cdot (3)^2 + 39 = 0$$
$$6 - 45 + 39 = 0$$
$$0 = 0$$

Explain why it is quite obvious that the other three pairs also satisfy the first equation.

CHECK: $(1, 3)$ in the second equation
$$x^2 + y^2 - 10 = 0$$
$$(1)^2 + (3)^2 - 10 = 0$$
$$1 + 9 - 10 = 0$$
$$0 = 0$$

Is it likewise clear that the other three pairs also satisfy this equation?

Thus, the solution set of the system is
$$\{(1, 3), \ (1, -3), \ (-1, 3), \ (-1, -3)\}$$

Example: *iii.* Find the solution set of the system
$$x^2 + y^2 = 5$$
$$xy = -2$$

We obtain a new equation equivalent to the second equation
$$2xy = -4$$

[How was this equation obtained from the second equation?]

Now we consider the new equivalent system
$$x^2 + y^2 = 5$$
$$\underline{\hspace{1.2em} 2xy = -4 \hspace{1.2em}}$$

By addition
$$x^2 + 2xy + y^2 = 1$$
$$(x + y)^2 = 1$$
$$x + y = 1 \qquad \text{or } x + y = -1$$
$$x = 1 - y \text{ or} \qquad x = -y - 1$$

Substituting $1 - y$ for x in the second equation
$$xy = -2$$
$$(1 - y)y = -2$$
$$y - y^2 = -2$$
$$y^2 - y - 2 = 0$$
$$(y - 2)(y + 1) = 0$$
$$y = 2 \text{ or } y = -1$$

Substituting $-y - 1$ for x in the second equation

$$xy = -2$$
$$(-y - 1)y = -2$$
$$-y^2 - y = -2$$
$$y^2 + y - 2 = 0$$
$$(y + 2)(y - 1) = 0$$
$$y = -2 \text{ or } y = 1$$

We now use the second equation, $xy = -2$, to find values of x

2 for y:

$$2x = -2$$
$$x = -1$$

-1 for y:

$$-x = -2$$
$$x = 2$$

-2 for y:

$$-2x = 2$$
$$x = 1$$

1 for y:

$$x = -2$$

Thus possible solution pairs are

$$(-1, 2) \quad (1, -2) \quad (2, -1) \quad (-2, 1)$$

CHECK:

$(-1, 2)$:

$$x^2 + y^2 = 5$$
$$(-1)^2 + (2)^2 = 5$$
$$1 + 4 = 5$$
$$5 = 5$$

$$xy = -2$$
$$(-1) \cdot (2) = -2$$
$$-2 = -2$$

Continue the checking to verify that the remaining three pairs satisfy both equations of the system. The solution set of the system is

$$\{(-1, 2), (2, -1), (-2, 1), (1, -2)\}$$

Example:

iv. Find the solution set of the system

$$4x^2 + 2y^2 = 1$$
$$4y + 5 = -4x^2$$

We form a new equation equivalent to the second equation

$$-4x^2 - 4y = 5$$

Now we use the equivalent system

$$4x^2 + 2y^2 = 1$$
$$-4x^2 - 4y = 5$$

By addition

$$2y^2 - 4y = 6$$
$$2y^2 - 4y - 6 = 0$$
$$y^2 - 2y - 3 = 0$$
$$(y + 1)(y - 3) = 0$$
$$y = -1 \text{ or } y = 3$$

Substituting in the equation $4x^2 + 2y^2 = 1$

-1 for y:

$$4x^2 + 2(-1)^2 = 1$$
$$4x^2 + 2 = 1$$
$$4x^2 = -1; \text{ no real number solution}$$

3 for y:

$$4x^2 + 2(3)^2 = 1$$
$$4x^2 + 18 = 1$$
$$4x^2 = -17; \text{ no real number solution}$$

Hence, the solution set of the system is ϕ.

EXERCISES

Find the solution sets of the following systems, using $R \times R$ as the universal set.

1. $x^2 + y^2 = 18$
   $3y = x^2$

2. $x^2 + y^2 - 8 = 0$
   $y^2 - x^2 = 0$

3. $x^2 + y^2 - 1 = 0$
   $xy = 1$

4. $\quad\quad y = x^2 + 2$
   $x^2 + y^2 - 4 = 0$

5. $x^2 + y^2 - 16 = 0$
   $y = x^2 + 4$

6. $\quad\quad xy = 1$
   $x^2 + y^2 = 2$

7. $4x^2 + 9y^2 - 36 = 0$
   $x^2 + y^2 = 4$

8. $x^2 - 2y^2 = 2$
   $xy + 2 = 0$

9. $2x^2 + 3y^2 - 1 = 0$
   $x^2 - 3y^2 - 8 = 0$

10. $y = x^2$
    $y = -x^2$

11. $y = x^2 + 3$
    $y = -x^2 + 5$

12. $y = 3x^2 + 1$
    $y = x^2 + 5$

13. $\quad\quad x^2 + y^2 = 16$
    $2y^2 - 32 + 2x^2 = 0$

14. $x^2 + y^2 = 9$
    $x^2 + y^2 = 4$

15. $x^2 + xy + y^2 = 9$
    $xy = 0$

16. $x^2 - y^2 = 10$
    $x^2 + y^2 = 22$

17. $x^2 + 3xy + y^2 = 0$
    $x^2 + y^2 = 0$

18. $\quad\quad xy = 0$
    $2x^2 + 3y^2 = 5$

19. $2x^2 + y^2 = 4$
    $2x^2 - y^2 = 4$

20. $x^2 + y^2 = 1$
    $2xy = 3$

21. $x^2 + y^2 = 100.01$
    $xy = 1$

22. $x^2 - y^2 = 0$
    $x^2 + y^2 = 1$

23. $x^2 = y + 1$
    $y^2 = x + 1$

24. $x^2 + 2xy + y^2 = 0$
    $x - y = 0$

GRAPHIC INTERPRETATION OF SYSTEMS OF TWO SECOND-DEGREE EQUATIONS

We shall now attempt to gain some additional insight into the solutions of systems of two second-degree equations by the use of graphs. We shall graph two of the systems we solved algebraically as examples above.

For the present, we choose only those systems which are fairly easy to graph.

Example: *i.* **Graph:** $x^2 + y^2 = 5$

$$xy = -2$$

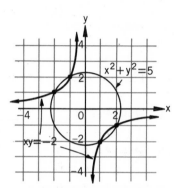

The graph of the first equation, $x^2 + y^2 = 5$, is a *circle* with the center at $(0, 0)$ and with a radius of length $\sqrt{5}$, which is approximately 2.2. Some pairs which satisfy the second equation, $xy = -2$, are: $(-1, 2)$, $(-2, 1)$, $(-3, \frac{2}{3})$, $(-4, \frac{1}{2})$, $(-\frac{1}{2}, 4)$, $(1, -2)$, $(2 - 1)$, $(3, -\frac{2}{3}), (4, -\frac{1}{2}), (\frac{1}{2}, -4)$. The graph of this equation is a *hyperbola* consisting of two branches, one located in the second quadrant, and the other in the fourth quadrant. Do you see that the graphs of the two equations intersect at four points? Does the graph verify that the solution set is $\{(-1, 2),\ (2, -1),\ (-2, 1),\ (1, -2)\}$, which we obtained previously for this system? See example *iii.* on page 319.

Example: *ii.* **Graph:** $4x^2 + 2y^2 = 1$

$$4y + 5 = -4x^2$$

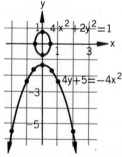

The graph of the first equation, $4x^2 + 2y^2 = 1$, is an *ellipse*. Verify that the points $(-\frac{1}{2}, 0)$, $(\frac{1}{2}, 0)$, $\left(0, \frac{\sqrt{2}}{2}\right)$, and $\left(0, -\frac{\sqrt{2}}{2}\right)$ belong to the ellipse. The graph of the second equation is a parabola. Verify that the following points belong to the parabola: $(0, -1\frac{1}{4})$, $(\frac{1}{2}, -1\frac{1}{2})$, $(-\frac{1}{2}, -1\frac{1}{2}), (1, -2\frac{1}{4}), (-1, -2\frac{1}{4}), (2, -5\frac{1}{4})$, and $(-2, -5\frac{1}{4})$. Does the graph verify that the solution set of this system is the empty set? See example *iv.* on page 320.

EXERCISES

1. Graph each of the following systems. Next to each system is given the number of the problem in the exercises on page 321 where the system appeared and was to be solved algebraically. Examine your graph to see whether it verifies the solution set you obtained previously.

a. (1) $x^2 + y^2 = 18$
$3y = x^2$

b. (2) $x^2 + y^2 - 8 = 0$
$y^2 - x^2 = 0$

c. (3) $x^2 + y^2 - 1 = 0$
$xy = 1$

d. (10) $y = x^2$
$y = -x^2$

e. (11) $y = x^2 + 3$
$y = -x^2 + 5$

f. (16) $x^2 - y^2 = 10$
$x^2 + y^2 = 22$

g. (18) $\quad xy = 0$
$2x^2 + 3y^2 = 5$

h. (19) $2x^2 + y^2 = 4$
$2x^2 - y^2 = 4$

i. (20) $x^2 + y^2 = 1$
$2xy = 3$

2. For each problem,

  i. write the system of equations which fits the problem

  ii. solve the system

  iii. check the solution in the original problem

a. The product of two positive numbers is 8. The sum of their reciprocals is $\frac{3}{4}$. What are the two numbers?

b. The sum of the squares of two positive numbers is 65. The difference of their squares is 33. What are the two numbers?

c. Given two positive numbers, such that the sum of the first number and the reciprocal of the second number is 4, and the sum of the second number and the reciprocal of the first number is $1\frac{1}{15}$, find the two numbers. (There are two pairs of such numbers. Find both.)

d. The product of two positive numbers is $\frac{8}{45}$. The sum of the reciprocals of these numbers is $4\frac{3}{4}$. Find the two numbers.

e. The area of a right triangle is 24 sq. in. The measure of the hypotenuse is 10 in. Find the measures of the two legs.

f. The sum of the areas of two circles is 3π sq. in. The difference of their areas is π sq. in. Find the lengths of the radii of the two circles.

g. The area of a rectangle is 60 sq. in. The measure of each of its diagonals is 13 in. Determine the width and the length of the rectangle.

h. The sum of the areas of two circles is 29π sq. in. The sum of the areas of two circles in which the radii are 1 inch longer than the radii in the previous circles is 45π sq. in. Determine the measures of the radii in the two smaller circles.

i. Increasing the speed of his jet by 190 mph., a pilot is able to reduce by 1 hour the time it takes to cover 3800 miles. What is the slower speed of the jet?

j. A factory worker normally produces 48,000 parts in a certain period of time. If his *hourly* output is increased by 2000 parts, he can produce the 48,000 parts in 2 hours less time. How many parts per hour does he normally produce?

SYSTEMS OF INEQUALITIES

The step from solving systems of equations to solving systems of inequalities is a very simple one. The most illuminating way of approaching the solutions of systems of inequalities is by graphing. We shall illustrate the ways of determining the solution sets of systems of inequalities by examples.

Example: *i.* Graph the solution set of $x + 2y > 3$.

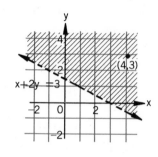

First, we graph $x + 2y = 3$. (We use dashed marks for this graph.) The line $x + 2y = 3$ separates the points of the plane not on the line into two half-planes. One of these half-planes is the graph of $x + 2y > 3$.

In chapter 6 we learned that the correct half-plane can be obtained by finding the y-form of the inequality. Another procedure for finding the correct half-plane consists of testing a point in either half-plane. For example, let us test one point which belongs to the upper half-plane, say, $(4, 3)$.

$$x + 2y > 3$$
$$(4) + 2 \cdot (3) > 3$$
$$4 + 6 > 3$$
$$10 > 3 \qquad [\text{True}]$$

Thus, $(4, 3)$ belongs to $\{(x, y) \mid x + 2y > 3\}$. Choose one point in the lower half-plane. Do its coordinates satisfy the inequality?

We conclude that the upper half-plane, a portion of which is shaded above, is the graph of $x + 2y > 3$. As usual, we show the graph of $x + 2y = 3$ by means of dashes to indicate that the line itself does *not* belong to the graph of $x + 2y > 3$.

Example: *ii.* The graph of $x + 2y \leq 3$ is shown at the right by means of shading. Notice that the graph of $x + 2y = 3$ is shown as a continuous line to bring out the fact that this line is a part of the graph of $x + 2y \leq 3$.

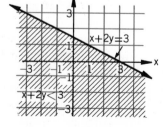

Explain why the graph of $\{(x, y) \mid x + 2y = 3\}$ is a proper subset of the graph of $\{(x, y) \mid x + 2y \leq 3\}$.

Example: *iii.* Graph the solution set of $3y + 4x \geq 2$. We first graph $3y + 4x = 2$ (see below). The graph of $3y + 4x \geq 2$ is the union of $\{(x, y) \mid 3y + 4x > 2\}$ and $\{(x, y) \mid 3y + 4x = 2\}$.

To decide which half-plane is the graph of $3y + 4x > 2$, we test one pair, say $(4, 1)$.

$$3 \cdot (1) + 4 \cdot (4) > 2$$
$$3 + 16 > 2$$
$$19 > 2 \quad \text{[True]}$$

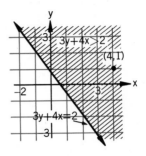

Therefore, the upper half-plane is the graph of our inequality. It is shown by the shaded portion at the right. Note that the boundary line is shown as a continuous line. Explain why.

Now we shall consider the graph of a *system of two inequalities.*

$$x + 2y \leq 3$$
$$3y + 4x \geq 2$$

To know what is meant by the *solution set of a system of two inequalities,* we make the following definition.

■   *Definition of Solution Set of a System of Two Inequalities*   The solution set of a system of two inequalities is the *intersection* of the solution sets of the respective inequalities.

Example: *i.* Graph the solution set of the system

$$x + 2y \leq 3$$
$$3y + 4x \geq 2$$

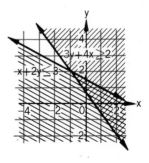

The portion which has double-shading is the graph of the solution set of the system. Tell which parts of the boundary lines belong to the graph. Explain why they are a part of the graph.

The solution set of the system can be described as

$$\{(x, y) \mid x + 2y \leq 3 \text{ and } 3y + 4x \geq 2\}$$

which is the same as

$$\{(x, y) \mid x + 2y \leq 3\} \cap \{(x, y) \mid 3y + 4x \geq 2\}$$

Example: *ii.*   By graphing, find the solution set of the system

$$y \geq x^2$$
$$x + y \leq -4$$

We first graph $y = x^2$. The graph of $y \geq x^2$ is the parabola and the portion shaded like this   . This set consists of the union of the *interior* of the parabola and the parabola itself.

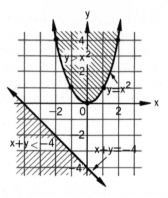

Why is the parabola included in the solution set of $y \geq x^2$? The graph of $x + y \leq -4$ is the straight line and the portion shaded like this   . From the graph of the system it is evident that the solution set of the system is the empty set. We have: $\{(x, y) \mid y \geq x^2\} \cap \{(x, y) \mid x + y \leq -4\} = \phi$.

Example: *iii.*   By graphing, find the solution set of

$$x^2 + y^2 \leq 9$$
$$x \leq 3$$

Examine the graph below.

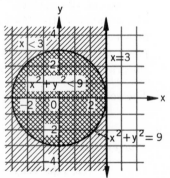

Explain why the following is true

$$\{(x,y)\,|\,x^2+y^2 \le 9\} \cap \{(x,y)\,|\,x \le 3\} = \{(x,y)\,|\,x^2+y^2 \le 9\}$$

The graph of the solution set here is the union of the circle and the *interior* of the circle.

Example: iv. By graphing, find the solution set of

$$x^2 + y^2 \le 9$$
$$xy \ge 2$$

The graph of $x^2 + y^2 \le 9$ is the circle and its interior which is shaded on the graph like this   .

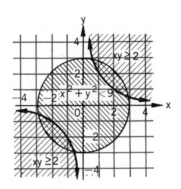

The graph of $xy \ge 2$ consists of the two portions shaded like this   , and the two branches of the hyperbola.

The graph of the system consists of the portions having double shading. Describe the boundaries of the solution set.

EXERCISES

1.   Graph the solution set of each system. If a boundary does not belong to a graph, show it by a dashed line. If it does belong, show it by a continuous line. Shade the intersection in such a way that it is distinct from any other portion.

a. $2x - y > 2$
    $y - 2x < 1$

b. $2x - y < 2$
    $y - 2x < 1$

c. $2x - y > 2$
    $y - 2x > 1$

d. $2x - y \ge 2$
    $y - 2x \le 1$

e. $3x + y > 1$
    $2y < 2 - 6x$

f. $3x + y > 1$
    $2y \le 2 - 6x$

g. $3x + y \ge 1$
    $2y \ge 2 - 6x$

h. $x > 1$
    $y > 2$

i. $x \le 1$
  $y \le 2$

n. $x \le y$
  $x \ge y$

j. $2x + y > 3$
  $y - x > 1$

o. $x < 0$
  $y < 0$

k. $2x + y \le 3$
  $y - x \ge 1$

p. $x < 0$
  $y > 0$

l. $2x + y \le 3$
  $y - x \le 1$

q. $x > 0$
  $y > 0$

m. $x > y$
  $-x > y$

r. $x > 0$
  $y < 0$

2.   Look at the graph in example *ii.* on page 326. Without doing any graphing, describe the graph of the solution set of each of the following systems.

a. $y \ge x^2$
  $x + y \ge -4$

c. $y < x^2$
  $x + y \le -4$

b. $y > x^2$
  $x + y > -4$

d. $y < x^2$
  $x + y < -4$

3.   Look at the graph in example *iii.* on page 326. Without doing any graphing, describe the graph of the solution set of each of the following systems.

a. $x^2 + y^2 \le 9$
  $x \ge 3$

c. $x^2 + y^2 \ge 9$
  $x \ge 3$

b. $x^2 + y^2 \ge 9$
  $x \le 3$

d. $x^2 + y^2 < 9$
  $x > 3$

4.   Look at the graph in example *iv.* on page 327. Without doing any graphing, describe the graph of the solution set of each of the following systems.

a. $x^2 + y^2 \le 9$
  $xy \le 2$

c. $x^2 + y^2 \ge 9$
  $xy \ge 2$

b. $x^2 + y^2 \le 9$
  $xy < 2$

d. $x^2 + y^2 \ge 9$
  $xy \le 2$

5.   Graph the solution set of each system. Show the boundaries and intersection as directed in problem **1,** on page 327.

a. $x^2 + y^2 \le 9$
  $x = 0$

g. $x^2 \le y$
  $x^2 + y^2 \le 9$

b. $x^2 + y^2 \le 9$
  $y = 0$

h. $x^2 \le y$
  $x^2 + y^2 \ge 9$

c. $x^2 + y^2 \le 9$
  $x \le 0$

i. $x^2 + y^2 \le 9$
  $x^2 \ge y$

d. $x^2 + y^2 \le 9$
  $x \ge 0$

j. $x^2 + y^2 \ge 9$
  $x^2 \ge y$

e. $x^2 + y^2 \le 9$
  $x > 0$

k. $xy \ge 4$
  $x^2 + y^2 \le 16$

f. $x^2 + y^2 \ge 9$
  $x > 0$

l. $xy \ge 4$
  $x^2 + y^2 \ge 16$

m. $xy \leq 4$
         $x^2 + y^2 \geq 16$

n. $xy \leq 4$
         $x^2 + y^2 \leq 16$

o. $x^2 + y^2 < 16$
              $x > 0$

p. $x^2 + y^2 < 16$
              $y < 0$

q. $x^2 + y^2 \leq 16$
        $x^2 + y^2 \leq 9$

r. $x^2 + y^2 \geq 16$
        $x^2 + y^2 \leq 9$

s. $x^2 + y^2 \geq 9$
        $x^2 + y^2 \leq 16$

t. $x^2 + y^2 > 9$
        $x^2 + y^2 < 16$

SYSTEMS INVOLVING ABSOLUTE VALUE

We shall now learn to solve systems which involve absolute value. First, we shall clarify some basic ideas about absolute value.

We recall the definition of the absolute value of a real number

$$\forall_{x \geq 0} \ |x| = x \ \textit{ and } \ \forall_{x < 0} \ |x| = -x$$

Example: *i.*   What is the solution set of $|x| < 5$?

As a consequence of the definition of absolute value, $\{x| \ |x| < 5\}$ consists of all numbers which are less than 5 *and* which are greater than -5. Thus, $\{x| \ |x| < 5\} = \{x| -5 < x < 5\}$. Recall that $-5 < x < 5$ is an abbreviation for $-5 < x \ \textit{and} \ x < 5$.

On the number line, the graph of $\{x| \ |x| < 5\}$ is

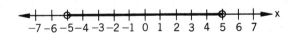

Example: *ii.*   What is the solution set of $|x| > 2$?

According to the definition of absolute value, $\{x| \ |x| > 2\}$ consists of all numbers which are greater than 2 or are less than -2. Thus, $\{x| \ |x| > 2\} = \{x| x > 2 \ or \ x < -2\}$. This is the same as the union

$$\{x| x > 2\} \cup \{x| x < -2\}$$

Its graph is as follows:

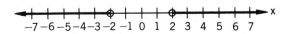

Having clarified these basic ideas in connection with absolute value, we are ready to consider some systems in two variables involving absolute value.

Example: By graphing, find the solution set of the system

$$|x| + |y| \leq 4$$
$$|y| \geq 2$$

Identify in the graph the shaded portion which is the graph of $|x| + |y| \leq 4$. Does its boundary belong to the set?

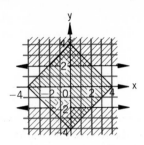

Identify the graph of $|y| \geq 2$. Does its boundary belong to the graph? Describe this boundary.

Describe the intersection of the two sets.

EXERCISES

1. Graph the solution set of each of the following on a separate number line. If the solution set is the empty set, write "ϕ".

a. $|x| < 3$	**c.** $|x| < -1$	**e.** $|x| \geq 0$
b. $|x| \leq 0$	**d.** $|x| \geq 2$	**f.** $|x| > -1$

2. For each non-empty set in problem **1**, give a different description for it, using the intersection or the union of two sets.

3. By graphing, find the solution set of each system in $R \times R$. Use dashed lines for boundaries which do not belong to the sets and continuous lines for boundaries which belong to the sets. Shade only the intersection.

a. $\begin{aligned} |x|+|y| &\leq 6 \\ |x| &\geq 2 \end{aligned}$	**f.** $\begin{aligned} |x| &> |y| \\ |y| &> 1 \end{aligned}$	**k.** $\begin{aligned} |x-y| &= 0 \\ |y| &\leq 2 \end{aligned}$
b. $\begin{aligned} |x|+|y| &\leq 1 \\ |x|+|y| &= 0 \end{aligned}$	**g.** $\begin{aligned} |x| &< 2 \\ |y| &> 1 \end{aligned}$	**l.** $\begin{aligned} y &> |x| \\ y &> x+2 \end{aligned}$
c. $\begin{aligned} |x|+|y| &\geq 1 \\ |x|+|y| &= 1 \end{aligned}$	**h.** $\begin{aligned} |y| &\geq 4 \\ |x| &\geq 4 \end{aligned}$	**m.** $\begin{aligned} y &= |x| \\ |x+1| &< y \end{aligned}$
d. $\begin{aligned} |x|+|y| &> 0 \\ |x|+|y| &< 0 \end{aligned}$	**i.** $\begin{aligned} |x+1| &> |y+1| \\ |x| &> 3 \end{aligned}$	**n.** $\begin{aligned} |x+3| &> y \\ |y+1| &< x \end{aligned}$
e. $\begin{aligned} |x| &= |y| \\ |x| &< 2 \end{aligned}$	**j.** $\begin{aligned} \left|\dfrac{x}{y}\right| &> 1 \\ |x| &= 0 \end{aligned}$	

VOCABULARY

Use each of the following correctly in a sentence. Numerals in parentheses refer to pages where these words were used. If you are not sure of the meaning of any word, turn to the indicated page.

absolute value (329)
addition method (300)
boundary (325)
circle (322)
comparison method (297)
conic (312)
dependent system (291)
determinant (305)
ellipse (322)
equivalent systems of equations (295)

half-plane (324)
hyperbola (322)
inconsistent system (291)
independent system (291)
interior (326)
linear equation (290)
second-degree equation (312)
substitution method (299)
system of equations (290)
system of inequalities (324)

REVIEW EXERCISES

1. Define each of the following:

a. an independent system

b. an inconsistent system

c. a dependent system

2. Graph each system of equations and tell whether it is independent, inconsistent, or dependent.

a. $x + y = 0$
$x - y = 0$

b. $2x + y + 1 = 0$
$y + 2x - 1 = 0$

c. $\dfrac{2x + y}{3} = 1$
$2y = 6 - 4x$

d. $\dfrac{3x - y}{2} = x$
$x = y$

e. $\dfrac{1}{x} = \dfrac{1}{y}$
$x = y$

f. $4(x - y) = 3(x + y)$
$x = 7y$

g. $2x + 1 = y$
$2y + 1 = x$

h. $\dfrac{x - y}{4} = \dfrac{x + y}{3}$
$x = y$

i. $\dfrac{1}{2}x + \dfrac{1}{3}y = \dfrac{1}{4}$
$6x + 4y = 3$

j. $\dfrac{x + 2y}{2} = 3$
$2(2y + x) = 3$

3. For each system of equations, give an equivalent system in which each equation is of the form $Ax + By + C = 0$.

a. $4x - y = 2$
$y - x = -1$

b. $2(3x - 2) = 3(y + 1)$
$\dfrac{x - 1}{2} = \dfrac{y + 3}{6}$

c. $\dfrac{2}{x} = \dfrac{3}{y - 2}$
$\dfrac{1}{x - 1} = \dfrac{2}{y + 1}$

d. $4(x - 1) + 3(y + 2) = 3$
$2(2y - 3) + 4(3x - 1) = 4$

e. $\dfrac{3}{2(x-1)} = \dfrac{4}{5(2y+1)}$

$2(1-2x) = 3(2+3y)$

f. $\dfrac{3}{x+1} = \dfrac{4}{y-1}$

$\dfrac{x+5}{-2} = \dfrac{3-2y}{-3}$

4. Solve each system of equations by using the most appropriate of the four methods: comparison, substitution, addition, determinants.

a. $2x - y = -2$
$4x + y = 2$

b. $2x + y = 1$
$y - x = 4$

c. $2(3x - y) = -10$
$3(2y - x) = 0$

d. $\dfrac{1}{2x+y} = \dfrac{4}{y-x}$
$3x - y = 6$

e. $4x + 3y + 1 = 0$
$6(x+y) = -1$

f. $x + y = -.1$
$x - y = .7$

g. $2(x-y) = 4(2x+y)$
$x - y = 6$

h. $3(y+x) = x$
$2(y+x) = -y$

5. Find the number named by each of the following determinants.

a. $\begin{vmatrix} -1 & 2 \\ 0 & 4 \end{vmatrix}$

b. $\begin{vmatrix} \sqrt{3} & -3 \\ -2 & -\sqrt{3} \end{vmatrix}$

c. $\begin{vmatrix} \dfrac{1}{2} & -\dfrac{1}{2} \\ \dfrac{1}{3} & \dfrac{1}{3} \end{vmatrix}$

d. $\begin{vmatrix} 3i & -2i \\ i & i \end{vmatrix}$

6. Find the solution set of each system.

a. $x - y = 1$
$4y = x^2$

b. $x^2 + y^2 = -2$
$x = y$

c. $x^2 + 2y^2 = 9$
$2x = y$

d. $2x^2 - 3xy = y^2$
$x = y$

e. $(2x - y + 3)(2x - y - 3) = 0$
$2x - y + 3 = 0$

f. $4x^2 - 12xy + 6y^2 = 0$
$2x = 3y$

g. $y + 7x = 0$
$7x^2 = y$

h. $16y^2 = x^2$
$4y + x = -1$

7. Find the solution set of each system.

a. $15x^2 - y^2 = -1$
$y = 4x^2$

b. $x^2 + y^2 = 4$
$xy = 0$

c. $x^2 + y^2 = 2$
$xy = 1$

d. $y^2 = x$
$y^2 = -x$

e. $x^2 - y^2 = 2$
$2x^2 + y^2 = 25$

f. $\dfrac{1}{x} + \dfrac{1}{y} = 5$
$36(x+y)^2 = 25$

g. $2y^2 - 1 = x^2 + 4$
$x^2 = y^2 - 1$

h. $x^2 = y^2 + 1$
$x^2 = -y - 1$

8. A jet covers a distance of 1200 miles in 2 hours with the help of a tailwind. On its return trip, with a headwind of the same speed as that of the tailwind, the jet takes $2\frac{1}{2}$ hours to cover the same distance. What was the speed of the wind and what was the jet's average speed in still air?

9. Two positive numbers are in the ratio of $\frac{2}{3}$. The product of the numbers is 54. What are the two numbers?

10. The measures of two supplementary angles are in the ratio of $\frac{1}{11}$. What are the measures of the two angles?

11. The square of a first number is 1 less than twice a second number. The second number subtracted from the first number gives the difference of -18. What are the two numbers?

12. Forty-four pounds of a mixture of candy is obtained by mixing one kind of candy worth 29¢ a pound and another kind of candy worth 35¢ a pound. The entire mixture is worth $13.12. How many pounds of each kind of candy were used?

13. Solve each system for x and for y.

a. $ax + y = 3$
  $bx - y = -1$

c. $\dfrac{a-x}{2} = \dfrac{b-y}{3}$
  $ax + 1 = by + 2$

b. $ax = my$
  $nx = by - 1$

d. $px + ry = s$
  $rx + px = t$

14. For each system, graph the conic and the line or the two conics. From the graph, tell whether the system's solution set is the empty set or if it consists of one ordered number pair, two ordered number pairs, or an infinite number of ordered number pairs.

a. $x = 2y^2$
  $x = 8$

e. $x^2 + y^2 = 16$
  $x = -4$

b. $xy = 1$
  $y = 1$

f. $(2x + y - 1)(2x + y + 1) = 0$
  $2x + y + 1 = 0$

c. $xy = 1$
  $x = y$

g. $(2x - y)^2 = 0$
  $2x - y = 0$

d. $x^2 + y^2 = 9$
  $y = -x^2$

h. $x^2 + y^2 = 4$
  $xy = 4$

15. Graph the solution set of each of the following. If a boundary does not belong to a graph, show it by a dashed line. If it does belong, show it by a continuous line.

a. $3x - y > 1$
  $x + y < 0$

d. $x^2 \leq y$
  $y \leq 3$

b. $\dfrac{2x + y}{3} \geq 1$
  $2x + y \leq 0$

e. $x^2 \leq y$
  $y < 0$

c. $\dfrac{2x + y}{3} \leq 1$
  $2x + y \geq 0$

f. $x^2 + y^2 \leq 9$
  $|x| \leq 3$

g. $x^2 + y^2 \le 9$
$|x| > 3$

h. $x^2 + y^2 \ge 4$
$xy \ge 1$

i. $|x| = |y|$
$x^2 + y^2 > 1$

j. $|x| \le |y|$
$x^2 + y^2 \ge 0$

k. $|x| + |y| \ge 1$
$x^2 + y^2 \le 1$

l. $x^2 + y^2 \le 1$
$|x| \le \dfrac{1}{2}$

16. Graph each set on the number line.

a. $\{x \,|\, |x| < 9\}$
b. $\{x \,|\, |x| \le 1\}$

c. $\{x \,|\, |x| > 4\}$
d. $\{x \,|\, |x| \ge 1\}$

17. Give a different description for each of the sets in problem **16,** using the intersection or union of two sets.

18. Explain why in the set of real numbers $|x^2| > y$ is equivalent to $x^2 > y$.

CHAPTER TEST

1. Next to each system of equations is given an ordered number pair (x, y). Tell whether this pair is a solution of the system.

a. $x + 3y = 7$
$y + 2x = 5$ $\quad (1, 2)$

b. $\dfrac{1}{x} - \dfrac{1}{y} = 1$
$x + y = \dfrac{30}{11}$ $\quad \left(\dfrac{1}{6}, \dfrac{1}{5}\right)$

c. $xy = -6$
$12x + y = 6$ $\quad \left(-\dfrac{1}{2}, 12\right)$

d. $3x^2 - 2y^2 = -5$
$2y^2 - 3x^2 = 5$ $\quad (-1, -2)$

2. For each system of equations tell whether it is independent, inconsistent, or dependent.

a. $2x + 2y = 1$
$3x = 2y$

b. $3x - 5y = -6$
$5y - 3x = 4$

c. $\dfrac{3x - y}{2} = 6$
$4 + \dfrac{1}{3}y = x$

d. $\dfrac{y - 3x}{3} = 1$
$y = 0$

3. Use determinants to solve the system

$$3x + y = 5$$
$$-4x - 2y = -1$$

4. Use the comparison method to solve the system

$$5x + 2y = 1$$
$$5x - 3y = 4$$

5. Use the addition method to solve the system

$$3x - 5y = 1$$
$$4x + 5y = 2$$

6. Use the substitution method to solve the system

$$y + 4x - 3 = 0$$
$$3x - 2y = 2$$

7. Solve the system for x and for y

$$\frac{ax + by}{2} = 3$$
$$cx + 3by = 1$$

8. Compute the number named by each of the following determinants.

a. $\begin{vmatrix} 3 & 1 \\ -6 & 2 \end{vmatrix}$

b. $\begin{vmatrix} \frac{1}{4} & -\frac{1}{6} \\ -\frac{1}{2} & \frac{1}{3} \end{vmatrix}$

c. $\begin{vmatrix} 5 & 0 \\ 7 & -2 \end{vmatrix}$

d. $\begin{vmatrix} .4 & .2 \\ 1.9 & 1.2 \end{vmatrix}$

e. $\begin{vmatrix} 2\sqrt{6} & \sqrt{21} \\ \sqrt{2} & \sqrt{7} \end{vmatrix}$

f. $\begin{vmatrix} 3i & 4i \\ -2i & i \end{vmatrix}$

9. Each graph below is a graph of a system of two equations, E_1 and E_2. By looking at the graph, tell whether the system has the empty set for its solution set, or a set consisting of one ordered number pair, two number pairs, four number pairs, or an infinite number of pairs.

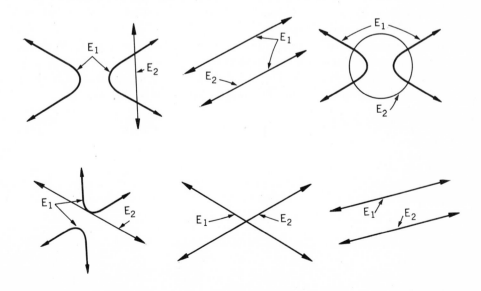

10. Find the solution set of each system.

a. $2y = x^2$
$4y + 2 = 5x$

c. $x^2 + y^2 = 8$
$2x^2 - y^2 = 4$

b. $2x^2 + y^2 = 9$
$y + 2x + 3 = 0$

d. $2y + 4 = x$
$xy = 6$

11. The sum of two numbers is 12. Their difference is 20. What are the two numbers?

12. The area of a square is equal to the area of a rectangle. The length of the rectangle is 4 times its width and the perimeter of the rectangle is 6 more than the perimeter of the square. Find the length and the width of the rectangle, and the length of a side of the square.

13. Graph the solution set of each system. If a boundary line does not belong to a graph, show it by a dashed line. If it does belong, show it by a continuous line.

a. $x - y > 0$
$y + 4 > 2x$

b. $x^2 + y^2 \leq 16$
$xy \leq 4$

c. $y \geq x^2$
$|x| < 1$

BIBLIOGRAPHY

Brixey, J. C. and Andree, R. V. *Fundamentals of College Mathematics*. New York: Holt, Rinehart and Winston, Inc., 1961. pp. 467-481.

Glicksman, A. M. and Ruderman, H. D. *Fundamentals for Advanced Mathematics*. New York: Holt, Rinehart and Winston, Inc., 1964. pp. 412-431.

Kane, R. B. "Linear Programming, An Aid to Decision Making." *The Mathematics Teacher*, March 1960. pp. 177-179.

Lichtenberg, D. and Zweng, M. "Linear Programming Problems for First-Year Algebra." *The Mathematics Teacher*, March 1960. pp. 171-176.

Nichols, Eugene D. *Modern Elementary Algebra*. New York: Holt, Rinehart and Winston, Inc., 1965. Chapter 9.

School Mathematics Study Group. *Intermediate Mathematics, Part I*. New Haven: Yale University Press, 1961. Chapters 6-8.

Western, D. W. and Haag, V. H. *An Introduction to Mathematics*. New York: Holt, Rinehart and Winston, Inc., 1959. pp. 328-342, 441-475.

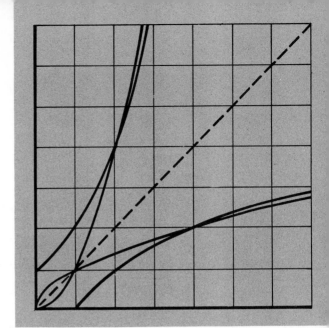

CHAPTER 11

Polynomial Functions

POLYNOMIAL FUNCTION, ITS DEGREE, AND ITS VALUE

In previous chapters you studied about polynomials and about functions. Now we shall consider *polynomial functions*. Here are four examples of polynomial functions.

$$\{(x, 3x^2 + 2)\} \qquad\qquad \{(x, 5)\}$$

$$\{(t, 5t^7 - 4t^3 + t)\} \qquad\qquad \left\{\left(t, \frac{2}{3} - \frac{5}{7}t^5 + t^2 - 3t^4\right)\right\}$$

We agree that the domain of each function is the set of all real numbers.

■ *Definition of Polynomial Function* A *polynomial function* is a set of ordered real number pairs $(x, f(x))$, where

$$f(x) = a_0x^n + a_1x^{n-1} + a_2x^{n-2} + \ldots + a_{n-1}x + a_n$$

In this chapter we shall be primarily concerned with polynomial functions in which the coefficients $a_0, a_1, a_2, \ldots, a_{n-1}, a_n$ are rational numbers and the replacement set of the variable x is the set of all real numbers.

In the definition of a polynomial function, the natural number exponent n ($a_0 \neq 0$) tells us the *degree* of the function. For example, the polynomial function defined by

$$f_1(x) = 5x^3 + \frac{1}{3}x^2 + 2x - 6$$

is of degree 3, since the highest-degree monomial is of degree 3.

In a previous chapter, we defined a *value of a function*. In this chapter, we shall refer frequently to a *value of a polynomial function;* for example, the value of the polynomial function $\{(x, 3x^2 + 2)\}$ at -4 is $3(-4)^2 + 2$ or 50; the value of $\{(t, 5t^7 - 4t^3 + t)\}$ at -1 is $5(-1)^7 - 4(-1)^3 + (-1)$ or -2.

■ *Definition of Value of a Polynomial Function* The *value* of the polynomial function $\{(x, a_0x^n + a_1x^{n-1} + a_2x^{n-2} + \ldots + a_{n-1}x + a_n)\}$ at c is $a_0c^n + a_1c^{n-1} + a_2c^{n-2} + \ldots + a_{n-1}c + a_n$.

From this definition you see that $P(c)$, the value of a polynomial function at c, is determined by substituting c for x.

EXERCISES

1. Tell the degree of each polynomial function.

Example: $g(x) = 2x^2 + 4x^7 - \frac{1}{2}x^9 + x - 4$

The degree is 9 since $-\frac{1}{2}x^9$ is the highest-degree monomial.

a. $h(x) = x^4 - \frac{1}{2}x^3 + 4x^2 - x + 4$ **d.** $f(x) = 2x^5 - 3x^{10}$

b. $k(x) = x^2 + 2x^3 - 4x^4 - \frac{1}{7}x - 1$ **e.** $p(x) = -x^3 + 2x^2 - \frac{1}{2}x + \frac{1}{4}$

c. $m(x) = 5 - x + x^2 - \frac{1}{4}x^4$ **f.** $s(x) = x^4 + 5 - \frac{1}{3}x^6$

2. Determine the value of each function at -1, at $\sqrt{2}$, and at 0.

Example: $g(x) = x^3 - 2x^2 + x - 1$

   i. $g(-1) = (-1)^3 - 2(-1)^2 + (-1) - 1$
      $= -1 - 2 - 1 - 1 = -5$

   ii. $g(\sqrt{2}) = (\sqrt{2})^3 - 2(\sqrt{2})^2 + (\sqrt{2}) - 1$
      $= 2\sqrt{2} - 2 \cdot 2 + \sqrt{2} - 1$
      $= 3\sqrt{2} - 4 - 1 = 3\sqrt{2} - 5$

   iii. $g(0) = 0^3 - 2 \cdot 0^2 + 0 - 1 = -1$

a. $f(x) = 3x^3 - x^2 + x - 3$ **c.** $m(x) = -x^5 + 2x^4 - x + \frac{1}{3}$

b. $h(x) = x^4 + x^3 - \frac{1}{2}$ **d.** $k(x) = x^6 + x^4 - x^2 + 3$

Division of polynomials by binomials of the form: x−a

You should recall that in a previous chapter we learned to work with polynomials in one or more variables. For the present, our study will be concerned with polynomials in one variable.

To simplify communication, we shall refer to

$$a_0x^n + a_1x^{n-1} + a_2x^{n-2} + \ldots + a_{n-1}x + a_n$$

as being a *polynomial in x*. Now, we shall review the problem of finding polynomial quotients and remainders when polynomials in x are divided by binomials of the form $x - a$, where a is a rational number. We illustrate such division by displaying all the steps in three examples. Study each example in detail.

Example: i.

$$
\begin{array}{r}
4x + 7 \quad \leftarrow \text{polynomial quotient} \\
\text{divisor} \rightarrow \quad x - 1 \,\overline{\big)\, 4x^2 + 3x - 2} \leftarrow \text{dividend} \\
\underline{4x^2 - 4x} \qquad\qquad \\
7x - 2 \qquad \\
\underline{7x - 7} \qquad \\
5 \leftarrow \text{remainder}
\end{array}
$$

Example: ii.

$$
\begin{array}{r}
\qquad\qquad\qquad \swarrow \text{polynomial} \\
3x^4 - 2x^3 + 3x^2 - 4x + 9 \qquad \text{quotient} \\
\text{divisor} \rightarrow \quad x + 2 \,\overline{\big)\, 3x^5 + 4x^4 - x^3 + 2x^2 + x - 4} \leftarrow \text{dividend} \\
\underline{3x^5 + 6x^4} \qquad\qquad\qquad\qquad\qquad \\
-2x^4 - x^3 \qquad\qquad\qquad\qquad \\
\underline{-2x^4 - 4x^3} \qquad\qquad\qquad\qquad \\
3x^3 + 2x^2 \qquad\qquad\qquad \\
\underline{3x^3 + 6x^2} \qquad\qquad\qquad \\
-4x^2 + x \qquad\qquad \\
\underline{-4x^2 - 8x} \qquad\qquad \\
9x - 4 \qquad \\
\underline{9x + 18} \qquad \\
-22 \leftarrow \text{remainder}
\end{array}
$$

Example: iii.

$$
\begin{array}{r}
\qquad\qquad\qquad \swarrow \text{polynomial} \\
-2x^3 + 12x^2 - 49x + 201 \qquad \text{quotient} \\
\text{divisor} \rightarrow \quad x + 4 \,\overline{\big)\, -2x^4 + 4x^3 - x^2 + 5x + 6} \leftarrow \text{dividend} \\
\underline{-2x^4 - 8x^3} \qquad\qquad\qquad\qquad \\
12x^3 - x^2 \qquad\qquad\qquad\qquad \\
\underline{12x^3 + 48x^2} \qquad\qquad\qquad \\
-49x^2 + 5x \qquad\qquad \\
\underline{-49x^2 - 196x} \qquad\qquad \\
201x + 6 \qquad \\
\underline{201x + 804} \qquad \\
-798 \leftarrow \text{remainder}
\end{array}
$$

EXERCISES

As in the examples, determine the polynomial quotients and the remainders.

1. $(x^3 + 2x^2 - 8x - 1) \div (x - 1)$ **4.** $(2x^5 - 3x^4 + 2x^3 - 4x + 5) \div (x + 4)$

2. $(3x^4 + x^3 - 2x^2 + x + 3) \div (x - 3)$ **5.** $(-4x^3 + 2x^2 - 3x + 1) \div (x + 1)$

3. $(x^5 - 2x^3 + x - 2) \div (x + 2)$ **6.** $(x^3 + 13x^2 - 2x + 1) \div (x - 5)$

DIVISIBILITY AND THE DIVISION ALGORITHM

We shall now attempt to understand the division of polynomials by first reviewing division of whole numbers. We shall say that one whole number is *divisible* by another whole number if and only if the quotient obtained from dividing the first number by the second is also a whole number; that is, the remainder is zero.

Examples: *i.* $20 \div 5 = 4$; 20 is divisible by 5.

          ii. $51 \div 3 = 17$; 51 is divisible by 3.

          iii. $25 \div 6 = 4\frac{1}{6}$; 25 is *not* divisible by 6.

We now extend the analogy to polynomials. For example

$$(x^3 - 3x - 2) \div (x - 2) = x^2 + 2x + 1$$

Therefore, $x^3 - 3x - 2$ is divisible by $x - 2$. But

$$(2x^2 + 4) \div (2x) = x + \frac{2}{x}$$

so $2x^2 + 4$ is *not* divisible by $2x$, since $x + \frac{2}{x}$ is not a polynomial.

Is $(5x + 7)$ divisible by 9? Why or why not?

■   *Definition of "is Divisible by" for Polynomials*   The polynomial $P(x)$ is *divisible by* the polynomial $D(x) \neq 0$ if and only if $P(x) \div D(x)$ is a polynomial.

EXERCISES

1.   Find the polynomial quotients and the remainders. In each case tell whether or not the first polynomial is divisible by the second polynomial.

    a. $(x^2 + x - 2) \div (x + 2)$

    b. $(2x^3 + x + 3) \div (x - 1)$

    c. $(4x^2 + x - 1) \div 2$ [Recall that 2 is a polynomial of degree 0.]

    d. $(6x^4 + 3x^3 - x^2) \div x^2$

    e. $(2x^5 + 2x^3 - x^2 - 1) \div (2x^3 - 1)$

    f. $(3x^3 + x^2 + 1) \div x^2$

    g. $(3x + 6) \div (x + 2)$

    h. $(2x^2 + 5x - 6) \div (2x^2 + 5x - 6)$

2. For each multiplication sentence write two division sentences and, for each sentence, tell what is the dividend, the divisor, and the quotient.

Example: $\qquad (x+1)(x-3) = x^2 - 2x - 3$

$\qquad$ *i.* $\quad (x^2 - 2x - 3) \div (x+1) = x - 3 \qquad (x \neq -1)$

$\qquad\qquad\qquad$ ↑ $\qquad\qquad$ ↑ $\qquad$ ↑

$\qquad\qquad\qquad$ dividend $\qquad$ divisor $\;$ quotient

$\qquad$ *ii.* $\quad (x^2 - 2x - 3) \div (x-3) = x + 1 \qquad (x \neq 3)$

$\qquad\qquad\qquad$ ↑ $\qquad\qquad$ ↑ $\qquad$ ↑

$\qquad\qquad\qquad$ dividend $\qquad$ divisor $\;$ quotient

a. $(x-1)(x+1) = x^2 - 1$

b. $(x-1)(x+2) = x^2 + x - 2$

c. $(2x-1)(x+3) = 2x^2 + 5x - 3$

d. $(x^2 + x + 1)(x-1) = x^3 - 1$

e. $(x+1)(x^3 + 1) = x^4 + x^3 + x + 1$

f. $(x-3)(x+3) = x^2 - 9$

g. $(2x-1)(2x+1) = 4x^2 - 1$

h. $(x^2 + x - 1)(x^2 + x + 1) = x^4 + 2x^3 + x^2 - 1$

i. $(2x^4 - 1)(x^5 + 1) = 2x^9 - x^5 + 2x^4 - 1$

Returning again to the division of whole numbers, we know that not every whole number is divisible by another whole number. For example, $25 \div 6 = 4\frac{1}{6}$ or $25 \div 6 = 4$, remainder 1. Thus, 25 is not divisible by 6.

Examples: $\quad$ *i.* $\qquad 30 \qquad \div \qquad 7 \qquad = \qquad 4, \qquad$ remainder 2

$\qquad\qquad\qquad\quad$ ↑ $\qquad\qquad\qquad$ ↑

$\qquad\qquad\qquad$ dividend $\qquad\quad$ divisor

$\qquad\qquad$ Also observe: $\;30 = 4 \times 7 + 2$

$\qquad\qquad$ *ii.* $\qquad 40 \qquad \div \qquad 7 \qquad = \qquad 5, \qquad$ remainder 5

$\qquad\qquad\qquad\qquad$ ↑ $\qquad\qquad\qquad$ ↑

$\qquad\qquad\qquad$ dividend $\qquad\quad$ divisor

$\qquad\qquad$ Also observe: $\;40 = 5 \times 7 + 5$

The situation with division of polynomials is similar.

Theorem 1 (Division Algorithm) $\qquad$ Given two polynomials $P(x)$ and $D(x)$, $D(x) \neq 0$, then either *i.* there is a unique polynomial $Q(x)$ such that

$$P(x) = Q(x) \cdot D(x)$$

or *ii.* there are two unique polynomials $Q(x)$ and $R(x)$ such that

$$P(x) = Q(x) \cdot D(x) + R(x)$$

In case *i.*, $P(x)$ is divisible by $D(x)$. In case *ii.*, $P(x)$ is *not* divisible by $D(x)$. Note that case *i.* may be viewed as a special instance of case *ii.*, namely the instance in which $R(x) = 0$.

Example: $P(x) = 2x^4 + x^3 + 2x^2 + x - 3$
$D(x) = x^3 + 1$
Find $P(x) \div D(x)$.

$$
\begin{array}{r}
2x + 1 \\
x^3 + 1 \enclose{longdiv}{2x^4 + x^3 + 2x^2 + x - 3} \\
\underline{2x^4 \qquad\qquad\quad + 2x} \\
x^3 + 2x^2 - x - 3 \\
\underline{x^3 \qquad\qquad\quad + 1} \\
2x^2 - x - 4
\end{array}
$$

Thus, $Q(x) = 2x + 1$ and $R(x) = 2x^2 - x - 4$.

What is the degree of $D(x)$? What is the degree of $R(x)$? Is the degree of $R(x)$ less than the degree of $D(x)$? Now let us verify that, for the above example

$$P(x) = Q(x) \cdot D(x) + R(x)$$

$$
\begin{aligned}
Q(x) \cdot D(x) + R(x) &= (2x + 1)(x^3 + 1) + (2x^2 - x - 4) \\
&= 2x^4 + x^3 + 2x + 1 + 2x^2 - x - 4 \\
&= 2x^4 + x^3 + 2x^2 + x - 3 \\
&= P(x)
\end{aligned}
$$

EXERCISES

1. In each problem, let $P(x)$ be the first polynomial and $D(x)$ be the second polynomial. Do the following:

  i. divide $P(x)$ by $D(x)$ to find $Q(x)$, the polynomial quotient, and $R(x)$, the remainder

  ii. verify that the degree of $R(x)$ is less than the degree of $D(x)$

  iii. verify that $P(x) = Q(x) \cdot D(x) + R(x)$

a. $x^3 + 1;\ x - 1$ **e.** $4x^2 + 3x;\ x$

b. $x^3 - 1;\ x + 1$ **f.** $3x^5 + 2x^4 + 5;\ 2$

c. $x^3 + 1;\ x + 1$ **g.** $-2x^4 + 5x^3 + 3x^2 - x + 3;\ -x + 3$

d. $3x^4 + x + 2;\ x - 1$ **h.** $5x^5 + x^4 - 3x^3 + 2x^2 - 1;\ x^4 + x^2 - 1$

2. If $P(x)$ is of degree 12 and $D(x)$ is of degree 3 and $P(x) = Q(x) \cdot D(x) + R(x)$, then what is the highest degree that $Q(x)$ may have? What is the highest degree that $R(x)$ may have?

REMAINDER THEOREM

Let us now return to the three examples we considered in the section on the division of polynomials.

Examples:
    i. $(4x^2 + 3x - 2) \div (x - 1) = 4x + 7$, remainder 5

    ii. $(3x^5 + 4x^4 - x^3 + 2x^2 + x - 4) \div (x + 2)$
$$= 3x^4 - 2x^3 + 3x^2 - 4x + 9, \text{ remainder } -22$$

    iii. $(-2x^4 + 4x^3 - x^2 + 5x + 6) \div (x + 4)$
$$= -2x^3 + 12x^2 - 49x + 201, \text{ remainder } -798$$

In each of these examples, we divided a polynomial by a binomial of the form $(x - a)$. In the first example, a is replaced by 1. In the second example, a is replaced by -2. [Note that $x - a = x - (-2) = x + 2$.] In the third example, a is replaced by -4.

Now, by substituting, we shall compute $P(a)$ for each $P(x)$ used in the examples.

Examples:
    i. $P(a) = P(1)$
$$= 4(1)^2 + 3(1) - 2$$
$$= 4 + 3 - 2 = 5$$

    ii. $P(a) = P(-2)$
$$= 3(-2)^5 + 4(-2)^4 - (-2)^3 + 2(-2)^2 + (-2) - 4$$
$$= 3(-32) + 4 \cdot 16 - (-8) + 2 \cdot 4 - 2 - 4$$
$$= -96 + 64 + 8 + 8 - 2 - 4$$
$$= 80 - 102 = -22$$

    iii. $P(a) = P(-4)$
$$= -2(-4)^4 + 4(-4)^3 - (-4)^2 + 5(-4) + 6$$
$$= -2 \cdot 256 - 16 - 20 + 6$$
$$= -804 + 6 = -798$$

Now compare $P(a)$ in each example with the remainder in that example. What do you find? This observation leads us to suspect a theorem which we now state and prove.

Theorem 2 (Remainder Theorem)   Given the polynomials $P(x)$, $D(x)$, and $(x - a)$, if $P(x) = D(x) \cdot (x - a) + R$ for some number R, then $R = P(a)$.

Proof

    If $P(x) = D(x) \cdot (x - a) + R$
    then $P(a) = D(a) \cdot (a - a) + R$
$$= D(a) \cdot 0 + R$$
$$= 0 + R$$
$$= R$$

Therefore $P(a) = R$

Thus, we have proved that $P(a) = R$. Note that this theorem is true whether $R = 0$ or $R \neq 0$.

The Remainder Theorem provides us with another way to evaluate any polynomial $P(x)$ at any number a.

> Find the remainder R obtained after dividing $P(x)$ by $x - a$. This remainder R is equal to $P(a)$, which is the value of $P(x)$ at a.

At first glance, this does not appear to be an efficient way to find the value of $P(x)$ at a. But, if we were able to find a shortcut for dividing any polynomial $P(x)$ by $x - a$, we would have a quick way of finding $P(a)$. In the next section we shall develop a method for rapidly dividing $P(x)$ by $x - a$.

EXERCISES

1. Prove that if $f(x) = g(x) \cdot (x - a) + c$, then $f(a) = c$.

2. In each problem, the first polynomial is $P(x)$ and the second is a binomial of the form $x - a$. Do the following:

> *i.* divide $P(x)$ by $x - a$ and find the remainder R in each case
>
> *ii.* evaluate $P(x)$ at a by substitution and verify that $P(a) = R$

a. $x^3 + x^2 - 3; \; x - 2$

b. $3x^2 + 4; \; x - 1$

c. $x^4 + 2x^3 - 3x^2 + 2x - 3; \; x + 2$

d. $5x^3 - x^2 + 2x + 4; \; x + 4$

e. $-\frac{1}{2}x^3 + 2x^2 - x + 1; \; x + 3$

f. $-2x^8 + x^4 + 2x^2 - 4; \; x + 1$

Synthetic division

Let us return to the second example of the section on division of polynomials. We reproduce this example here.

$$
\begin{array}{r}
3x^4 - 2x^3 + 3x^2 - 4x + 9 \\
\text{divisor} \rightarrow \quad x + 2 \overline{\smash{)}\, 3x^5 + 4x^4 - x^3 + 2x^2 + x - 4} \\
\underline{\textcircled{3}x^5 + 6x^4} \\
-2x^4 - x^3 \\
\underline{\textcircled{-2}\, x^4 - 4x^3} \\
3x^3 + 2x^2 \\
\underline{\textcircled{3}\,x^3 + 6x^2} \\
-4x^2 + x \\
\underline{\textcircled{-4}\, x^2 - 8x} \\
9x - 4 \\
\underline{\textcircled{9}\,x + 18} \\
-22
\end{array}
$$

This can be written in a much simpler form. Let us observe a few things which will show us how some simplification can be achieved.

i. In the divisor the coefficient of x is 1, because we are concerned only with division by binomials of the form $x - a$. Thus, we need not write x; just keep in mind that it is omitted.

ii. Note that the circled coefficients are a repetition of the coefficients immediately above them. Thus, we need not show these coefficients twice.

iii. Since we have arranged monomials in descending powers of x, we will not write x at all and simply keep in mind what the powers of x should be if we need to supply them.

With these three points in mind, we can now have the following simpler version.

$$
\begin{array}{r}
\;\; 3 \quad -2 \quad\;\; 3 \quad -4 \quad\;\; 9 \\
\hline
2\;\lfloor\; 3 \quad\;\; 4 \quad -1 \quad\;\; 2 \quad\;\; 1 \quad -4 \\
 6 \\
 -2 \;\;\textcircled{-1} \\
 -4 \\
 3 \;\;\textcircled{2} \\
 6 \\
 -4 \;\;\textcircled{1} \\
 -8 \\
 9 \;\;\textcircled{-4} \\
 18 \\
 -22
\end{array}
$$

This abbreviated version can be condensed even more. We show this below and then explain how it was obtained.

$$
\begin{array}{r}
\;\; 3 \quad -2 \quad\;\; 3 \quad -4 \quad\;\; 9, \quad \text{remainder } -22 \\
\hline
2\;\lfloor\; 3 \quad\;\; 4 \quad -1 \quad\;\; 2 \quad\;\; 1 \quad -4 \\
 6 \quad -4 \quad\;\; 6 \quad -8 \quad\;\; 18
\end{array}
$$

We simply did not write the circled coefficients, because they are seen above as coefficients of the terms in the dividend.

Below we make a slight change in the form given above. Compare it with the above form and tell what changes have been introduced.

$$
\begin{array}{r}
2\;\lfloor\;\; 3 \quad\;\; 4 \quad -1 \quad\;\; 2 \quad\;\; 1 \quad -4 \\
 6 \quad -4 \quad\;\; 6 \quad -8 \quad\;\; 18 \\
\hline
 3 \quad -2 \quad\;\; 3 \quad -4 \quad\;\; 9\;\textcircled{-22} \leftarrow \text{remainder}
\end{array}
$$

Now, if we recall each step as we divide the polynomial

$$3x^5 + 4x^4 - x^3 + 2x^2 + x - 4$$

by the binomial $x + 2$, we can decide on the simplest way of doing it. The last form is explained at the top of the next page.

i. The first number in the last row is simply a repetition of the coefficient of the highest power of x.

ii. Multiply 3 by 2 and write 6 under 4.

iii. Subtract 6 from 4 and write -2 in the last line.

iv. Multiply -2 by 2 and write -4 under -1.

v. Subtract -4 from -1 and write 3 in the last line.

vi. Continue this procedure.

vii. The last number (-22) is the remainder.

The simplified scheme shown above is called *synthetic division*. Now we illustrate this procedure on the division of other polynomials by binomials of the form $x - a$.

Example: i. $(3x^4 + 4x^3 - 2x^2 + x - 3) \div (x + 3)$

$$
\begin{array}{r|rrrrr}
3 & 3 & 4 & -2 & 1 & -3 \\
  &   & 9 & -15 & 39 & -114 \\
\hline
  & 3 & -5 & 13 & -38 & \boxed{111} \leftarrow \text{remainder}
\end{array}
$$

If you were not able to follow the example, restudy steps *i.* through *vii.* above.

Now by the Remainder Theorem we know that the value of the polynomial $3x^4 + 4x^3 - 2x^2 + x - 3$ at -3 is 111. Explain why the last statement is true. [HINT: $x - a = x + 3 = x - (-3)$.]

If we are interested in the polynomial quotient, it is easily supplied from the scheme above.

$(3x^4 + 4x^3 - 2x^2 + x - 3) \div (x + 3) = 3x^3 - 5x^2 + 13x - 38$, remainder 111

Example: ii. $(-7x^5 + 3x^3 + x^2 - 3) \div (x + 4)$

$$
\begin{array}{r|rrrrrr}
4 & -7 & 0 & 3 & 1 & 0 & -3 \\
  &   & -28 & 112 & -436 & 1748 & -6992 \\
\hline
  & -7 & 28 & -109 & 437 & -1748 & \boxed{6989} \leftarrow \text{remainder}
\end{array}
$$

Note that since the terms in x to the exponents 4 and 1 are missing, we are using 0 as the coefficients for these terms. Thus, the value of the polynomial $-7x^5 + 3x^3 + x^2 - 3$ at -4 is 6989.

To state the problem and the answer in one equation

$(-7x^5 + 3x^3 + x^2 - 3) \div (x + 4)$
$\qquad = -7x^4 + 28x^3 - 109x^2 + 437x - 1748$, remainder 6989

Example: iii. $(2x^3 - 3x + 4) \div (x - 2)$

$$
\begin{array}{r|rrrr}
-2 & 2 & 0 & -3 & 4 \\
   &   & -4 & -8 & -10 \\
\hline
   & 2 & 4 & 5 & \boxed{14}
\end{array}
$$

Why did we write 0 for the second coefficient in the first row? What is the value of the polynomial $2x^3 - 3x + 4$ at 2? What is the polynomial quotient and the remainder?

EXERCISES

For each problem

    i. use synthetic division

    ii. state the value of the dividend at a

    iii. state the problem and the answer in one equation

Example: $(x^3 + x^2 - 1) \div (x + 1)$

    i. synthetic division:

$$\underline{1 \,|\, 1 \quad\quad 1 \quad\quad 0 \quad -1}$$
$$ 1 \quad\quad 0 \quad\quad 0$$
$$ 1 \quad\quad 0 \quad\quad 0 \quad \boxed{-1} \leftarrow \text{remainder}$$

    ii. if $x^3 + x^2 - 1 = f(x)$, then $f(-1) = (-1)^3 + (-1)^2 - 1 = -1$

    iii. $(x^3 + x^2 - 1) \div (x + 1) = x^2$, remainder -1

1. $(2x^4 + x^3 - 2x^2 + x - 2) \div (x + 2)$
2. $(-3x^3 + 2x - 4) \div (x - 1)$
3. $(-4x^3 + 3) \div (x + 3)$
4. $(2x^5 + x^4 - 2x^3 + 3x^2 + x - 2) \div (x - 3)$
5. $(x^6 + 2x^4 + x^2 - 2) \div (x - 4)$
6. $(2x^6 + 1) \div (x - 1)$
7. $(3x^4 + x - 4) \div (x + 5)$
8. $(6x^3 - 5x^2 + 3) \div \left(x + \dfrac{1}{2}\right)$

ZEROS OF A POLYNOMIAL

We have already defined divisibility of polynomials. We say that the polynomial $D(x)$ is a *divisor* or *factor* of the polynomial $P(x)$ if and only if the remainder is 0, when $P(x)$ is divided by $D(x)$. For example, $x - 1$ is a divisor of

$$2x^5 + x^4 - 3x^3 + 2x^2 + x - 3$$

as can be seen from this synthetic division.

$$\underline{-1 \,|\, 2 \quad\quad 1 \quad -3 \quad\quad 2 \quad\quad 1 \quad -3}$$
$$ \; -2 \quad -3 \quad\quad 0 \quad -2 \quad -3$$
$$ 2 \quad\quad 3 \quad\quad 0 \quad\quad 2 \quad\quad 3 \quad \boxed{0} \leftarrow \text{remainder}$$

We know that $P(1) = 0$, since, on dividing $P(x) = 2x^5 + x^4 - 3x^3 + 2x^2 + x - 3$ by $D(x) = x - 1$, the remainder is 0. The number 1, therefore, is called a *zero* of the polynomial $2x^5 + x^4 - 3x^3 + 2x^2 + x - 3$.

■   *Definition of a Zero of a Polynomial* r is called a *zero* of a polynomial $P(x)$ if and only if $P(r) = 0$.

EXERCISES

1.   Use synthetic division to see whether the number listed next to each polynomial is a zero of that polynomial.

   a. $x^3 + 2x^2 + 7x + 14$; -2 [HINT: If the remainder is 0 when the polynomial is divided by $x + 2$, then -2 is a zero.]

   b. $2x^6 + 14x^5 - x^4 - 7x^3 + x + 7$; -7

   c. $3x^7 - 63x^6 - 2x^5 + 42x^4 + x^2 - 23x + 42$; 21

   d. $3x^8 - 12x^7 - 2x + 4$; 4

   e. $2x^5 + 10x^4 - x^3 - 5x^2 + 4x + 20$; 5

2.   Explain how it is possible, just by glancing at

$$P(x) = 2x^{10} + 3x^6 + 4x^5 + x^2 + 3$$

to tell that no positive number is a zero of $P(x)$.

3.   Explain how it is possible, just by glancing at

$$Q(x) = x^8 + 3x^6 + 5x^2 + 1$$

to tell that no real number is a zero of $Q(x)$.

4.   Explain why no negative number can be a zero of the polynomial

$$R(x) = 2x^7 + 3x^5 + x - 21$$

FACTOR THEOREM

From problem **1** above, you learned that r is a zero of a polynomial $P(x)$ if and only if the remainder is 0 when $P(x)$ is divided by $x - r$. In this case

$$P(x) = Q(x) \cdot (x - r)$$

and we see that $x - r$ is a factor of $P(x)$. We state this as a theorem.

   Theorem 3 (Factor Theorem) $x - r$ is a factor of $P(x)$ if and only if $P(r) = 0$.

   Proof   Since the theorem contains the phrase, *if and only if*, we must prove two parts.

   PART I: If $x - r$ is a factor of $P(x)$, then $P(r) = 0$.

        $x - r$ is a factor of $P(x)$ means that there exists a polynomial $Q(x)$ such that

$$P(x) = Q(x) \cdot (x - r)$$

     then $$\begin{aligned} P(r) &= Q(r) \cdot (r - r) \\ &= Q(r) \cdot 0 \\ &= 0 \end{aligned}$$

PART II: If $P(r) = 0$, then $x - r$ is a factor of $P(x)$.

If $P(r) = 0$, then the remainder is 0 when $P(x)$ is divided by $x - r$. [Why?]

That is $P(x) = Q(x) \cdot (x - r) + 0$
$$= Q(x) \cdot (x - r)$$

and we have proved that $x - r$ *is* a factor of $P(x)$.

Example: Is $x + 3$ a factor of the polynomial

$$P(x) = 2x^5 + 7x^4 + 2x^3 - 3x^2 - 5x - 15?$$

To answer this question, we need to find out whether $P(-3) = 0$. We do this by the use of synthetic division.

$$
\begin{array}{r|rrrrrr}
3 & 2 & 7 & 2 & -3 & -5 & -15 \\
  &   & 6 & 3 & -3 & 0 & -15 \\
\hline
  & 2 & 1 & -1 & 0 & -5 & 0 \\
\end{array}
\;\leftarrow \text{remainder}
$$

Since the remainder is 0 when $P(x)$ is divided by $x + 3$, $P(-3) = 0$ and $x + 3$ is a factor of $P(x)$.

EXERCISES

1. **a.** Given that 1, 4, and -2 are zeros of $P(x) = x^3 - 3x^2 - 6x + 8$, tell three first-degree factors of $P(x)$.

   b. Give three second-degree factors of $P(x)$.

   c. If some polynomial $Q(x)$ has the same zeros as $P(x)$ in this problem, could $Q(x)$ be a polynomial of degree lower than 3?

   d. Could $Q(x)$ be a polynomial of degree higher than 3?

   e. Could $Q(x)$ be a polynomial of degree 3 and be different from $P(x)$?

2. Using synthetic division, determine whether each polynomial has the binomial given to its right as a factor.

   a. $x^4 - 9x^3 + x - 9$; $x - 9$

   b. $x^4 - 9x^3 + x - 9$; $x + 9$

   c. $x^3 - 14x^2 - 14x - 30$; $x - 15$

   d. $x^3 - 14x^2 - 14x - 15$; $x - 15$

   e. $\frac{1}{3}x^3 - \frac{2}{3}x^2 - 4x + 8$; $x - 2$

   f. $\sqrt{2}\, x^3 + 7\sqrt{2}\, x^2 + x + 7$; $x + 7$

   g. $ix^5 + (i - 1)x^4 - x^3 + ix + i$; $x + 1$

INTEGRAL POLYNOMIALS

From problem **2f** on page 349 you have seen that a polynomial with irrational coefficients may have an integer for one of its zeros; from problem **2g** you have seen that a polynomial with complex coefficients may have an integer for one of its zeros.

We shall now examine the nature of the zeros of a polynomial which has only integers for its coefficients. Recall that such a polynomial is called *a polynomial over the integers* or an *integral polynomial*.

We can prove by examples that an integral polynomial may have the following:

a complex number for a zero

Example: $x^2 + 1$ What are the two zeros of this polynomial?

an irrational number for a zero

Example: $x^2 - 2$ What are the two zeros of this polynomial?

a non-integral rational number for a zero

Example: $2x - 1$ What is the zero of this polynomial?

May an integral polynomial have an integer as one of its zeros? Again we can prove that the answer to this question is "yes" by showing an example.

$$x^2 - 1 \qquad \text{What are its zeros?}$$

Such zeros will be called *integral zeros*.

The question which we would now like to answer is the following: Given an integral polynomial, is there a systematic way of searching for its integral zeros?

Let us answer this question by investigating an example. Rather than trying one integer after another to see whether or not it is a zero of $P(x)$, we shall take another approach. Read each step and see how it leads to an answer to the question we raised above.

$$P(x) = 2x^3 + 3x^2 - 32x + 15$$
$$P(x) = x(2x^2 + 3x - 32) + 15$$

If r is an integral zero of $P(x)$, then $P(r) = 0$; that is

$$r(2r^2 + 3r - 32) + 15 = 0$$

and therefore $r(2r^2 + 3r - 32) = -15$

Since r is an integer, $2r^2 + 3r - 32$ must also be an integer. Explain.

Now, if the product of two integers is -15, each of the integers is a factor of -15. We know then that r is a factor of -15. So the only integers which can be zeros of $P(x)$ are: $1, -1, 3, -3, 5, -5, 15, -15$.

Note that what we concluded is that *if $P(x)$ has any integral zero, it must be a factor of -15.*

To clarify the situation, answer the following questions.

Must $P(x)$ have an integral zero?

May $P(x)$ have an integral zero which is not a factor of -15?

Must each of the factors of -15 be an integral zero of $P(x)$?

We see that the set of factors of -15 contains the *potential* integral zeros of $P(x) = 2x^3 + 3x^2 - 32x + 15$. We start checking the factors of -15 to see which of them are zeros of this polynomial. We begin doing this by means of synthetic division.

$$
\begin{array}{r|rrrr}
-1 & 2 & 3 & -32 & 15 \\
   &   & -2 & -5 & 27 \\
\hline
   & 2 & 5 & -27 & \boxed{-12}
\end{array}
\qquad
\begin{array}{r|rrrr}
-3 & 2 & 3 & -32 & 15 \\
   &   & -6 & -27 & 15 \\
\hline
   & 2 & 9 & -5 & \boxed{0}
\end{array}
$$

So far we found that 3 is an integral zero of $P(x) = 2x^3 + 3x^2 - 32x + 15$. Therefore, $(x - 3)$ is a factor of $2x^3 + 3x^2 - 32x + 15$.

Rather than continuing the search for other integral zeros by means of synthetic division, we use the fact that $(x - 3)$ is a factor of $2x^3 + 3x^2 - 32x + 15$ to obtain a new polynomial of a lower degree

$$(2x^3 + 3x^2 - 32x + 15) \div (x - 3) = 2x^2 + 9x - 5$$

We now have

$$P(x) = 2x^3 + 3x^2 - 32x + 15 = (x - 3)(2x^2 + 9x - 5)$$

Thus, the remaining zeros of $P(x)$, in addition to 3, are also zeros of $2x^2 + 9x - 5$. We find these zeros using the Quadratic Formula.

$$\frac{-9 \pm \sqrt{81 - 4 \cdot 2 \cdot (-5)}}{4} = \frac{-9 \pm \sqrt{121}}{4} = \frac{-9 \pm 11}{4}$$

The two remaining zeros are $\frac{1}{2}$ and -5. Since we are seeking only integral zeros, we found 3 and -5 to be the only integral zeros of $P(x) = 2x^3 + 3x^2 - 32x + 15$.

We are now ready to take a look at the matter of integral zeros of an integral polynomial in general.

$$P(x) = a_0 x^n + a_1 x^{n-1} + a_2 x^{n-2} + \ldots + a_{n-1} x + a_n$$

We shall call a_n the *constant term* of $P(x)$.

We proceed as in the example above.

$$P(x) = x(a_0 x^{n-1} + a_1 x^{n-2} + a_2 x^{n-3} + \ldots + a_{n-1}) + a_n$$

If r is an integral zero of $P(x)$, then $P(r) = 0$.

$$P(r) = r(a_0 r^{n-1} + a_1 r^{n-2} + a_2 r^{n-3} + \ldots + a_{n-1}) + a_n = 0$$

Hence

$$r(a_0 r^{n-1} + a_1 r^{n-2} + a_2 r^{n-3} + \ldots + a_{n-1}) = -a_n$$

Since r is an integer, $a_0 r^{n-1} + a_1 r^{n-2} + a_2 r^{n-3} + \ldots + a_{n-1}$ is also an integer. Since the product of the two is also an integer, namely $-a_n$ [why is $-a_n$ an integer?], r is a factor of $-a_n$. Observe that the set of integral factors of $-a_n$ is the same as that of a_n, for every integer a_n.

We thus proved a theorem which we now state.

Theorem 4 (Integral Zero Theorem)   If an integer r is a zero of an integral polynomial $P(x)$, then r is a factor of the constant term of $P(x)$.

EXERCISES

1. **a.** What is an integral polynomial?

   b. The definition of an integral polynomial should suggest to you a definition of a *rational* polynomial. What is it?

2. **a.** Give an example of an integral polynomial which has a rational non-integral zero.

   b. Give an example of an integral polynomial which has an irrational zero.

   c. Give an example of an integral polynomial which has a complex zero.

3. For each integral polynomial, find all of its integral zeros.

   a. $2x^3 - 3x^2 - 28x - 12$ **f.** $2x^4 + x^3 - 8x^2 - x + 6$

   b. $3x^3 - 10x^2 - 9x + 4$ **g.** $x^5 - 9x^3 - x^2 + 9$

   c. $x^4 - 6x^2 - 27$ **h.** $2x^4 + 6x^3 - 15x^2 + 15x - 50$

   d. $x^5 - 4x^3 - x^2 + 4$ **i.** $x^5 - 4x^3 - 8x^2 + 32$

   e. $x^8 - x^5 - x^3 + 1$ **j.** $x^3 - 2x^2 - 5x + 6$

4. Explain why any integral polynomial of the form

$$a_0 x^n + a_1 x^{n-1} + a_2 x^{n-2} + \ldots + a_{n-1} x + 1$$

has at most *two* integral zeros. What two integers are potential zeros of such a polynomial?

5. If a polynomial $P(x)$ has $x - 3$ and $x + 1$ as two of its factors, then what second-degree factor must $P(x)$ have?

6. Given that $2x^2 + 11x + 12$ has $x + 4$ for one of its factors, use synthetic division to determine its other first-degree factor.

7. Given that $3x^3 - 2x^2 - 17x - 12$ has $x - 3$ and $x + 1$ for two of its factors, determine its other first-degree factor.

8. Consider any two *integral* polynomials $P(x)$ and $Q(x)$

$$P(x) = a_0 x^n + a_1 x^{n-1} + \ldots + a_{n-1} x + a_n$$
$$Q(x) = b_0 x^n + b_1 x^{n-1} + \ldots + b_{n-1} x + b_n$$

Prove that the set of integral polynomials is closed under addition and under subtraction by proving that $P(x) + Q(x)$ and $P(x) - Q(x)$ are also integral polynomials.

9. Write out a brief argument showing that the set of integral polynomials is closed under multiplication.

10. **a.** Write out an argument showing that the value of the non-integral polynomial

$$2x^3 + \sqrt{3}\, x^2 - \sqrt{2}\, x + \sqrt{7}$$

   at each real number is a real number.

   b. Which property of the set of real numbers is vital in supporting your argument in problem **10a**?

RATIONAL POLYNOMIALS

From the previous section you know that a rational polynomial has rational numbers for its coefficients. Since the set of integers is a subset of the set of rational numbers, the set of integral polynomials is a subset of the set of rational polynomials. Here are some examples of rational polynomials in x.

$$\frac{1}{2}x^4 + 4x^3 - 2x^2 + \frac{2}{3}x - \frac{1}{4} \qquad\qquad 2.6x^3 - 2x^2 + 6x - 9$$

$$4x^2 - \frac{1}{5} \qquad\qquad x^4 + 3x - 5$$

Which one of the rational polynomials above is also an integral polynomial?

To get some insight into the problem of determining all rational zeros of rational polynomials, let us consider how we can determine all rational zeros of

$$P(x) = 2x^4 - \frac{4}{5}x^3 - 4\frac{1}{10}x^2 + 1\frac{3}{5}x + \frac{1}{5}$$

Let us observe that

$$P(x) = \frac{1}{10}(20x^4 - 8x^3 - 41x^2 + 16x + 2)$$

Thus, we have shown $P(x)$ as the product of the rational number $\frac{1}{10}$ and the integral polynomial $Q(x) = 20x^4 - 8x^3 - 41x^2 + 16x + 2$. Thus, $P(x) = \frac{1}{10} \cdot Q(x)$. It should be clear that every zero of $Q(x)$ is also a zero of $P(x)$. Prove this.

Our problem is thus reduced to finding all rational zeros of the *integral* polynomial

$$Q(x) = 20x^4 - 8x^3 - 41x^2 + 16x + 2$$

We already know that every rational number has a name of the form $\frac{a}{b}$, where a and b are relatively prime *integers* ($b \neq 0$); that is, a and b have no common divisor other than 1 and -1.

Suppose $\frac{a}{b}$ is a zero of $Q(x)$. Then

$$20 \cdot \left(\frac{a}{b}\right)^4 - 8 \cdot \left(\frac{a}{b}\right)^3 - 41 \cdot \left(\frac{a}{b}\right)^2 + 16 \cdot \left(\frac{a}{b}\right) + 2 = 0$$

Now we carry out some algebraic manipulations. Examine each step and justify it.

$$20 \cdot \frac{a^4}{b^4} - 8 \cdot \frac{a^3}{b^3} - 41 \cdot \frac{a^2}{b^2} + 16 \cdot \frac{a}{b} + 2 = 0$$

$$b^4\left(20 \cdot \frac{a^4}{b^4} - 8 \cdot \frac{a^3}{b^3} - 41 \cdot \frac{a^2}{b^2} + 16 \cdot \frac{a}{b} + 2\right) = 0$$

$$20a^4 - 8a^3b - 41a^2b^2 + 16ab^3 + 2b^4 = 0$$

$$20a^4 = 8a^3b + 41a^2b^2 - 16ab^3 - 2b^4$$

$$20a^4 = b(8a^3 + 41a^2b - 16ab^2 - 2b^3)$$

We are now ready to make some observations which are needed in deciding about the nature of rational zeros of an integral polynomial.

Recall that a and b ($b \neq 0$) are relatively prime integers.

$\forall_{a \in I} \forall_{b \in I}$ $8a^3 + 41a^2b - 16ab^2 - 2b^3$ is an integer. Explain why.

Therefore, $\dfrac{20a^4}{b}$ is an integer. Why?

Since a and b are relatively prime, for $\dfrac{20a^4}{b}$ to be an integer, b must be a divisor of 20.

Observe that 20 is the coefficient of the highest-degree term in the integral polynomial $Q(x)$. Thus, we have reached the following conclusion for this problem.

If $\dfrac{a}{b}$ ($b \neq 0$, a and b relatively prime integers) is a zero of an integral polynomial, then b is a divisor of the coefficient of the highest degree term in this polynomial.

To find out whether a has any relation to any of the coefficients, we rewrite the third step from the bottom in our development on page 353. Examine each step.

$$20a^4 - 8a^3b - 41a^2b^2 + 16ab^3 + 2b^4 = 0$$
$$2b^4 = -20a^4 + 8a^3b + 41a^2b^2 - 16ab^3$$
$$2b^4 = a(-20a^3 + 8a^2b + 41ab^2 - 16b^3)$$

Now we make observations similar to those above

Are a and b ($b \neq 0$) relatively prime integers? Why or why not?

Is $-20a^3 + 8a^2b + 41ab^2 - 16b^3$ an integer for every integer a and every integer b?

Is $\dfrac{2b^4}{a}$ ($a \neq 0$) an integer? Why or why not?

Is a a divisor of 2?

If you have given correct answers to the questions above, then the conclusion was that a is a divisor of 2. Now, observe that 2 is the constant term of the integral polynomial $Q(x)$. Thus, we have reached the following conclusion for this problem.

If $\dfrac{a}{b}$ ($b \neq 0$, a and b relatively prime integers) is a zero of an integral polynomial, then a is a divisor of the constant term in this polynomial.

Combining and generalizing the two conclusions, we obtain the following:

Theorem 5 (Rational Zero Theorem)   If $\dfrac{a}{b}$ ($b \neq 0$, a and b relatively prime integers) is a zero of the integral polynomial

$$P(x) = a_0x^n + a_1x^{n-1} + a_2x^{n-2} + \ldots + a_{n-1}x + a_n$$

then a is a divisor of a_n and b is a divisor of a_0.

To prove this theorem, every step we carried out in the previous example can be generalized when working with $P(x)$ as given in the theorem. As an exercise, write out these steps following the pattern established.

We now make use of the Rational Zero Theorem in finding rational zeros of an integral polynomial.

Example: Find all rational zeros of $P(x) = 6x^4 + x^3 - 13x^2 - 2x + 2$.

If $\dfrac{a}{b}$ ($b \neq 0$, a and b relatively prime integers) is a zero of $P(x)$, then a is a divisor of 2 and b is a divisor of 6.

Divisors of 2: 1, -1, 2, -2

Divisors of 6: 1, -1, 2, -2, 3, -3, 6, -6

If $P(x)$ has any rational zeros, then they are found among the following:

$$1,\ -1,\ \frac{1}{2},\ -\frac{1}{2},\ \frac{1}{3},\ -\frac{1}{3},\ \frac{1}{6},\ -\frac{1}{6},\ 2,\ -2,\ \frac{2}{3},\ -\frac{2}{3}$$

Each of these twelve potential zeros may be tested by synthetic division. In some cases it is easier to test by substitution. For example, it is easier to test 1 and -1 by substitution.

$$6 \cdot (1)^4 + (1)^3 - 13 \cdot (1)^2 - 2 \cdot (1) + 2$$
$$= 6 + 1 - 13 - 2 + 2 = -6 \neq 0$$

$$6 \cdot (-1)^4 + (-1)^3 - 13 \cdot (-1) - 2 \cdot (-1) + 2$$
$$= 6 - 1 + 13 + 2 + 2 = 22 \neq 0$$

Thus, 1 and -1 are not zeros.

We test further using synthetic division.

$$
\begin{array}{r|rrrrr}
\frac{1}{2} & 6 & 1 & -13 & -2 & 2 \\
 & & 3 & -1 & -6 & 2 \\
\hline
 & 6 & -2 & -12 & 4 & \boxed{0}
\end{array}
$$
$\leftarrow$ Therefore, $-\dfrac{1}{2}$ is a zero.

Since $-\dfrac{1}{2}$ is a zero, $x + \dfrac{1}{2}$ is a factor of

$$P(x) = 6x^4 + x^3 - 13x^2 - 2x + 2$$

From the synthetic division above we see that

$$(6x^4 + x^3 - 13x^2 - 2x + 2) \div \left(x + \frac{1}{2}\right) = 6x^3 - 2x^2 - 12x + 4$$

and, therefore

$$6x^4 + x^3 - 13x^2 - 2x + 2 = \left(x + \frac{1}{2}\right)(6x^3 - 2x^2 - 12x + 4)$$

We know that the zeros of $6x^3 - 2x^2 - 12x + 4$ are the same as those of $3x^3 - x^2 - 6x + 2$. Explain why.

According to the Rational Zero Theorem, the *potential* zeros of $3x^3 - x^2 - 6x + 2$ are

$$\frac{1}{3} \qquad -\frac{1}{3} \qquad \frac{2}{3} \qquad -\frac{2}{3} \qquad 2 \qquad -2$$

We start testing these by synthetic division

$$\frac{1}{3} \begin{array}{|rrrr} 3 & -1 & -6 & 2 \\ & 1 & -\dfrac{2}{3} & \\ \hline 3 & -2 & & \end{array}$$

← We do not need to complete this to see that the remainder will be different from 0; thus, $-\dfrac{1}{3}$ is not a zero.

$$-\frac{1}{3} \begin{array}{|rrrr} 3 & -1 & -6 & 2 \\ & -1 & 0 & 2 \\ \hline 3 & 0 & -6 & \boxed{0} \end{array}$$

← Therefore, $\dfrac{1}{3}$ is a zero.

From this synthetic division we obtain

$$(3x^3 - x^2 - 6x + 2) \div \left(x - \frac{1}{3}\right) = 3x^2 - 6$$

and, therefore

$$3x^3 - x^2 - 6x + 2 = \left(x - \frac{1}{3}\right)(3x^2 - 6)$$

Thus, the remaining zeros of $3x^3 - x^2 - 6x + 2$ are the zeros of $3x^2 - 6$, which are irrational numbers. [Determine the remaining zeros.] Thus, we found that the only rational zeros of

$$P(x) = 6x^4 + x^3 - 13x^2 - 2x + 2 \text{ are } -\frac{1}{2} \text{ and } \frac{1}{3}.$$

EXERCISES

1. Using the Rational Zero Theorem, determine the rational zeros of each polynomial.

   a. $8x^2 - 6x + 1$

   b. $6x^2 - x - 2$

   c. $12x^3 - 4x^2 - 3x + 1$

   d. $4x^3 - 4x^2 - x + 1$

   e. $2x^3 - 5x^2 - 2x + 5$

   f. $3x^3 + 4x^2 - 12x - 16$

   g. $2x^3 - x^2 + 18x - 9$

   h. $2x^4 + 3x^3 - 2x - 3$

2. Find an *integral* polynomial of degree 4 which has the following zeros

$$1 \qquad -2 \qquad \frac{1}{2} \qquad -\frac{1}{3}$$

Rational and irrational zeros of integral polynomials

Let us examine the example of the previous section from a slightly different approach. We found that $-\frac{1}{2}$ and $\frac{1}{3}$ are two zeros of

$$P(x) = 6x^4 + x^3 - 13x^2 - 2x + 2$$

This means that $(x + \frac{1}{2})$ and $(x - \frac{1}{3})$ are factors of $P(x)$. Therefore, $(2x + 1)$ and $(3x - 1)$ are also factors of $P(x)$. Explain.

It follows that $(2x + 1)(3x - 1) = 6x^2 + x - 1$ is also a factor.

Now we divide

$$
\require{enclose}
\begin{array}{r}
x^2 - 2 \\
6x^2 + x - 1 \enclose{longdiv}{6x^4 + x^3 - 13x^2 - 2x + 2} \\
\underline{6x^4 + x^3 - x^2 } \\
-12x^2 - 2x + 2 \\
\underline{-12x^2 - 2x + 2} \\
0
\end{array}
$$

We thus found

$$6x^4 + x^3 - 13x^2 - 2x + 2 = (6x^2 + x - 1)(x^2 - 2) = (2x + 1)(3x - 1)(x^2 - 2)$$

The only remaining zeros to be found come from $x^2 - 2 = 0$. They are $\sqrt{2}$ and $-\sqrt{2}$. We see then that the set of zeros of $P(x) = 6x^4 + x^3 - 13x^2 - 2x + 2$ is $\{-\frac{1}{2}, \frac{1}{3}, \sqrt{2}, -\sqrt{2}\}$. All four zeros are real numbers; two are rational and two are irrational. Knowing the four zeros gives us the complete factorization of $P(x)$ into first-degree factors (expressions of the form $ax + b$; $a \in R$, $b \in R$).

$$6x^4 + x^3 - 13x^2 - 2x + 2 = (2x + 1)(3x - 1)(x - \sqrt{2})(x + \sqrt{2})$$

EXERCISES

1. Find all rational and irrational zeros of each polynomial using the method illustrated above.

    a. $4x^4 - 13x^2 + 3$

    b. $6x^4 - 5x^3 - 11x^2 + 10x - 2$

    c. $80x^4 - 4x^3 - 64x^2 + 3x + 3$

    d. $2x^4 - x^3 - 15x^2 + 6x + 18$

    e. $2x^5 - x^4 - 6x^3 + 3x^2 + 4x - 2$

    f. $x^4 + x^3 - 5x^2 - 3x + 6$

2. For each polynomial in problem **1**, give its complete factorization into first-degree factors.

3. Each set given below is a set of zeros of a third-degree polynomial. For each set, give one such third-degree *integral* polynomial.

    a. $\left\{1, -\frac{1}{2}, 2\right\}$ **c.** $\left\{\frac{1}{2}, \sqrt{2}, -\sqrt{2}\right\}$

    b. $\left\{2, \frac{3}{2}, -\frac{3}{4}\right\}$ **d.** $\left\{\frac{4}{5}, \sqrt{3}, -\sqrt{3}\right\}$

THE FUNDAMENTAL THEOREM OF ALGEBRA

So far we have developed a number of ways to obtain information about the zeros of an integral polynomial. We have not yet, however, raised the question about the *number* of zeros a given polynomial may have.

In order to tackle the problem in its most general form, we shall assume that we are dealing with polynomials having complex numbers as coefficients. Viewing the set of real numbers as a subset of the set of complex numbers permits us to consider the set of polynomials over real numbers; that is, polynomials with real numbers for coefficients are a subset of the polynomials over the complex numbers.

The answer to the question

How many zeros does a given polynomial have?

is found in the theorem which was first proved by the German mathematician, Karl Fredrick Gauss. We state this theorem here without proof, since the proof is beyond the scope of this book.

Theorem 6 (Fundamental Theorem of Algebra)   If $P(x)$ is a polynomial over the complex numbers and of degree greater than 0, then there is a complex number r for which $P(r) = 0$.

This theorem assures us that $P(x)$ has at least one zero. We shall now derive a very important consequence of this theorem.

Suppose we are given a polynomial $P(x)$ over the complex numbers of degree $n \geq 1$. If the coefficient of the highest-degree term is a_0, we can factor it and obtain

$$P(x) = a_0 \cdot Q_1(x)$$

According to the Fundamental Theorem of Algebra, $Q_1(x)$, which is of degree n, has at least one zero. Call it r_1. If $P(x)$ is of degree 1, then

$$P(x) = a_0(x - r_1)$$

and $P(x)$ is completely factored. If $P(x)$ is of degree higher than 1, then

$$P(x) = a_0(x - r_1) \cdot Q_2(x)$$

$Q_2(x)$ is of degree $n - 1$. It also has at least one zero, according to the same theorem. Call this zero r_2. Then

$$P(x) = a_0(x - r_1)(x - r_2) \cdot Q_3(x)$$

We can repeat this argument until we obtain

$$P(x) = a_0(x - r_1)(x - r_2) \ldots (x - r_n)$$

that is, $P(x)$ is shown as the product of a constant and n first-degree factors in x. Now it may happen that some of the zeros: $r_1, r_2, \ldots, r_n$ are not distinct. For example, if

$$P(x) = x^2 + 2x + 1 = (x + 1)(x + 1)$$

then $r_1 = r_2 = -1$. We shall say that, in this case, -1 is a zero of *multiplicity* two of $x^2 + 2x + 1$; that is, the polynomial $x^2 + 2x + 1$ has *one* zero, which has the multiplicity *two*.

For another example, consider

$$T(x) = x^3 + x^2 - x - 1 = (x + 1)(x + 1)(x - 1)$$

Then $T(x)$ has two distinct zeros, 1 and -1. One zero, namely 1, is of multiplicity one; the other zero, namely -1, is of multiplicity two. The sum of the multiplicities of both zeros is three. Do you see that the sum of the multiplicities of all zeros of a polynomial of nth degree is n, whether or not all zeros are distinct?

The argument above is partial proof of a theorem which we now state. As you have seen, this theorem is a consequence of the Fundamental Theorem of Algebra.

Theorem 7 (Unique Factorization Theorem)   Every polynomial $P(x)$ of degree $n \geq 1$ over the complex numbers can be factored uniquely into n first-degree factors, not all of which are necessarily distinct, and a constant factor which is the coefficient of the highest degree term of $P(x)$.

We stated that the argument preceding the statement of the theorem is a *partial* proof of the Unique Factorization Theorem. We still need to prove that this factorization is *unique*; that is, for every polynomial there is only *one* set of first-degree factors. We prove this as follows (we shall ignore the constant factor a_0, because it is of no consequence to this portion of the discussion).

Suppose $P(x)$ has two factorizations which differ in at least one factor

$$P(x) = (x - r_1)(x - r_2) \ldots (x - r_n)$$

and

$$P(x) = (x - k)(x - r_2) \ldots (x - r_n)$$

This implies that $P(x)$ has $n + 1$ zeros: $k, r_1, r_2, \ldots, r_n$. But implicit in the portion of the proof given above is the conclusion that $P(x)$ *of degree n can have at most n zeros, or zeros of multiplicity n.* Thus, our assumption that $P(x)$ has two factorizations is false.

EXERCISES

1.   Find the zeros of each polynomial and then give its complete factorization.
   a. $x^3 - x^2 + x - 1$
   b. $2x^3 + x^2 + 2x + 1$
   c. $x^4 - 2x^2 + 1$
   d. $x^6 - 1$ [HINT: $\forall_x \ x^6 - 1 = (x^3 - 1)(x^3 + 1)$]
   e. $x^4 - 4$
   f. $x^8 - 1$

2. $P(x)$ is a polynomial of degree 4. The coefficient of the fourth-degree term is 5. The four zeros of $P(x)$ are: $-1, 1 - i, 1 + i, \frac{1}{5}$.
   a. Give a complete factorization of $P(x)$.
   b. Give $P(x)$ in the form $a_0x^4 + a_1x^3 + a_2x^2 + a_3x + a_4$, where $a_0 = 5$.

3.   **a.** Give a complete factorization of a polynomial of degree 3, with the set of zeros $\{1, i, -i\}$, where 1 is the coefficient of the third-degree term.
   b. Give the polynomial in problem **3a** in the form: $a_0x^3 + a_1x^2 + a_2x + a_3$

4. If $P(x) = (x - 4)^2(x - 2i + 1)^2$, then

    a. What is the set of zeros of $P(x)$?

    b. What is the multiplicity of each zero?

    c. What is the degree of $P(x)$?

GRAPHING POLYNOMIAL FUNCTIONS

Much of the information we gained about the zeros of a polynomial will be helpful in graphing polynomial functions. Graphs, in turn, will be helpful in obtaining some additional information about the zeros.

Example: *i.* Graph $\{(x, y) \mid y = 2x^2 + x + 3\}$.

To obtain the graph, we first determine several number pairs (x, y) which belong to this function. We obtain the second member, y, of each pair by substituting for x. We then assemble the pairs in a table.

x	y
0	3
1	6
−1	4
−2	9

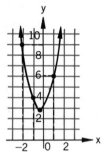

Explain why the graph will not intersect the x-axis. This means that the polynomial $2x^2 + x + 3$ has no real zeros. Using the quadratic formula, find the complex zeros of $2x^2 + x + 3$.

Example: *ii.* Graph $\{(x, y) \mid y = x^2 + 4x + 4\}$.

Let us first tabulate several number pairs which belong to this function.

x	y
0	4
1	9
−1	1
−2	0
−3	1
−4	4
−5	9

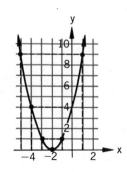

We see that the graph has one point in common with the x-axis, namely $(-2, 0)$. Therefore, $x^2 + 4x + 4$ has one zero of multiplicity two and is factored as follows:

$$x^2 + 4x + 4 = (x + 2)(x + 2)$$

Example: iii.   Graph $\{(x, y) \mid y = -x^2 - 2x + 3\}$.

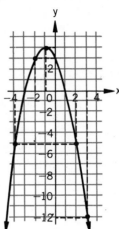

x	y
0	3
1	0
-1	4
2	-5
-2	3
3	-12
-3	0
-4	-5

At what two points does the graph intersect the x-axis? What are the zeros of $-x^2 - 2x + 3$? Why does $-x^2 - 2x + 3$ have no more than two zeros?

Example: iv.   Graph $\{(x, y) \mid y = 2x^3 - 3x^2 - 3x + 2\}$.

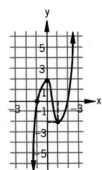

x	y
0	2
1	-2
-1	0
2	0
-2	-20
3	20

We did not show the points $(-2, -20)$ and $(3, 35)$ on the graph, but these points give us an idea as to how the graph would continue. How do we know that the graph will not intersect the x-axis in more than three points? Verify that the following is a correct factorization.

$$2x^3 - 3x^2 - 3x + 2 = (x + 1)(2x - 1)(x - 2)$$

Example: *v.*   Graph $\{(x, y) \mid y = 4x^3 + 12x^2 + 9x + 2\}$.

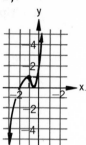

x	y
0	2
1	27
-1	1
-2	0
-3	-25
$-\frac{1}{2}$	0

The graph has the points $(-2, 0)$ and $(-\frac{1}{2}, 0)$ in common with the x-axis. Thus, the polynomial $4x^3 + 12x^2 + 9x + 2$ has two zeros: -2 and $-\frac{1}{2}$. The multiplicity of -2 is one and the multiplicity of $-\frac{1}{2}$ is two. Is the following a correct factorization?

$$4x^3 + 12x^2 + 9x + 2 = (x + 2)(2x + 1)(2x + 1)$$

Example: *vi.*   Graph $\{(x, y) \mid y = x^4 - x^3 - 11x^2 + 9x + 18\}$.

To illustrate an approach different from that used in the previous examples, we first attempt to locate zeros of the polynomial $P(x) = x^4 - x^3 - 11x^2 + 9x + 18$. If $P(x)$ has any integral zeros, then they are found among the factors of 18, which are $1, -1, 2, -2, 3, -3, 6, -6, 9, -9, 18, -18$. We proceed to try these.

$$P(1) = (1)^4 - (1)^3 - 11 \cdot (1)^2 + 9 \cdot (1) + 18$$
$$= 1 - 1 - 11 + 9 + 18 = 16$$
$$P(-1) = (-1)^4 - (-1)^3 - 11 \cdot (-1)^2 + 9 \cdot (-1) + 18$$
$$= 1 + 1 - 11 - 9 + 18 = 0$$

-1 is a zero of $P(x)$; therefore, $x + 1$ is a factor of $P(x)$. Using synthetic division, we divide $P(x)$ by $x + 1$.

$$
\begin{array}{r|rrrrr}
1 & 1 & -1 & -11 & 9 & 18 \\
  &   & 1 & -2 & -9 & 18 \\
\hline
  & 1 & -2 & -9 & 18 & 0 \\
\end{array}
$$

Thus, $x^4 - x^3 - 11x^2 + 9x + 18 = (x + 1)(x^3 - 2x^2 - 9x + 18)$.

The potential integral zeros of $x^3 - 2x^2 - 9x + 18$ are the factors of 18. We test whether 2 is a zero.

$$
\begin{array}{r|rrrr}
-2 & 1 & -2 & -9 & 18 \\
   &   & -2 & 0 & 18 \\
\hline
   & 1 & 0 & -9 & 0 \\
\end{array}
$$

Thus, 2 is a zero of $x^3 - 2x^2 - 9x + 18$.

We now know that $(x + 1)$ and $(x - 2)$ are factors of $P(x)$. Therefore, $x^2 - x - 2$ is also a factor of $P(x)$. From the last line of the last synthetic division it follows that $x^2 - 9$ is also a factor of $P(x)$. Thus, $P(x) = x^4 - x^3 - 11x^2 + 9x + 18 = (x^2 - x - 2)(x^2 - 9)$. Therefore, the remaining zeros of $P(x)$ are 3 and -3. Explain why. The set of zeros of $P(x)$ is $\{-1, 2, 3, -3\}$; therefore, the graph of $P(x)$ intersects the x-axis at $(-3, 0)$, $(-1, 0)$, $(2, 0)$, and $(3, 0)$.

We make another important observation which will help us to decide on the approximate course of the graph of $P(x)$. Note that the coefficient of the highest-degree term, x^4, is positive. Furthermore, the exponent of the highest-degree term is an even number. Therefore, for values of x less than -3 and for those greater than 3, the values of $P(x)$ will be positive numbers. Thus, to the left of $(-3, 0)$ and to the right of $(3, 0)$, the graph will continue upward.

Using all of the information obtained above, we are ready to sketch the graph of

$$\{(x, y) \mid y = x^4 - x^3 - 11x^2 + 9x + 18\}$$

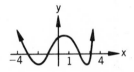

This is just a rough sketch. In order to obtain a more accurate graph, we would have to obtain a few more values of $P(x)$, especially for values of x between -3 and -1, between -1 and 2, and between 2 and 3. For our purposes, however, such a sketch is sufficient.

EXERCISES

Sketch the graph of each of the following polynomial functions.

1. $\{(x, y) \mid y = 2x^2 + 3x - 5\}$
2. $\{(x, y) \mid y = 4x^2 - 4x + 1\}$
3. $\{(x, y) \mid y = x^2 + 4\}$
4. $\{(x, y) \mid y = x^3 + x^2 - 2x + x\}$
5. $\{(x, y) \mid y = 2x^3 - 8x^2 + 3x - 12\}$
6. $\{(x, y) \mid y = x^4 + 4x^3 - 2x^2 - 12x + 9\}$
7. $\{(x, y) \mid y = 2x^4 - 9x^3 + 6x^2 - 9x + 4\}$
8. $\{(x, y) \mid y = 6x^4 - x^3 - 7x^2 + x + 1\}$
9. $\{(x, y) \mid y = 2x^4 - x^3 + 5x^2 - 4x - 12\}$
10. $\{(x, y) \mid y = -3x^4 + x^3 + 9x^2 + 3x - 2\}$

Approximating irrational zeros

The polynomials with which we have dealt so far in this chapter were chosen so that we would get rather "nice" zeros. But what happens if we take, say, a third-degree polynomial and discover that it does not have any rational zeros. We must answer the question: Does it have any irrational zeros and if it does, what are they?

Unfortunately, there does not exist as systematic a method of finding the irrational zeros of an integral polynomial as the method for finding the rational zeros. There are general formulas for finding *all* zeros of third- and fourth-degree polynomials. These formulas are a great deal more involved than the quadratic formula which you derived for second-degree polynomials and, therefore, we shall not develop them. It was proved a long time ago that no such formula can be developed for polynomials of degree 5 and higher.

We shall resort to graphs to provide us with some insight into the problem of approximating irrational zeros of a polynomial. Consider the polynomial

$$P(x) = -2x^3 + 6x + 1$$

To obtain the graph of $P(x)$, we obtain a number of ordered pairs belonging to the set

$$\{(x, P(x)) \mid P(x) = -2x^3 + 6x + 1\}$$

x	$P(x)$
0	1
1	5
-1	-3
2	-3
-2	5
$\frac{1}{2}$	$3\frac{3}{4}$
$-\frac{1}{2}$	$-2\frac{3}{4}$
$1\frac{1}{2}$	$3\frac{1}{4}$
$-1\frac{1}{2}$	$-1\frac{1}{4}$

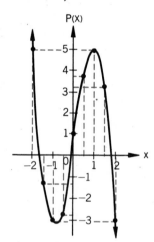

The graph of $P(x) = -2x^3 + 6x + 1$ above reveals a great deal about the zeros of $P(x)$. Before we elicit all possible information from the graph, answer these three questions by referring to the graph of $P(x) = -2x^3 + 6x + 1$.

How do we know that for values of x greater than 2, the values of $P(x)$ will be less than -3?

How do we know that for values of x less than -2, the values of $P(x)$ will be greater than 5?

How do we know that the graph will not intersect the x-axis in more than the three points shown on the graph?

Since we know that for every zero r of $P(x)$, $P(r) = 0$, the zeros are the first coordinates of points at which the graph intersects the x-axis. From the graph, we can tell that one zero is between -1.5 and -2; one zero is between $-.5$ and 0; and one zero is between 1.5 and 2.

First, we determine whether or not $P(x)$ has any rational zeros. The only potential rational zeros are: 1, -1, $\frac{1}{2}$, and $-\frac{1}{2}$. Explain how this is a consequence of the Rational Zero Theorem. It is probably easier to check whether any of these numbers is a zero by substitution than by synthetic division.

$$P(1) = -2 \cdot 1 + 6 \cdot 1 + 1 = 5 \neq 0$$

$$P(-1) = -2 \cdot (-1) + 6 \cdot (-1) + 1 = -3 \neq 0$$

$$P\left(\frac{1}{2}\right) = -2 \cdot \left(\frac{1}{8}\right) + 6 \cdot \left(\frac{1}{2}\right) + 1 = 3\frac{3}{4} \neq 0$$

$$P\left(-\frac{1}{2}\right) = -2 \cdot \left(-\frac{1}{8}\right) + 6 \cdot \left(-\frac{1}{2}\right) + 1 = -1\frac{3}{4} \neq 0$$

Now we know that $P(x)$ has no rational zeros. Since the graph tells us that it has three real zeros, none of which we found to be rational, it follows that it has three irrational zeros.

We shall now attempt to approximate each irrational zero to one decimal place. To do this, we shall make use of the following important fact.

> If $P(r_1) > 0$ and $P(r_2) < 0$, then there is at least one r, such that r is between r_1 and r_2, for which $P(r) = 0$; that is, there is at least one zero between r_1 and r_2.

For example, for $P(x) = -2x^3 + 6x + 1$, $P(1) = 5$ and $5 > 0$; $P(2) = -3$ and $-3 < 0$; therefore, there is at least one zero of $P(x)$ between 1 and 2. From the graph we know that there is *one* zero between 1 and 2.

To "close in" on the zero between 1 and 2 for $P(x) = -2x^3 + 6x + 1$, we resort to synthetic division. First, we find the value of $P(x)$ at 1.8.

$$\begin{array}{r|rrrr} -1.8 & -2 & 0 & 6 & 1 \\ & & 3.6 & 6.48 & .864 \\ \hline & -2 & -3.6 & -.48 & .136 \end{array}$$

Thus, $P(1.8) = .136$.

Next, to find out whether $P(x)$ has a zero between 1.8 and 1.9, we find $P(1.9)$. If the value of $P(x)$ at 1.9 turns out to be negative, then we shall know that $P(x)$ has a zero between 1.8 and 1.9.

$$\begin{array}{r|rrrr} -1.9 & -2 & 0 & 6 & 1 \\ & & 3.8 & 7.22 & 2.318 \\ \hline & -2 & -3.8 & -1.22 & -1.318 \end{array}$$

Since $P(1.8) = .136$ and $P(1.9) = -1.318$, we know that $P(x)$ has a zero between 1.8 and 1.9. [Why?] To be able to give the zero to one place accuracy, we need to know whether it is closer to 1.8 or 1.9.

We find the value of $P(x)$ at 1.85.

$$\begin{array}{r|rrrr} -1.85 & -2 & 0 & 6 & 1 \\ & & 3.7 & 6.845 & 1.56325 \\ \hline & -2 & -3.7 & -.845 & -.56325 \end{array}$$

Thus, $P(1.85) = -.56325$. From the graph, we can tell that the value of $P(x)$ at any number greater than 1.85 is negative. Explain why. We know then that $P(x)$ has a zero which is between 1.80 and 1.85. Therefore, we can now state a zero to one decimal place to be 1.8.

EXERCISES

1. Using the method illustrated above, approximate to one decimal place the two remaining irrational zeros of $P(x) = -2x^3 + 6x + 1$.

2. Sketch the graph of each of the following:

    a. $x^3 - x^2 - 5x + 5$ **c.** $2x^4 - 7x^3 - 15x^2 + 10x + 9$

    b. $2x^3 + 3x^2 - 4x + 1$ **d.** $9x^4 + 16x^3 - 18x^2 - 16x + 3$

3. Use the graphs from problem **2** to tell how many real zeros each of the four polynomials in **a–d** has.

4.   **a.** Test to see whether each of the polynomials in problem **2** has any rational zeros.

    b. Tell how many irrational zeros each of these polynomials has.

    c. Approximate to one decimal place all irrational zeros for each polynomial in problem **2**.

5. For some $P(x)$ of degree twenty, $P(a) > 0$ and $P(b) < 0$, where a and b are real numbers. On the basis of this information, answer each of the following questions.

    a. Must $P(x)$ have at least one zero which is a real number between a and b?

    b. May $P(x)$ have more than one zero between a and b?

    c. May $P(x)$ have exactly two distinct zeros, each of multiplicity one, between a and b? Why or why not?

    d. May $P(x)$ have exactly three distinct zeros, each of multiplicity one, between a and b?

    e. May $P(x)$ have an even number of distinct zeros, each of multiplicity one, between a and b? Why or why not?

    f. May $P(x)$ have an odd number of distinct zeros, each of multiplicity one, between a and b? Why or why not?

COMPLEX ZEROS OF REAL POLYNOMIALS

We shall now return to the consideration of polynomials with *real number* coefficients. We have already seen that such a polynomial may have zeros which are complex numbers or real numbers. Real zeros may be rational numbers or irrational numbers. Rational zeros may be integers or non-integral rational numbers. You already learned to find rational zeros and approximate irrational zeros. We shall now inquire into the nature of complex zeros.

Let us first recall that the complex numbers $a + bi$ and $a - bi$ are called *conjugates*. Now, if $a + bi$ is a zero of

$$P(x) = c_0 x^n + c_1 x^{n-1} + \ldots + c_{n-1} x + c_n$$

then

$$P(a + bi) = c_0(a + bi)^n + c_1(a + bi)^{n-1} + \ldots + c_{n-1}(a + bi) + c_n = 0$$

We shall show that if $P(a + bi) = 0$, then $P(a - bi) = 0$.

Theorem 8 (Conjugate Zero Theorem)   If $a + bi$ is a zero of a real polynomial $P(x)$, then $a - bi$ is also a zero of $P(x)$.

First we show that if $P(a + bi) = x + yi$, then $P(a - bi) = x - yi$; that is, if the value of a polynomial $P(x)$ at some complex number $a + bi$ is some complex number $x + yi$, then the value of $P(x)$ at the conjugate of $a + bi$ is the conjugate of $x + yi$.

This result is based on the following facts.

    i. the conjugate of any real number is that real number

    ii. the conjugate of the sum of two complex numbers is the sum of the conjugates of these numbers

    iii. the conjugate of the product of two complex numbers is the product of the conjugates of these numbers

    iv. if $(a + bi)^n = x + yi$, then $(a - bi)^n = x - yi$

    v. $P(a + bi) = c_0(a + bi)^n + c_1(a + bi)^{n-1} + \ldots + c_{n-1}(a + bi) + c_n$
       $P(a - bi) = c_0(a - bi)^n + c_1(a - bi)^{n-1} + \ldots + c_{n-1}(a - bi) + c_n$

The facts *i.* through *v.* lead to the conclusion

$$P(a - bi) = \text{the conjugate of } P(a + bi)$$

Now, if $a + bi$ is a zero of $P(x)$, then

$$P(a + bi) = 0$$

Then $P(a - bi)$ is the conjugate of 0, which is 0. Hence

$$P(a - bi) = 0$$

which means that $a - bi$ is also a zero of $P(x)$, which was to be proved.

The Conjugate Zero Theorem tells us that, if a complex number $a + bi$ is a zero of a polynomial with real coefficients, then $a - bi$ is also a zero. Thus, complex zeros occur in conjugate pairs.

EXERCISES

1. A third-degree real polynomial $P(x)$ has 2 and $1 + 2i$ for two of its zeros.
    a. What is the third zero of $P(x)$?
    b. Give a factorization of $P(x)$ into first-degree factors.
    c. If the coefficient of the third-degree term is 1, give $P(x)$ in the form
$$x^3 + ax^2 + bx + c$$

2. Find all zeros of each of the following polynomials.
    a. $2x^3 - 5x^2 + 6x - 2$ **c.** $9x^4 + 12x^3 - 37x^2 + 22x - 6$
    b. $2x^3 + 15x^2 + 38x + 30$ **d.** $4x^4 + 11x^3 + 26x^2 - 89x - 78$

3. Show that for $P(x) = ax^2 + bx + c$, if $P(p + qi) = m + ni$, then $P(p - qi) = m - ni$.

4. Prove that any real polynomial of an even degree either has no real zeros or the sum of multiplicities of its real zeros is an even number.

5. Prove that any real polynomial of an odd degree has real zeros whose multiplicities add to an odd number.

6. Given that $1 + 2i$ and $-3 - i$ are two zeros of

$$Q(x) = x^4 + 4x^3 + 27x^2 + 10x + 50$$

find the other two zeros. Factor $Q(x)$ into first-degree factors.

Descartes' Rule of Signs

We shall make one more observation about the zeros of a polynomial with real coefficients which will be helpful in determining the zeros. Before doing so, let us recall how to determine $P(-x)$ for a given $P(x)$.

Consider the polynomial

$$P(x) = 3x^5 - 4x^4 + 2x^3 + x^2 - 6x + 4$$

To obtain $P(-x)$, we replace x by $-x$ in $P(x)$.

$$P(-x) = 3(-x)^5 - 4(-x)^4 + 2(-x)^3 + (-x)^2 - 6(-x) + 4$$
$$= -3x^5 - 4x^4 - 2x^3 + x^2 + 6x + 4$$

Now, we shall establish what we call the number of *changes in sign* in $P(x)$.

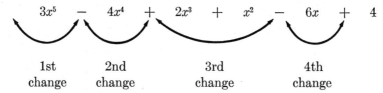

Thus, $P(x)$ has four changes of sign.

Do the same for $P(-x)$ to verify that it has *one* change in sign.

Now we shall state the following:

Theorem 9 (Descartes' Rule of Signs) The sum of multiplicities of positive real zeros of a polynomial $P(x)$ with real coefficients is at most equal to the number of changes in sign. If this sum of multiplicities is less than the number of changes in sign, then it differs from it by an even number. The sum of multiplicities of negative real zeros of $P(x)$ is at most equal to the number of changes in sign in $P(-x)$. Again, if this sum of multiplicities is less than the number of changes in sign, then it differs from it by an even number.

We illustrate this rule by means of an example.

Example: . Determine the possible sum of multiplicities of positive real zeros and of negative real zeros of

$$P(x) = 2x^4 + 5x^3 - 9x^2 - 15x + 9$$

Since there are two changes in sign in $P(x)$, it may have positive zeros whose multiplicities add to two, or it may have no positive zeros.

$$P(-x) = 2x^4 - 5x^3 - 9x^2 + 15x + 9$$

Since $P(-x)$ has two changes in sign, $P(x)$ may have negative zeros, whose multiplicities add to two or it may have no negative zeros.

We determine the zeros of $P(x)$ by first testing for possible rational zeros. If there are any, they would be in the set

$$\left\{ 1, -1, \frac{1}{2}, -\frac{1}{2}, 3, -3, \frac{3}{2}, -\frac{3}{2}, 9, -9, \frac{9}{2}, -\frac{9}{2} \right\}$$

We can easily verify that 1 and -1 are not zeros. We test $\frac{1}{2}$.

$$
\begin{array}{r|rrrrr}
-\frac{1}{2} & 2 & 5 & -9 & -15 & 9 \\
 & & -1 & -3 & 3 & 9 \\
\hline
 & 2 & 6 & -6 & -18 & \boxed{0}
\end{array}
$$

Thus, $\frac{1}{2}$ is a rational zero.

Verify to see that $-\frac{1}{2}$ is not a zero. We next test 3.

$$
\begin{array}{r|rrrrr}
-3 & 2 & 5 & -9 & -15 & 9 \\
 & & 6 & -33 & & \\
\hline
 & 2 & 11 & 24 & &
\end{array}
$$

It is clear at this point that 3 is not a zero.

Test -3.

$$
\begin{array}{r|rrrrr}
3 & 2 & 5 & -9 & -15 & 9 \\
 & & 6 & -3 & -18 & 9 \\
\hline
 & 2 & -1 & -6 & 3 & \boxed{0}
\end{array}
$$

Thus, -3 is a zero.

Since -3 and $\frac{1}{2}$ are two zeros, $x - \frac{1}{2}$ and $x + 3$ are two factors of $P(x) = 2x^4 + 5x^3 - 9x^2 - 15x + 9$. Since the coefficient of the fourth-degree term is 2, we take the factor $2x - 1$ in place of $x - \frac{1}{2}$. Then

$$(2x - 1)(x + 3) = 2x^2 + 5x - 3$$

is also a factor. Therefore

$$2x^4 + 5x^3 - 9x^2 - 15x + 9 = (2x^2 + 5x - 3) \cdot Q(x)$$

We determine $Q(x)$ by division.

$$
\begin{array}{r}
x^2 - 3 \\
2x^2 + 5x - 3 \overline{\smash{\big)}\; 2x^4 + 5x^3 - 9x^2 - 15x + 9} \\
\underline{2x^4 + 5x^3 - 3x^2} \\
-6x^2 - 15x + 9 \\
\underline{-6x^2 - 15x + 9} \\
0
\end{array}
$$

Thus, $Q(x) = x^2 - 3$ and we have

$$2x^4 + 5x^3 - 9x^2 - 15x + 9 = (2x^2 + 5x - 3)(x^2 - 3)$$

Solving $x^2 - 3 = 0$ yields the remaining two zeros: $\sqrt{3}$, $-\sqrt{3}$. Thus, the set of zeros of $P(x)$ is $\{-3, \frac{1}{2}, \sqrt{3}, -\sqrt{3}\}$. This agrees with what we found according to Descartes' Rule of Signs. There are two positive real zeros (sum of their multiplicities is two) and two negative real zeros (sum of their multiplicities is also two).

EXERCISES

For each polynomial below

    i. predict the possible sum of multiplicities of its positive real zeros

    ii. predict the possible sum of multiplicities of its negative real zeros

    iii. find all zeros

1. $3x^3 + x^2 - 3x - 1$
2. $3x^4 - 5x^3 - 17x^2 - 25x + 10$
3. $6x^4 - 13x^3 + 12x^2 - 13x + 6$
4. $x^5 - 8x^4 + 28x^3 - 58x^2 + 67x - 30$

VOCABULARY

Use each of the following correctly in a sentence. Numerals in parentheses refer to pages where these words were used. If you are not sure of the meaning of any word, turn to the indicated page.

change in sign (368)

complex zero (366)

Conjugate Zero Theorem (367)

constant term (351)

degree of a polynomial function (338)

Descartes' Rule of Signs (368)

divisible (340)

Division Algorithm (341)

Factor Theorem (348)

first-degree factor (352)

Fundamental Theorem of Algebra (358)

integral polynomial (350)

integral zero (350)

Integral Zero Theorem (351)

irrational zero (357)

multiplicity (358)

polynomial (339)

polynomial function (337)

rational polynomial (353)

rational zero (353)

Rational Zero Theorem (354)

Remainder Theorem (343)

synthetic division (344)

Unique Factorization Theorem (359)

value of a polynomial function (338)

zero of a polynomial (347)

REVIEW EXERCISES

1. Tell the degree of each of the following polynomials in x.

    a. $2x^3 + x - 7 + x^5$

    b. $\sqrt{7}\,x - 3x^2 + x^7$

    c. $(1 + i)x^3 - \sqrt{2}\,x^2 + ix^4 - (3 - 2i)\,x + (2 + i)$

    d. $2x^6 - x^5 + 3x^4 - \frac{1}{2}x^3 + 6x^2 - 7x + 1$

2. Determine the value of each polynomial at 0, at -1, and at $\sqrt{2}$.

   a. $2x^3 - 2x^2 + x - 1$ **b.** $x^4 + x^3 - x^2 + 2x - 2$ **c.** $3x^5 - 2x^3 + x - 1$

3. Define

   a. divisibility of $P(x)$ by $D(x) \neq 0$
   f. complex polynomial

   b. zero of a polynomial
   g. integral zero of a polynomial

   c. integral polynomial
   h. irrational zero of a polynomial

   d. rational polynomial
   i. multiplicity of a zero of a polynomial

   e. real polynomial
   j. conjugate complex numbers

4. State the

   a. Division Algorithm
   e. Rational Zero Theorem

   b. Remainder Theorem
   f. Fundamental Theorem of Algebra

   c. Factor Theorem
   g. Unique Factorization Theorem

   d. Integral Zero Theorem
   h. Conjugate Zero Theorem

5. In each problem, the first given polynomial is $P(x)$ and the second is a binomial of the form $x - a$. Do the following:

   i. using synthetic division, find the remainder R when $P(x)$ is divided by $x - a$

   ii. evaluate $P(x)$ at a by substitution to verify that $P(a) = R$

   iii. write an equation in the form: $P(x) = Q(x) \cdot (x - a) + R$

   a. $3x^4 - 8x^3 - 5x^2 + 7x - 1; \; x - 3$

   b. $x^4 + 4x^3 - 11x^2 + 2x - 29; \; x + 6$

   c. $2x^5 + 23x^4 - 11x^3 + 13x^2 + 11x - 12; \; x + 12$

6. a. Is there a *real* polynomial which has the following set of zeros: $\{1, 1 - 2i, i\}$? Why or why not?

   b. Is there a complex polynomial which has the set of zeros given in problem **6a**?

7. For each set of zeros, construct the real polynomial in which the coefficient of the highest-degree term is as specified and which has the given set for its zeros.

   a. $\{-1, 1, -2\}$; coefficient 1

   b. $\left\{-\dfrac{1}{2}, \dfrac{1}{3}, 2, 1\right\}$; coefficient 6

   c. $\{\sqrt{2}, -\sqrt{2}, 1 + i, 1 - i\}$; coefficient 1

   d. $\left\{\dfrac{1}{3}, 2 + 3i, 2 - 3i\right\}$; coefficient 3

   e. $\{i, -i, 1 + i, 1 - i\}$; coefficient 1

   f. $\{2 + i, 2 - i, 3 + 2i, 3 - 2i\}$; coefficient 1

8. Give all *potential integral* zeros of each of the following polynomials.

   a. $x^3 + 2x^2 - x + 7$ **b.** $2x^4 + x^2 - 2$ **c.** $6x^7 + 3x^3 + 2x^2 - 7x - 1$

9. Write an argument proving that the value of

$$P(x) = \frac{1}{3}x^4 - \frac{1}{2}x^3 + 2x^2 - \frac{4}{5}x + \frac{1}{7}$$

at any rational number is a rational number.

10. Tell why it is impossible to tell whether the value of

$$P(x) = \sqrt{2}\,x^5 + 2x^3 - x^2 + x - 1$$

at any irrational number is an irrational number.

11. If a polynomial has $3 + 2i$ and $3 - 2i$ as two of its zeros, then what second-degree polynomial is one of its factors?

12. For each polynomial, give all of its *potential rational* zeros.

   a. $3x^3 + 2x^2 - x - 1$ c. $17x^3 + 2x^2 - 3x + 1$

   b. $8x^4 + 3x^3 - 2x^2 + x + 4$ d. $12x^4 + 3x^3 - x^2 + x + 2$

13. For each polynomial

        i. sketch its graph

       ii. find all of its rational zeros

      iii. find its irrational zeros to one decimal place

   a. $4x^4 - 6x^3 - 10x^2 + 15x - 5$

   b. $15x^4 - 64x^3 + 17x^2 - 36x - 20$

   c. $2x^4 + 2x^3 - 7x^2 - 3x + 6$

14. For each polynomial, tell the possible sum of multiplicities of positive real zeros and the possible sum of multiplicities of negative real zeros.

   a. $2x^4 - x^3 + x^2 - 2x + 3$

   b. $-3x^5 + x^4 - 2x^3 + 4x^2 + x - 4$

   c. $-x^6 + x^5 - 6x^4 + 2x^3 - x^2 - x - 1$

15. A fourth-degree real polynomial has $2 + 5i$ and $1 - 3i$ for two of its zeros.

   a. What are the other two zeros of this polynomial?

   b. Construct this polynomial with 1 as the coefficient of the fourth-degree term.

16. For some $P(x)$ of degree 10, $P(a) > 0$ and $P(b) < 0$, where a and b are real numbers. On the basis of this information, answer the following questions.

   a. Must $P(x)$ have at least one real zero which is a number between a and b?

   b. May $P(x)$ have exactly two distinct real zeros between a and b, the sum of whose multiplicities is two?

   c. May $P(x)$ have exactly three distinct real zeros between a and b, the sum of whose multiplicities is three?

   d. What is the largest possible number of real zeros $P(x)$ may have?

   e. What is the smallest number of real zeros $P(x)$ must have?

CHAPTER TEST

1. Use substitution to determine the value of each given polynomial at 0; at -1; at .1; and at i.

    a. $2x^4 + x^2 - 3$

    b. $4x^3 + x^2 + 2x + 2$

    c. $2x^4 - 4x^3 + x^2 - x + 4$

2. Tell the degree of each polynomial.

    a. $7x - 5 - x^5 + 8x^3$

    b. $(4 - i)x^2 - x^4 + x + 9x^3$

3. Use synthetic division to determine

    a. $P(-3)$ if $P(x) = 7x^4 + 22x^3 + 6$

    b. $Q(10)$ if $Q(x) = 5x^3 + 7x^2 + 9x + 2$

    c. $T(2)$ if $T(x) = x^7 - x^5 - 7x^4 + 15$

4. Construct a fourth-degree *integral* polynomial which has the following zeros.

$$\frac{2}{3} \qquad -\frac{1}{2} \qquad 3i \qquad -3i$$

5. For $P(x) = 3x^3 - \sqrt{2}\,x^2 + \frac{5}{7}x - 1.42$, argue that for any *real* number x, $P(x)$ is a real number.

6. Given $Q(x) = 4(x - 7)(x + 3)(x + 3)$.

    a. Determine the degree of $Q(x)$.

    b. Determine the number of zeros of $Q(x)$.

    c. What is the sum of multiplicities of zeros of $Q(x)$?

    d. How many points of the x-axis belong to the graph of $Q(x)$?

7. For each polynomial, list all of its *potential rational* zeros.

    a. $x^3 + 2x^2 - 2$

    b. $5x^4 - 3x^3 + 2x^2 - 3$

    c. $2x^5 + 3x^4 - x^3 + x^2 + 3x - 8$

8. For $P(x) = 2x^7 - x^6 + 3x^5 - x^4 + x^3 - 2x^2 + 3x - 2$, determine the polynomial $Q(x)$ and the real number R for which $P(x) = Q(x) \cdot (x - 2) + R$.

9. Find all zeros of $P(x) = x^4 - 5x^2 + 10x - 6$.

10. Given polynomials $P(x)$ and $Q(x)$ and real numbers a and b such that $P(x) = Q(x) \cdot (x - a) + b$.

    a. Determine $P(a)$.   **b.** If $b = 0$, list two divisors of $P(x)$.

11. Define "*zero* of the polynomial $P(x)$."

12. Give an example of a complex polynomial of the third degree that is not a real polynomial.

13. Choose the one correct conclusion. If $P(x)$ is a real polynomial with $P(a) > 0$ and $P(b) < 0$, a and b being real numbers, then

    a. $P(x)$ cannot have a real zero between a and b

    b. $P(x)$ must have at least one real zero between a and b

    c. $P(x)$ may have exactly two distinct zeros between a and b, the sum of whose multiplicities is two

    d. $P(x)$ must have at least one zero greater than b

14. If $(x - 2)$, $(x + 1)$, and $(x + 2)$ are three first-degree divisors of $P(x)$, then list three second-degree divisors of $P(x)$.

15. If $-2 - 3i$ and $2i$ are zeros of the real fourth-degree polynomial $P(x)$, then determine two other zeros of $P(x)$.

16. True or false?

    a. $(3i)x + 12$ does not have a zero.

    b. The constant function $\{(x, 4)\}$ is not a polynomial function.

    c. The set of non-zero real polynomials is closed under division.

    d. The set of real polynomials is closed under multiplication.

    e. $(2x^2 + 4x)$ is divisible by $2x$.

    f. $(3x^2 + 6)$ is divisible by $3x$.

    g. $(5x^2 + 7)$ is divisible by 5.

    h. If $P(x) = x^3 - 8x^2 + 19x - 12$ and $D(x) = x^2 - 7x + 12$ and $Q(x) = x - 1$, then $P(x) = Q(x) \cdot D(x)$ and $P(x) \div D(x) = Q(x)$ and $P(x) \div Q(x) = D(x)$.

    i. If $P(x) = 3x^7 + 4x^3 - 9$ and if $P(t) = 0$, then $(x + t)$ must be a factor of $P(x)$.

    j. Each real polynomial of degree 6 has a real zero.

    k. Each real polynomial of degree 7 has a real zero.

    l. A real polynomial of degree 8 may have 8 complex zeros.

    m. A real polynomial of degree 8 may have 8 real zeros.

    n. A real polynomial of degree 9 may have 9 complex zeros.

    o. A real polynomial of degree 9 may have 9 real zeros.

BIBLIOGRAPHY

Birkhoff, G. and MacLane, S. *A Survey of Modern Algebra.* New York: The Macmillan Co., 1958. Chapter 4.

Haag, V. H. *Structure of Elementary Algebra.* SMSG Studies in Mathematics, Volume III. Yale University Press, 1961. Chapter 6.

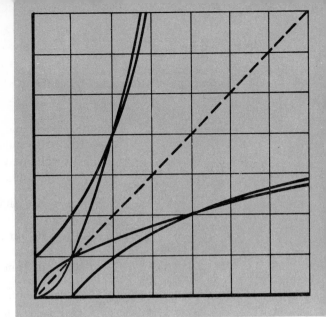

CHAPTER 12

Logarithmic Functions

COMMON LOGARITHMIC FUNCTION

In this chapter you will study another group of functions called the *logarithmic* functions. This type of function has applications in the sciences, in higher mathematics, and in computing approximations of products, quotients, powers, and roots of numbers.

As you recall, in a *function f* each element x of its domain is paired with the unique element $f(x)$ in its range. For example, in the function f, defined by

$$f(x) = x^2 + 2$$

1 is paired with 3 since $f(1) = (1)^2 + 2 = 3$

-2 is paired with 6 since $f(-2) = (-2)^2 + 2 = 6$

$\frac{1}{3}$ is paired with $2\frac{1}{9}$ since $f(\frac{1}{3}) = (\frac{1}{3})^2 + 2 = 2\frac{1}{9}$

Using set notation, we write: $f = \{(x, f(x)) \mid f(x) = x^2 + 2\}$. The domain of f is R, the set of all real numbers, and the range of f is $\{y \mid y \geq 2\}$.

The first logarithmic function that we shall study is the *common* logarithmic function, denoted by *log*.

■ *Definition of Common Logarithmic Function* $\forall_{x>0} \forall_y$, if $x = 10^y$, then $\log(x) = y$; and if $\log(x) = y$, then $10^y = x$.

$$\text{Thus } 1000 = 10^3 \text{ and } \log(1000) = 3$$
$$100 = 10^2 \text{ and } \log(100) = 2$$
$$10 = 10^1 \text{ and } \log(10) = 1$$
$$1 = 10^0 \text{ and } \log(1) = 0$$

$$\frac{1}{10} = .1 = 10^{-1} \text{ and } \log(.1) = -1$$

$$\frac{1}{10^2} = .01 = 10^{-2} \text{ and } \log(.01) = -2$$

$$\frac{1}{10^3} = .001 = 10^{-3} \text{ and } \log(.001) = -3$$

In set notation, the common logarithmic function, log, is

$$\{(x, y) \mid x = 10^y\} \quad \text{or} \quad \{(x, \log(x)) \mid x = 10^{\log(x)}\}$$

EXERCISES

Solve each equation for a or for b.

1. $\log(10^8) = b$
2. $\log(.0001) = b$
3. $\log(10,000) = b$

4. $\log(10^{-6}) = b$
5. $\log(a) = 5$
6. $\log(a) = -2$

7. $\log(a) = -5$
8. $\log(a) = 0$

Graph of log

A portion of the graph of log is pictured in figure 1.

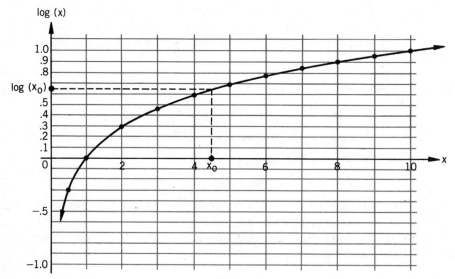

Fig. 1

Verify each of the following statements by examining the graph in figure 1.

  i. The domain of log is the set of all *positive* real numbers.

  ii. The range of log is the set of *all* real numbers.

  iii. To estimate $\log(x)$ for a given positive real number x, say x_0, we plot x_0 on the x-axis and then go up or down to the graph of log and then over to the vertical axis to determine $\log(x_0)$.

  iv. For each real number $x_1 > 0$ and each real number $x_2 > 0$, if $x_2 > x_1$, then $\log(x_2) > \log(x_1)$.

  v. For each real number x, if $0 < x < 1$, then $\log(x) < 0$.

EXERCISES

1. Using the graph of figure 1, estimate each of the following to the nearest tenth by using the "up and over" method.

  a. $\log(2)$ e. $\log(3.2)$

  b. $\log(4)$ f. $\log(6.3)$

  c. $\log(5)$ g. $\log(2.5)$

  d. $\log(1)$ h. $\log(7.9)$

2. True or false?

  a. For each real number x, if $x > 10$, then $\log(x) > 1$.

  b. $0.7 < \log(7) < 0.8$

  c. For each real number x, if $0 < x < 1$, then $\log(x) < 0$.

  d. For each real number x_1 and each real number x_2, if $0 < x_1 < x_2$, then $\log(x_1) > \log(x_2)$.

Reading the log table

By the definition of a common logarithm, we can readily determine that

$$\log(1000) = \log(10^3) = 3$$
$$\log(1) = \log(10^0) = 0$$
$$\log(.01) = \log(10^{-2}) = -2$$

and from the graph of figure 1 we can estimate that

$\log(6.4) \doteq 0.8$ ["$\doteq$" means "is approximately equal to"]

but from this graph we cannot approximate $\log(3.72)$ to more than one decimal place. To determine the log of a number that is not an *integer power* of ten, we can find an approximation of the log of that number in a table. A portion of such a table is reproduced on the next page. The means of determining these approximations is beyond the scope of this book. If you study calculus later, you will learn how this is done.

N	0	1	2	3
40	6021	6031	6042	6053
41	6128	6138	6149	6160
42	6232	6243	6253	6263
43	6335	6345	6355	6365
44	6435	6444	6454	6464

In this table, all decimal points have been omitted. In the column headed "*N*", a decimal point should occur *after* the first digit. In the other columns, a decimal point should occur *before* the first digit. Two rows of the above table are repeated below with decimal points in their proper positions.

N	0	1	2	3
4.1	.6128	.6138	.6149	.6160
4.2	.6232	.6243	.6253	.6263

Figure 2 below shows how to read the table to determine that $\log(4.21) \doteq .6243$.

N	0	1	2	3
40	6021			6053
41	6128			6160
42		6243		6263
43	6335	6345		6365
44			6454	6464

Fig. 2

First, find "42" (the first two digits of "4.21") in the left column, and then find "1" (the third digit of "4.21") in the top row. Now go to the right from "42" and down from "1" until you find "6243". Figure 2 also shows how to determine that

$$\log(4.42) \doteq .6454$$

Use the table on page 562 to verify each of the following:

$$\log(2.53) \doteq .4031 \qquad\qquad .7839 \doteq \log(6.08)$$
$$\log(4.75) \doteq .6767 \qquad\qquad .9731 \doteq \log(9.40)$$

EXERCISES

Use the table on page 562 to determine x to two decimal places and to determine y to four decimal places. Be sure to place the decimal points in the correct positions.

1. $\log(1.42) \doteq y$
2. $\log(x) \doteq .1523$
3. $\log(5.34) \doteq y$
4. $\log(x) \doteq .7275$

5. $\log(7.56) \doteq y$
6. $\log(x) \doteq .9269$
7. $\log(6.51) \doteq y$
8. $\log(x) \doteq .3729$

9. $\log(1.11) \doteq y$
10. $\log(x) \doteq .7574$
11. $\log(9.69) \doteq y$
12. $\log(x) \doteq .9335$

THEOREMS CONCERNING LOG

Study the following examples.

Examples: i. $\log(10 \times 100) = \log(1000) = 3$

Also $\log(10) + \log(100) = 1 + 2 = 3$

Therefore $\log(10 \times 100) = \log(10) + \log(100)$

ii. $\log\left(\frac{1}{10} \times \frac{1}{100}\right) = \log\left(\frac{1}{1000}\right) = -3$

Also $\log\left(\frac{1}{10}\right) + \log\left(\frac{1}{100}\right) = -1 + (-2) = -3$

Therefore $\log\left(\frac{1}{10} \times \frac{1}{100}\right) = \log\left(\frac{1}{10}\right) + \log\left(\frac{1}{100}\right)$

These examples suggest the following theorem.

Theorem 1 $\forall_{m>0} \ \forall_{n>0} \ \log(m \times n) = \log(m) + \log(n)$

Proof   Justify each step.

$$\log(10^{a+b}) = \log(10^a \times 10^b)$$
$$\log(10^{a+b}) = a + b$$
$$\therefore a + b = \log(10^a \times 10^b)$$

But $a + b = \log(10^a) + \log(10^b)$

Hence $\log(10^a \times 10^b) = \log(10^a) + \log(10^b)$

Let $m = 10^a$ and $n = 10^b$

$$\log(m \times n) = \log(m) + \log(n)$$

Theorem 1 can be used to approximate products. Study the following examples.

Examples: i.   Approximate 5.46×1.13 to two decimal places.

$\log(5.46 \times 1.13) = \log(5.46) + \log(1.13)$ Theorem 1

$\doteq .7372 + .0531$ Table

$= .7903$ Addition

$\therefore 5.46 \times 1.13 \doteq 6.17$ $.7903 \doteq \log(6.17)$

ii.   Approximate 3.29×2.16 to two decimal places.

$\log(3.29 \times 2.16) = \log(3.29) + \log(2.16)$

$\doteq .5172 + .3345$

$= .8517$

[In the table "8517" occurs between "8513" and "8519". Since .8517 is closer to .8519 than it is to .8513, we choose the closer number.]

$\log(3.29 \times 2.16) \doteq .8519$

$\therefore 3.29 \times 2.16 \doteq 7.11$ $[.8519 \doteq \log(7.11)]$

Example: *iii.*   Approximate 2.76×3.24 to two decimal places. Notice the use of a vertical or column arrangement.

$$\log(2.76) \doteq .4409$$
$$\log(3.24) \doteq .5105$$

$$\log(2.76 \times 3.24) \doteq .9514 \doteq 9513 \quad [.9513 \text{ is the nearest}$$
$$\text{Therefore}\;\; 2.76 \times 3.24 \doteq 8.94 \qquad\qquad\qquad \text{entry in the table.}]$$

EXERCISES

1.   By using Theorem 1 and the table, approximate each answer to two decimal places.

a. 4.83×1.75 d. 5.83×1.42 g. $2.34 \times 2.76 \times 1.53$

b. 3.17×2.23 e. 1.08×3.98 h. $1.09 \times 2.41 \times 1.87$

c. 3.00×2.00 f. 7.77×1.11 i. $2.76 \times 1.32 \times 2.53$

2.   Supply the reasons in the proof of the following theorem.

Theorem 2 $\log(1) = 0$

Proof
$$\log(1) = \log(1 \times 1)$$
$$\log(1) = \log(1) + \log(1)$$
$$-\log(1) + \log(1) = -\log(1) + \log(1) + \log(1)$$
$$0 = \log(1)$$

3.   Supply the reasons in the proof of the following theorem.

Theorem 3 $\forall_{n>0} \log\!\left(\dfrac{1}{n}\right) = -\log(n)$

Proof $\log(n) + \log\!\left(\dfrac{1}{n}\right) = \log\!\left(n \times \dfrac{1}{n}\right)$
$$= \log(1)$$

$$\log(n) + \log\!\left(\dfrac{1}{n}\right) = 0$$

Hence $\log\!\left(\dfrac{1}{n}\right) = -\log(n)$

4.   Supply the reasons in the proof of the following theorem.

Theorem 4 $\forall_{m>0} \forall_{n>0} \;\; \log\!\left(\dfrac{m}{n}\right) = \log(m) - \log(n)$

Proof $\log\!\left(\dfrac{m}{n}\right) = \log\!\left(m \times \dfrac{1}{n}\right)$
$$= \log(m) + \log\!\left(\dfrac{1}{n}\right)$$
$$= \log(m) + [-\log(n)]$$
$$= \log(m) - \log(n)$$

Approximating quotients

Theorem 4 can be used to approximate quotients. Study the following examples.

Example: *i.* Approximate $\dfrac{8.23}{3.46}$ to two decimal places.

$$\log\left(\frac{8.23}{3.46}\right) = \log(8.23) - \log(3.46) \quad \text{Theorem 4}$$

$$\doteq .9154 - .5391 \qquad\qquad \text{Table}$$
$$= .3763 \qquad\qquad\quad \text{Subtraction}$$
$$\doteq .3766 \qquad\qquad\quad \text{Closest entry}$$

Therefore $\dfrac{8.23}{3.46} \doteq 2.38$ $.3766 \doteq \log(2.38)$

Example: *ii.* Approximate $\dfrac{6.49}{4.17}$ to two decimal places.

Justify each step.

$$\log\left(\frac{6.49}{4.17}\right) = \log(6.49) - \log(4.17)$$

$$\doteq .8122 - .6201$$
$$= .1921$$
$$\doteq .1931$$

Therefore $\dfrac{6.49}{4.17} \doteq 1.56$

Example: *iii.* Approximate $\dfrac{8.21}{1.04}$ to two decimal places.

Notice the use of a *vertical* or *column* arrangement.

$$\log(8.21) \doteq .9143$$
$$\log(1.04) \doteq .0170$$

$$\log\left(\frac{8.21}{1.04}\right) \doteq .8973 \doteq .8971$$

$$\frac{8.21}{1.04} \doteq 7.89$$

EXERCISES

1. By using Theorem 4 and the table, approximate each answer to two decimal places.

a. $\dfrac{8.88}{2.22}$ **c.** $\dfrac{4.91}{1.32}$ **e.** $\dfrac{6.82}{4.37}$

b. $\dfrac{9.76}{3.15}$ **d.** $\dfrac{5.55}{3.29}$ **f.** $\dfrac{7.68}{5.18}$

2. Give a proof of the following theorem.

Theorem 5 $\forall_{a>0} \forall_{b>0} \forall_{c>0}$ $\log\left(\dfrac{ab}{c}\right) = \log(a) + \log(b) - \log(c)$

3. Give a proof of the following theorem.

Theorem 6 $\forall_{a>0} \forall_{b>0} \forall_{c>0}$ $\log\left(\dfrac{a}{bc}\right) = \log(a) - [\log(b) + \log(c)]$

4. Use Theorems 5 and 6 and the table to approximate each answer to two decimal places.

a. $\dfrac{4.36 \times 3.27}{5.14}$ c. $\dfrac{3.72 \times 1.79}{2.16}$ e. $\dfrac{5.89 \times 2.37}{4.76}$

b. $\dfrac{9.36}{2.21 \times 3.14}$ d. $\dfrac{9.75}{2.23 \times 3.01}$ f. $\dfrac{8.89}{1.04 \times 3.71}$

5. Simplify.

a. $\log\left(\dfrac{10}{1000}\right)$ f. $\log\left(\dfrac{100}{100,000}\right)$

b. $\dfrac{\log(10)}{\log(1000)}$ g. $\dfrac{\log(100)}{\log(100,000)}$

c. $\dfrac{\log(10)}{1000}$ h. $\dfrac{\log(100)}{100,000}$

d. $\log(10) - \log(1000)$ i. $\log(100) - \log(100,000)$

e. $\dfrac{10}{1000}$ j. $\dfrac{100}{100,000}$

6. True or false? For all positive real numbers a and b

a. $\log\left(\dfrac{a}{b}\right) = \dfrac{\log(a)}{\log(b)}$ d. $\log\left(\dfrac{a}{b}\right) = \log(a) - \log(b)$ g. $\dfrac{a}{b} = \log(a) - \log(b)$

b. $\log\left(\dfrac{a}{b}\right) = \dfrac{\log(a)}{b}$ e. $\dfrac{\log(a)}{\log(b)} = \log(a) - \log(b)$ h. $\log\left(\dfrac{b}{b}\right) = 0$

c. $\dfrac{a}{b} = \dfrac{\log(a)}{\log(b)}$ f. $\dfrac{\log(a)}{b} = \log(a) - \log(b)$

Approximating powers

The next theorems may be used to approximate powers and roots of numbers.

Theorem 7 $\forall_{m \in R, m>0} \forall_{c \in N}$ $\log(m^c) = c \cdot \log(m)$

Proof $\log(m^c) = \log(\underbrace{m \times m \times m \times \ldots \times m}_{c \text{ factors}})$

$\log(m^c) = \underbrace{\log(m) + \log(m) + \log(m) + \ldots + \log(m)}_{c \text{ terms}}$

$\log(m^c) = c \cdot \log(m)$

Study the following examples in which Theorem 7 is used.

Example: *i.* Approximate 1.23^5 to two decimal places.

$$\begin{aligned}
\log(1.23^5) &= 5 \cdot \log(1.23) && \text{Theorem 7} \\
&\doteq 5 \cdot (.0899) && \text{Table} \\
&= .4495 && \text{Multiplication} \\
&\doteq .4502 && \text{Closest entry} \\
\text{Therefore, } 1.23^5 &\doteq 2.82 && .4502 \doteq \log(2.82)
\end{aligned}$$

Example: *ii.* Approximate 2.14^3 to two decimal places.

Notice the use of a *vertical* or *column* arrangement.

$$\log(2.14^3) = 3 \cdot \log(2.14) \doteq .3304$$
$$\underline{\times\, 3}$$
$$\log(2.14^3) \doteq .9912$$
$$2.14^3 \doteq 9.80$$

EXERCISES

1. Use Theorem 7 and the table to approximate each answer to two decimal places.

   a. 2.96^2 **b.** 2.05^3 **c.** 1.74^4 **d.** 1.01^6

2. Give a proof of the following theorem.

   Theorem 8 $\forall_{a \epsilon R,\, a>0}\ \forall_{b \epsilon R,\, b>0}\ \forall_{c \epsilon N}\quad \log((ab)^c) = c \cdot [\log(a) + \log(b)]$

3. Give a proof of the following theorem.

   Theorem 9 $\forall_{a \epsilon R,\, a>0}\ \forall_{b \epsilon R,\, b>0}\ \forall_{c \epsilon N}\quad \log\left(\left(\dfrac{a}{b}\right)^c\right) = c \cdot [\log(a) - \log(b)]$

4. Use Theorems 8 and 9 and the table to approximate each answer to two decimal places.

   a. $(2.36 \times 1.14)^2$ **d.** $\left(\dfrac{7.89}{4.53}\right)^2$ **g.** $(1.05 \times 1.10)^4$

   b. $\left(\dfrac{5.79}{4.18}\right)^5$ **e.** $(1.34 \times 2.21)^2$ **h.** $\left(\dfrac{5.99}{4.08}\right)^4$

   c. $(1.01 \times 2.13)^3$ **f.** $\left(\dfrac{9.81}{7.65}\right)^3$ **i.** $(1.22 \times 1.22)^5$

5. Justify each step in the proof of the following theorem.

   Theorem 10 $\forall_{a \epsilon R,\, a>0}\ \forall_{n \epsilon N}\quad \log\left(a^{\frac{1}{n}}\right) = \dfrac{\log(a)}{n}$

   Proof $\log\left(\left(a^{\frac{1}{n}}\right)^n\right) = \log(a)$

   $\log\left(\left(a^{\frac{1}{n}}\right)^n\right) = n \cdot \log\left(a^{\frac{1}{n}}\right)$

   $n \cdot \log\left(a^{\frac{1}{n}}\right) = \log(a)$

   $\log\left(a^{\frac{1}{n}}\right) = \dfrac{\log(a)}{n}$

Approximating roots

Theorem 10 can be used to approximate roots of numbers. Study the following examples.

Example: i.   Approximate $\sqrt{8.63}$ to two decimal places.

$$\log(\sqrt{8.63}) = \log(8.63^{\frac{1}{2}}) \qquad \forall_{x>0}\sqrt{x} = x^{\frac{1}{2}}$$

$$= \frac{\log(8.63)}{2} \qquad \text{Theorem 10}$$

$$\doteq \frac{.9360}{2} \qquad \text{Table}$$

$$= .4680 \qquad \text{Division}$$

$$\doteq .4683 \qquad \text{Closest entry}$$

Therefore, $\sqrt{8.63} \doteq 2.94$ $\qquad .4683 \doteq \log(2.94)$

Example: ii.   Approximate $\sqrt[5]{8.63}$ to two decimal places.
Justify each step.

$$\log(\sqrt[5]{8.63}) = \log(8.63^{\frac{1}{5}}) \qquad \forall_{x>0}\sqrt[5]{x} = x^{\frac{1}{5}}$$

$$= \frac{\log(8.63)}{5}$$

$$\doteq \frac{.9360}{5}$$

$$= .1872$$

$$\doteq .1875$$

Therefore $\sqrt[5]{8.63} \doteq 1.54$

EXERCISES

1.   Use Theorem 10 and the table to approximate each answer to two decimal places.

a. $\sqrt{7.77}$ $\qquad\qquad\qquad$ d. $\sqrt[5]{7.77}$

b. $\sqrt[3]{7.77}$ $\qquad\qquad\qquad$ e. $\sqrt[3]{4.04}$

c. $\sqrt[4]{7.77}$ $\qquad\qquad\qquad$ f. $\sqrt{2.39}$

2.   Give a proof of the following theorem.

Theorem 11 $\forall_{a\epsilon R,\ a>0}\ \forall_{b\epsilon R,\ b>0}\ \forall_{n\epsilon N}\ \ \log\left((ab)^{\frac{1}{n}}\right) = \dfrac{\log(a) + \log(b)}{n}$

3.   Give a proof of the following theorem.

Theorem 12 $\forall_{a\epsilon R,\ a>0}\ \forall_{b\epsilon R,\ b>0}\ \forall_{n\epsilon N}\ \ \log\left(\left(\dfrac{a}{b}\right)^{\frac{1}{n}}\right) = \dfrac{\log(a) - \log(b)}{n}$

4. Use Theorems 11 and 12 and the table to approximate each answer to two decimal places.

a. $\sqrt{6.57 \times 5.01}$

b. $\sqrt{\dfrac{6.57}{5.01}}$

c. $\sqrt[3]{8.31 \times 2.24}$

d. $\sqrt[3]{\dfrac{8.31}{2.24}}$

e. $\sqrt[4]{3.77 \times 1.75}$

f. $\sqrt[4]{\dfrac{3.77}{1.75}}$

5. Justify each step in the proof of the following theorem.

Theorem 13 $\forall_{a \epsilon R,\ a>0}\ \forall_{m \epsilon N}\ \forall_{n \epsilon N}\quad \log\left(a^{\frac{m}{n}}\right) = \dfrac{m \cdot \log(a)}{n}$

Proof

$$\log\left(a^{\frac{m}{n}}\right) = \log\left((a^m)^{\frac{1}{n}}\right)$$

$$= \dfrac{\log(a^m)}{n}$$

$$= \dfrac{m \cdot \log(a)}{n}$$

Study the application of Theorem 13 in the following problem.

Example: Approximate $\sqrt[3]{5.13^2}$ to two decimal places.

$$\log(\sqrt[3]{5.13^2}) = \log(5.13^{\frac{2}{3}}) \qquad \sqrt[q]{x^p} = x^{\frac{p}{q}}$$

$$= \dfrac{2 \cdot \log(5.13)}{3} \qquad \text{Theorem 13}$$

$$\doteq \dfrac{2 \cdot (.7101)}{3} \qquad \text{Table}$$

$$= \dfrac{1.4202}{3} \qquad \text{Multiplication}$$

$$= .4734 \qquad \text{Division}$$

$$\doteq .4728 \qquad \text{Closest entry}$$

Therefore $\sqrt[3]{5.13^2} \doteq 2.97$ $.4728 \doteq \log(2.97)$

EXERCISES

1. Use Theorem 13 and the table to approximate each answer to two decimal places.

a. $\sqrt[5]{7.12^3}$

b. $\sqrt[3]{6.87^2}$

c. $\sqrt[5]{3.21^4}$

d. $\sqrt[4]{2.24^5}$

2. Use any of the Theorems 1–13 to simplify each expression to the form $\log(a)$.

Example: $\dfrac{\log(t) - \log(k)}{r} = \dfrac{\log\left(\frac{t}{k}\right)}{r} = \log\left(\left(\frac{t}{k}\right)^{\frac{1}{r}}\right) = \log\left(\sqrt[r]{\frac{t}{k}}\right)$

a. $\log(p) - [\log(q) + \log(r)]$

b. $\log(p) - \log(q) - \log(r)$

c. $\log(p) - \log(q) + \log(r)$

d. $s \cdot [\log(t) - \log(d)]$

e. $s \cdot \log(t) - \log(d)$

f. $\log(c) - \log(d)$

g. $\dfrac{\log(c)}{d}$

h. $ab \cdot \log(t)$

i. $\log(r) + \log(t) + \log(7)$

j. $\log(t) - \log(t)$

k. $m \cdot \log(d) + m \cdot \log(t)$

l. $\log(d) + m \cdot \log(t)$

m. $\log(r) + \log(st) - \log(rt)$

n. $-\log(p)$

o. $r \cdot \dfrac{\log(d)}{t}$

p. $\dfrac{\log(r)}{t} + \dfrac{\log(d)}{t}$

SCIENTIFIC NOTATION

In all our computations thus far we have considered only numbers between one and ten. But the procedures and theorems developed thus far can be used for *all* positive real numbers. The use of *scientific notation* will help us to deal with positive numbers greater than ten or less than one. Study the following examples.

$$43{,}400 = 4.34 \times 10^4 \qquad\qquad 4.34 = 4.34 \times 10^0$$
$$4340 = 4.34 \times 10^3 \qquad\qquad .434 = 4.34 \times 10^{-1}$$
$$434 = 4.34 \times 10^2 \qquad\qquad .0434 = 4.34 \times 10^{-2}$$
$$43.4 = 4.34 \times 10^1 \qquad\qquad .00434 = 4.34 \times 10^{-3}$$

The right member in each example above is expressed in *scientific notation*.

■ *Definition of Scientific Notation*   A numeral is in *scientific notation* if and only if it is written in the form $a \times 10^b$ where $1 < a < 10$ and b is an integer.

Study the following table in which some numbers are expressed first in ordinary decimal notation and then in scientific notation.

Decimal Notation	Scientific Notation
5390	5.39×10^3
.00632	6.32×10^{-3}
7.46	7.46×10^0
389,000	3.89×10^5
.0000121	1.21×10^{-5}

EXERCISES

1. Express each of the following in scientific notation.

   a. 62,500

   b. .000151

   c. 83.2

   d. 7250

   e. .222

   f. 105

   g. .0173

   h. 7.63

   i. .00194

   j. 4,080,000

2. Express each of the following in ordinary decimal notation.

   a. 1.73×10^{-2}

   b. 7.25×10^3

   c. 4.08×10^6

   d. 2.22×10^{-1}

   e. 1.51×10^{-4}

   f. 1.05×10^2

   g. 7.63×10^0

   h. 2.48×10^{-3}

3. Tell whether each numeral is or is not in scientific notation.

   a. 5,290,000

   b. 6.31×10^8

   c. .000521

   d. 834×10^2

   e. $.642 \times 10^{-7}$

   f. 2.34×10^{-6}

   g. 2.84

   h. $7.63 \times 10^{\frac{3}{4}}$

4. Describe all the replacements of n and of m for which $n \times 10^m$ will be in scientific notation.

Characteristic and mantissa

We are now ready to approximate the log of a number that is greater than ten or less than one. For example, since $53,900 = 5.39 \times 10^4$ and $\log(5.39) \doteq .7316$, it follows that

$$
\begin{array}{ll}
\log(53,900) = \log(5.39 \times 10^4) & \text{Scientific notation} \\
= \log(5.39) + \log(10^4) & \text{Theorem 1} \\
= \log(5.39) + 4 & \text{Def. common log} \\
\doteq .7316 + 4 & \text{Table} \\
= 4 + .7316 & \text{CPA}
\end{array}
$$

and that

$$
\begin{array}{l}
\log(.00539) = \log(5.39 \times 10^{-3}) \\
= \log(5.39) + \log(10^{-3}) \\
= \log(5.39) + (-3) \\
\doteq .7316 + (-3) \\
= -3 + .7316
\end{array}
$$

Notice that in both examples we left the answer in the form $c + m$ where c is an integer and $0 < m < 1$; c is called the *characteristic* and m is called the *mantissa*.

EXERCISES

1. For each number

  i. express it in scientific notation

  ii. express the log of the number in the form $c + m$ where c is an integer and $0 < m < 1$

Example: .00236

   i. $.00236 = 2.36 \times 10^{-3}$

   ii. $\log(.00236) = -3 + .3729$

a. 714,000	**c.** 6.26	**e.** 8670	**g.** 435
b. .0359	**d.** .0000482	**f.** .721	**h.** 99.9

2. For the log of each number below, determine

  i. the characteristic

  ii. the mantissa

a. 8,420,000	**e.** 3.24	**i.** 281
b. .000842	**f.** 32.4	**j.** 28,100
c. .617	**g.** .324	**k.** 2,810,000,000
d. 6.17	**h.** .0324	**l.** .300

Let us now reverse the procedure; that is, given the log of a number, we shall then find the number. For example, to find an approximation of the number, say x, if $\log(x) \doteq 4 + .8998$, we proceed as follows:

Example: *i.*

$$\begin{aligned}
\log(x) &\doteq 4 + .8998 \\
&= \log(10^4) + .8998 &&\text{Def. common log} \\
&\doteq \log(10^4) + \log(7.94) &&\text{Table} \\
&= \log(10^4 \times 7.94) &&\text{Theorem 1} \\
&= \log(79{,}400) &&\text{Multiplication}
\end{aligned}$$

Therefore $x = 79{,}400$

For another example, to find an approximation of the number, say p, if $\log(p) \doteq -2 + .8162$, we proceed as follows:

Example: *ii.*

$$\begin{aligned}
\log(p) &\doteq -2 + .8162 \\
&= \log(10^{-2}) + .8162 \\
&\doteq \log(10^{-2}) + \log(6.55) \\
&= \log(10^{-2} \times 6.55) \\
&= \log(.0655)
\end{aligned}$$

Therefore $p \doteq .0655$

EXERCISES

In each problem, the log of a number is given. Express, in ordinary decimal notation, an approximation of this number.

Example: 5 + .2430
From the table, we find that .2430 ≐ log(1.75). Since $1.75 \times 10^5 = 175{,}000$, an approximation of this number is 175,000.

1. 3 + .9175   **3.** 0 + .7959   **5.** −5 + .6830   **7.** 1 + .5752

2. −2 + .7419   **4.** 2 + .6385   **6.** −1 + .8579   **8.** −3 + .4014

APPROXIMATIONS INVOLVING ANY POSITIVE RATIONAL NUMBER

We are now ready to compute approximations involving *any* positive rational number. Study the following examples.

Examples: i. Approximate $43{,}600 \times .00578$ to three digits.

$$\log(43{,}600) \doteq \quad 4 + \ \ .6395$$
$$\log(.00578) \doteq -3 + \ \ .7619$$

$$\log(43{,}600 \times .00578) \doteq \quad 1 + 1.4014$$
$$= \quad 2 + \ \ .4014$$

Theorem 1
The mantissa must be between 0 and 1.
$.4014 \doteq \log(2.52)$

Therefore
$$43{,}600 \times .00578 \doteq 10^2 \times 2.52$$
$$= 252$$

ii. Approximate $43.6 \times .000578$ to four decimal places.

$$\log(43.6) \doteq \quad 1 + \ \ .6395$$
$$\log(.000578) \doteq -4 + \ \ .7619$$

$$\log(43.6 \times .000578) \doteq -3 + 1.4014$$
$$= -2 + \ \ .4014$$

The mantissa must be between 0 and 1.

Therefore
$$43.6 \times .000578 \doteq 10^{-2} \times 2.52$$
$$= .0252$$

EXERCISES

Approximate each answer as in the examples above.

1. $317 \times .00223$

2. $14.2 \times .0583$

3. $77{,}700 \times .111$

4. $.0428 \times 7290$

5. 954×62.1

6. $.00309 \times .852$

7. $2340 \times .00276 \times 15.3$

8. $.0187 \times 555{,}000 \times .224$

Approximating quotients

Examples: i.   Approximate $\dfrac{5780}{436}$ to one decimal place.

$$\log(5780) \doteq 3 + .7619$$
$$\log(436) \doteq 2 + .6395$$

$$\log\left(\frac{5780}{436}\right) \doteq 1 + .1224 \qquad \text{Theorem 4}$$

$$\doteq 1 + .1239 \qquad \text{Closest entry}$$

Therefore $\dfrac{5780}{436} \doteq 13.\overset{\text{'}}{3}$

ii.   Approximate $\dfrac{.578}{43.6}$ to four decimal places.

$$\log(.578) \doteq -1 + .7619$$
$$\log(43.6) \doteq \ \ 1 + .6395$$

$$\log\left(\frac{.578}{43.6}\right) \doteq -2 + .1224$$

$$\doteq -2 + .1239$$

Therefore $\dfrac{.578}{43.6} \doteq .0133$

iii.   Approximate $\dfrac{436}{5780}$ to four decimal places.

$$\log(436) \doteq 2 + .6395 = \ \ 1 + 1.6395$$
$$\log(5780) \doteq 3 + .7619 = \ \ 3 + .7619$$

$$\log\left(\frac{436}{5780}\right) \doteq -2 + \ \ .8776$$

$$\doteq -2 + \ \ .8774$$

Hence $\dfrac{436}{5780} \doteq .0754$

iv.   Approximate $\dfrac{.0436}{57.8}$ to six decimal places.

$$\log(.0436) \doteq -2 + .6395 = -3 + 1.6395$$
$$\log(57.8) \doteq \ \ 1 + .7619 = \ \ 1 + \ .7619$$

$$\log\left(\frac{.0436}{57.8}\right) \doteq -4 + \ \ .8776$$

$$\doteq -4 + \ \ .8774$$

Hence $\dfrac{.0436}{57.8} \doteq .000754$

EXERCISES

Approximate each answer as in the examples above.

1. $\dfrac{9760}{.315}$

2. $\dfrac{.0132}{491}$

3. $\dfrac{68.2}{.00437}$

4. $\dfrac{.518}{76,800}$

5. $\dfrac{801}{313,000}$

6. $\dfrac{.00227}{.0942}$

7. $\dfrac{93,600}{221 \times .314}$

8. $\dfrac{.0372 \times .00179}{.000216}$

9. $\dfrac{889}{10.4 \times 3710}$

10. $\dfrac{7210 \times .405}{558}$

11. $\dfrac{.00667}{13,900 \times 72.7}$

12. $\dfrac{.0112 \times 29.3}{88.5}$

Approximating powers

Examples: i.   Approximate 3750^4, stating the answer in scientific notation.

$$\log(3750) \doteq 3 + .5740$$
$$\log(3750^4) \doteq 3 + .5740$$
$$\underline{\times 4}$$
$$= 12 + 2.2960$$
$$= 14 + .2960$$
$$\doteq 14 + .2967$$

Hence $3750^4 \doteq 1.98 \times 10^{14}$

ii.   Approximate $.0375^2$ to five decimal places.

$$\log(.0375) \doteq -2 + .5740$$
$$\log(.0375^2) \doteq -2 + .5740$$
$$\underline{\times 2}$$
$$= -4 + 1.1480$$
$$= -3 + .1480$$
$$\doteq -3 + .1492$$

Hence $.0375^2 \doteq .00141$

EXERCISES

Approximate each answer as in the examples above.

1. $.00294^2$

2. $79,600^3$

3. 418^6

4. $.118^5$

5. $(2960 \times 20.5)^3$

6. $(.00632 \times .415)^2$

7. $(311 \times .0891)^4$

8. $(54.7 \times .00103)^{10}$

9. $\left(\dfrac{4180}{.579}\right)^5$

10. $\left(\dfrac{78.9}{.00453}\right)^2$

11. $\left(\dfrac{.0765}{981}\right)^3$

12. $\left(\dfrac{.599}{40.8}\right)^4$

Approximating roots

Examples: *i.*   Approximate $\sqrt[3]{37.5}$ to two decimal places.

$$\log(\sqrt[3]{37.5}) = \log(37.5^{\frac{1}{3}}) \qquad \forall_{x>0} \ \sqrt[3]{x} = x^{\frac{1}{3}}$$

$$= \frac{\log(37.5)}{3} \qquad \text{Theorem 10}$$

$$\doteq \frac{1 + .5740}{3} \qquad \text{Table}$$

$$= \frac{0 + 1.5740}{3} \qquad \begin{array}{l}\text{The numerator is regrouped} \\ \text{here since the characteristic} \\ \text{in the next line must be an} \\ \text{integer.}\end{array}$$

$$\doteq 0 + .5247$$

$$\doteq 0 + .5250 \qquad \text{Nearest entry}$$

Hence $\sqrt[3]{37.5} \doteq 3.35$

ii.   Approximate $\sqrt[4]{.00375}$ to three decimal places.

$$\log(\sqrt[4]{.00375}) = \log(.00375^{\frac{1}{4}})$$

$$= \frac{\log(.00375)}{4}$$

$$\doteq \frac{-3 + .5740}{4}$$

$$= \frac{-4 + 1.5740}{4} \qquad \begin{array}{l}\text{The numerator is regrouped} \\ \text{here since the character-} \\ \text{istic in the next line must} \\ \text{be an integer.}\end{array}$$

$$= -1 + .3935$$

$$\doteq -1 + .3927$$

Hence $\sqrt[4]{.00375} \doteq .247$

EXERCISES

1.   Approximate as in the examples above.

a. $\sqrt{777}$

b. $\sqrt[3]{.0777}$

c. $\sqrt{77,700}$

d. $\sqrt[5]{77.7}$

e. $\sqrt[3]{.00404}$

f. $\sqrt{.239}$

g. $\sqrt{657 \times 50.1}$

h. $\sqrt{\dfrac{657}{50.1}}$

i. $\sqrt[3]{8310 \times .00224}$

j. $\sqrt[3]{\dfrac{8310}{.00224}}$

k. $\sqrt[4]{.377 \times .0175}$

l. $\sqrt[4]{\dfrac{.377}{.0175}}$

m. $\sqrt{\dfrac{.723}{602 \times 1620}}$

n. $\sqrt[3]{\dfrac{.0417 \times 22.4}{51,000}}$

o. $\sqrt[4]{\dfrac{.0912}{48.1 \times 113}}$

p. $\sqrt{\dfrac{.00344 \times .237}{8960}}$

q. $\sqrt[3]{\dfrac{584}{.0104 \times 2820}}$

r. $\sqrt[5]{\dfrac{59,600 \times 38.4}{.118}}$

s. $\sqrt{4320^3}$

t. $\sqrt[3]{.0176^2}$

u. $\sqrt[5]{78.1^4}$

v. $\sqrt[3]{\left(\dfrac{63.1}{1.76}\right)^4}$

2. The formula for the energy, E, of a moving object is $E = \dfrac{Wv^2}{2g}$. Solving for v in terms of the other variables, we obtain $v = \sqrt{\dfrac{2Eg}{W}}$. Thus

$$\log(v) = \tfrac{1}{2}[\log(2) + \log(E) + \log(g) - \log(W)]$$

For each formula

     i. solve for the indicated variable in terms of the other variables

     ii. express the log of this variable in "expanded form" as above

a. $d = \dfrac{1}{2}gt^2$; g

b. $d = \dfrac{1}{2}gt^2$; t

c. $v^2 = 2gh$; v

d. $v = \sqrt{2gh}$; g

e. $\dfrac{P_1V_1}{T_1} = \dfrac{P_2V_2}{T_2}$; V_1

f. $\dfrac{P_1V_1}{T_1} = \dfrac{P_2V_2}{T_2}$; T_1

g. $E = \dfrac{Wv^2}{2g}$; g

3. Approximate.

a. $\dfrac{6120}{11.9}$

b. $(.0345 \times 2.17)^4$

c. $\sqrt{\dfrac{43,800}{407}}$

d. $3060 \times .206$

e. $\dfrac{316 \times 52,600}{.00691}$

f. $(98.5)^3$

g. $\sqrt[5]{333 \times 444}$

h. $\left(\dfrac{.0469}{.591}\right)^2$

i. $\dfrac{7.17}{34.2 \times .986}$

j. $\sqrt[10]{826,000}$

k. $\left(\dfrac{.000433 \times 472}{65.7}\right)^3$

l. $\sqrt[3]{\dfrac{.0898 \times 14.9}{.534}}$

m. $\sqrt[7]{132^3}$

n. $\left(\dfrac{991}{6940 \times 1.28}\right)^5$

o. $\sqrt[4]{(.0230 \times .164)^3}$

p. $\sqrt[5]{\left(\dfrac{61.3}{3820 \times 8.90}\right)}$

4. If P dollars is invested at an interest rate r, then the number of dollars, A, accumulated at the end of n years, when interest is compounded annually, is given by the formula: $A = P(1 + r)^n$. This formula is called the *compound interest formula*.

    a. Find A if P is 2,000, n is 30, and r is 6%.

    b. Find A if P is 400, n is 10, and r is 4%.

EXPONENTIAL EQUATIONS

There are many phases of science today where *exponential equations* occur and need to be solved. Some examples of exponential equations are

$$5 = 3^x \qquad\qquad 7 = 2^{x-1} \qquad\qquad 18 = 4^{3x+2}$$
$$6^{2x} = 3^{x-1} \qquad\qquad 5^{x^2} = 625 \qquad\qquad 2^{3x} = 4^{3x}$$

We shall learn to solve such equations by the study of examples.

Our method of solving exponential equations depends on the following fact which was used before.

$$\forall_{a>0} \ \forall_{b>0}, \ (a = b) \text{ if and only if } [\log(a) = \log(b)]$$

You should study the graph of log in figure 1 to see that this statement is true.

Example: i.   Solve $5 = 3^x$.

$$\log(5) = \log(3^x)$$
$$\log(5) = x \cdot \log(3)$$
$$\frac{\log(5)}{\log(3)} = x$$
$$\frac{0 + .6990}{0 + .4771} \doteq x$$
$$\frac{.699}{.477} \doteq x$$
$$x \doteq 1.47$$

Example: ii.   Solve $4 = 7^{2x}$.

$$\log(4) = \log(7^{2x})$$
$$\log(4) = 2x \cdot \log(7)$$
$$\frac{\log(4)}{\log(7)} = 2x$$
$$\frac{0 + .6021}{0 + .8451} \doteq 2x$$
$$\frac{.602}{.845} \doteq 2x$$
$$2x \doteq .712$$
$$x = .356$$

Example: iii.   Solve $5 = 3^{2x-1}$.

$$\log(5) = \log(3^{2x-1})$$
$$\log(5) = (2x - 1) \cdot \log(3)$$
$$\frac{\log(5)}{\log(3)} = 2x - 1$$
$$\frac{.699}{.477} \doteq 2x - 1$$

$$2x - 1 \doteq 1.47$$
$$2x \doteq 2.47$$
$$x \doteq 1.24$$

EXERCISES

Solve for x, then approximate its value as in the examples above.

1. $9 = 4^x$

2. $9 = 4^{3x+1}$

3. $4 = 9^x$

4. $4 = 9^{2x-3}$

5. $12 = 7^x$

6. $12 = 7^{1-x}$

7. $23.4 = 1.76^x$

8. $2.34 = 17.6^x$

9. $8 = 3 \cdot 5^x$

10. $7^{2x} = 4^{x-1}$

OTHER LOGARITHMIC FUNCTIONS

At the beginning of this chapter we said that there is a group of functions called logarithmic functions. You have been studying one of this group, the common logarithmic function, denoted by *log* and defined to be $\{(x, y) \mid x = 10^y\}$. This function is sometimes called the *base-ten* logarithmic function.

Now any positive real number (except the number one) may be used as the base of a logarithmic function. For example, the *base-five* logarithmic function is $\{(x, y) \mid x = 5^y\}$. Some of its members are $(25, 2)$, $(125, 3)$, $(5, 1)$, $(1, 0)$, $(\frac{1}{25}, -2)$, and $(\sqrt[3]{5}, \frac{1}{3})$. This function is denoted by "$\log_5$"; using set notation, we write $\log_5 = \{(x, y) \mid x = 5^y\}$. Study the following:

$$\log_5(25) \quad = 2 \text{ since } 25 = 5^2$$
$$\log_5(5) \quad = 1 \text{ since } 5 = 5^1$$
$$\log_5(\tfrac{1}{125}) \quad = -3 \text{ since } \tfrac{1}{125} = 5^{-3}$$
$$\log_5(\sqrt[3]{5}) = \tfrac{1}{3} \text{ since } \sqrt[3]{5} = 5^{\frac{1}{3}}$$

The *base-four* logarithmic function is $\{(x, y) \mid x = 4^y\}$. Some of its members are $(64, 3)$, $(2, \frac{1}{2})$, $(1, 0)$, $(\frac{1}{16}, -2)$, and $(16, 2)$. This function is denoted by "$\log_4$". Study the following:

$$\log_4(64) = 3 \text{ since } 64 = 4^3$$
$$\log_4(2) \quad = \tfrac{1}{2} \text{ since } 2 = 4^{\frac{1}{2}}$$
$$\log_4(1) \quad = 0 \text{ since } 1 = 4^0$$
$$\log_4(\tfrac{1}{16}) = -2 \text{ since } \tfrac{1}{16} = 4^{-2}$$
$$\log_4(16) = 2 \text{ since } 16 = 4^2$$

In general, for each positive real number a (except 1), the *base a* logarithmic function is $\{(x, y) \mid x = a^y\}$.

EXERCISES

Evaluate each of the following:

1. $\log_5(625)$

2. $\log_5(1)$

3. $\log_5(5)$

4. $\log_5(125)$

5. $\log_5(\sqrt{5})$

6. $\log_5(\sqrt[4]{5^3})$

7. $\log_5(\sqrt[4]{125})$

8. $\log_5(\sqrt[3]{25})$

9. $\log_3(3)$

10. $\log_3(81)$

11. $\log_3\left(\dfrac{1}{9}\right)$

12. $\log_2(32)$

13. $\log_2\left(\dfrac{1}{16}\right)$

14. $\log_2(2)$

15. $\log_7(\sqrt{7})$

16. $\log_7\left(\dfrac{1}{49}\right)$

17. $\log_8\left(\dfrac{1}{8}\right)$

18. $\log_2\left(\dfrac{1}{8}\right)$

19. $\log_3\left(\dfrac{1}{81}\right)$

20. $\log_{\frac{1}{2}}\left(\dfrac{1}{8}\right)$

21. $\log_{\frac{1}{2}}\left(\dfrac{1}{2}\right)$

22. $\log_{\frac{1}{2}}(2)$

23. $\log_{\frac{1}{2}}(4)$

24. $\log_{\frac{1}{6}}(36)$

25. $\log_c(c)$ $(c > 0, c \neq 1)$

26. $\log_c(c^3)$ $(c > 0, c \neq 1)$

27. $\log_c(c^{2k-1})$ $(c > 0, c \neq 1)$

28. $\log_e(e^\pi)$

Change of base

You probably used your knowledge of exponents to solve most of the exercises above, that is, you found $\log_3(\frac{1}{9})$ to be -2 because you knew that $3^{-2} = \frac{1}{9}$. But how does one determine $\log_3(4)$? $\log_3(4)$ is an irrational number that can be approximated by a rational number. Study the following examples to see how this may be done.

Example: *i.* Approximate $\log_3(4)$ to two decimal places.

First let $n = \log_3(4)$

Then $3^n = 4$

$$\log(3^n) = \log(4)$$
$$n \cdot \log(3) = \log(4)$$
$$n = \frac{\log(4)}{\log(3)}$$

Second $n = \dfrac{\log(4)}{\log(3)} \doteq \dfrac{.602}{.477}$

Therefore $n \doteq 1.26$

And thus $\log_3(4) \doteq 1.26$

Example: *ii.*   Approximate $\log_7(5)$ to three decimal places.

Let $\qquad\qquad n = \log_7(5)$

Then $\qquad\qquad 7^n = 5$

$$\log(7^n) = \log(5)$$

$$n = \frac{\log(5)}{\log(7)}$$

$$n \doteq \frac{.699}{.845}$$

Therefore $\qquad\quad n \doteq .827$

Thus $\qquad\log_7(5) \doteq .827$

EXERCISES

1.   Express in ordinary decimal notation as in the examples above.

   a. $\log_2(6)$

   b. $\log_6(2)$

   c. $\log_5(14)$

   d. $\log_3(8.6)$

   e. $\log_{12}(6)$

   f. $\log_2(\sqrt[3]{7})$

   g. $\log_3(100{,}000)$

   h. $\log_{2.5}(9.6)$

2.   Prove that for all positive real numbers a and x, $a \neq 1$, $\log_a(x) = \dfrac{\log(x)}{\log(a)}$.

VOCABULARY

Use each of the following correctly in a sentence. Numerals in parentheses refer to pages where these words were used. If you are not sure of the meaning of any words, turn to the indicated pages.

base (395)

characteristic (387)

common logarithmic function (375)

exponential equation (394)

mantissa (387)

scientific notation (386)

SUMMARY OF BASIC THEOREMS

For all positive real numbers x and y and for all natural numbers a and b

$$\log(xy) = \log(x) + \log(y)$$

$$\log\left(\frac{1}{x}\right) = -\log(x)$$

$$\log\left(\frac{x}{y}\right) = \log(x) - \log(y)$$

$$\log(x^a) = a \cdot \log(x)$$

$$\log\left(x^{\frac{m}{n}}\right) = \frac{m \cdot \log(x)}{n}$$

REVIEW EXERCISES

1. Simplify.

a. $\log(10^7)$

b. $\log(.0001)$

c. $\log_3(81)$

d. $\log_{73}(73)$

e. $\log_{73}(1)$

f. $\log_{73}(\sqrt{73})$

g. $\log\left(\dfrac{1000}{10}\right)$

h. $\dfrac{\log(1000)}{\log(10)}$

i. $\dfrac{\log(1000)}{10}$

j. $\log_{\frac{1}{3}}\left(\dfrac{1}{27}\right)$

k. $\log_3\left(\dfrac{1}{27}\right)$

l. $\log_{\frac{1}{3}}(27)$

2. What is the domain of the log function?

3. What is the range of the log function?

4. $\mathrm{Log}(2) \doteq .3010$ and $\log(3) \doteq .4771$; approximate each of the following without using a table.

a. $\log(6)$

b. $\log(\frac{3}{2})$

c. $\log(3^4)$

d. $\log(12)$

e. $\log(\frac{8}{3})$

f. $\log(300)$

g. $\log(\sqrt{2})$

h. $\log(15)$

i. $\log(\frac{1}{2})$

j. $\log(\sqrt[3]{6})$

k. $\log(\frac{2}{3})$

l. $\log(.006)$

5. If $\log(x_1) = -5 + 2.3076$, then determine

a. the characteristic of $\log(x_1)$

b. the mantissa of $\log(x_1)$

6. Simplify to obtain an equivalent expression of the form $\log(x)$.

a. $\log(t) - \log(c) + \log(5)$

b. $2 \cdot \log(a + b)$

c. $\dfrac{\log(3m)}{2}$

7. Express in scientific notation.

a. .000604

b. .604

c. 6.04

d. 6040

e. 604,000

f. .0604

8. Suppose $7 = 3^x$. Then x is equal to which of the following?

a. $\dfrac{\log(3)}{\log(7)}$

b. $\dfrac{\log(7)}{\log(3)}$

c. $\dfrac{\log(7)}{3}$

d. $\log_7(3)$

e. $\log\left(\dfrac{7}{3}\right)$

9. Solve for x (do not approximate).

a. $5^x = 10$

b. $12 = 7^{2x}$

c. $4 = 12^{4x+1}$

d. $8 = 4 \cdot 3^x$

e. $2^x = 3^{x+1}$

f. $3 \cdot 3^{x+2} = 5 \cdot 2^{x+2}$

10. Solve for x and approximate the answer.

a. $3^x = 6$

b. $6^{2x} = 5$

CHAPTER TEST

Directions: Each question is followed by five choices lettered **a, b, c, d,** and **e.** Select the letter in front of the correct answer. In each case, the fifth choice, **e,** is "none of these". You are to select the letter **e,** only if none of the four preceding choices is the correct answer. There is *only one* correct choice to each question.

1. The domain of log is
   a. the set of all real numbers
   b. the set of all positive real numbers
   c. the set of all non-negative real numbers
   d. the set of all real numbers between 1 and 10
   e. none of these

2. The range of log is
   a. the set of all real numbers
   b. the set of all positive real numbers
   c. the set of all non-negative real numbers
   d. the set of all real numbers between zero and one
   e. none of these

3. Which of the following is given in the table of common logarithms of numbers?
   a. characteristics only
   b. mantissas only
   c. both characteristics and mantissas
   d. powers
   e. none of these

4. What is true about the characteristic of the logarithm of a number?
   a. It is always positive.
   b. It is always negative.
   c. It is always an integer.
   d. It is always zero.
   e. none of these

5. If x is a real number between 0 and 1, then $\log(x)$ is
   a. greater than one
   b. between zero and one
   c. less than zero
   d. undefined
   e. none of these

6. What is the characteristic of $\log(6760)$?
   a. 5   **b.** 4   **c.** 3   **d.** 2   **e.** none of these

7. What is the characteristic of $\log (0.00675)$?
   a. -3 **b.** -2 **c.** 2   **d.** 3   **e.** none of these

8. Which of the following is in scientific notation?
   a. $3.22 \times 10^{\frac{1}{3}}$
   b. $.537 \times 10^5$
   c. 816
   d. 5.63×10^{-4}
   e. none of these

9. $\log(1000)$ is
   a. 3   **b.** 2   **c.** 1   **d.** .0000   **e.** none of these

10. Log(1) is

    a. 3   **b.** 2   **c.** 1   **d.** 0   **e.** none of these

11. Log(.001) is

    a. 0   **b.** -1 **c.** -2 **d.** -3 **e.** none of these

12. Log(699) is

    a. between 0 and 1   **c.** between 2 and 3   **e.** none of these

    b. between 1 and 2   **d.** between 3 and 4

13. Log(xy) is equal to

    a. $\log(x + y)$ **c.** $y \cdot \log(x)$ **e.** none of these

    b. $\log(x) \cdot \log(y)$ **d.** $\log(x) + \log(y)$

14. $\log\left(\dfrac{x}{y}\right)$ is equal to

    a. $\dfrac{\log(x)}{\log(y)}$ **b.** $\log(y) - \log(x)$ **d.** $\log(x) - \log(y)$

                               c. $\log(x - y)$ **e.** none of these

15. What is $\log(\sqrt[4]{16})$ equal to?

    a. $4 \times \log(16)$ **c.** $\log(16^4)$ **e.** none of these

    b. $\frac{1}{4} \times \log(16)$ **d.** $4 \times \log(4)$

16. What is $\log(8)$ equal to?

    a. $2 \times \log(8)$ **c.** $3 \times \log(2)$ **e.** none of these

    b. $2 \times \log(4)$ **d.** $2 \times \log(2)$

17. Log(2) $\doteq 0 + .3010$; what is log(8) approximately?

    a. $0 + .9030$ **c.** $0 + .6020$ **e.** none of these

    b. $1 + .2040$ **d.** $0 + .0021$

18. Log(27) $\doteq 1 + .4314$; what is log(3) approximately?

    a. $0 + .1590$ **c.** $0 + .7157$ **e.** none of these

    b. $0 + .4771$ **d.** $2 + .0489$

19. Log(x) $+ c \cdot \log(y)$ is equal to

    a. $\log(xyc)$ **c.** $\log((xy)^c)$ **e.** none of these

    b. $\log (xy^c)$ **d.** $\log(x + y^c)$

20. $\log\left(\dfrac{a^3 \times \sqrt{b}}{c}\right)$ is equal to

    a. $\frac{1}{3} \log(a) + 2 \log(b) - \log(c)$ **d.** $3 \log(a) - \frac{1}{2} \log(b) - \log(c)$

    b. $3 \log(a) + \frac{1}{2} \log(b) - \log(c)$ **e.** none of these

    c. $\frac{1}{3} \log(a) + \frac{1}{2} \log(b) - \log(c)$

21. What is $\log(x^y \times x^v)$ equal to?

    a. $y \log(x) - v \log(x)$ **d.** $\log (x^y) \times \log(x^v)$

    b. $(y + v) \log(x)$ **e.** none of these

    c. $y \log(x) + \log(x)$

22. Which of the following is equivalent to $\log_a(A) = C$?

  a. $A^C = a$ **c.** $a^C = A$ **e.** none of these

  b. $C^a = A$ **d.** $A^a = C$

23. $\text{Log}(5) \doteq 0 + .6990$; what is $\log(\frac{1}{5})$ approximately?

  a. $-1 + .6990$ **c.** $0 + .3010$ **e.** none of these

  b. $-1 + .3010$ **d.** $-(0 + .3010)$

24. If $V = \frac{4}{3}\pi r^3$, then what is $\log(V)$ equal to?

  a. $\log(\pi) - \log(3) + \log(4) + 3\log(r)$ **d.** $\log(4) + \log(3) - \log(\pi) + 3\log(r)$

  b. $\log(4) + \log(3) + \log(\pi) + 3\log(r)$ **e.** none of these

  c. $\log(4) - \log(3) + \log(\pi) + \frac{1}{3}\log(r)$

25. If $a = bc$, then what is $\log(b)$ equal to?

  a. $\log(a) + \log(c)$

  b. $\log(c) - \log(a)$ **d.** $\dfrac{\log(a)}{\log(c)}$

  c. $\log(a) - \log(c)$ **e.** none of these

26. If $x = \dfrac{cy}{z}$, then what is $\log(x)$ equal to?

  a. $\log(c + y) - \log(z)$

  b. $\log(c) - \log(z) - \log(y)$ **d.** $\log(c) + \log\left(\dfrac{y}{z}\right)$

  c. $\log(c - z) + \log(y)$ **e.** none of these

27. If $s = \frac{1}{2}gt^2$, then $\log(t)$ is equal to

  a. $\frac{1}{2}[\log(s) + \log(2) - \log(g)]$

  b. $\log(s) - \log(2) - \log(g)$ **d.** $\log\left(\dfrac{s}{g}\right)$

  c. $\log(sg)$ **e.** none of these

28. If $a^x = b$, then what is x equal to?

  a. $\dfrac{\log(b)}{\log(a)}$ **c.** $\log(b) - \log(a)$

                      d. $\log(a) - \log(b)$

  b. $\log\left(\dfrac{b}{a}\right)$ **e.** none of these

29. $\text{Log}(\sqrt[4]{7^3})$ is equal to

  a. $\frac{1}{4}\log(7)$ **d.** $\log(7) - \log(4) + \log(3)$

  b. $\frac{4}{3}\log(7)$ **e.** none of these

  c. $\frac{3}{4}\log(7)$

30. What is $\log_3(27)$ equal to?

  a. 1   **c.** 3   **e.** none of these

  b. 2   **d.** 4

31. $\text{Log}_2(\frac{1}{4})$ is equal to

  a. 2   **c.** -2 **e.** none of these

  b. -1 **d.** -3

32. What is $\log_5(625)$ equal to?

    a. 5   **c.** 3   **e.** none of these

    b. 4   **d.** 2

33. If $y = a^{4x}$, then what is $\log(y)$ equal to?

    a. $x \log(4a)$ **c.** $4x \log(a)$ **e.** none of these

    b. $4 \log(xa)$ **d.** $a \log(4x)$

34. If $2 \times 10^x = 2000$, then what is x equal to?

    a. 2   **c.** $\frac{1}{100}$ **e.** none of these

    b. 100   **d.** $\frac{1}{10}$

35. If $\log_x(\frac{1}{8}) = 3$, then what is x equal to?

    a. $\frac{1}{2}$ **c.** 3   **e.** none of these

    b. 10   **d.** $\frac{1}{8}$

36. The equation $\log_a(B) = x$ is equivalent to which one of the following equations?

    a. $a^{\log_B(a)} = B$ **c.** $a^{\log_a(B)} = B$ **e.** none of these

    b. $B^{\log_a(B)} = B$ **d.** $x^{\log_a(B)} = x$

37. $\text{Log}_5(5)$ is the same as

    a. $\log_{10}(5)$ **c.** $\log_{10}(10)$ **e.** none of these

    b. $\log_5(10)$ **d.** $\log_{10}(100)$

38. If $4^{\log(x)} = \frac{1}{16}$, then what is x equal to?

    a. 2   **c.** $\frac{1}{100}$ **e.** none of these

    b. -2 **d.** 100

39. $\text{Log}_4(5)$ is equal to

    a. $\dfrac{\log(4)}{\log(5)}$ **c.** $\log\left(\dfrac{4}{5}\right)$ **e.** none of these

    b. $\log\left(\dfrac{5}{4}\right)$ **d.** $\dfrac{\log(5)}{\log(4)}$

40. $\log\left(\sqrt[3]{\dfrac{473^2 \times .00316}{28.7}}\right)$ is equal to

    a. $3[2 + \log(4.73) + \log(3.16) - \log(2.87)]$

    b. $\dfrac{2 \cdot \log(473)}{3} - \log(28.7) + \log(.00316)$

    c. $\dfrac{2 \cdot \log(4.73) + \log(3.16) - \log(2.87)}{3}$

    d. $\dfrac{2 + \log(4.73) + \log(3.16) - \log(2.87)}{3}$

    e. none of these

CUMULATIVE REVIEW

The following exercises cover the material in chapters 9 through 12.

1. Compute and express the answers in standard form, $a + bi$.

   a. $(5 - 3i) + (-7 + 5i)$ **c.** $(2 + 3i) \cdot (3 - 4i)$

   b. $(6 + 8i) - (9 - 10i)$ **d.** $(1 + 2i) \div (2 - 3i)$

2. Determine each of the following:

   a. $\overline{-6 - 2i}$, the conjugate of $-6 - 2i$

   b. $|3 - 5i|$, the absolute value of $3 - 5i$

   c. $(2i)^5$, the fifth power of $2i$

   d. the two square roots of $-21 - 20i$

3. Simplify.

   a. $\sqrt{-36}$ **c.** $(\sqrt{-2})(\sqrt{-8})$

   b. $-\sqrt{-8} + \sqrt{-32}$ **d.** $(-7 + \sqrt{-3})(-7 - \sqrt{-3})$

4. Solve. The replacement set for x is the set of all complex numbers.

   a. $x^2 + 4 = 0$ **b.** $x^2 + 3x + 5 = 0$

5. Use the comparison method to solve the system
   $$5x + 2y = 8$$
   $$9 - 7x = 2y$$

6. Use the substitution method to solve the system
   $$\frac{4 - 3x}{5} = \frac{2 + 3y}{4}$$
   $$y = 2x + 1$$

7. Use the addition method to solve the system
   $$3(x - 2y) = 4$$
   $$2x + 7 = 3y$$

8. Use determinants to solve the system
   $$5x + 3y = 7$$
   $$6x - 2y = 9$$

9. For each system, tell whether it is independent, inconsistent, or dependent.

   a. $5(x - 2) = 3(4 - y)$

   $7 + 6y = 2(1 - 5x)$

   b. $3 - (x + y) = 4 - 2x$

   $y + 5 = 3 - x$

   c. $\dfrac{x + 2}{5} = \dfrac{y - 2}{2}$

   $x - 2y - 7 = \dfrac{1}{2}y$

10. Expand and simplify each determinant

    a. $\begin{vmatrix} -2 & 4 \\ 3 & 5 \end{vmatrix}$ **b.** $\begin{vmatrix} a + b & b \\ a & a + b \end{vmatrix}$

11. Find the solution set of the system
    $$x^2 + 2y^2 - 38 = 0$$
    $$y = 3x$$

12. Graph the solution set of the system

$$x^2 + y^2 \le 9$$
$$y \ge |x|$$

13. Determine the value of the polynomial $2x^3 + 4x + 5$ at each of the following

    a. 10   **b.** -1 **c.** i **d.** $\sqrt{2}$

14. Suppose $P(x) = 3x^3 + x - 6$.

    a. Use synthetic division to determine $P(-2.1)$

    b. Determine the polynomial $Q(x)$ and the number R such that

$$P(x) = (x - 1) \cdot Q(x) + R$$

15. Determine all the rational zeros of $T(x) = 3x^4 - x^3 - 8x^2 + 2x + 4$.

16. Construct a third-degree real polynomial such that two of its three zeros are 4 and $1 + 2i$.

17. Simplify.

    a. $\log(100)$ **d.** $\dfrac{\log(1000)}{10}$

    b. $\log_2(16)$ **e.** $\dfrac{\log(1000)}{\log(10)}$

    c. $\log_{25}(5)$ **f.** $\log\left(\dfrac{1000}{10}\right)$

18. $\log(47.6) \doteq 1 + .6776$; determine the following:

    a. $\log(.0476)$ **d.** $\log((47.6)^3)$

    b. $\log(47{,}600)$ **e.** the characteristic of $\log(47.6)$

    c. $\log(\sqrt{47.6})$ **f.** the mantissa of $\log(47.6)$

19. For each of the following, determine an equivalent expression of the form $\log(a)$.

    a. $\log(r) - \log(k) + \log(t)$ **c.** $\dfrac{\log(16d^8)}{4}$

    b. $2 \cdot \log(m - 2)$ **d.** $\log(r + t) + \log(r - t)$

BIBLIOGRAPHY

Allendoerfer, C. B. and Oakley, C. O. *Fundamentals of Freshman Mathematics.* New York: McGraw-Hill Book Co., Inc., 1959. pp. 215–232.

Hogben, L. *Mathematics for the Million.* New York: W. W. Norton and Co., Inc., 1951. Chapter 10.

Kasner, E. and Newman, J. *Mathematics and the Imagination.* New York: Simon and Schuster, Inc., 1940. pp. 80–89.

Moore, J. T. *Fundamental Principles of Mathematics.* New York: Holt, Rinehart and Winston, Inc., 1960. pp. 53–63, 99–105.

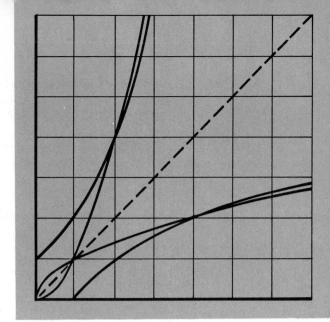

CHAPTER 13

Introduction to Trigonometry

PATHS

Let us consider moves along certain geometric figures. The course traveled during a move will be called a *path*. One simple kind of move is along a straight line. Consider the line of figure 1. Ten of its points have been labeled. These ten points separate the line so as to form disjoint sets of points: nine open segments and two half-lines.

Suppose each of the nine segments has a length of one unit. If a move is made along the line starting at T and ending 3 units away, will the ending point be C or B? Of course, we cannot tell whether it will be C or B unless we also know the *direction* of the move.

For figure 2, we have decided arbitrarily that any move along the line in the direction from B towards T is to be considered as a move in the *positive* direction and that any move from T towards B is to be considered as a move in the *negative* direction.

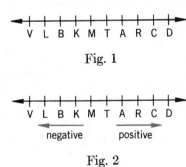

V L B K M T A R C D

Fig. 1

V L B K M T A R C D

negative   positive

Fig. 2

405

Thus, the path for a move from L to A will be traversed by beginning at L and moving 5 units in the positive direction without change of direction. L is called the *initial* point and A is called the *terminal* point of this path. This path will be denoted by the ordered pair $(L, 5)$. The path from R to T will be denoted by $(R, -2)$ signifying the path covered by a move 2 units in the negative direction beginning at R. What is the terminal point of $(R, -2)$? Describe the path denoted by

$$(T, 3) \qquad (C, -3) \qquad (M, -2.3) \qquad (K, 8.6)$$

Another kind of move is along a square. Consider the square $TCRV$ of figure 3. Suppose that each side of the square is 2 units in length and that A, K, L, and M are midpoints of the sides as shown.

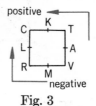

Fig. 3

If a move is made along this square from A to C by passing T and then K, then the move will be 3 units long and we shall consider the direction of this move as positive. The path will be denoted by $(A, 3)$ signifying a move beginning at A and continuing 3 units along the square in the positive direction. A is the *initial* point and C is the *terminal* point of this path. $(V, -4)$ is the path traversed by a move from V along the square 4 units in the negative direction. Observe that C is the terminal point of this path. Describe the path denoted by

$(K, 5)$	$(A, 8)$	$(C, 3\frac{1}{2})$	$(R, 8)$
$(K, -3)$	$(A, -4)$	$(C, -3\frac{1}{2})$	$(M, 0)$
$(A, 4)$	$(A, -8)$	$(R, 0)$	$(M, -8)$

For the square of figure 3, the length of a move may be greater than 8, even though the perimeter of the square is 8.

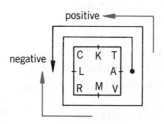

Fig. 4

Observe in figure 4 that part which shows the path $(A, 12)$. $(A, 12)$ is the path covered by a move in the positive direction from A along the square and traversing 12 units. Its terminal point is L. In what respects are the paths $(A, 12)$ and $(A, 4)$ alike? In what respect are $(A, 12)$ and $(A, 4)$ different?

Draw pictures as in figure 4 corresponding to the following paths for the square $TCRV$: $(A, -2)$; $(A, -10)$; $(A, 10)$. Do any of these paths have the same terminal point? If so, which ones? In what respect are the paths $(A, 10)$ and $(A, -14)$ alike and in what respect are they different?

A third kind of move we want to consider is a move along a circle. Consider the circle of figure 5. Its radius is 4 units. Therefore, the circumference is 8π ($C = 2\pi r$). The circle has been separated by eight points forming eight arcs, each of length π.

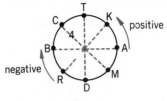

Fig. 5

A move along this circle from A to C, passing K and then T, is 3π units long. We consider the *counter-clockwise* direction as positive. The path is denoted by $(A, 3\pi)$; the terminal point is C. $(A, -2\pi)$ is the path traversed by a move from A along the circle 2π units in the negative, or *clockwise*, direction. Observe that D is the terminal point of this path, $(A, -2\pi)$.

For the circle of figure 5, describe the path denoted by

$(A, 4\pi)$	$(A, 5\pi)$	$(A, 8\pi)$	$(A, 0)$	$(A, 10\pi)$
$(A, -4\pi)$	$(A, -5\pi)$	$(A, -8\pi)$	$(A, 16\pi)$	$(A, -14\pi)$

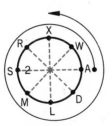

Fig. 6

The circle of figure 6 has a radius of 2 units and therefore a circumference of 4π units. A move in the clockwise direction along this circle shall be considered to be in the negative direction. The circle has been separated by eight points forming eight arcs, each of the same length, namely $\frac{\pi}{2}$ units. Observe the portion of the picture that shows the path $(A, 5\pi)$. Its terminal point is X. Draw pictures as in figure 6 corresponding to the following paths for this circle.

$$\left(A, \frac{\pi}{2}\right) \quad (A, -3\pi) \quad \left(A, -\frac{5\pi}{2}\right) \quad (A, 6\pi) \quad (A, -6\pi) \quad \left(A, \frac{15\pi}{2}\right) \quad \left(A, -\frac{15\pi}{2}\right)$$

EXERCISES

1.   For the adjoining figure, the radius of the circle is 1. Eight points of the circle separate the circle into eight arcs, each of the same length. Consider counter-clockwise moves to have positive direction.

a. Determine the circumference of the circle.

b. Determine the length of one of the eight arcs.

c. The picture shows the path $\left(A, \dfrac{3\pi}{4}\right)$. Draw similar pictures showing the following paths.

$i.\ \left(A, \dfrac{3\pi}{2}\right)$ $\qquad$ $v.\ (A, 4\pi)$ $\qquad$ $viii.\ \left(A, -\dfrac{5\pi}{4}\right)$

$ii.\ \left(A, -\dfrac{3\pi}{4}\right)$ $\qquad$ $vi.\ \left(A, \dfrac{5\pi}{4}\right)$ $\qquad$ $ix.\ \left(A, -\dfrac{5\pi}{2}\right)$

$iii.\ (A, 3\pi)$
$iv.\ (A, -3\pi)$ $\qquad$ $vii.\ \left(A, \dfrac{13\pi}{4}\right)$ $\qquad$ $x.\ (A, -6\pi)$

d. List five paths that have the same initial and terminal points as the path

$i.\ \left(A, \dfrac{3\pi}{4}\right)$ $\qquad\qquad$ $ii.\ \left(A, -\dfrac{7\pi}{4}\right)$

2.   For the adjoining figure, the radius of the circle is 1. Twelve points of the circle separate it into twelve arcs of equal length. Consider counter-clockwise moves to be positive.

a. Determine the circumference of the circle.

b. Determine the length of one of the twelve arcs.

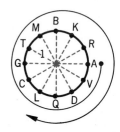

c. The picture shows the path $\left(A, -\dfrac{16\pi}{6}\right)$ which

is equal to the path $\left(A, -\dfrac{8\pi}{3}\right)$. Draw similar

pictures showing the following paths.

$i.\ \left(A, \dfrac{5\pi}{6}\right)$ $\qquad$ $iv.\ \left(A, -\dfrac{7\pi}{6}\right)$ $\qquad$ $vii.\ (A, -3\pi)$

$ii.\ \left(A, \dfrac{\pi}{3}\right)$ $\qquad$ $v.\ \left(A, -\dfrac{11\pi}{6}\right)$ $\qquad$ $viii.\ \left(A, \dfrac{7\pi}{6}\right)$

$iii.\ \left(A, \dfrac{3\pi}{2}\right)$ $\qquad$ $vi.\ \left(A, \dfrac{8\pi}{3}\right)$ $\qquad$ $ix.\ \left(A, -\dfrac{7\pi}{3}\right)$
$\qquad\qquad\qquad\qquad\qquad\qquad\qquad$ $x.\ (A, -2\pi)$

d. List five paths that have the same initial and terminal points as the path

$i.\ \left(A, \dfrac{5\pi}{6}\right)$ $\qquad\qquad$ $ii.\ \left(A, -\dfrac{2\pi}{3}\right)$

The unit circle

A circle whose radius is 1 is called a *unit circle*. Consider the unit circle of figure 7. Points A, B, C, and D separate it into four arcs of equal length, namely $\frac{\pi}{2}$.

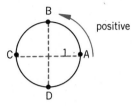

Fig. 7

Observe that many paths for this circle have their initial point at A and their terminal point at B. These paths are

$$\left(A, \frac{\pi}{2}\right) \qquad\qquad \left(A, \frac{\pi}{2} - 2\pi\right) = \left(A, -\frac{3\pi}{2}\right)$$

$$\left(A, \frac{\pi}{2} + 2\pi\right) \qquad\qquad \left(A, \frac{\pi}{2} - 4\pi\right)$$

$$\left(A, \frac{\pi}{2} + 4\pi\right) \qquad\qquad \left(A, \frac{\pi}{2} - 6\pi\right)$$

$$\left(A, \frac{\pi}{2} + 6\pi\right) \qquad\qquad \vdots$$

$$\vdots \qquad\qquad \left(A, \frac{\pi}{2} - 2n\pi\right)$$

$$\left(A, \frac{\pi}{2} + 2n\pi\right)$$

$$\vdots$$

Hence, for any number n of the set $\{0, 1, 2, 3, \ldots\}$, the path $\left(A, \frac{\pi}{2} \pm 2n\pi\right)$ has initial point A and terminal point B. In a similar manner it can be shown that any path $(A, \pi \pm 2n\pi)$ for this circle will have initial point A and terminal point C, and that any path $\left(A, \frac{3\pi}{2} \pm 2n\pi\right)$ will have initial point A and terminal point D. In general, for any point P of this unit circle and for any real number θ, if (A, θ) has terminal point P, then $(A, \theta \pm 2n\pi)$ also has terminal point P. See figure 8.

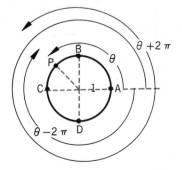

Fig. 8

EXERCISES

1. Consider the *unit* circle of the adjoining figure. The eight points separate the circle into eight arcs of equal length.

a. Determine the circumference of the circle.

b. Determine the length of one of the eight arcs.

c. What is the terminal point of each of the following paths?

i. $\left(A, \dfrac{3\pi}{4} \pm 2n\pi\right)$

ii. $\left(A, \dfrac{5\pi}{4} \pm 2n\pi\right)$

iii. $(A, \pi \pm 2n\pi)$

iv. $(A, 0 \pm 2n\pi)$

v. $\left(A, -\dfrac{\pi}{2} \pm 2n\pi\right)$

2. Consider the *unit* circle of the adjoining figure. The twelve points separate the circle into twelve arcs of equal length.

a. Determine the circumference of the circle.

b. Determine the length of one of the twelve arcs.

c. What is the terminal point of each of the following paths?

i. $\left(A, \dfrac{\pi}{6} \pm 2n\pi\right)$

ii. $\left(A, \dfrac{5\pi}{6} \pm 2n\pi\right)$

iii. $\left(A, \dfrac{\pi}{3} \pm 2n\pi\right)$

iv. $\left(A, \dfrac{4\pi}{3} \pm 2n\pi\right)$

v. $\left(A, \dfrac{3\pi}{2} \pm 2n\pi\right)$

vi. $\left(A, -\dfrac{2\pi}{3} \pm 2n\pi\right)$

vii. $(A, -\pi \pm 2n\pi)$

viii. $\left(A, -\dfrac{5\pi}{6} \pm 2n\pi\right)$

3. Consider the *unit* circle of the adjoining figure. Three paths with the same initial point A and the same terminal point have been pictured. Observe that one such path is $(A, 2\frac{1}{2})$. Determine each of the following:

a. θ_1 for (A, θ_1)

b. θ_2 for (A, θ_2)

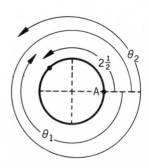

The unit circle and a coordinate system

We have been considering unit circles such as the one pictured in figure 9. We shall now establish a coordinate system on the plane having x and y-axes in which the origin is the center of the unit circle. We shall consider only those moves which are along this unit circle and whose initial point is $A(1, 0)$.   Each counter-clockwise move shall be considered as being in the positive direction. Thus, for each real number θ, the terminal point of the path (A, θ) is some point P on the circle. This point P has coordinates (x, y) which satisfy the equation of this unit circle: $x^2 + y^2 = 1$.

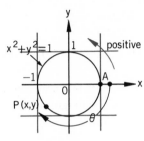

Fig. 9

The coordinates of certain points of this unit circle are readily determined. Consider the following three cases.

CASE 1:

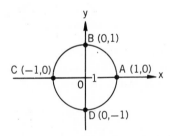

The coordinates of four points are readily determined

$$A(1, 0) \qquad B(0, 1) \qquad C(-1, 0) \qquad D(0, -1)$$

These are the points of intersection of the circle and the axes. What is the degree-measure of $\angle AOB$?

Since the circumference is 2π, the terminal points of the paths $\left(A, \dfrac{\pi}{2}\right)$, (A, π), and $\left(A, \dfrac{3\pi}{2}\right)$ are B, C, and D respectively. Determine the terminal point and its x and y-coordinates for each of the following paths.

$$(A, \pi \pm 2n\pi) \qquad \left(A, \frac{\pi}{2} \pm 2n\pi\right) \qquad (A, 0 \pm 2n\pi) \qquad \left(A, -\frac{\pi}{2} \pm 2n\pi\right)$$

CASE 2: Consider the square $EFGH$ of the diagram below. Its diagonals are each 2 units in length and they intersect at O. We shall now compute the length of the sides of this square. Justify each statement.

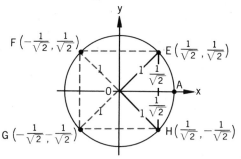

$$(EH)^2 + (GH)^2 = (GE)^2$$
$$(EH)^2 + (EH)^2 = (2)^2$$
$$2(EH)^2 = 4$$
$$(EH)^2 = 2$$

$$EH = \sqrt{2} = \frac{2}{\sqrt{2}}$$

Thus $EH = GH = \dfrac{2}{\sqrt{2}}$

Let T be the midpoint of EH; then $ET = TH = OT = \dfrac{1}{\sqrt{2}}$.

Consider again the square $EFGH$ but now inscribed in the unit circle and with each side parallel to an axis as in the diagram below.

The coordinates of the vertices of the square were determined from the preceding computations as given in the figure. What is the degree-measure of $\angle AOE$? Observe that the points E, F, G, and H bisect the arcs in their respective quadrants. Why?

Since the circumference is 2π, the terminal point of $\left(A, \dfrac{\pi}{4}\right)$ is E; the terminal points of the paths $\left(A, \dfrac{3\pi}{4}\right)$, $\left(A, \dfrac{5\pi}{4}\right)$, and $\left(A, \dfrac{7\pi}{4}\right)$ are F, G, and H respectively. Determine the terminal point and its x and y-coordinates for each of the following paths.

$$\left(A, \frac{3\pi}{4} \pm 2n\pi\right) \qquad \left(A, \frac{7\pi}{4} \pm 2n\pi\right) \qquad \left(A, \frac{5\pi}{4} \pm 2n\pi\right)$$

CASE 3: Consider the rectangle $JKLM$ of the adjoining diagram. Its diagonals are each 2 units in length and they intersect at O; also, $JM = KL = 1$. We shall now compute the lengths of the sides of this rectangle. Justify each statement.

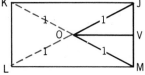

$OJ = OM = JM = 1$ and $\triangle JOM$ is equilateral and thus equiangular.

Let V be the midpoint of JM; then $\triangle JOV$ is a right triangle.

The degree-measures of angles JOV and OJV are 30 and 60, respectively.

$$(OV)^2 + (JV)^2 = (OJ)^2$$

$$(OV)^2 + \left(\frac{1}{2}\right)^2 = (1)^2$$

$$(OV)^2 + \frac{1}{4} = 1$$

$$(OV)^2 = \frac{3}{4}$$

$$OV = \frac{\sqrt{3}}{2}$$

Consider again the rectangle $JKLM$ but now inscribed in the unit circle and with each side parallel to an axis as in the diagram which follows:

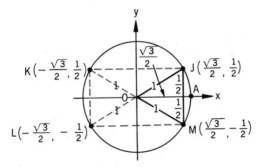

From the computations above, the coordinates of the vertices of the rectangle are determined as given in the figure. What is the degree-measure of $\angle AOJ$?

Now consider the rectangle $NPQR$ inscribed in the unit circle and with each side parallel to an axis as in the following diagram. Its diagonals are each 2 units in length and they intersect at O; $NP = QR = 1$. By an argument similar to the preceding one, the coordinates of the vertices of this rectangle are determined as given in the figure which follows. What is the degree-measure of angle AON?

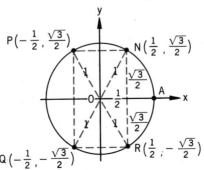

In case 3 observe that the points J, N, P, K, L, Q, R, and M are trisection points of the arcs in their respective quadrants. Why? Since the circumference of the unit circle is 2π, the terminal points of $\left(A, \dfrac{\pi}{6}\right)$ and $\left(A, \dfrac{\pi}{3}\right)$ are J and N, respectively, with coordinates $\left(\dfrac{\sqrt{3}}{2}, \dfrac{1}{2}\right)$ and $\left(\dfrac{1}{2}, \dfrac{\sqrt{3}}{2}\right)$, respectively. Determine the terminal point and its x and y-coordinates for each of these paths for this unit circle.

$$\left(A, \frac{2\pi}{3} \pm 2n\pi\right) \qquad \left(A, \frac{5\pi}{6} \pm 2n\pi\right) \qquad \left(A, -\frac{2\pi}{3} \pm 2n\pi\right)$$

$$\left(A, \frac{5\pi}{3} \pm 2n\pi\right) \qquad \left(A, -\frac{\pi}{6} \pm 2n\pi\right)$$

EXERCISES

1. For the *unit* circle of the adjoining figure: K, L, M, and N bisect the arcs in their respective quadrants.

a. Determine three values of θ for which each of the following is the terminal point of (A, θ).

   i. K *iv.* C

   ii. B *v.* M

   iii. N

b. Determine the x, y-coordinates of the following points.

   i. K *iii.* C *v.* N *vii.* L

   ii. B *iv.* M *vi.* A *viii.* D

c. Determine the terminal points of the following paths.

   i. $(A, 8\pi)$ *iv.* $\left(A, -\dfrac{9\pi}{4}\right)$

   ii. $(A, -7\pi)$

   iii. $\left(A, \dfrac{5\pi}{2}\right)$ *v.* $\left(A, -\dfrac{65\pi}{4}\right)$

                           vi. $(A, 321\pi)$

2. For the *unit* circle of the adjoining figure: E, F, G, H, Q, R, S, and T trisect the arcs in their respective quadrants.

a. Determine three values of θ for which each of the following is the terminal point of (A, θ).

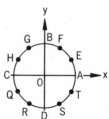

   i. F *v.* A

   ii. E *vi.* G

   iii. R *vii.* D

   iv. T

b. Determine the x and y-coordinates of the following points.

   i. F   *iii.* E   *v.* T   *vii.* S

   ii. H   *iv.* R   *vi.* G   *viii.* Q

c. Determine the terminal point of each path.

   i. $\left(A, \dfrac{7\pi}{3}\right)$ *iv.* $\left(A, \dfrac{23\pi}{6}\right)$

   ii. $\left(A, -\dfrac{17\pi}{6}\right)$ *v.* $\left(A, -\dfrac{29\pi}{6}\right)$

   iii. $(A, -12\pi)$ *vi.* $\left(A, -\dfrac{7\pi}{2}\right)$

THE WRAPPING FUNCTION, *W*

We have seen that for certain paths (A, θ) for the unit circle, we could determine the terminal point of the path and its x and y-coordinates. See figure 10.

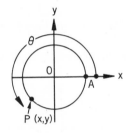

Fig. 10

We shall now introduce the *wrapping function*, W: For each real number θ, the wrapping function W takes us from θ to the ordered pair of real numbers (x, y) which are the coordinates of the terminal point of the path (A, θ). Study the following two examples.

Example: *i.* The terminal point of $\left(A, \dfrac{5\pi}{6}\right)$ is *H*. The coordinates of *H*

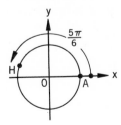

are $\left(-\dfrac{\sqrt{3}}{2}, \dfrac{1}{2}\right)$. Thus $W\left(\dfrac{5\pi}{6}\right) = \left(-\dfrac{\sqrt{3}}{2}, \dfrac{1}{2}\right)$.

Example:　　*ii.* The terminal point of $\left(A, -\dfrac{9\pi}{4} \right)$ is N. The coordinates of N are

$\left(\dfrac{1}{\sqrt{2}}, -\dfrac{1}{\sqrt{2}} \right)$. Thus, $W\left(-\dfrac{9\pi}{4} \right) = \left(\dfrac{1}{\sqrt{2}}, -\dfrac{1}{\sqrt{2}} \right)$.

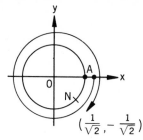

■　*Definition of Wrapping Function, W*　For each path (A, θ) for the unit circle specified by $x^2 + y^2 = 1$ and for each real number θ, if A is the point corresponding to $(1, 0)$, then the *wrapping function, W* is specified by

$$W(\theta) = (x, y)$$

where (x, y) are the coordinates of the terminal point of (A, θ).

Study figure 11 in regard to the preceding definition of W.

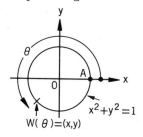

Fig. 11

EXERCISES

1.　Consider the *unit* circle of the adjoining figure. Determine the coordinates of each of the following points.

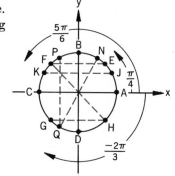

a. A	**h.** F	
b. E	**i.** D	
c. J	**j.** H	
d. B	**k.** N	
e. P	**l.** Q	
f. G	**m.** K	
g. C		

2.   Express each of the following as an ordered pair of real numbers (x, y).

a. $W\left(\dfrac{\pi}{6}\right)$

b. $W\left(\dfrac{3\pi}{4}\right)$

c. $W\left(\dfrac{4\pi}{3}\right)$

d. $W(\pi)$

e. $W\left(-\dfrac{\pi}{3}\right)$

f. $W\left(-\dfrac{\pi}{2}\right)$

g. $W(4\pi)$

h. $W(-5\pi)$

i. $W\left(\dfrac{17\pi}{6}\right)$

j. $W(0)$

k. $W\left(-\dfrac{7\pi}{3}\right)$

l. $W\left(\dfrac{7\pi}{2}\right)$

m. $W\left(-\dfrac{31\pi}{2}\right)$

n. $W\left(\dfrac{-17\pi}{6}\right)$

o. $W\left(\dfrac{5\pi}{4}\right)$

p. $W\left(\dfrac{13\pi}{4}\right)$

3.   True or false?

a. $W\left(\dfrac{\pi}{4}\right) = W\left(\dfrac{3\pi}{4}\right)$

b. $W\left(\dfrac{\pi}{4}\right) = W\left(-\dfrac{\pi}{4}\right)$

c. $W\left(\dfrac{3\pi}{4}\right) = W\left(-\dfrac{5\pi}{4}\right)$

d. $W\left(\dfrac{2\pi}{3}\right) = W\left(-\dfrac{4\pi}{3}\right)$

e. $W\left(\dfrac{\pi}{6}\right) = W\left(\dfrac{13\pi}{6}\right)$

f. $W(2\pi) = W(-2\pi)$

g. $W(3\pi) = W(-3\pi)$

h. $W\left(\dfrac{3\pi}{2}\right) = W\left(-\dfrac{3\pi}{2}\right)$

i. $W(\pi) = W(-\pi)$

j. $W(5\pi) = W(-5\pi)$

k. $\forall_\theta\ W(\theta) = W(-\theta)$

l. $W(\pi) = W(3\pi)$

m. $\forall_\theta\ W(\theta) = W(3\theta)$

n. $W(3\pi) = W(9\pi)$

o. $\forall_{k\epsilon N}\ W(k\pi) = W(k^2\pi)$

p. $(.8, .6)$ satisfies $x^2 + y^2 = 1$

q. $(1, 1)$ satisfies $x^2 + y^2 = 1$

r. $\left(\dfrac{5}{13}, \dfrac{12}{13}\right)$ satisfies $x^2 + y^2 = 1$

s. $\left(\dfrac{-4}{5}, \dfrac{3}{5}\right)$ satisfies $x^2 + y^2 = 1$

t. $(-.6, -.8)$ satisfies $x^2 + y^2 = 1$

u. $W\left(\dfrac{4\pi}{3}\right) = W\left(\dfrac{4\pi}{3} + 6\pi\right)$

v. $W\left(\dfrac{4\pi}{3}\right) = W\left(\dfrac{4\pi}{3} - 8\pi\right)$

w. $W(2\pi) = W(0)$

x. $\forall_\theta\ W(\theta) = W(\theta + 4\pi)$

y. $\forall_\theta\ W(\theta) = W(\theta - 6\pi)$

z. $\forall_\theta\ W(\theta) = W(\theta + \pi)$

a'. $\forall_\theta\forall_{k\epsilon I}\ W(\theta) = W(\theta + 2k\pi)$

PERIODIC FUNCTIONS

By now you have probably observed that the wrapping function W possesses an unusual property. This property is stated as follows:

$$\forall_\theta \, \forall_{k \in I} \quad W(\theta + 2k\pi) = W(\theta)$$

According to this property, each of the following is true.

$$W\left(\frac{\pi}{6} + 8\pi\right) = W\left(\frac{\pi}{6}\right) \qquad\qquad W\left(\frac{5\pi}{4} + 10\pi\right) = W\left(\frac{5\pi}{4}\right)$$

$$W\left(\frac{2\pi}{3} - 6\pi\right) = W\left(\frac{2\pi}{3}\right) \qquad\qquad W\left(\frac{-\pi}{2} - 4\pi\right) = W\left(\frac{-\pi}{2}\right)$$

A function that possesses this property is said to be a *periodic* function.

■   *Definition of Periodic Function*   For each function f and for all real numbers x and p, if $f(x) = f(x + p)$, then f is said to be a *periodic function* and p is called a *period* of f.

Is 4π a period of W? Is -6π? Is 3π? What is the least positive period of W?

EXERCISES

Each of the functions specified below is a periodic function. For each function, determine the least positive period of the function.

1. $\{\ldots, (2, 7), (2\frac{1}{2}, -3), (3, 7), (3\frac{1}{2}, -3), (4, 7), (4\frac{1}{2}, -3), \ldots\}$

2. $\{\ldots, (-7, \pi), (-3, \pi), (1, \pi), (5, \pi), (9, \pi), \ldots\}$

3. $\{\ldots, (3.2, \sqrt{2}), (3.3, \sqrt{3}), (3.4, \sqrt{2}), (3.5, \sqrt{3}), (3.6, \sqrt{2}), (3.7, \sqrt{3}), \ldots\}$

4. $f = \{(x, y) \mid y = 8 \text{ and } (x \text{ is an even integer or } x \text{ is a multiple of } 3)\}$

5.

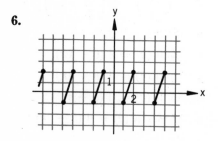

7.

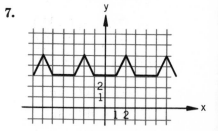

6.

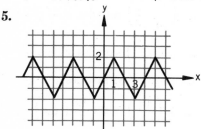

8.

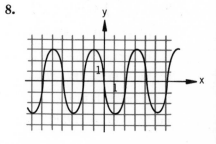

Other values of θ

For the most part, our examples and problems thus far have involved only values of θ which are either

$$\text{multiples of } \frac{\pi}{6}: \quad 0, \ \pm\frac{\pi}{6}, \ \pm\frac{\pi}{3}, \ \pm\frac{\pi}{2}, \ \pm\frac{2\pi}{3}, \ \pm\frac{5\pi}{6}, \ \pm\pi, \ \pm\frac{7\pi}{6}, \ \cdots$$

$$\text{or multiples of } \frac{\pi}{4}: \quad 0, \ \pm\frac{\pi}{4}, \ \pm\frac{\pi}{2}, \ \pm\frac{3\pi}{4}, \ \pm\pi, \ \pm\frac{5\pi}{4}, \ \pm\frac{3\pi}{2}, \ \pm\frac{7\pi}{4}, \ \cdots$$

Now, we shall briefly consider other values of θ. Observe the unit circle of figure 12 which has its center at the origin. Its circumference is 2π, a real number between 6.2 and 6.3. A number scale has been established along the circle. From this we can take approximate readings by perpendicular projections into the axes; the figure shows for $(A, 2.5)$ how one might approximate that $W(2.5)$ is $(-.8, .6)$, each coordinate correct to the nearest tenth.

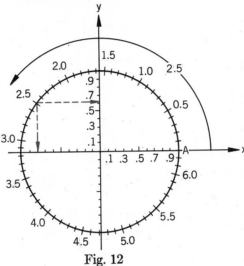

Fig. 12

EXERCISES

Using figure 12, express each of the following as an ordered pair of real numbers, each coordinate correct to the nearest tenth.

1. $W(0.8)$

2. $W(6.2)$

3. $W(1.1)$

4. $W(3.9)$

5. $W(2.4)$

6. $W(4.3)$

7. $W(4.7)$

8. $W(2.2)$

9. $W(5.2)$

10. $W(5.6)$

11. $W(3.6)$

12. $W(0.4)$

The cosine function

We shall now introduce another function, the *cosine* function: For each real number θ, if $W(\theta) = (x, y)$, then the *cosine of* θ is x. We abbreviate *the cosine of* θ as: $\cos(\theta)$. Study the following statements.

$$W\left(\frac{\pi}{6}\right) = \left(\frac{\sqrt{3}}{2}, \frac{1}{2}\right) \text{ and } \cos\left(\frac{\pi}{6}\right) = \frac{\sqrt{3}}{2}$$

$$W\left(\frac{2\pi}{3}\right) = \left(-\frac{1}{2}, \frac{\sqrt{3}}{2}\right) \text{ and } \cos\left(\frac{2\pi}{3}\right) = -\frac{1}{2}$$

$$W\left(\frac{7\pi}{4}\right) = \left(\frac{1}{\sqrt{2}}, -\frac{1}{\sqrt{2}}\right) \text{ and } \cos\left(\frac{7\pi}{4}\right) = \frac{1}{\sqrt{2}}$$

$$W(\pi) = (-1, 0) \text{ and } \cos(\pi) = -1$$

$$W\left(-\frac{\pi}{3}\right) = \left(\frac{1}{2}, -\frac{\sqrt{3}}{2}\right) \text{ and } \cos\left(-\frac{\pi}{3}\right) = \frac{1}{2}$$

$$W\left(-\frac{3\pi}{2}\right) = (0, 1) \text{ and } \cos\left(-\frac{3\pi}{2}\right) = 0$$

$$W\left(-\frac{5\pi}{6}\right) = \left(-\frac{\sqrt{3}}{2}, -\frac{1}{2}\right) \text{ and } \cos\left(-\frac{5\pi}{6}\right) = -\frac{\sqrt{3}}{2}$$

$$W\left(\frac{11\pi}{4}\right) = \left(-\frac{1}{\sqrt{2}}, \frac{1}{\sqrt{2}}\right) \text{ and } \cos\left(\frac{11\pi}{4}\right) = -\frac{1}{\sqrt{2}}$$

$$W(-9\pi) = (-1, 0) \text{ and } \cos(-9\pi) = -1$$

$$W(6\pi) = (1, 0) \text{ and } \cos(6\pi) = 1$$

■   *Definition of Cosine Function*   Cosine is $\{(\theta, x)\}$ for which $W(\theta) = (x, y)$.

From the definition of cosine and from figure 13, you should observe that the *domain* of cosine, the set of all values of θ, is the set of all real numbers.

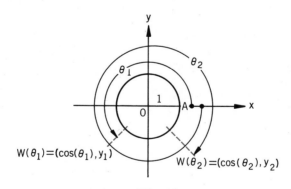

Fig. 13

You should also observe that the *range* of cosine, that is, the set of all values of $\cos(\theta)$, is $\{x \mid -1 \le x \le 1\}$.

EXERCISES

1. Determine the value of each of the following:

a. $\cos\left(\dfrac{\pi}{6}\right)$

b. $\cos\left(\dfrac{\pi}{4}\right)$

c. $\cos(-\pi)$

d. $\cos\left(\dfrac{5\pi}{6}\right)$

e. $\cos\left(\dfrac{5\pi}{4}\right)$

f. $\cos(2\pi)$

g. $\cos\left(-\dfrac{3\pi}{4}\right)$

h. $\cos\left(\dfrac{7\pi}{6}\right)$

i. $\cos\left(\dfrac{2\pi}{3}\right)$

j. $\cos\left(\dfrac{11\pi}{6}\right)$

k. $\cos\left(\dfrac{15\pi}{4}\right)$

l. $\cos\left(-\dfrac{\pi}{6}\right)$

m. $\cos\left(\dfrac{3\pi}{2}\right)$

n. $\cos(\pi)$

o. $\cos(-4\pi)$

p. $\cos(0)$

q. $\cos\left(\dfrac{\pi}{3}\right)$

r. $\cos\left(-\dfrac{13\pi}{4}\right)$

s. $\left[\cos\left(\dfrac{\pi}{4}\right)\right]^2$

t. $\left[\cos\left(\dfrac{5\pi}{6}\right)\right]^2$

u. $\left[\cos\left(\dfrac{2\pi}{3}\right)\right]^2$

v. $[\cos(-\pi)]^2$

2. True or false?

a. $\cos\left(\dfrac{\pi}{4}\right) = \cos\left(\dfrac{3\pi}{4}\right)$

b. $\cos\left(\dfrac{\pi}{4}\right) = \cos\left(-\dfrac{\pi}{4}\right)$

c. $\cos\left(\dfrac{3\pi}{4}\right) = \cos\left(\dfrac{5\pi}{4}\right)$

d. $\cos\left(\dfrac{2\pi}{3}\right) = \cos\left(\dfrac{4\pi}{3}\right)$

e. $\cos\left(\dfrac{2\pi}{3}\right) = \cos\left(-\dfrac{2\pi}{3}\right)$

f. $\cos\left(\dfrac{2\pi}{3}\right) = -\cos\left(\dfrac{2\pi}{3}\right)$

g. $\cos\left(\dfrac{2\pi}{3}\right) = \cos\left(-\dfrac{4\pi}{3}\right)$

h. $\cos\left(\dfrac{2\pi}{3}\right) = \cos\left(\dfrac{8\pi}{3}\right)$

i. $\cos\left(\dfrac{\pi}{6}\right) = \cos\left(\dfrac{5\pi}{6}\right)$

j. $\cos\left(\dfrac{\pi}{6}\right) = \cos\left(-\dfrac{\pi}{6}\right)$

k. $\cos\left(\dfrac{\pi}{6}\right) = \cos\left(\dfrac{11\pi}{6}\right)$

l. $\cos\left(\dfrac{\pi}{6}\right) = -\cos\left(\dfrac{5\pi}{6}\right)$

m. $\cos\left(\dfrac{\pi}{6}\right) = -\cos\left(\dfrac{\pi}{6}\right)$

n. $\cos\left(\dfrac{\pi}{6}\right) = \cos\left(-\dfrac{11\pi}{6}\right)$

o. $\cos\left(\dfrac{\pi}{6}\right) = \cos\left(\dfrac{13\pi}{6}\right)$

p. $\cos\left(\dfrac{\pi}{6}+\dfrac{\pi}{3}\right) = \cos\left(\dfrac{\pi}{6}\right)+\cos\left(\dfrac{\pi}{3}\right)$

q. $\cos\left(\dfrac{\pi}{4}+\dfrac{3\pi}{4}\right) = \cos\left(\dfrac{\pi}{4}\right)+\cos\left(\dfrac{3\pi}{4}\right)$

r. $\forall_\theta \forall_\alpha \cos(\theta+\alpha) = \cos(\theta)+\cos(\alpha)$

s. $\forall_\theta \ -1 \le \cos(\theta) \le 1$

t. $\forall_\theta \ 0 \le [\cos(\theta)]^2 \le 1$

u. $\forall_\theta \ \cos(\theta) = \cos(\theta + 3\pi)$

v. $\forall_\theta \ \cos(\theta) = \cos(\theta + 6\pi)$

w. $\forall_\theta \forall_{k\epsilon I} \ \cos(\theta) = \cos(\theta + 2k\pi)$

x. The cosine function is a periodic function.

y. 2π is a period of the cosine function.

z. $\forall_\theta \ 0 \le \cos(\theta) \le 1$

The sine function

We shall now introduce another function, the *sine* function: for each real number θ, if $W(\theta) = (x, y)$, then the *sine of* θ is y. We abbreviate *the sine of* θ as $\sin(\theta)$. Study the following statements.

$$W\left(\frac{\pi}{6}\right) = \left(\frac{\sqrt{3}}{2}, \frac{1}{2}\right) \text{ and } \sin\left(\frac{\pi}{6}\right) = \frac{1}{2}$$

$$W\left(\frac{2\pi}{3}\right) = \left(-\frac{1}{2}, \frac{\sqrt{3}}{2}\right) \text{ and } \sin\left(\frac{2\pi}{3}\right) = \frac{\sqrt{3}}{2}$$

$$W\left(\frac{7\pi}{4}\right) = \left(\frac{1}{\sqrt{2}}, -\frac{1}{\sqrt{2}}\right) \text{ and } \sin\left(\frac{7\pi}{4}\right) = -\frac{1}{\sqrt{2}}$$

$$W(\pi) = (-1, 0) \text{ and } \sin(\pi) = 0$$

$$W\left(-\frac{\pi}{3}\right) = \left(\frac{1}{2}, -\frac{\sqrt{3}}{2}\right) \text{ and } \sin\left(-\frac{\pi}{3}\right) = -\frac{\sqrt{3}}{2}$$

$$W\left(-\frac{3\pi}{2}\right) = (0, 1) \text{ and } \sin\left(-\frac{3\pi}{2}\right) = 1$$

$$W\left(-\frac{5\pi}{6}\right) = \left(-\frac{\sqrt{3}}{2}, -\frac{1}{2}\right) \text{ and } \sin\left(-\frac{5\pi}{6}\right) = -\frac{1}{2}$$

$$W\left(\frac{11\pi}{4}\right) = \left(-\frac{1}{\sqrt{2}}, \frac{1}{\sqrt{2}}\right) \text{ and } \sin\left(\frac{11\pi}{4}\right) = \frac{1}{\sqrt{2}}$$

$$W(-9\pi) = (-1, 0) \text{ and } \sin(-9\pi) = 0$$

$$W(6\pi) = (1, 0) \text{ and } \sin(6\pi) = 0$$

■   *Definition of Sine Function*   Sine is $\{(\theta, y)\}$ for which $W(\theta) = (x, y)$.

From the definition of sine and from figure 14, you should observe that the *domain* of sine, the set of all values of θ, is the set of all real numbers.

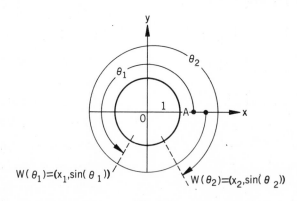

Fig. 14

You should also observe that the *range* of sine, that is, the set of all values of $\sin(\theta)$, is $\{y \mid -1 \le y \le 1\}$.

EXERCISES

1. Determine the value of each of the following:

a. $\sin\left(\dfrac{\pi}{6}\right)$

b. $\sin\left(\dfrac{\pi}{4}\right)$

c. $\sin(-\pi)$

d. $\sin\left(\dfrac{5\pi}{6}\right)$

e. $\sin\left(\dfrac{5\pi}{4}\right)$

f. $\sin(2\pi)$

g. $\sin\left(-\dfrac{3\pi}{4}\right)$

h. $\sin\left(\dfrac{7\pi}{6}\right)$

i. $\sin\left(\dfrac{2\pi}{3}\right)$

j. $\sin\left(\dfrac{11\pi}{6}\right)$

k. $\sin\left(\dfrac{15\pi}{4}\right)$

l. $\sin\left(-\dfrac{\pi}{6}\right)$

m. $\sin\left(\dfrac{3\pi}{2}\right)$

n. $\sin(\pi)$

o. $\sin(-4\pi)$

p. $\sin(0)$

q. $\sin\left(\dfrac{\pi}{3}\right)$

r. $\sin\left(-\dfrac{4\pi}{3}\right)$

s. $\left[\sin\left(\dfrac{\pi}{4}\right)\right]^2$

t. $\left[\sin\left(\dfrac{5\pi}{6}\right)\right]^2$

u. $\left[\sin\left(\dfrac{2\pi}{3}\right)\right]^2$

v. $[\sin(-\pi)]^2$

2. True or false?

a. $\sin\left(\dfrac{\pi}{4}\right) = \sin\left(\dfrac{3\pi}{4}\right)$

b. $\sin\left(\dfrac{\pi}{4}\right) = -\sin\left(\dfrac{\pi}{4}\right)$

c. $\sin\left(\dfrac{\pi}{4}\right) = -\sin\left(\dfrac{5\pi}{4}\right)$

d. $\sin\left(\dfrac{4\pi}{3}\right) = \sin\left(\dfrac{2\pi}{3}\right)$

e. $\sin\left(\dfrac{\pi}{6}\right) = \sin\left(-\dfrac{\pi}{6}\right)$

f. $\sin\left(\dfrac{\pi}{6}\right) = -\sin\left(\dfrac{\pi}{6}\right)$

g. $\sin\left(\dfrac{2\pi}{3}\right) = \sin\left(-\dfrac{4\pi}{3}\right)$

h. $\sin\left(\dfrac{5\pi}{6}\right) = \sin\left(\dfrac{17\pi}{6}\right)$

i. $\sin\left(\dfrac{2\pi}{3}\right) = \sin\left(\dfrac{\pi}{3}\right)$

j. $\sin\left(\dfrac{\pi}{6}\right) = \sin\left(\dfrac{5\pi}{6}\right)$

k. $\sin\left(\dfrac{\pi}{3}\right) = \sin\left(\dfrac{2\pi}{3}\right)$

l. $\sin\left(\dfrac{2\pi}{3}\right) = -\sin\left(-\dfrac{2\pi}{3}\right)$

m. $\sin\left(\dfrac{4\pi}{3}\right) = -\sin\left(-\dfrac{4\pi}{3}\right)$

n. $\sin\left(\dfrac{\pi}{2}\right) = \sin\left(-\dfrac{3\pi}{2}\right)$

o. $\sin\left(\dfrac{5\pi}{4}\right) = \sin\left(\dfrac{13\pi}{4}\right)$

p. $\sin\left(\dfrac{\pi}{6} + \dfrac{\pi}{3}\right) = \sin\left(\dfrac{\pi}{6}\right) + \sin\left(\dfrac{\pi}{3}\right)$

q. $\sin\left(\dfrac{\pi}{4} + \dfrac{3\pi}{4}\right) = \sin\left(\dfrac{\pi}{4}\right) + \sin\left(\dfrac{3\pi}{4}\right)$

r. $\forall_\theta \forall_\alpha \ \sin(\theta + \alpha) = \sin(\theta) + \sin(\alpha)$

s. $\forall_\theta \ -1 \leq \sin(\theta) \leq 1$

t. $\forall_\theta \ 0 \leq [\sin(\theta)]^2 \leq 1$

u. $\forall_\theta \ \sin(\theta) = \sin(\theta + 5\pi)$

v. $\forall_\theta \ \sin(\theta) = \sin(\theta + 8\pi)$

w. $\forall_\theta \forall_{k \in I} \ \sin(\theta) = \sin(\theta + 2k\pi)$

x. The sine function is a periodic function.

y. 2π is a period of the sine function.

z. $\forall_\theta \ 0 \leq \sin(\theta) \leq 1$

3. Simplify.

a. $\left(\dfrac{1}{\sqrt{2}}\right)^2$

b. $\left(\dfrac{\sqrt{3}}{2}\right)^2$

c. $\left(-\dfrac{1}{\sqrt{2}}\right)^2$

d. $\left(\dfrac{1}{\sqrt{2}}\right)^2 + \left(-\dfrac{1}{\sqrt{2}}\right)^2$

e. $\left(-\dfrac{\sqrt{3}}{2}\right)^2 + \left(-\dfrac{1}{2}\right)^2$

f. $\left(\dfrac{1}{\sqrt{2}}\right) \div \left(\dfrac{1}{\sqrt{2}}\right)$

g. $\left(\dfrac{\sqrt{3}}{2}\right) \div \left(\dfrac{1}{2}\right)$

h. $\left(\dfrac{1}{2}\right) \div \left(\dfrac{\sqrt{3}}{2}\right)$

i. $\left[\sin\left(\dfrac{\pi}{6}\right)\right]^2 + \left[\cos\left(\dfrac{\pi}{6}\right)\right]^2$

j. $\left[\sin\left(\dfrac{3\pi}{4}\right)\right]^2 + \left[\cos\left(\dfrac{3\pi}{4}\right)\right]^2$

k. $\left[\cos\left(-\dfrac{2\pi}{3}\right)\right]^2 + \left[\cos\left(\dfrac{\pi}{6}\right)\right]^2$

l. $\left[\sin\left(\dfrac{\pi}{6}\right)\right] \div \left[\cos\left(\dfrac{\pi}{6}\right)\right]$

m. $\left[\sin\left(-\dfrac{2\pi}{3}\right)\right] \div \left[\cos\left(-\dfrac{2\pi}{3}\right)\right]$

n. $\left[\sin\left(\dfrac{5\pi}{4}\right)\right] \div \left[\cos\left(\dfrac{5\pi}{4}\right)\right]$

o. $[\sin(\pi)] \div [\cos(\pi)]$

p. $[\cos(\pi)] \div [\sin(\pi)]$

The tangent function

We now introduce another function, the *tangent* function. For each real number θ, if $W(\theta) = (x, y)$, then the *tangent* of θ is $\dfrac{y}{x}$ ($x \neq 0$). We abbreviate *the tangent of θ* as: $\tan(\theta)$. Study the following statements.

$W\left(\dfrac{\pi}{6}\right) = \left(\dfrac{\sqrt{3}}{2}, \dfrac{1}{2}\right)$ and $\tan\left(\dfrac{\pi}{6}\right) = \left(\dfrac{1}{2}\right) \div \left(\dfrac{\sqrt{3}}{2}\right) = \dfrac{1}{\sqrt{3}}$

$W\left(\dfrac{2\pi}{3}\right) = \left(-\dfrac{1}{2}, \dfrac{\sqrt{3}}{2}\right)$ and $\tan\left(\dfrac{2\pi}{3}\right) = \left(\dfrac{\sqrt{3}}{2}\right) \div \left(-\dfrac{1}{2}\right) = -\sqrt{3}$

$W\left(\dfrac{7\pi}{4}\right) = \left(\dfrac{1}{\sqrt{2}}, -\dfrac{1}{\sqrt{2}}\right)$ and $\tan\left(\dfrac{7\pi}{4}\right) = -1$

$W(\pi) = (-1, 0)$ and $\tan(\pi) = 0$

$W\left(-\dfrac{\pi}{3}\right) = \left(\dfrac{1}{2}, -\dfrac{\sqrt{3}}{2}\right)$ and $\tan\left(-\dfrac{\pi}{3}\right) = -\sqrt{3}$

$W\left(-\dfrac{3\pi}{2}\right) = (0, 1)$ and $\tan\left(-\dfrac{3\pi}{2}\right)$ is undefined, since $\dfrac{1}{0}$ is undefined.

$W\left(-\dfrac{5\pi}{6}\right) = \left(-\dfrac{\sqrt{3}}{2}, -\dfrac{1}{2}\right)$ and $\tan\left(-\dfrac{5\pi}{6}\right) = \dfrac{1}{\sqrt{3}}$

$W\left(\dfrac{11\pi}{4}\right) = \left(-\dfrac{1}{\sqrt{2}}, \dfrac{1}{\sqrt{2}}\right)$ and $\tan\left(\dfrac{11\pi}{4}\right) = -1$

$W(-9\pi) = (-1, 0)$ and $\tan(-9\pi) = 0$

$W\left(\dfrac{5\pi}{2}\right) = (0, 1)$ and $\tan\left(\dfrac{5\pi}{2}\right)$ is undefined.

■ *Definition of Tangent Function*   *Tangent* is $\left\{\left(\theta, \frac{y}{x}\right)\right\}$ for which $W(\theta) = (x, y)$
and $x \neq 0$.

From the definition of tangent and from figure 11 on page 416, you should observe that the *domain* of tangent, the set of values of θ, is the set of all real numbers except for members of $\left\{\frac{\pi}{2} \pm n\pi\right\}$. Why are these values of θ not included in the domain of tangent?

EXERCISES

1. Determine the value if the symbol is defined.

   a. $\tan\left(\dfrac{\pi}{6}\right)$

   b. $\tan\left(\dfrac{\pi}{4}\right)$

   c. $\tan(-\pi)$

   d. $\tan\left(\dfrac{5\pi}{6}\right)$

   e. $\tan\left(\dfrac{2\pi}{3}\right)$

   f. $\tan\left(\dfrac{5\pi}{4}\right)$

   g. $\tan(2\pi)$

   h. $\tan\left(-\dfrac{3\pi}{4}\right)$

   i. $\tan\left(\dfrac{7\pi}{6}\right)$

   j. $\tan\left(\dfrac{7\pi}{3}\right)$

   k. $\tan\left(\dfrac{11\pi}{6}\right)$

   l. $\tan\left(\dfrac{15\pi}{4}\right)$

   m. $\tan\left(-\dfrac{\pi}{6}\right)$

   n. $\tan\left(\dfrac{3\pi}{2}\right)$

   o. $\tan(\pi)$

   p. $\tan(-4\pi)$

   q. $\tan\left(-\dfrac{5\pi}{2}\right)$

   r. $\tan\left(\dfrac{7\pi}{2}\right)$

   s. $\tan\left(\dfrac{\pi}{3}\right)$

   t. $\tan\left(-\dfrac{4\pi}{3}\right)$

2. True or false?

   a. $\tan\left(\dfrac{\pi}{4}\right) = \tan\left(\dfrac{3\pi}{4}\right)$

   b. $\tan\left(\dfrac{\pi}{4}\right) = -\tan\left(\dfrac{3\pi}{4}\right)$

   c. $\tan\left(\dfrac{\pi}{4}\right) = \tan\left(-\dfrac{3\pi}{4}\right)$

   d. $\tan\left(\dfrac{\pi}{6}\right) = \tan\left(\dfrac{7\pi}{6}\right)$

   e. $\tan\left(\dfrac{2\pi}{3}\right) = \tan\left(\dfrac{5\pi}{3}\right)$

   f. $\tan\left(\dfrac{4\pi}{3}\right) = \tan\left(\dfrac{5\pi}{3}\right)$

   g. $\tan\left(\dfrac{4\pi}{3}\right) = -\tan\left(\dfrac{5\pi}{3}\right)$

   h. $\tan\left(\dfrac{\pi}{3}\right) = \tan\left(\dfrac{\pi}{3} + \pi\right)$

   i. $\tan\left(\dfrac{3\pi}{4}\right) = \tan\left(\dfrac{3\pi}{4} + \pi\right)$

   j. $\tan\left(\dfrac{7\pi}{6}\right) = \tan\left(\dfrac{7\pi}{6} + 3\pi\right)$

   k. $\tan\left(\dfrac{5\pi}{3}\right) = \tan\left(\dfrac{5\pi}{3} - \pi\right)$

   l. $\tan(\pi) = 0$

   m. $\tan(0) = 0$

   n. $\tan(-5\pi) = 0$

   o. $\tan(6\pi) = 0$

   p. $\forall_{k \epsilon I} \ \tan(k\pi) = 0$

q. $\forall_{k\epsilon I} \ \tan\left(\dfrac{\pi}{2} + k\pi\right) = 0$

r. $\dfrac{\sin\left(\dfrac{3\pi}{4}\right)}{\cos\left(\dfrac{3\pi}{4}\right)} = \tan\left(\dfrac{3\pi}{4}\right)$

s. $\dfrac{\sin\left(\dfrac{4\pi}{3}\right)}{\cos\left(\dfrac{4\pi}{3}\right)} = \tan\left(\dfrac{4\pi}{3}\right)$

t. $\forall_\theta$, if $\cos(\theta) \neq 0$, then
$\dfrac{\sin(\theta)}{\cos(\theta)} = \tan(\theta).$

u. $\forall_\theta$, if $\cos(\theta) \neq 0$, then $-1 \leq \tan(\theta) \leq 1$.

v. $\forall_\theta \forall_{k\epsilon I}$, if $\theta \epsilon \left\{\dfrac{\pi}{2} + k\pi\right\}$, then $\tan(\theta)$ is undefined.

w. $\forall_{k\epsilon I} \ \tan\left(\dfrac{\pi}{4} + k\pi\right) = 1$

x. $\forall_\theta \forall_{k\epsilon I}$, if $\cos(\theta) \neq 0$, then $\tan(\theta) = \tan(\theta + 2k\pi)$.

y. The tangent function is a periodic function.

z. 2π is a period of the tangent function.

TRIGONOMETRIC EQUATIONS

Here are six examples of *trigonometric equations*.

$$2 \cdot \sin(\theta) = 1$$
$$5 + 5 \cdot \cos(\theta) = 3 \cdot \cos(\theta) + 4$$
$$4 \cdot \cos^2(\theta) = 3 \quad [\text{NOTE}: \cos^2(\theta) \text{ means } (\cos(\theta))^2]$$
$$2 \cdot \sin^2(\theta) + \sin(\theta) = 1$$
$$2 \cdot \cos(2\theta) = -1$$
$$\tan^2(\theta) = 3$$

To solve a trigonometric equation, such as one of the above, means to find all values of θ which satisfy the equation. Consider the following examples as we explore various techniques for solving trigonometric equations.

Example: *i.* Solve $2 \cdot \sin(\theta) = 1$.

$$\sin(\theta) = \tfrac{1}{2}$$

From our previous work with the unit circle, we can readily determine two points of the circle for which $y = \sin(\theta) = \tfrac{1}{2}$.

From the adjoining diagram we find two values of θ between 0 and 2π, namely $\dfrac{\pi}{6}$ and $\dfrac{5\pi}{6}$, for which $\sin(\theta) = \tfrac{1}{2}$. Hence, the solution set is

$$\left\{\dfrac{\pi}{6} \pm 2n\pi\right\} \cup \left\{\dfrac{5\pi}{6} \pm 2n\pi\right\}$$

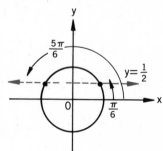

Example: ii. Solve $4 \cos^2(\theta) = 3$ and $0 \leq \theta < 2\pi$.

$$4 \cos^2(\theta) = 3$$

$$\cos^2(\theta) = \frac{3}{4}$$

$$\cos(\theta) = \frac{\sqrt{3}}{2} \text{ or } \cos(\theta) = -\frac{\sqrt{3}}{2}$$

From our previous work with the unit circle, we can readily determine four points for which $\left(x = \cos(\theta) = \dfrac{\sqrt{3}}{2} \right)$ or $\left(x = \cos(\theta) = -\dfrac{\sqrt{3}}{2} \right)$.

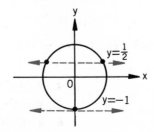

The four values of θ are $\dfrac{\pi}{6}, \dfrac{5\pi}{6}, \dfrac{7\pi}{6},$ and $\dfrac{11\pi}{6}.$

Example: iii. Solve $2 \sin^2(\theta) + \sin(\theta) = 1$ and $0 \leq \theta < 2\pi$.

$$2 \sin^2(\theta) + \sin(\theta) = 1$$

$$2 \sin^2(\theta) + \sin(\theta) - 1 = 0$$

$$(2 \sin(\theta) - 1)(\sin(\theta) + 1) = 0$$

$$2 \sin(\theta) - 1 = 0 \text{ or } \sin(\theta) + 1 = 0$$

If $2 \sin(\theta) - 1 = 0$, then by the first example we know that two solutions are $\dfrac{\pi}{6}$ and $\dfrac{5\pi}{6}$; and if $\sin(\theta) + 1 = 0$, then $\sin(\theta) = y = -1$ and $\dfrac{3\pi}{2}$ is also a solution. Hence, the solution set is $\left\{ \dfrac{\pi}{6}, \dfrac{5\pi}{6}, \dfrac{3\pi}{2} \right\}.$

Example: *iv.* Solve $2 \cdot \cos(2\theta) = -1$ and $0 \le \theta < 2\pi$.

$$2 \cdot \cos(2\theta) = -1$$
$$\cos(2\theta) = -\tfrac{1}{2}$$

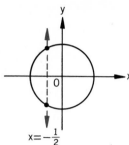

$x = -\tfrac{1}{2}$

Since $\cos(2\theta) = x = -\tfrac{1}{2}$, we can readily determine that 2θ must belong to $\left\{ \dfrac{2\pi}{3}, \dfrac{2\pi}{3} + 2\pi, \dfrac{2\pi}{3} + 4\pi, \ldots \right\}$ or to $\left\{ \dfrac{4\pi}{3}, \dfrac{4\pi}{3} + 2\pi, \dfrac{4\pi}{3} + 4\pi, \ldots \right\}$.

Hence, values of θ in these sets for which $0 \le \theta < 2\pi$ are $\dfrac{\pi}{3}, \dfrac{\pi}{3} + \pi, \dfrac{2\pi}{3}$, and $\dfrac{2\pi}{3} + \pi$.

Example: *v.* Solve $\tan^2(\theta) = 3$ and $0 \le \theta < 2\pi$.

$$\tan^2(\theta) = 3$$
$$\tan(\theta) = \sqrt{3} \ \text{ or } \ \tan(\theta) = -\sqrt{3}$$

Verify that, at each of the four points marked in the diagram below, either $\tan(\theta) = \dfrac{y}{x} = \sqrt{3}$ or $\tan(\theta) = \dfrac{y}{x} = -\sqrt{3}$.

Hence, the solution set is $\left\{ \dfrac{\pi}{3}, \dfrac{2\pi}{3}, \dfrac{4\pi}{3}, \dfrac{5\pi}{3} \right\}$.

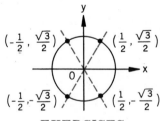

EXERCISES

Find all values of θ which satisfy each of the following equations and such that $0 \le \theta < 2\pi$.

1. $\tan(\theta) = 1$
2. $\sin(\theta) = 1$
3. $\cos(\theta) = -1$

4. $2 \cdot \cos^2(\theta) = 1$
5. $\sin(2\theta) = \tfrac{1}{2}$
6. $4 \cdot \sin(\theta) + 4 = 3 \cdot \sin(\theta) + 3$

7. $\tan^2(\theta) = 1$
8. $4 \cdot \sin(\theta) + \sqrt{12} = 0$
9. $5 + 5 \cdot \cos(\theta) = 3 \cdot \cos(\theta) + 4$
10. $\dfrac{1}{\sin(\theta)} - 2 = 0$
11. $3 \cdot \tan^2(\theta) - 1 = 0$
12. $4 \cdot \cos^2(\theta) = 1$
13. $2 \cdot \sin^2(\theta) + \sin(\theta) = 0$
14. $\tan^2(\theta) - \tan(\theta) = 0$
15. $2 \cdot \sin^2(\theta) + 7 \cdot \sin(\theta) - 4 = 0$
16. $\sin(\theta) \cdot \cos(\theta) + \sin(\theta) +$
$\cos(\theta) + 1 = 0$

17. $\tan(2\theta) = 1$
18. $\sin^2(\theta) - \cos^2(\theta) = 0$
19. $\sin^2(\theta) + \tfrac{1}{2} = \cos^2(\theta)$
   [HINT: $\forall_\theta \ \sin^2(\theta) + \cos^2(\theta) = 1$]
20. $\sin(\theta) = 0$
21. $\sin^2(\theta) = 1$
22. $\sin(\theta) + \cos(\theta) = 0$
23. $\dfrac{1}{\cos(\theta)} = 2$
24. $\sin^2(\theta) + \cos^2(\theta) = 1$
25. $\sin^2(\theta) + \cos^2(\theta) = 0$
26. $\sin^3(\theta) = -1$

Two values from one value

The first function that we introduced was the wrapping function, W: for each path (A, θ) for the *unit* circle and for each real number θ, $W(\theta) = (x, y)$, where x and y are the coordinates of the terminal point of the path. See figure 15.

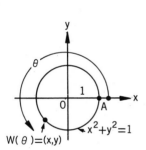

Fig. 15

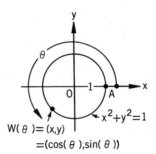

Fig. 16

Then, we introduced two functions, cosine and sine: $\cos(\theta) = x$ and $\sin(\theta) = y$. See figure 16.

Now, with the following three facts

$$\text{an equation of the } unit \text{ circle is } x^2 + y^2 = 1$$
$$\cos(\theta) = x$$
$$\sin(\theta) = y$$

and the substitution property, it follows that

$$\forall_\theta \ \cos^2(\theta) + \sin^2(\theta) = 1$$

Furthermore, since $\tan(\theta) = \dfrac{y}{x}$, it follows that

$$\forall_\theta, \text{ if } \cos(\theta) \neq 0, \text{ then } \frac{\sin(\theta)}{\cos(\theta)} = \tan(\theta)$$

These conclusions may be used in solving problems of the type illustrated by the following examples. Justify each step.

Example: i.   Suppose $\cos(\theta) = -\dfrac{3}{5}$ and $\dfrac{\pi}{2} < \theta < \pi$; determine $\sin(\theta)$ and $\tan(\theta)$.

Since $x^2 + y^2 = 1$ and $\cos(\theta) = x = -\dfrac{3}{5}$, it follows that

$$\left(-\frac{3}{5}\right)^2 + y^2 = 1$$

$$\frac{9}{25} + y^2 = 1$$

$$y^2 = \frac{16}{25}$$

and hence $\qquad\qquad y = \dfrac{4}{5}$ or $y = -\dfrac{4}{5}$

Since $\dfrac{\pi}{2} < \theta < \pi$, $y = \dfrac{4}{5}$. Why is $y \neq -\dfrac{4}{5}$?

Now, $\dfrac{y}{x} = \tan(\theta) = \dfrac{\sin(\theta)}{\cos(\theta)} = \left(\dfrac{4}{5}\right) \div \left(-\dfrac{3}{5}\right) = -\dfrac{4}{3}$.

Thus, if $\cos(\theta) = -\dfrac{3}{5}$ and $\dfrac{\pi}{2} < \theta < \pi$, then $\sin(\theta) = \dfrac{4}{5}$ and $\tan(\theta) = -\dfrac{4}{3}$.

Example: ii.   Suppose $\sin(\theta) = -\dfrac{2}{5}$ and $\dfrac{3\pi}{2} < \theta < 2\pi$; determine $\cos(\theta)$ and $\tan(\theta)$.

Since $x^2 + y^2 = 1$ and $\sin(\theta) = y = -\dfrac{2}{5}$, it follows that

$$x^2 + \left(-\frac{2}{5}\right)^2 = 1$$

$$x^2 + \frac{4}{25} = 1$$

$$x^2 = \frac{21}{25}$$

and hence $\qquad\qquad x = \dfrac{\sqrt{21}}{5}$ or $x = -\dfrac{\sqrt{21}}{5}$

Since $\dfrac{3\pi}{2} < \theta < 2\pi$, $x = \dfrac{\sqrt{21}}{5}$. Why is $x \neq -\dfrac{\sqrt{21}}{5}$?

Now, $\dfrac{y}{x} = \tan(\theta) = \dfrac{\sin(\theta)}{\cos(\theta)} = \left(-\dfrac{2}{5}\right) \div \left(\dfrac{\sqrt{21}}{5}\right) = -\dfrac{2}{\sqrt{21}}$.

Thus, if $\sin(\theta) = -\dfrac{2}{5}$ and $\dfrac{3\pi}{2} < \theta < 2\pi$, then $\cos(\theta) = \dfrac{\sqrt{21}}{5}$ and $\tan(\theta) = -\dfrac{2}{\sqrt{21}}$.

Example: **iii.** Suppose $\tan(\theta) = \dfrac{\sqrt{5}}{6}$ and $\pi < \theta < \dfrac{3\pi}{2}$; determine $\cos(\theta)$ and $\sin(\theta)$.

Since $\tan(\theta) = \dfrac{y}{x} = \dfrac{\sqrt{5}}{6}$, it follows that $y = \dfrac{\sqrt{5}}{6}x$;

and since
$$x^2 + y^2 = 1$$

it follows that
$$x^2 + \left(\frac{\sqrt{5}}{6}x \right)^2 = 1$$

$$x^2 + \frac{5x^2}{36} = 1$$

$$\frac{41}{36}x^2 = 1$$

$$x^2 = \frac{36}{41}$$

and hence
$$x = \frac{6}{\sqrt{41}} \text{ or } x = -\frac{6}{\sqrt{41}}$$

Since $\pi < \theta < \dfrac{3\pi}{2}$, $x = -\dfrac{6}{\sqrt{41}}$. Why is $x \neq \dfrac{6}{\sqrt{41}}$?

Thus, since $x = \cos(\theta) = -\dfrac{6}{\sqrt{41}}$ and $y = \dfrac{\sqrt{5}}{6}x = \sin(\theta)$,

it follows that $\sin(\theta) = \dfrac{\sqrt{5}}{6} \cdot \left(-\dfrac{6}{\sqrt{41}} \right) = -\dfrac{\sqrt{5}}{\sqrt{41}}$.

So, if $\tan(\theta) = \dfrac{\sqrt{5}}{6}$ and $\pi < \theta < \dfrac{3\pi}{2}$, then $\sin(\theta) = -\dfrac{\sqrt{5}}{\sqrt{41}}$

and $\cos(\theta) = -\dfrac{6}{\sqrt{41}}$.

EXERCISES

1. For each condition on θ, where $W(\theta) = (x, y)$, state whether $(x > 0$ or $x < 0)$ and whether $(y > 0$ or $y < 0)$. The adjoining diagram may be helpful to you.

a. $0 < \theta < \dfrac{\pi}{2}$

b. $\dfrac{\pi}{2} < \theta < \pi$

c. $\pi < \theta < \dfrac{3\pi}{2}$

d. $\dfrac{3\pi}{2} < \theta < 2\pi$

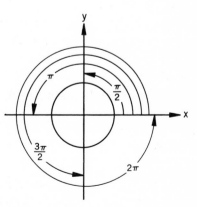

2. Use the diagram of problem **1,** if you need it, in solving the following problems. Determine which of $\cos(\theta)$, $\sin(\theta)$, and $\tan(\theta)$ are positive for each value of θ such that

a. $0 < \theta < \dfrac{\pi}{2}$

c. $\pi < \theta < \dfrac{3\pi}{2}$

b. $\dfrac{\pi}{2} < \theta < \pi$

d. $\dfrac{3\pi}{2} < \theta < 2\pi$

3. For each given set of conditions, determine $\cos(\theta)$, $\sin(\theta)$, and $\tan(\theta)$.

a. $\cos(\theta) = \dfrac{5}{13}$ and $\dfrac{3\pi}{2} < \theta < 2\pi$

f. $\tan(\theta) = -\dfrac{12}{5}$ and $\dfrac{3\pi}{2} < \theta < 2\pi$

b. $\sin(\theta) = .8$ and $\dfrac{\pi}{2} < \theta < \pi$

g. $\cos(\theta) = \dfrac{\sqrt{7}}{4}$ and $0 < \theta < \dfrac{\pi}{2}$

c. $\tan(\theta) = \dfrac{3}{4}$ and $\pi < \theta < \dfrac{3\pi}{2}$

h. $\sin(\theta) = -\dfrac{\sqrt{6}}{3}$ and $\pi < \theta < \dfrac{3\pi}{2}$

d. $\cos(\theta) = -\dfrac{5}{8}$ and $\dfrac{\pi}{2} < \theta < \pi$

i. $\tan(\theta) = -2$ and $\dfrac{\pi}{2} < \theta < \pi$

e. $\sin(\theta) = -\dfrac{4}{9}$ and $\pi < \theta < \dfrac{3\pi}{2}$

j. $\cos(\theta) = \dfrac{5}{\sqrt{30}}$ and $\dfrac{3\pi}{2} < \theta < 2\pi$

THE BASIC FORMULA

We shall now recall the Distance Formula and its use in the real number plane. In Chapter 5 we found that the distance between any two points on the plane could be determined as shown in the following example.

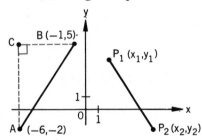

Fig. 17

The distance AB between $A(-6, -2)$ and $B(-1, 5)$ in figure 17 is

$$AB = \sqrt{(BC)^2 + (AC)^2}$$
$$= \sqrt{[-1 - (-6)]^2 + [5 - (-2)]^2}$$
$$= \sqrt{5^2 + 7^2}$$
$$= \sqrt{25 + 49}$$
$$= \sqrt{74}$$

where $C(-6, 5)$ is the vertex of the right angle of right triangle ABC. And in general, the distance between any two points of the plane, $P_1(x_1, y_1)$ and $P_2(x_2, y_2)$, is determined by the Distance Formula

$$P_1 P_2 = \sqrt{(x_1 - x_2)^2 + (y_1 - y_2)^2}$$

We shall now use the Distance Formula to develop a formula for $\cos(\theta_1 - \theta_2)$, where θ_1 and θ_2 is any pair of real numbers. Then several more formulas will be derived from this formula. In figure 18, consider the unit circle and the four paths (A, θ_1), (A, θ_2), (D, θ_3), and (A, θ_3).

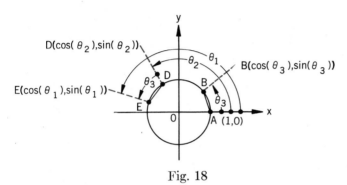

Fig. 18

Observe that

  B is the terminal point of (A, θ_3)

  D is the terminal point of (A, θ_2) and also the initial point of (D, θ_3)

  E is the terminal point of (A, θ_1) and of (D, θ_3)

  $\theta_1 = \theta_2 + \theta_3$

  the coordinates of A, B, D, and E are as given in figure 18

  the chords $\overline{DE}$ and $\overline{AB}$ have the same length

Therefore, since $AB = DE$, it follows that

$$[1 - \cos(\theta_3)]^2 + [0 - \sin(\theta_3)]^2 = [\cos(\theta_1) - \cos(\theta_2)]^2 + [\sin(\theta_1) - \sin(\theta_2)]^2$$

$$1 - 2 \cdot \cos(\theta_3) + \cos^2(\theta_3) + \sin^2(\theta_3) = \cos^2(\theta_1) - 2 \cdot \cos(\theta_1) \cdot \cos(\theta_2)$$
$$+ \cos^2(\theta_2) + \sin^2(\theta_1) - 2 \cdot \sin(\theta_1) \cdot \sin(\theta_2) + \sin^2(\theta_2)$$

$$1 - 2 \cdot \cos(\theta_3) + 1 = 1 - 2 \cdot \cos(\theta_1) \cdot \cos(\theta_2) + 1 - 2 \cdot \sin(\theta_1) \cdot \sin(\theta_2)$$

$$2 - 2 \cdot \cos(\theta_3) = 2 - 2 \cdot \cos(\theta_1) \cdot \cos(\theta_2) - 2 \cdot \sin(\theta_1) \cdot \sin(\theta_2)$$

$$\cos(\theta_3) = \cos(\theta_1) \cdot \cos(\theta_2) + \sin(\theta_1) \cdot \sin(\theta_2)$$

Since $\theta_1 = \theta_2 + \theta_3$, it follows that $\theta_3 = \theta_1 - \theta_2$.

Replacing θ_3 by $\theta_1 - \theta_2$ in the last equation above, we obtain

$$\cos(\theta_1 - \theta_2) = \cos(\theta_1) \cdot \cos(\theta_2) + \sin(\theta_1) \cdot \sin(\theta_2)$$

This last equation will be called our *Basic Formula*.

Theorem 1 (Basic Formula)   For all real numbers θ_1 and θ_2,

$$\cos(\theta_1 - \theta_2) = \cos(\theta_1) \cdot \cos(\theta_2) + \sin(\theta_1) \cdot \sin(\theta_2)$$

We shall now verify one instance of the Basic Formula.

Suppose $\theta_1 = \dfrac{7\pi}{3}$ and $\theta_2 = \dfrac{\pi}{6}$; by computing we shall verify that

$$\cos\left(\frac{7\pi}{3} - \frac{\pi}{6}\right) = \cos\left(\frac{7\pi}{3}\right) \cdot \cos\left(\frac{\pi}{6}\right) + \sin\left(\frac{7\pi}{3}\right) \cdot \sin\left(\frac{\pi}{6}\right)$$

$$= \cos\left(\frac{14\pi}{6} - \frac{\pi}{6}\right) \qquad = \cos\left(\frac{\pi}{3} + 2\pi\right) \cdot \cos\left(\frac{\pi}{6}\right) + \sin\left(\frac{\pi}{3} + 2\pi\right) \cdot \sin\left(\frac{\pi}{6}\right)$$

$$= \cos\left(\frac{13\pi}{6}\right) \qquad = \cos\left(\frac{\pi}{3}\right) \cdot \cos\left(\frac{\pi}{6}\right) + \sin\left(\frac{\pi}{3}\right) \cdot \sin\left(\frac{\pi}{6}\right)$$

$$= \cos\left(\frac{\pi}{6} + 2\pi\right) \qquad = \frac{1}{2} \cdot \frac{\sqrt{3}}{2} + \frac{\sqrt{3}}{2} \cdot \frac{1}{2}$$

$$= \cos\left(\frac{\pi}{6}\right) \qquad = \frac{\sqrt{3}}{4} + \frac{\sqrt{3}}{4}$$

$$= \frac{\sqrt{3}}{2} \qquad = \frac{\sqrt{3}}{2}$$

Since we have shown that

$$\cos\left(\frac{7\pi}{3} - \frac{\pi}{6}\right) \text{ and } \cos\left(\frac{7\pi}{3}\right) \cdot \cos\left(\frac{\pi}{6}\right) + \sin\left(\frac{7\pi}{3}\right) \cdot \sin\left(\frac{\pi}{6}\right)$$

each represent the same real number, we have verified one instance of the Basic Formula.

EXERCISES

By computing, verify instances of the Basic Formula for the given values of θ_1 and θ_2.

1. $\dfrac{7\pi}{4}$ for θ_1; $\dfrac{\pi}{2}$ for θ_2

2. $\dfrac{2\pi}{3}$ for θ_1; $\dfrac{\pi}{6}$ for θ_2

3. $\dfrac{4\pi}{3}$ for θ_1; $-\dfrac{5\pi}{6}$ for θ_2

4. $\dfrac{7\pi}{6}$ for θ_1; 0 for θ_2

5. 0 for θ_1; $\dfrac{7\pi}{6}$ for θ_2

6. π for θ_1; 3π for θ_2

7. $-\dfrac{3\pi}{4}$ for θ_1; $-\pi$ for θ_2

8. 2π for θ_1; -3π for θ_2

TRIGONOMETRIC THEOREMS

From the *Basic Formula*

$$\forall_{\theta_1} \forall_{\theta_2} \quad \cos(\theta_1 - \theta_2) = \cos(\theta_1) \cdot \cos(\theta_2) + \sin(\theta_1) \cdot \sin(\theta_2)$$

We shall now derive several other formulas. Supply reasons where necessary.

Theorem 2 $\forall_\theta \cos(-\theta) = \cos(\theta)$

Proof Suppose $\theta_1 = 0$; then the Basic Formula tells us that

$$\cos(0 - \theta_2) = \cos(0) \cdot \cos(\theta_2) + \sin(0) \cdot \sin(\theta_2)$$
$$\cos(-\theta_2) = 1 \cdot \cos(\theta_2) + 0 \cdot \sin(\theta_2)$$
$$\cos(-\theta_2) = \cos(\theta_2)$$

Theorem 3 $\forall_\theta \cos\left(\dfrac{\pi}{2} - \theta\right) = \sin(\theta)$

Proof Suppose $\theta_1 = \dfrac{\pi}{2}$; then, according to the Basic Formula

$$\cos\left(\frac{\pi}{2} - \theta_2\right) = \cos\left(\frac{\pi}{2}\right) \cdot \cos(\theta_2) + \sin\left(\frac{\pi}{2}\right) \cdot \sin(\theta_2)$$
$$= 0 \cdot \cos(\theta_2) + 1 \cdot \sin(\theta_2)$$
$$= \sin(\theta_2)$$

Theorem 4 $\forall_\alpha \sin\left(\dfrac{\pi}{2} - \alpha\right) = \cos(\alpha)$

Proof Using the symmetric property of equality, Theorem 3 can be stated as

$$\forall_\theta \sin(\theta) = \cos\left(\frac{\pi}{2} - \theta\right)$$

Now suppose $\theta = \dfrac{\pi}{2} - \alpha$; replacing θ by $\dfrac{\pi}{2} - \alpha$, we obtain

$$\sin\left(\frac{\pi}{2} - \alpha\right) = \cos\left(\frac{\pi}{2} - \left(\frac{\pi}{2} - \alpha\right)\right)$$
$$= \cos(\alpha)$$

Observe in Theorem 4 that $\left(\dfrac{\pi}{2} - \alpha\right) + (\alpha) = \dfrac{\pi}{2}$ for each real number α.

Theorem 5 $\forall_\theta \sin(-\theta) = -\sin(\theta)$

Proof $\sin(-\theta) = \cos\left(\dfrac{\pi}{2} - (-\theta)\right)$

$$= \cos\left(\frac{\pi}{2} + \theta\right)$$
$$= \cos\left(-\frac{\pi}{2} - \theta\right)$$
$$= \cos\left(-\frac{\pi}{2}\right) \cdot \cos(\theta) + \sin\left(-\frac{\pi}{2}\right) \cdot \sin(\theta)$$
$$= 0 \cdot \cos(\theta) + (-1) \cdot \sin(\theta)$$
$$= 0 - \sin(\theta)$$
$$= -\sin(\theta)$$

Theorem 6 $\forall_{\theta_1} \forall_{\theta_2} \; \cos(\theta_1 + \theta_2) = \cos(\theta_1) \cdot \cos(\theta_2) - \sin(\theta_1) \cdot \sin(\theta_2)$

Proof   According to the Basic Formula

$$\forall_{\theta_1} \forall_{\beta} \; \cos(\theta_1 - \beta) = \cos(\theta_1) \cdot \cos(\beta) + \sin(\theta_1) \cdot \sin(\beta)$$

Now, suppose that $\beta = -\theta_2$; we replace β by $(-\theta_2)$ in the formula above and obtain

$$\cos(\theta_1 - (-\theta_2)) = \cos(\theta_1) \cdot \cos(-\theta_2) + \sin(\theta_1) \cdot \sin(-\theta_2)$$

$$\cos(\theta_1 + \theta_2) = \cos(\theta_1) \cdot \cos(\theta_2) + \sin(\theta_1) \cdot [-\sin(\theta_2)]$$

Theorems 2 and 5

$$\cos(\theta_1 + \theta_2) = \cos(\theta_1) \cdot \cos(\theta_2) - \sin(\theta_1) \cdot \sin(\theta_2)$$

Theorem 7 $\forall_{\theta_1} \forall_{\theta_2} \; \sin(\theta_1 + \theta_2) = \sin(\theta_1) \cdot \cos(\theta_2) + \cos(\theta_1) \cdot \sin(\theta_2)$

Proof
$$\sin(\theta_1 + \theta_2) = \cos\left(\frac{\pi}{2} - (\theta_1 + \theta_2)\right) \qquad \text{Theorem 3}$$

$$= \cos\left(\frac{\pi}{2} - \theta_1 - \theta_2\right)$$

$$= \cos\left(\left(\frac{\pi}{2} - \theta_1\right) - \theta_2\right)$$

$$= \cos\left(\frac{\pi}{2} - \theta_1\right) \cdot \cos(\theta_2)$$

$$+ \sin\left(\frac{\pi}{2} - \theta_1\right) \cdot \sin(\theta_2) \qquad \text{Basic formula}$$

$$= \sin(\theta_1) \cdot \cos(\theta_2) + \cos(\theta_1) \cdot \sin(\theta_2) \quad \text{Theorems 3 and 4}$$

Theorem 8 $\forall_{\theta_1} \forall_{\theta_2} \; \sin(\theta_1 - \theta_2) = \sin(\theta_1) \cdot \cos(\theta_2) - \cos(\theta_1) \cdot \sin(\theta_2)$

Proof   According to Theorem 7

$$\forall_{\theta_1} \forall_{\beta} \; \sin(\theta_1 + \beta) = \sin(\theta_1) \cdot \cos(\beta) + \cos(\theta_1) \cdot \sin(\beta)$$

Now, suppose that $\beta = -\theta_2$; we replace β by $(-\theta_2)$ in the formula above and obtain

$$\sin(\theta_1 + (-\theta_2)) = \sin(\theta_1) \cdot \cos(-\theta_2) + \cos(\theta_1) \cdot \sin(-\theta_2)$$

$$\sin(\theta_1 - \theta_2) = \sin(\theta_1) \cdot \cos(\theta_2) + \cos(\theta_1) \cdot (-\sin(\theta_2))$$

Theorems 2 and 5

$$\sin(\theta_1 - \theta_2) = \sin(\theta_1) \cdot \cos(\theta_2) - \cos(\theta_1) \cdot \sin(\theta_2)$$

At this point, we list the theorems and formulas derived thus far. For all real numbers θ_1 and θ_2

$i.$ $\cos^2(\theta_1) + \sin^2(\theta_1) = 1$

$ii.$ $\tan(\theta_1) = \dfrac{\sin(\theta_1)}{\cos(\theta_1)}, \; (\cos(\theta_1) \neq 0)$

$iii.$ $\cos(\theta_1 - \theta_2) = \cos(\theta_1) \cdot \cos(\theta_2) + \sin(\theta_1) \cdot \sin(\theta_2)$

$iv.$ $\cos(\theta_1 + \theta_2) = \cos(\theta_1) \cdot \cos(\theta_2) - \sin(\theta_1) \cdot \sin(\theta_2)$

$v.$ $\sin(\theta_1 + \theta_2) = \sin(\theta_1) \cdot \cos(\theta_2) + \cos(\theta_1) \cdot \sin(\theta_2)$

$vi.$ $\sin(\theta_1 - \theta_2) = \sin(\theta_1) \cdot \cos(\theta_2) - \cos(\theta_1) \cdot \sin(\theta_2)$

$vii.$ $\cos(-\theta_1) = \cos(\theta_1)$

$viii.$ $\sin(-\theta_1) = -\sin(\theta_1)$

$ix.$ $\sin\left(\dfrac{\pi}{2} - \theta_1\right) = \cos(\theta_1)$

$x.$ $\cos\left(\dfrac{\pi}{2} - \theta_1\right) = \sin(\theta_1)$

EXERCISES

1. Prove the following:

   a. $\forall_\theta\ \sin(2\theta) = 2 \cdot \sin(\theta) \cdot \cos(\theta)$
   [HINT: Begin with $v.$ from the above list and replace θ_2 by θ_1.]

   b. $\forall_\theta\ \cos(2\theta) = \cos^2(\theta) - \sin^2(\theta)$
   [HINT: Begin with $iv.$ from the above list and replace θ_2 by θ_1.]

   c. $\forall_\theta\ \cos(2\theta) = 1 - 2 \cdot \sin^2(\theta)$
   [HINT: Use the result of problem **b** and then use $i.$ from the above list.]

   d. $\forall_\theta\ \cos(2\theta) = 2 \cdot \cos^2(\theta) - 1$

   e. $\forall_\theta\ \tan(-\theta) = -\tan(\theta),\ (\cos(\theta) \neq 0).$
   [HINT: Use $ii.$ from the above list; replace θ_1 by $-\theta_2$; then use $vii.$ and $viii.$]

2. $\forall_{\theta_1} \forall_{\theta_2}\ \tan(\theta_1 + \theta_2) = \dfrac{\tan(\theta_1) + \tan(\theta_2)}{1 - \tan(\theta_1) \cdot \tan(\theta_2)},$

   $(\cos(\theta_1 + \theta_2) \neq 0,\ \cos(\theta_1) \neq 0,\ \text{and } \cos(\theta_2) \neq 0).$

   Complete the following proof of this formula.

   $$\tan(\theta_1 + \theta_2) = \frac{\sin(\theta_1 + \theta_2)}{\cos(\theta_1 + \theta_2)}$$

   $$= \frac{\sin(\theta_1) \cdot \cos(\theta_2) + \cos(\theta_1) \cdot \sin(\theta_2)}{\cos(\theta_1) \cdot \cos(\theta_2) - \sin(\theta_1) \cdot \sin(\theta_2)}$$

   $$= \frac{\dfrac{\sin(\theta_1) \cdot \cos(\theta_2)}{\cos(\theta_1) \cdot \cos(\theta_2)} + \dfrac{\cos(\theta_1) \cdot \sin(\theta_2)}{\cos(\theta_1) \cdot \cos(\theta_2)}}{\dfrac{\cos(\theta_1) \cdot \cos(\theta_2)}{\cos(\theta_1) \cdot \cos(\theta_2)} - \dfrac{\sin(\theta_1) \cdot \sin(\theta_2)}{\cos(\theta_1) \cdot \cos(\theta_2)}}$$

3. Prove that $\forall_\theta\ \tan(2\theta) = \dfrac{2 \cdot \tan(\theta)}{1 - \tan^2(\theta)},\ (\cos(\theta) \neq 0)$

4. Prove that $\forall_{\theta_1} \forall_{\theta_2} \ \tan(\theta_1 - \theta_2) = \dfrac{\tan(\theta_1) - \tan(\theta_2)}{1 + \tan(\theta_1) \cdot \tan(\theta_2)}$,

$(\cos(\theta_1 - \theta_2) \neq 0, \ \cos(\theta_1) \neq 0, \ \text{and} \ \cos(\theta_2) \neq 0).$

5. Simplify.

Example: $\qquad \sin(\pi + \theta)$

$$\forall_\theta \ \sin(\pi + \theta) = \sin(\pi) \cdot \cos(\theta) + \cos(\pi) \cdot \sin(\theta)$$
$$= 0 \cdot \cos(\theta) + (-1) \cdot \sin(\theta)$$
$$= -\sin(\theta)$$

a. $\cos(\pi - \theta)$

b. $\cos(\theta - \pi)$

c. $\cos(\theta + \pi)$

d. $\sin(\pi - \theta)$

e. $\sin(\theta - \pi)$

f. $\sin(\theta + \pi)$

g. $\cos(\theta + 2\pi)$

h. $\sin(\theta + 2\pi)$

i. $\cos(\theta + 2n\pi)$, (for each integer n)

j. $\sin(\theta + 2n\pi)$, (for each integer n)

k. $\tan(\theta + \pi), \ \left(\theta \epsilon \left\{\dfrac{\pi}{2} + n\pi\right\}\right)$

[HINT: Use the result of problem 2.]

l. $\tan(\theta + 2\pi), \ \left(\theta \epsilon \left\{\dfrac{\pi}{2} + n\pi\right\}\right)$

m. $\tan(\theta + 3\pi), \ \left(\theta \epsilon \left\{\dfrac{\pi}{2} + n\pi\right\}\right)$

n. $\tan(\theta + n\pi), \ \Big($for each integer

$n; \ \theta \epsilon \left\{\dfrac{\pi}{2} + n\pi\right\}\Big)$

o. $\sin^2\left(\dfrac{7\pi}{6}\right) + \cos^2\left(\dfrac{7\pi}{6}\right)$

p. $\cos(-(2t - 5))$

q. $\cos(-7 - r)$

r. $-\sin(2k - 5)$

s. $-\sin(-8 - 4m)$

t. $\dfrac{\sin(ab)}{\cos(ab)}, \ (\cos(ab) \neq 0)$

u. $\dfrac{\sin(-\theta)}{\cos(-\theta)}, \ (\cos(-\theta) \neq 0)$

v. $\dfrac{\sin(\theta)}{\cos(-\theta)}, \ (\cos(-\theta) \neq 0)$

w. $\dfrac{\sin(-\theta)}{\cos(\theta)}, \ (\cos(\theta) \neq 0)$

x. $\sin\left(\dfrac{\pi}{2} - 5a\right)$

y. $\cos\left(\dfrac{\pi}{2} - 3b\right)$

z. $\sin\left(\dfrac{\pi}{2} + 7k\right)$

a'. $\cos(3m) \cdot \cos(2c) + \sin(3m) \cdot \sin(2c)$

b'. $\sin(5a) \cdot \cos(4d) + \cos(5a) \cdot \sin(4d)$

c'. $\cos(8t) \cdot \cos(3t) - \sin(8t) \cdot \sin(3t)$

d'. $\sin(2d) \cdot \cos(d) - \cos(2d) \cdot \sin(d)$

6. True or false?

a. $\forall_\theta \ \sin\left(\dfrac{7\pi}{6} + \theta\right) = \sin\left(\dfrac{\pi}{6} - \theta\right)$

b. $\forall_\theta \ \sin\left(\dfrac{5\pi}{4} + \theta\right) = \sin\left(\dfrac{3\pi}{4} - \theta\right)$

c. $\forall_\theta \ \cos\left(\theta - \dfrac{2\pi}{3}\right) = \cos\left(\dfrac{\pi}{3} + \theta\right)$

d. $\forall_\theta \ \cos\left(\theta + \dfrac{2\pi}{3}\right) = \cos\left(\theta + \dfrac{\pi}{3}\right)$

e. $\forall_\theta \, \sin\left(\dfrac{7\pi}{6}+\theta\right) = \sin\left(\dfrac{\pi}{6}+\theta\right)$

f. $\forall_\theta \, \sin\left(\dfrac{7\pi}{6}-\theta\right) = \sin\left(\theta-\dfrac{\pi}{6}\right)$

g. $\forall_\theta \, \cos\left(\dfrac{7\pi}{6}+\theta\right) = -\cos\left(\dfrac{\pi}{6}+\theta\right)$

h. $\forall_\theta \, \cos\left(\dfrac{7\pi}{6}-\theta\right) = -\cos\left(\theta-\dfrac{\pi}{6}\right)$

i. $\forall_\theta \forall_{n\epsilon I} \, \sin(\theta) = \sin(\theta+n\pi)$

j. $\forall_\theta \forall_{n\epsilon I} \, \cos(\theta) = \cos(\theta+2n\pi)$

k. $\forall_\theta \forall_{n\epsilon I}$, if $\tan(\theta)$ is defined, then
$\tan(\theta) = \tan(\theta+2n\pi)$.

l. $\forall_\theta \forall_{n\epsilon I}$, if $\tan(\theta)$ is defined, then
$\tan(\theta) = \tan(\theta+n\pi)$.

m. $\forall_\theta \, \sin\left(\dfrac{\pi}{2}-\theta\right) = \cos(\theta)$

n. $\forall_\theta \, \cos\left(\dfrac{\pi}{2}-\theta\right) = \sin(\theta)$

o. $\forall_\theta \, \sin\left(\dfrac{\pi}{2}-\theta\right) = -\cos(\theta)$

p. $\forall_\theta \, \cos\left(\theta-\dfrac{\pi}{2}\right) = -\sin(\theta)$

q. $\forall_\theta \, \cos(\theta) = \cos(-\theta)$

r. $\forall_\theta \, \cos(\theta) = -\cos(\theta)$

s. $\forall_\theta \, \cos(\theta) = -\cos(-\theta)$

7. Since the wrapping function W is a periodic function, we know that sine, cosine, and tangent are periodic functions. 2π is a period of sine, of cosine, and of tangent. 2π is the least positive period of sine and of cosine. Let us find out whether tangent has a positive period which is less than 2π. Justify each step.

For each integer n

$$\tan(\theta+n\pi) = \frac{\sin(\theta+n\pi)}{\cos(\theta+n\pi)} \qquad \left[\theta\epsilon\left\{\dfrac{\pi}{2}+2n\pi\right\}\right]$$

$$= \frac{\sin(\theta)\cdot\cos(n\pi)+\cos(\theta)\cdot\sin(n\pi)}{\cos(\theta)\cdot\cos(n\pi)-\sin(\theta)\cdot\sin(n\pi)}$$

Hence, if n is an *odd* integer

$$\tan(\theta+n\pi) = \frac{\sin(\theta)\cdot(-1)+\cos(\theta)\cdot(0)}{\cos(\theta)\cdot(-1)-\sin(\theta)\cdot(0)}$$

$$= \frac{-\sin(\theta)}{-\cos(\theta)}$$

$$= \tan(\theta)$$

And, if n is an *even* integer

$$\tan(\theta+n\pi) = \frac{\sin(\theta)\cdot(1)+\cos(\theta)\cdot(0)}{\cos(\theta)\cdot(1)-\sin(\theta)\cdot(0)}$$

$$= \frac{\sin(\theta)}{\cos(\theta)}$$

$$= \tan(\theta)$$

Thus, whether n is an even or an odd integer

$$\tan(\theta+n\pi) = \tan(\theta) \qquad \text{and} \qquad \pi \text{ is a positive period of tangent}$$

GRAPHS OF SINE, COSINE, AND TANGENT

You have no doubt had the experience of gaining insight into a mathematical concept by means of a picture. For this reason we shall now present the graphs of the three trigonometric functions that we have studied.

First, let us recall that sine $= \{(\theta, y)\}$ where $W(\theta) = (x, y)$. To construct the graph of sine, we shall plot several ordered pairs (θ, y), for which $W(\theta) = (x, y)$. Study figures 19a and 19b.

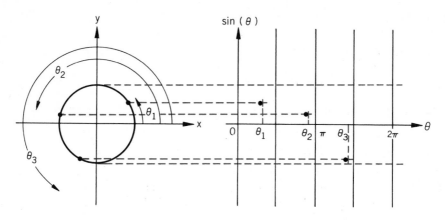

Fig. 19-a	Fig. 19-b

In figure 19a we determined three points (x, y) for which $W(\theta) = (x, y)$. Then, by projecting from the unit circle, we have located three points (θ, y) in figure 19b which are points of the sine function, $\{(\theta, y)\}$. Explain how the points labeled θ_1, θ_2, and θ_3 on the θ-axis were obtained.

Figure 20 shows the completed graph of sine for $0 \leq \theta \leq 2\pi$.

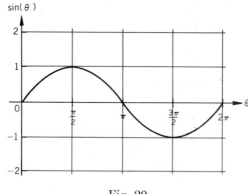

Fig. 20

Since the sine function is periodic with a period of 2π, we can easily extend the graph of figure 20 without having to plot any more points. See figure 21.

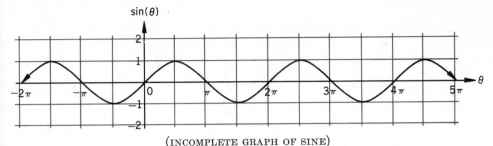

(INCOMPLETE GRAPH OF SINE)

Fig. 21

From the graph of sine shown in figure 21, you should be able to observe several things.

    i. the domain of sine is R, the set of all real numbers

    ii. the range of sine is $\{y|-1 \leq y \leq 1\}$

    iii. sine is a periodic function and $\forall_\theta \forall_{k\epsilon I} \sin(\theta) = \sin(\theta + 2k\pi)$

    iv. the zeros of the sine function are the members of $\{n\pi\}$

Since $\forall_\theta \cos(\theta) = \cos(-\theta) = \sin\left(\frac{\pi}{2} + \theta\right)$ the graph of cosine is readily obtained from the graph of sine by "shifting" the graph of sine to the left $\frac{\pi}{2}$ units. The graphs of sine and of cosine are shown in figure 22.

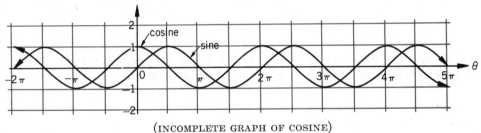

(INCOMPLETE GRAPH OF COSINE)

Fig. 22

Next, let us recall that tangent $= \left\{\left(\theta, \frac{y}{x}\right)\right\}$ where $W(\theta) = \frac{y}{x}$, $(x \neq 0)$. To construct the graph of tangent by projecting from the unit circle, we first develop a procedure as shown in figure 23.

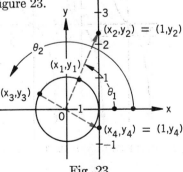

Fig. 23

Observe in figure 23 on page 441 that the three points (x_1, y_1), (x_2, y_2), and the origin are collinear. Therefore the slope of the line through these points may be expressed as $\dfrac{y_1}{x_1}$ or $\dfrac{y_2}{x_2}$. Note $x_2 = 1$; hence, $\tan(\theta_1) = \dfrac{y_1}{x_1} = \dfrac{y_2}{x_2} = \dfrac{y_2}{1} = y_2$.

Observe also that $\tan(\theta_2) = \dfrac{y_3}{x_3} = \dfrac{y_4}{x_4} = y_4$ since each of $\dfrac{y_3}{x_3}$ and $\dfrac{y_4}{x_4}$ is the slope of the line through the points: (x_3, y_3), (x_4, y_4), and the origin; and $x_4 = 1$.

To construct the graph of tangent, we shall plot several ordered pairs $\left(\theta, \dfrac{y}{x}\right)$ for which $W(\theta) = (x, y)$. Study figure 24.

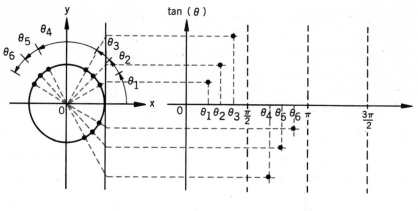

Fig. 24

In figure 24 we plotted six points $(\theta, \tan(\theta))$ of the graph of tangent. Figure 25 shows several completed parts of the graph of tangent.

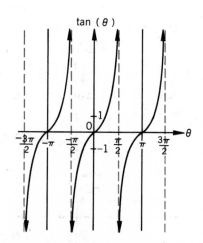

(INCOMPLETE GRAPH OF TANGENT)

Fig. 25

EXERCISES

Use the graphs of sine, of cosine, and of tangent as given in figures 21, 22 and 25 to answer the following:

1. Determine the domain of
   a. sine   b. cosine   c. tangent

2. Determine the range of
   a. sine   b. cosine   c. tangent

3. Determine the smallest positive period of
   a. sine   b. cosine   c. tangent

4. For each given range of values of θ, tell whether each of $\sin(\theta)$, $\cos(\theta)$, and $\tan(\theta)$ is positive or negative.

   a. $0 < \theta < \dfrac{\pi}{2}$ c. $\pi < \theta < \dfrac{3\pi}{2}$ e. $-\dfrac{\pi}{2} < \theta < \dfrac{\pi}{2}$

   b. $\dfrac{\pi}{2} < \theta < \pi$ d. $\dfrac{3\pi}{2} < \theta < 2\pi$

5. Determine the zeros of
   a. sine   b. cosine   c. tangent

VOCABULARY

Use each of the following correctly in a sentence. Numerals in parentheses refer to pages where these words were used. If you are not sure of the meaning of any word, turn to the indicated page.

clockwise (407)
cosine (420)
counterclockwise (407)
initial point (406)
path (405)
periodic (418)

sine (422)
tangent (424)
terminal point (406)
trigonometric equations (426)
unit circle (409)
wrapping function (415)

REVIEW EXERCISES

1. Consider the path $\left(A, -\dfrac{\pi}{6}\right)$ for a unit circle. List five other paths for this circle that have the same initial point and the same terminal point as the path $\left(A, -\dfrac{\pi}{6}\right)$.

2. What is the least positive period of each of the following periodic functions?
   a. wrapping function   c. tangent
   b. sine   d. cosine
   e. $\{\ldots, (-3, 5), (-1, 2), (1, 5), (3, 2), (5, 5), (7, 2), \ldots\}$

3.   Express each of the following as an ordered pair of real numbers. W is the wrapping function.

a. $W\left(\dfrac{\pi}{4}\right)$

b. $W\left(-\dfrac{2\pi}{3}\right)$

c. $W\left(\dfrac{7\pi}{6}\right)$

d. $W\left(-\dfrac{\pi}{2}\right)$

e. $W(\pi)$

f. $W(6\pi)$

g. $W(0)$

h. $W\left(\dfrac{8\pi}{3}\right)$

i. $W\left(\dfrac{7\pi}{2}\right)$

j. $W\left(-\dfrac{5\pi}{4}\right)$

4.   Determine the value of

a. $\sin(0)$

b. $\tan\left(\dfrac{3\pi}{4}\right)$

c. $\cos\left(\dfrac{\pi}{2}\right)$

d. $\tan\left(\dfrac{\pi}{6}\right)$

e. $\tan(0)$

f. $\sin\left(\dfrac{5\pi}{3}\right)$

g. $\cos\left(-\dfrac{5\pi}{6}\right)$

h. $\cos\left(\dfrac{5\pi}{4}\right)$

i. $\sin\left(-\dfrac{\pi}{4}\right)$

j. $\cos(0)$

k. $\tan(-\pi)$

l. $\sin\left(\dfrac{\pi}{6}\right)$

m. $\sin\left(-\dfrac{\pi}{2}\right)$

n. $\cos\left(\dfrac{\pi}{6}\right)$

o. $\tan\left(\dfrac{5\pi}{6}\right)$

p. $\cos(2\pi)$

5. Specify the domain and the range of each function in problem **2.**

6. Solve each equation for all values of θ where $0 \le \theta < 2\pi$.

a. $2 \cdot \cos(\theta) + 1 = 0$

b. $4 \cdot \tan(\theta) - 7 = 5 \cdot \tan(\theta) - 6$

c. $4 \cdot \sin^2(\theta) = 3$

d. $\cos(2\theta) = \frac{1}{2}$

e. $\tan(\theta) \cdot (\sin(\theta) + 1) = 0$

f. $\dfrac{1}{\cos(\theta)} = -2$

7. Suppose $\sin(\theta) = -\dfrac{2}{3}$ and $\dfrac{3\pi}{2} < \theta < 2\pi$. Determine $\cos(\theta)$ and $\tan(\theta)$.

8. Simplify.

a. $\cos\left(\dfrac{\pi}{2} - 3c\right)$

b. $\sin\left(\dfrac{\pi}{2} + 5a\right)$

c. $\sin^2(4d) + \cos^2(4d)$

d. $\dfrac{\sin(3b)}{\cos(3b)}$

e. $\cos\left(\dfrac{-3c}{4}\right)$

f. $-\sin(-5t)$

g. $\cos(4a) \cdot \cos(5a) - \sin(4a) \cdot \sin(5a)$

h. $\sin(7m) \cdot \cos(3m) - \cos(7m) \cdot \sin(3m)$

9. Draw the graphs of sine, of cosine, and of tangent for two complete periods beginning at $-\dfrac{\pi}{2}$.

CHAPTER TEST

1. Which one of the following paths for a unit circle has the same terminal point as the path $(A, 7)$ for the same circle?

  a. $(A, 7\pi)$ **c.** $(A, 7 + \pi)$ **e.** $(A, 0)$

  b. $\left(A, \dfrac{\pi}{7}\right)$ **d.** $(A, 7 - 4\pi)$ **f.** $(A, 2 + 7\pi)$

2. Express each of the following as an ordered pair of real numbers. W is the wrapping function.

  a. $W\left(\dfrac{3\pi}{4}\right)$ **c.** $W\left(\dfrac{\pi}{6}\right)$ **e.** $W\left(\dfrac{7\pi}{3}\right)$

  b. $W(-\pi)$ **d.** $W(4\pi)$ **f.** $W\left(-\dfrac{\pi}{2}\right)$

3. Determine the least positive period of each of the following:

  a. the cosine function

  b. the tangent function

  c. $\{\ldots, (5, 3), (9, -3), (13, 3), (17, -3), (21, 3), (25, -3), \ldots\}$

4. For the unit circle specified by $x^2 + y^2 = 1$ and for all paths (A, θ) of this circle, where A has coordinates $(1, 0)$, which one of the following is the cosine function?

  a. $\{(\theta,\, y)\}$ **c.** $\{(y,\, \theta)\}$ **e.** $\{(x,\, y)\}$

  b. $\{(\theta,\, x)\}$ **d.** $\{(x,\, \theta)\}$ **f.** $\left\{\left(\theta,\, \dfrac{y}{x}\right)\right\}$

5. Determine the value of

  a. $\cos(\pi)$ **d.** $\cos\left(\dfrac{2\pi}{3}\right)$ **g.** $\sin\left(\dfrac{\pi}{2}\right)$

  b. $\sin\left(\dfrac{\pi}{4}\right)$ **e.** $\tan\left(-\dfrac{\pi}{3}\right)$ **h.** $\sin(-4\pi)$

  c. $\tan\left(\dfrac{\pi}{6}\right)$ **f.** $\cos(2\pi)$

6. Specify the range of cosine.

7. Specify the range of tangent.

8. What two real numbers between 0 and 2π are not members of the domain of tangent?

9. Determine all values of θ between 0 and 2π that satisfy each of the following:

  a. $\tan^2(\theta) = 1$ **b.** $(2 \cdot \sin(\theta) + 1) \cdot \cos(\theta) = 0$

10. Suppose that $\cos(\theta) = -\dfrac{2}{5}$ and $\pi < \theta < \dfrac{3\pi}{2}$.

  a. Determine $\sin(\theta)$.   **b.** Determine $\tan(\theta)$.

11. Sketch the graphs of sine, of cosine, and of tangent for $0 \leq \theta < 2\pi$.

12. If $\sin(\theta) > 0$ and $\tan(\theta) < 0$ and $0 < \theta < 2\pi$, then which one of the following must be true?

a. $0 < \theta < \dfrac{\pi}{2}$ 　　　　　　　　　　 d. $\dfrac{3\pi}{2} < \theta < 2\pi$

b. $\dfrac{\pi}{2} < \theta < \pi$ 　　　　　　　　　　 e. $\theta = \dfrac{\pi}{2}$

c. $\pi < \theta < \dfrac{3\pi}{2}$ 　　　　　　　　　　 f. $\theta = \pi$

13. Which one of the following is undefined?

a. $\cos(\pi)$ 　　　　　 c. $\tan\left(\dfrac{\pi}{2}\right)$ 　　　　　 e. $\dfrac{1}{\cos(\pi)}$

b. $\dfrac{1}{\cos(0)}$ 　　　　 d. $\tan(0)$ 　　　　　 f. $\sin(\pi)$

14. $\forall_\alpha \forall_\beta \; \cos(\alpha + \beta) = \cos(\alpha) \cdot \cos(\beta) - \sin(\alpha) \cdot \sin(\beta)$.　Suppose $\cos(\theta) = \frac{3}{5}$. Compute $\cos(2\theta)$.

15. True or false?

a. $\forall_\theta \; \sin(-\theta) = \sin(\theta)$

b. $\forall_\theta \; \cos(-\theta) = \cos(\theta)$

c. $\forall_\theta \; \sin(\pi + \theta) = -\sin(\theta)$

d. $\forall_\theta \; \cos\left(\dfrac{\pi}{2} - \theta\right) = \sin(\theta)$

e. $\forall_\theta \; \cos\left(\dfrac{\pi}{2} + \theta\right) = \sin(-\theta)$

f. If $\sin(\theta) = \dfrac{-6}{35}$ and $\cos(\theta) = \dfrac{9}{20}$, then $\tan(\theta) = \dfrac{-8}{21}$.

BIBLIOGRAPHY

Allendoerfer, C. and Oakley, C. *Fundamentals of Freshman Mathematics.* New York: McGraw-Hill Book Co., Inc., 1959. pp. 265–298.

Dubisch, R. *Trigonometry.* New York: Ronald Press Co., 1955. Chapters 2, 3, 4, 7.

Hogben, L. *Mathematics for the Million.* New York: W. W. Norton and Co., Inc., 1951. Chapter 6.

Moore, J. T. *Fundamental Principles of Mathematics.* New York: Holt, Rinehart and Winston, Inc., 1960. pp. 105–125, 172–210.

Sanford, V. *A Short History of Mathematics.* New York: Houghton Mifflin Co., 1930. pp. 291–307.

School Mathematics Study Group. *Elementary Functions.* New Haven: Yale University Press, 1961. pp. 225–242.

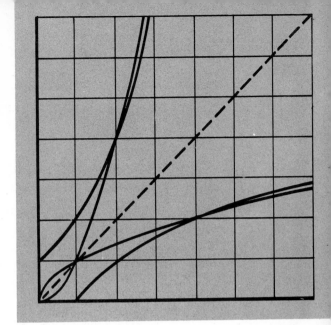

CHAPTER 14

Numerical Trigonometry

The subject of trigonometry originated over 2000 years ago. It began when man had a need to solve triangles; that is, for a given triangle if he knew the measures of some of its angles and sides, he had the problem of computing the measures of remaining angles and sides. In fact, the word "trigonometry" is derived from Greek words meaning "triangle measurement."

Consider triangles ABC and DEF of figure 1. These two triangles are related in a special way. $\triangle ABC$ and $\triangle DEF$ are *similar* triangles. Angles A and D have the same measure; angles B and E have the same measure; and the same is true of angles C and F. What markings are used in the figure to indicate pairs of angles that have equal measure?

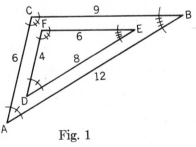

Fig. 1

447

Notice that the measures of the sides are related in the following way.

$$\frac{12}{8} = \frac{9}{6} \text{ and } \frac{9}{6} = \frac{6}{4}; \text{ that is, } \frac{AB}{DE} = \frac{BC}{EF} \text{ and } \frac{BC}{EF} = \frac{AC}{DF}$$

In geometry the following is proved.

For *any* two triangles ABC and DEF, if angles A and D have the same measure and angles B and E have the same measure, then $\triangle ABC$ is *similar* to $\triangle DEF$ and $\dfrac{AB}{DE} = \dfrac{BC}{EF}$ and $\dfrac{BC}{EF} = \dfrac{AC}{DF}$.

The converse is also proved in geometry.

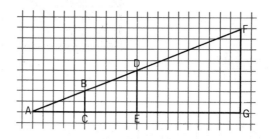

Fig. 2

Consider the three right triangles of figure 2: $\triangle ABC$, ADE, and AFG. By counting units, we can determine that $AC = 5$, $AE = 10$, and $AG = 20$; and that $BC = 2$, $DE = 4$, and $FG = 8$. Using the Pythagorean Relation, we can compute and find that

$(AB)^2 = 5^2 + 2^2 = 25 + 4 = 29$; hence, $AB = \sqrt{29}$
$(AD)^2 = 10^2 + 4^2 = 100 + 16 = 116 = 4 \times 29$; hence, $AD = 2\sqrt{29}$
$(AF)^2 = 20^2 + 8^2 = 400 + 64 = 464 = 16 \times 29$; hence, $AF = 4\sqrt{29}$

Verify that

$$\frac{BC}{AC} = \frac{2}{5} = \frac{DE}{AE} = \frac{FG}{AG}$$

$$\frac{AC}{AB} = \frac{5}{\sqrt{29}} = \frac{AE}{AD} = \frac{AG}{AF}$$

$$\frac{BC}{AB} = \frac{2}{\sqrt{29}} = \frac{DE}{AD} = \frac{FG}{AF}$$

Thus, each pair of the right triangles — ABC, ADE, and AFG — is a pair of *similar* right triangles.

You recall that the longest side of a right triangle is called the *hypotenuse;* the other two sides are called the *legs.* The legs of a right triangle are often named relative to the vertex of an acute angle. The names are assigned in this manner: for the right triangle KLM of figure 3 the *leg* containing point K is called the leg *adjacent* to K; the leg not containing K is called the leg *opposite* to K.

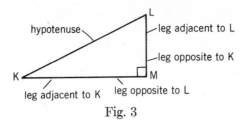

Fig. 3

Observe in figure 2 that for all three right triangles, △ABC, ADE, and AFG

$$\frac{\text{measure of leg opposite to } A}{\text{measure of hypotenuse}}$$ is the same, namely $\frac{2}{\sqrt{29}}$

$$\frac{\text{measure of leg adjacent to } A}{\text{measure of hypotenuse}}$$ is the same, namely $\frac{5}{\sqrt{29}}$

$$\frac{\text{measure of leg opposite to } A}{\text{measure of leg adjacent to } A}$$ is the same, namely $\frac{2}{5}$

EXERCISES

1. For the right triangle of the adjoining diagram, compute each of the following to three decimal places.

    a. $\dfrac{AC}{AB}$ **b.** $\dfrac{BC}{AB}$ **c.** $\dfrac{BC}{AC}$

2. For the right triangle of the adjoining diagram, compute each of the following to three decimal places.

    a. $\dfrac{DF}{DE}$ **b.** $\dfrac{EF}{DE}$ **c.** $\dfrac{EF}{DF}$

3. For the right triangles of the adjoining diagram, compute each of the following to three decimal places.

    a. $\dfrac{GJ}{GH}$ **d.** $\dfrac{HJ}{GH}$ **g.** $\dfrac{HJ}{GJ}$

    b. $\dfrac{GL}{GK}$ **e.** $\dfrac{KL}{GK}$ **h.** $\dfrac{KL}{GL}$

    c. $\dfrac{GN}{GM}$ **f.** $\dfrac{MN}{GM}$ **i.** $\dfrac{MN}{GN}$

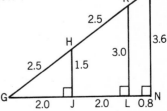

4. For each problem, the degree-measures of two angles of a triangle are given. Determine the degree-measure of the third angle.

a. 40, 60	**g.** x, y
b. 20, 30	**h.** $3x, 4x$
c. 110, 40	**i.** $x - 3, x - 7$
d. $27\frac{1}{2}, 45\frac{1}{2}$	**j.** 90, 20
e. $82\frac{1}{2}, 63$	**k.** 90, 84
f. $80\frac{1}{3}, 20\frac{1}{2}$	**l.** 90, 89

5. For each problem, the degree-measure of one *acute* angle of a *right* triangle is given. Determine the degree-measure of the other acute angle.

a. 40	**f.** 45
b. 23	**g.** $x - 6$
c. 68	**h.** $x + 3$
d. $36\frac{1}{2}$	**i.** $5 - 2x$
e. $47\frac{2}{3}$	**j.** $x - y$

TRIGONOMETRIC RATIOS

Consider the right triangles of figure 4.

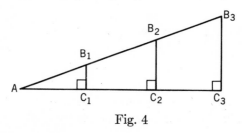

Fig. 4

You should note the following:

   i. There are three *right* triangles: $\triangle AB_1C_1$, AB_2C_2, and AB_3C_3.

   ii. Each pair of these three triangles is a pair of similar triangles. [How do we know that angles C_1, C_2, and C_3 have the same degree-measure? How do we know that the acute angles B_1, B_2, and B_3 have the same degree-measure?]

   iii. Since the pairs of triangles are similar, it follows that

$$\frac{B_1C_1}{AC_1} = \frac{B_2C_2}{AC_2} = \frac{B_3C_3}{AC_3}$$

$$\frac{B_1C_1}{AB_1} = \frac{B_2C_2}{AB_2} = \frac{B_3C_3}{AB_3}$$

$$\frac{AC_1}{AB_1} = \frac{AC_2}{AB_2} = \frac{AC_3}{AB_3}$$

We shall now name these ratios. Study figure 5. For the right triangle ABC of figure 5, with right angle at C, the measure of the hypotenuse is c, the measure of the leg opposite to A is a, and the measure of the leg adjacent to A is b. The three ratios

$$\frac{a}{b}, \frac{a}{c}, \text{ and } \frac{b}{c}$$

are called *trigonometric ratios*. Specifically

$\dfrac{a}{b}$ is the *tangent ratio* of angle A

$\dfrac{a}{c}$ is the *sine ratio* of angle A

$\dfrac{b}{c}$ is the *cosine ratio* of angle A

For example, consider the right triangle of figure 6. The tangent of angle A is $\frac{4}{3}$; the sine of angle A is $\frac{4}{5}$; and the cosine of angle A is $\frac{3}{5}$. We abbreviate these three statements thus

$$\tan (A) = \frac{4}{3}$$

$$\sin (A) = \frac{4}{5}$$

$$\cos (A) = \frac{3}{5}$$

To be precise, for each right triangle ABC with right angle at C

$$\tan (A) = \frac{\text{measure of leg opposite to } A}{\text{measure of leg adjacent to } A}$$

$$\sin (A) = \frac{\text{measure of leg opposite to } A}{\text{measure of hypotenuse}}$$

$$\cos (A) = \frac{\text{measure of leg adjacent to } A}{\text{measure of hypotenuse}}$$

Thus, for the right triangle of figure 7

$$\tan(D) = \frac{d}{e} \qquad\qquad \tan(E) = \frac{e}{d}$$

$$\sin(D) = \frac{d}{f} \qquad\qquad \sin(E) = \frac{e}{f}$$

$$\cos(D) = \frac{e}{f} \qquad\qquad \cos(E) = \frac{d}{f}$$

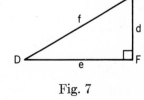

Fig. 7

EXERCISES

1. Refer to the two figures and decide on replacements for the question marks.

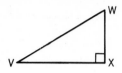
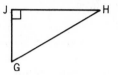

a. $\cos(H) = \dfrac{?}{?}$

b. $\cos(G) = \dfrac{?}{?}$

c. $\tan(?) = \dfrac{JG}{JH}$

d. $\sin(?) = \dfrac{JH}{GH}$

e. $\cos(?) = \dfrac{WX}{VW}$

f. $\cos(?) = \dfrac{VX}{VW}$

g. $\sin(?) = \dfrac{JG}{GH}$

h. $\tan(?) = \dfrac{VX}{WX}$

i. $\sin(G) = \dfrac{?}{?}$

j. $\sin(H) = \dfrac{?}{?}$

k. $\underline{\ ?\ }(V) = \dfrac{WX}{VW}$

l. $\underline{\ ?\ }(V) = \dfrac{WX}{VX}$

m. $\underline{\ ?\ }(W) = \dfrac{VX}{WX}$

n. $\underline{\ ?\ }(W) = \dfrac{WX}{VW}$

o. $(VX)^2 + (WX)^2 = (?)^2$

p. $(GJ)^2 + (?)^2 = (?)^2$

q. $(VW)^2 - (?)^2 = (WX)^2$

r. $(GH)^2 - (?)^2 = (?)^2$

2. Compute to two decimal places. Use the data given in the figures.

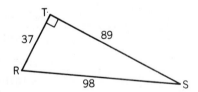

a. $\tan(K)$

b. $\sin(K)$

c. $\cos(K)$

d. $\tan(L)$

e. $\sin(L)$

f. $\cos(L)$

g. $\tan(R)$

h. $\sin(R)$

i. $\cos(R)$

j. $\tan(S)$

k. $\sin(S)$

l. $\cos(S)$

USING THE TRIGONOMETRIC TABLES

In the table on page 561 the trigonometric ratios for each acute angle measured to the nearest degree are listed to four decimal places. Study the table and notice that, if the degree-measure of an angle A is 37, then

$$\tan (A) \doteq .7536$$
$$\sin (A) \doteq .6018$$
$$\cos (A) \doteq .7986$$

From the table we also read that

if $\tan (B) \doteq 3.7321$, then the degree-measure of angle B is 75
if $\sin (K) \doteq .8660$, then the degree-measure of angle K is 60
and if $\cos (T) \doteq .6820$, then the degree-measure of angle T is 47

Be sure to verify these statements in the table. When we compute a ratio to four decimal places, we may find that it is not listed in the table. In such cases we use the nearest entry. For example, if we compute for some angle R

$$\sin (R) = \frac{4.63}{8.14} \doteq .5688,$$

we discover that .5688 is not listed in the table. But, since .5688 is between two entries, .5592 and .5736, and it is closer to .5736, we shall say that the degree-measure of angle R is 35, to the nearest degree. Use the table to verify this.

EXERCISES

1. Use the table to determine $\sin(M)$, $\cos(M)$, and $\tan(M)$, if
   a. the degree-measure of angle M is 62
   b. the degree-measure of angle M is 29
   c. the degree-measure of angle M is 12

2. Determine to the nearest whole number the degree-measure of angle A if

a. $\sin(A) = .2419$	e. $\cos(A) = .2419$	i. $\tan(A) = .5982$
b. $\cos(A) = .9135$	f. $\tan(A) = 2.6051$	j. $\sin(A) = .8356$
c. $\tan(A) = .3443$	g. $\sin(A) = .4197$	k. $\cos(A) = .2782$
d. $\sin(A) = .8988$	h. $\cos(A) = .8451$	l. $\tan(A) = 3.5029$

3. Determine to the nearest whole number the degree-measure of angle A for the accompanying figure.

Example: i. $\tan (A) = \dfrac{3.4}{5.6}$ Def. tangent ratio

$\doteq .6071$

$\doteq .6009$ Nearest entry in tangent column

Hence, the degree-measure of angle A is approximately 31.

Example: ii. $\cos (A) = \dfrac{41}{65}$ Def. cosine ratio

$\doteq .6308$

$\doteq .6293$ Nearest entry in cosine column

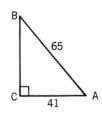

Hence, the degree-measure of angle A is approximately 51.

a.

c.

b.

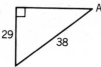

d.

4.   Determine to two digits the length of the side whose measure is m for the accompanying figure.

Example: i. $\tan (A) = \dfrac{m}{4.6}$ Def. tangent ratio

$m = 4.6 \times \tan (A)$

$\doteq 4.6 \times 1.2799$ From tangent

$\doteq 5.9$ column

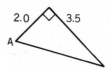

ii. $\sin (B) = \dfrac{3.29}{m}$ Def. sine ratio

$m = \dfrac{3.29}{\sin (B)}$

$\doteq \dfrac{3.29}{.8090}$ From sine

$\doteq 4.1$ column

a.

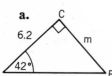

c.

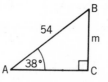

e.

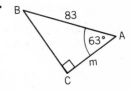

b.

d.

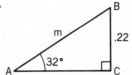

f.

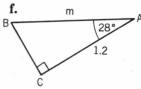

SOLVING RIGHT TRIANGLES

There are six measures associated with each right triangle: the degree-measures of its three angles and the measures of its three sides. Since the triangle is a right triangle, we always know one of these measures. Which one? If we are told two of the remaining five measures including the measure of at least one side, then we can compute the other three by the use of

> the trigonometric ratios
> the table of trigonometric ratios
> the fact that the acute angles are complementary
> the Pythagorean Relation

After we have determined the six measures, we say that the *triangle is solved*. Study the following examples in which certain right triangles are solved, beginning with the data given in the corresponding figure.

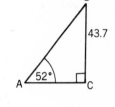

Example: *i.* The degree-measure of
angle B is 38.   **Why?**

$$\tan (A) = \frac{43.7}{AC}$$ Def. tangent
ratio

$$1.2799 \doteq \frac{43.7}{AC}$$ From tangent
column

$$AC \doteq \frac{43.7}{1.2799} \doteq 34.1$$

$$\sin (A) = \frac{43.7}{AB}$$ Def. sine ratio

$$.7880 \doteq \frac{43.7}{AB}$$ From sine column

$$AB \doteq \frac{43.7}{.7880} \doteq 55.3$$

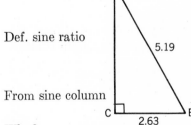

Example: *ii.* $\sin (A) = \dfrac{2.63}{5.19}$ Def. sine ratio

$$\doteq .5067$$

The degree-measure of
angle A is 30.   From sine column

The degree-measure of
angle B is 60.   **Why?**

$$\cos (A) = \frac{AC}{5.19}$$ Def. cosine ratio

$$.8660 \doteq \frac{AC}{5.19}$$ From cosine column

$$AC \doteq (5.19)(.8660)$$
$$AC \doteq 4.49$$

EXERCISES

Solve the following right triangles. Determine lengths to two digits and degree-measures to the nearest whole number.

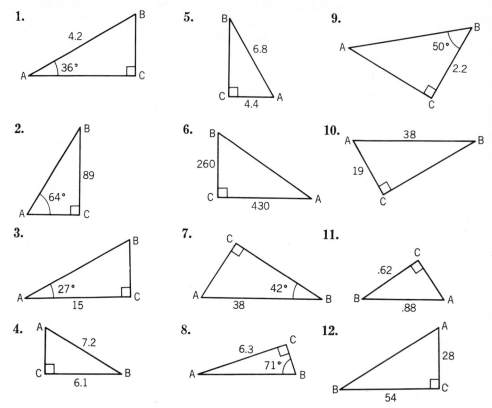

1. 4.2, 36°, A, B, C

2. 89, 64°, A, B, C

3. 27°, 15, A, B, C

4. A, 7.2, 6.1, C, B

5. B, 6.8, 4.4, C, A

6. B, 260, 430, C, A

7. C, 42°, 38, A, B

8. 6.3, 71°, C, A, B

9. A, 50°, 2.2, B, C

10. A, 38, 19, B, C

11. .62, .88, C, B, A

12. A, 28, 54, B, C

APPLIED PROBLEMS

We can compute the height of a given tree by making certain measurements and then solving a right triangle. See figure 8.

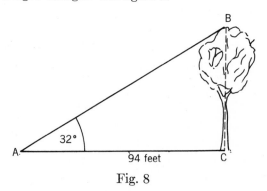

Fig. 8

If we measure a length away from the base of the tree and then measure the angle to the top of the tree, we can compute the tree's height. There is an instrument, called a sextant, that is used to sight and measure such angles. Suppose these measurements are as recorded in figure 8. Then

$$\tan (A) = \frac{BC}{94}$$

$$.6249 \doteq \frac{BC}{94}$$

$$BC \doteq 94(.6249)$$

$$BC \doteq 58.7, \text{ or } 59 \text{ to the nearest foot.}$$

The tree is *approximately* 59 feet in height. Give several reasons why the answer is approximate and not exact.

EXERCISES

Make a drawing for each problem. Find lengths to the nearest foot and degree-measures to the nearest whole number.

1.   Seventy feet from the base of the tallest monument in Granite City, the angle of elevation to the top of the monument is 42°. How high is the monument?

2.   A 45-foot ladder must be placed for safety at an angle of 74° with the ground. To what height on a wall will such a ladder reach?

3.   In problem **2,** how far from the wall is a person when he stands at the base of the ladder? How far is he from the wall after he has climbed half-way up?

4.   Al and Charles are 2500 feet apart at bird-watching stations. When Charles sees a huge flock of birds pass directly above him, he radios immediately to Al who sights the flock at a 48° angle of elevation. How high above Charles was the flock at the time he saw them?

5.   A boy 5 feet 3 inches tall casts a shadow 6 feet 6 inches long. What is the angle of elevation of the sun?

6.

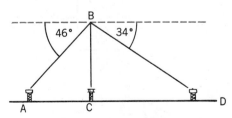

A pilot and his copilot are flying at an altitude of 2400 feet directly above a tower. The pilot measures the angle of depression to a tower due east to be 34° while the copilot measures the angle of depression to a tower due west to be 46°. How far apart are the two towers that they sighted?

30—60—90 TRIANGLES

Triangle KLM of figure 9 is an equilateral triangle. P is between K and L, and the line through M and P is perpendicular to the line through K and L. What is the degree-measure of angle K? of angle L? of angle 1 [$\angle 1$]? of $\angle 2$? of $\angle 3$? If $KM = 2x$ for some number x, then what is ML? KL? KP? PL?

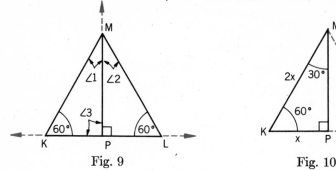

Fig. 9   Fig. 10

We shall now determine MP in terms of x. See figure 10.

$$\text{Since } (KP)^2 + (MP)^2 = (KM)^2$$
$$\text{it follows that} \quad x^2 + (MP)^2 = (2x)^2$$
$$x^2 + (MP)^2 = 4x^2$$
$$(MP)^2 = 3x^2$$
$$MP = x\sqrt{3}$$

Thus, for each right triangle, if one acute angle is a 30° angle, then

    i. the other acute angle is a 60° angle

    ii. the shorter leg is one-half the length of the hypotenuse

    iii. the length of the longer leg is $\sqrt{3}$ times the length of the shorter leg

Verify statements *i.*, *ii.*, and *iii.* for the following figures.

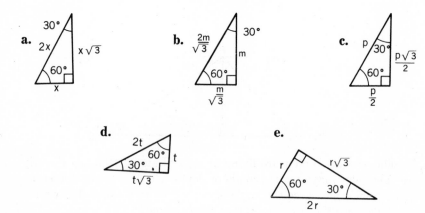

EXERCISES

1. For these problems, do *not* use the trigonometric tables. Solve the following right triangles.

Example:

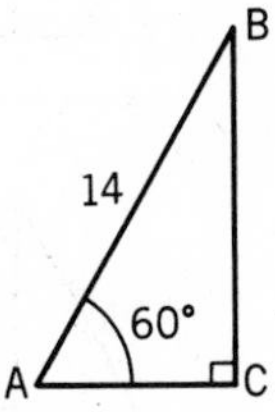

The degree-measure of angle B is 30.

$AC = 7$
$BC = 7\sqrt{3}$

a.

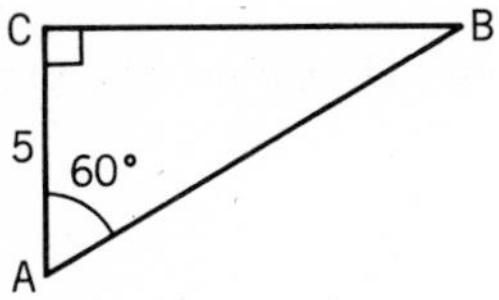

b.

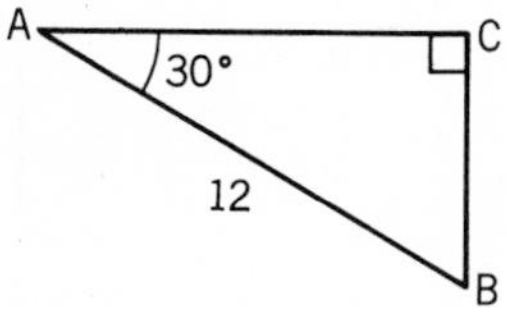

c.

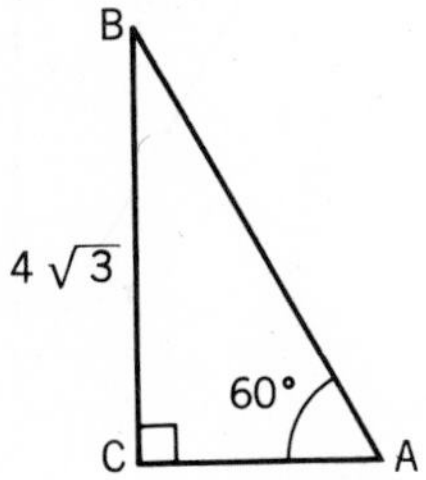

d.

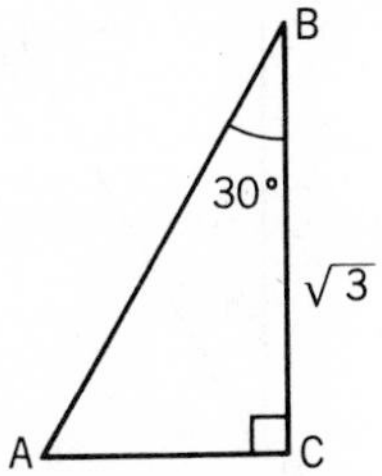

e.

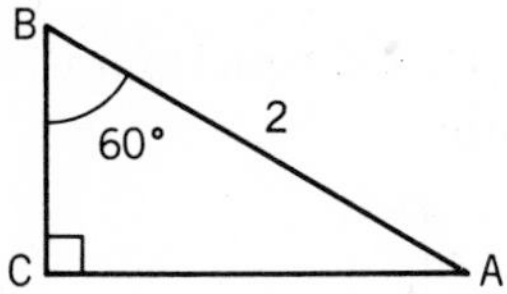

f.

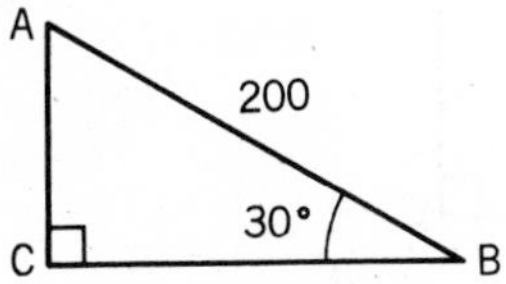

g.

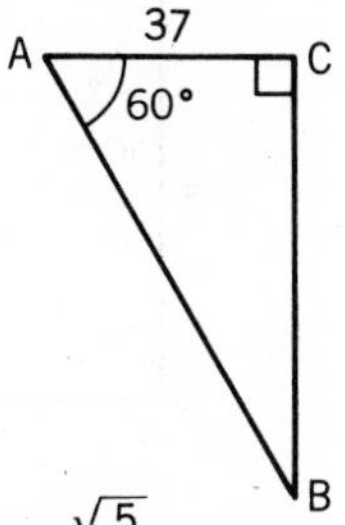

h.

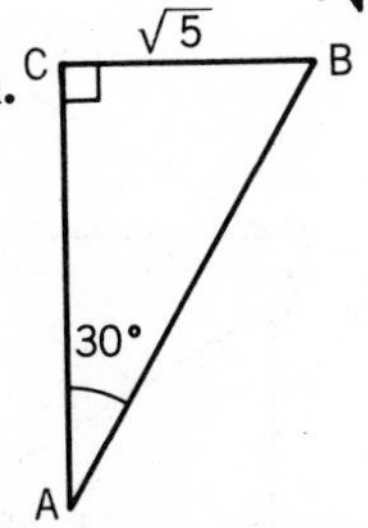

i.

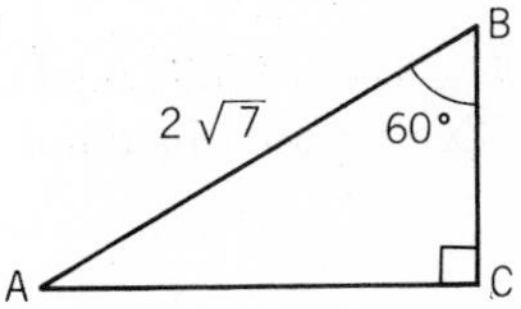

j.

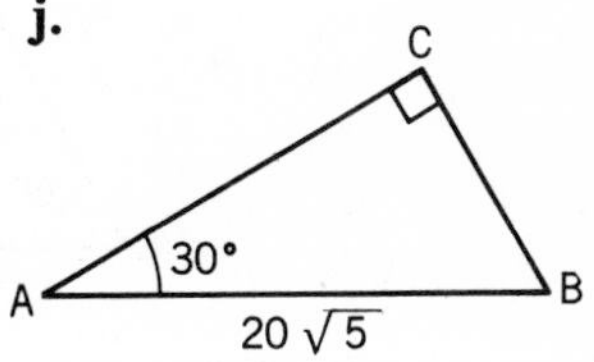

k.

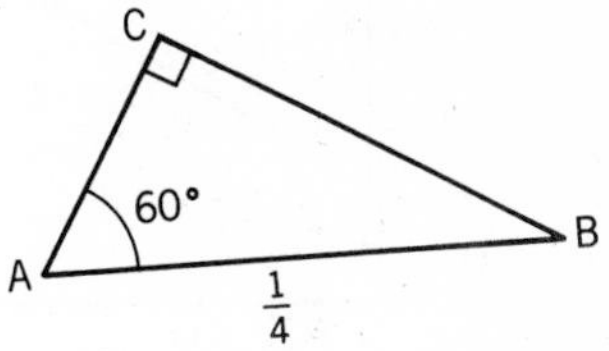

2. There are three right triangles pictured at the right. Find the length of every side of each triangle.

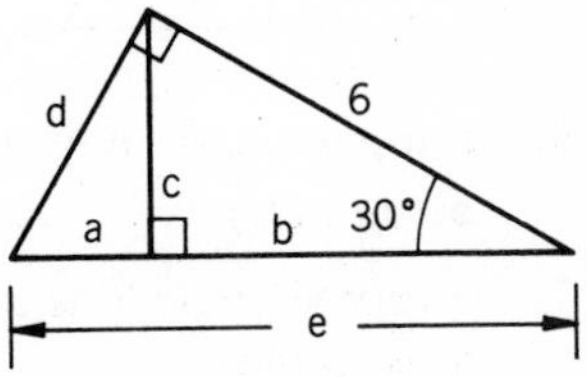

3.   There are three right triangles pictured at the right. Find the length of every side of each triangle.

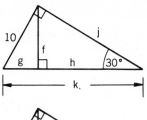

4.   There are three right triangles pictured at the right. In each triangle find the length of every side in terms of x.

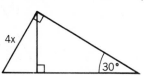

5.   Determine $\tan(A)$, $\sin(A)$, and $\cos(A)$ for each problem. Do *not* use the tables. Give answers in simplest form.

Example:

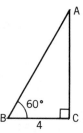

$$\tan(A) = \frac{4}{4\sqrt{3}} = \frac{1}{\sqrt{3}}$$

$$\sin(A) = \frac{4}{8} = \frac{1}{2}$$

$$\cos(A) = \frac{4\sqrt{3}}{8} = \frac{\sqrt{3}}{2}$$

a.

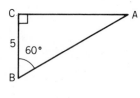

b.

c.

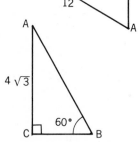

d.

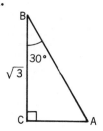

e.

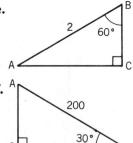

f.

g.

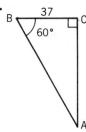

h.

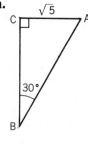

6.   Suppose angle K is a 30° angle. Determine each of the following:
   a. $\tan(K)$ **b.** $\sin(K)$ **c.** $\cos(K)$

7.   Suppose angle T is a 60° angle. Determine each of the following:
   a. $\tan(T)$ **b.** $\sin(T)$ **c.** $\cos(T)$

45—45—90 TRIANGLES

Consider the *square KLMN* of figure 11 and the diagonal *LN*. What is the degree-measure of angle *K*? Of ∠1? Of ∠2? If *KN* = 3, then determine *KL* and *NL*. [HINT: Make use of the definition of a square and then the Pythagorean Relation.] If *KN* = 2, then determine *KL* and *NL*. If *KN* = $\sqrt{5}$, then determine *KL* and *NL*. If *KN* = *x* for some positive real number *x*, then determine *KL* and *NL* in terms of *x*.

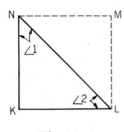

Fig. 11

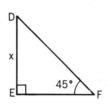

Fig. 12

Now we shall consider the right triangle *DEF* of figure 12. The degree-measure of angle *F* is 45. What is the degree-measure of angle *E*? Of angle *D*? If *DE* = *x* for some positive real number *x*, then what is *EF*? We shall now determine *DF* in terms of *x*.

Since $(DE)^2 + (EF)^2 = (DF)^2$

It follows that $x^2 + x^2 = (DF)^2$
$$2x^2 = (DF)^2$$
$$(DF)^2 = x^2 \cdot 2$$
$$DF = x \cdot \sqrt{2}$$

Thus, for each right triangle, if one acute angle is a 45° angle, then

i. the other acute angle is a 45° angle

ii. both legs have the same length

iii. the length of the hypotenuse is $\sqrt{2}$ times the length of a leg

Verify statements *i.*, *ii.*, and *iii.* for the following figures.

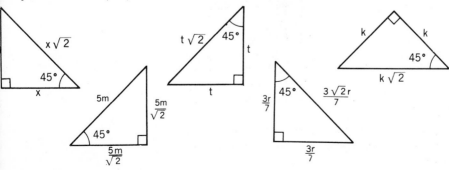

EXERCISES

1. In these problems, do *not* use the trigonometric tables. Solve the following right triangles.

Example:

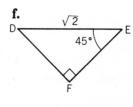

The degree-measure of angle B is 45.

$AC = 5$

$AB = 5\sqrt{2}$

a.

c.

e.

b.

d.

f.

2. There are three right triangles pictured below. Find the length of every side of each triangle.

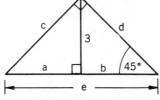

3. The circle meets each of the two squares in four points. A radius of the circle is 10 inches long. [All answers must be exact. You may use radical signs and π.]

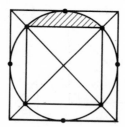

a. What is the length of a side of the smaller square?

b. What is the length of a side of the larger square?

c. What is the length of a diagonal of the smaller square?

d. What is the length of a diagonal of the larger square?

e. What is the area of the larger square? of the circle? of the smaller square?

f. What is the area of the shaded region?

4. Determine $\tan(A)$, $\sin(A)$, and $\cos(A)$ for each problem. Do *not* use the table. Give answers in simplest form.

Example:

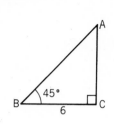

$$\tan(A) = \frac{6}{6} = 1$$

$$\sin(A) = \frac{6}{6\sqrt{2}} = \frac{1}{\sqrt{2}}$$

$$\cos(A) = \frac{6}{6\sqrt{2}} = \frac{1}{\sqrt{2}}$$

a.

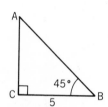

b.

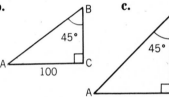

c.

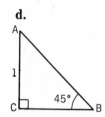

d.

5. Suppose angle M is a 45° angle. Determine each of the following:

a. $\tan(M)$ **b.** $\sin(M)$ **c.** $\cos(M)$

6. For the triangle of the adjoining figure, angle C is a right angle. Tell whether the following statements are true or false?

a. $a^2 + b^2 = c^2$

b. $a^2 = c^2 - b^2$

c. $b^2 = a^2 - c^2$

d. Angles A and B are complementary angles.

e. $\cos(A) = \dfrac{a}{c}$

f. $\sin(A) = \dfrac{a}{c}$

g. $\cos(B) = \dfrac{a}{b}$

h. $\cos(B) = \dfrac{a}{c}$

i. $\cos(A) = \sin(B)$

j. $\sin(A) = \cos(B)$

k. $\left(\dfrac{a}{c}\right) \div \left(\dfrac{b}{c}\right) = \dfrac{a}{b}$

l. $\dfrac{\sin(A)}{\cos(A)} = \tan(A)$

m. $\dfrac{\cos(B)}{\sin(B)} = \tan(A)$

n. $\dfrac{a^2 + b^2}{c^2} = 1$

o. $\sin^2(A) = \dfrac{a^2}{c^2}$

p. $\cos^2(A) = \dfrac{b^2}{c^2}$

q. $\sin^2(A) + \cos^2(A) = 1$

7. For the adjoining figure, determine each of the following:

    a. $\sin(A)$ **f.** $\tan(B)$

    b. $\cos(A)$ **g.** $\sin(D)$

    c. $\tan(A)$ **h.** $\cos(D)$

    d. $\sin(B)$ **i.** $\tan(D)$

    e. $\cos(B)$

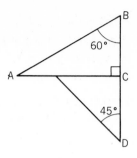

TRIGONOMETRY AND DEGREE-MEASURE

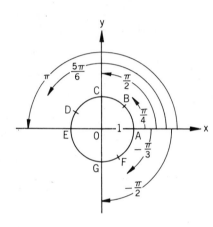

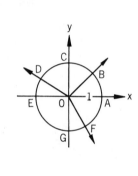

Fig. 13   Fig. 14

For the unit circle of figure 13, consider the six paths

$$\left(A, \frac{\pi}{4}\right), \left(A, \frac{\pi}{2}\right), \left(A, \frac{5\pi}{6}\right), (A, \pi), \left(A, -\frac{\pi}{3}\right), \text{ and } \left(A, -\frac{\pi}{2}\right)$$

with the terminal points B, C, D, E, F, and G, respectively. Each of these terminal points determines a ray whose initial point is the origin, O. In figure 14, these six rays are shown

$$\overrightarrow{OB}, \overrightarrow{OC}, \overrightarrow{OD}, \overrightarrow{OE}, \overrightarrow{OF}, \text{ and } \overrightarrow{OG}$$

The union of any one of these rays and the ray $\overrightarrow{OA}$ is an angle whose vertex is the origin, O. In figure 14 these six angles are shown

$$\angle AOB, \angle AOC, \angle AOD, \angle AOE, \angle AOF, \text{ and } \angle AOG$$

The ray $\overrightarrow{OA}$ is called the *initial side* of the angle and the other ray is called the *terminal side* of the angle. Which ray is the terminal side of $\angle AOD$?

Degree-measures are assigned to such angles by the following rule.

For each path (A, θ) with terminal point P,

a degree-measure of $\angle AOP$ is $\dfrac{180}{\pi} \cdot \theta$.

For figure 15 a degree-measure of

$$\angle AOP_1 \text{ is } \frac{180}{\pi} \cdot \theta_1$$

and a degree-measure of

$$\angle AOP_2 \text{ is } \frac{180}{\pi} \cdot \theta_2$$

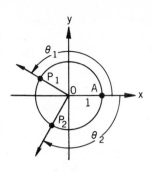

Fig. 15

Thus, for figures 13 and 14 a degree-measure of

$$\angle AOB \text{ is } \frac{180}{\pi} \cdot \frac{\pi}{4} \text{ or } 45 \qquad\qquad \angle AOE \text{ is } \frac{180}{\pi} \cdot \pi \text{ or } 180$$

$$\angle AOC \text{ is } \frac{180}{\pi} \cdot \frac{\pi}{2} \text{ or } 90 \qquad\qquad \angle AOF \text{ is } \frac{180}{\pi} \cdot \frac{-\pi}{3} \text{ or } -60$$

$$\angle AOD \text{ is } \frac{180}{\pi} \cdot \frac{5\pi}{6} \text{ or } 150 \qquad\qquad \angle AOG \text{ is } \frac{180}{\pi} \cdot \frac{-\pi}{2} \text{ or } -90$$

Observe that we speak of "a degree-measure of such an angle." Each such angle has many degree-measures assigned to it. For example, in figures 13 and 14 consider the many paths $\left(A, \dfrac{5\pi}{6} \pm 2n\pi \right)$. Each of these paths has terminal point D which determines $\angle AOD$. The degree-measures of $\angle AOD$ are $\dfrac{180}{\pi} \cdot \left(\dfrac{5\pi}{6} \pm 2n\pi \right)$ or $150 \pm 360n$. Some of these degree-measures which are assigned to $\angle AOD$ are 150, 510, 870, -210, and -570. List five degree-measures that are assigned to $\angle AOB$; to $\angle AOF$; to $\angle AOC$; to $\angle AOG$.

We are now able to compute a degree-measure c of the $\angle AOP$ which is determined by the path (A, θ) with terminal point P. One such number c is $\dfrac{180}{\pi} \cdot \theta$.

Examples: *i.* Determine a degree-measure c of the $\angle AOP$ for which P is the terminal point of the path $\left(A, \dfrac{5\pi}{3} \right)$.

$$c = \frac{180}{\pi} \cdot \frac{5\pi}{3} = 300; \text{ thus, } \angle AOP \text{ is a } 300° \text{ angle.}$$

ii. Determine a degree-measure c of the $\angle AOP$ for which P is the terminal point of the path $\left(A, -\dfrac{3\pi}{4} \right)$.

$$c = \frac{180}{\pi} \cdot \frac{-3\pi}{4} = -135; \text{ thus, } \angle AOP \text{ is a } -135° \text{ angle.}$$

Example: *iii.* Determine a degree-measure c of the $\angle AOP$ for which P is the terminal point of the path $(A, 0)$.

$$c = \frac{180}{\pi} \cdot 0 = 0; \text{ thus, } \angle AOP \text{ is a } 0° \text{ angle.}$$

Is $\angle AOP$ a $360°$ angle? [HINT: $(A, 0)$ and $(A, 2\pi)$ have the same terminal point.]

Is $\overrightarrow{OP}$ the same ray as $\overrightarrow{OA}$?

Conversely, we may determine a real number θ for which P is the terminal point of the path (A, θ) and for which the $\angle AOP$ is an angle of c degrees. Since $c = \dfrac{180}{\pi} \cdot \theta$, it follows that $\theta = c \cdot \dfrac{\pi}{180}$.

Examples: *i.* Determine a real number θ for which P is the terminal point of the path (A, θ) and for which the $\angle AOP$ is a $300°$ angle.

$$\theta = 300 \cdot \frac{\pi}{180} = \frac{5\pi}{3}; \text{ thus, the path } \left(A, \frac{5\pi}{3}\right) \text{ has } P \text{ as its}$$

terminal point.

ii. Determine θ so that P is the terminal point of the path (A, θ) and so that $\angle AOP$ is a $-225°$ angle.

$$\theta = -225 \cdot \frac{\pi}{180} = -\frac{5\pi}{4}$$

EXERCISES

1. For each path listed below, let its terminal point be P. Draw a unit circle as shown at the right and then draw the angle AOP.

a. $\left(A, \dfrac{\pi}{2}\right)$

b. $\left(A, \dfrac{3\pi}{4}\right)$

c. $\left(A, -\dfrac{3\pi}{4}\right)$

d. $\left(A, \dfrac{7\pi}{12}\right)$

e. (A, π)

f. $\left(A, \dfrac{\pi}{6}\right)$

g. $\left(A, -\dfrac{3\pi}{2}\right)$

h. $\left(A, -\dfrac{\pi}{3}\right)$

i. $(A, -\pi)$

j. $(A, -2\pi)$

k. $\left(A, \dfrac{5\pi}{2}\right)$

l. $(A, 0)$

2. For each angle AOP of problem **1**, determine a degree-measure of that angle.

3. Determine a value of θ such that the path (A, θ) will have its terminal point on the terminal side of the angle whose initial side is $\overrightarrow{OA}$ and whose degree-measure is given below.

   a. $60°$ **d.** $180°$ **g.** $-30°$ **j.** $360°$

   b. $-135°$ **e.** $-75°$ **h.** $70°$ **k.** $18°$

   c. $105°$ **f.** $195°$ **i.** $1°$ l $36°$

DEFINITION OF COSINE, SINE, AND TANGENT

As you might surmise from pages 464–465, every real number which describes the length of a path along a unit circle, can be given in terms of a degree-measure of an angle which corresponds to this path. It would be convenient to have a definition for degree-measure which would define the same range value, given in degree-measure symbolism and in θ symbolism, for corresponding domain values. Hence we state the following:

■ *Definition of Cosine, Sine, and Tangent for Degree-Measures*   For all real numbers c and θ, if $c = \dfrac{180}{\pi} \cdot \theta$, then

$$\cos(c°) = \cos(\theta)$$
$$\sin(c°) = \sin(\theta)$$
$$\tan(c°) = \tan(\theta), \quad (c \neq 90 \pm 180n)$$

Examples:
i. Compute $\cos(135°)$.

If $135 = \dfrac{180}{\pi} \cdot \theta$, then $\theta = \dfrac{\pi}{180} \cdot 135$ and $\theta = \dfrac{3\pi}{4}$.

Hence, $\cos(135°) = \cos\left(\dfrac{3\pi}{4}\right) = -\dfrac{1}{\sqrt{2}}$.

ii. Compute $\sin(180°)$.

If $180 = \dfrac{180}{\pi} \cdot \theta$, then $\theta = \dfrac{\pi}{180} \cdot 180$ and $\theta = \pi$.

Hence, $\sin(180°) = \sin(\pi) = 0$.

iii. Compute $\tan(-120°)$.

If $-120 = \dfrac{180}{\pi} \cdot \theta$, then $\theta = \dfrac{\pi}{180} \cdot (-120)$ and $\theta = -\dfrac{2\pi}{3}$.

Hence, $\tan(-120°) = \tan\left(-\dfrac{2\pi}{3}\right) = \dfrac{\sqrt{3}}{2}$.

On pages 436–437 ten important formulas were listed. We restate them here in terms of degree-measures x.

i. $\cos^2(x°) + \sin^2(x°) = 1$

ii. $\tan(x°) = \dfrac{\sin(x°)}{\cos(x°)}, \quad (x \neq 90 \pm 180n)$

iii. $\cos((x_1 - x_2)°) = \cos(x_1°) \cdot \cos(x_2°) + \sin(x_1°) \cdot \sin(x_2°)$

iv. $\cos((x_1 + x_2)°) = \cos(x_1°) \cdot \cos(x_2°) - \sin(x_1°) \cdot \sin(x_2°)$

v. $\sin((x_1 + x_2)°) = \sin(x_1°) \cdot \cos(x_2°) + \cos(x_1°) \cdot \sin(x_2°)$

vi. $\sin((x_1 - x_2)°) = \sin(x_1°) \cdot \cos(x_2°) - \cos(x_1°) \cdot \sin(x_2°)$

vii. $\cos(-x°) = \cos(x°)$

viii. $\sin(-x°) = -\sin(x°)$

ix. $\sin((90 - x)°) = \cos(x°)$

x. $\cos((90 - x)°) = \sin(x°)$

The following examples illustrate some uses of these formulas.

Examples: i. Verify that $\cos^2(60°) + \sin^2(60°) = 1$.

To verify this, recall that

$$\cos(60°) = \cos\left(\frac{\pi}{3}\right) = \frac{1}{2}$$

and that $\sin(60°) = \sin\left(\dfrac{\pi}{3}\right) = \dfrac{\sqrt{3}}{2}$

Thus $\cos^2(60°) + \sin^2(60°) = \left(\dfrac{1}{2}\right)^2 + \left(\dfrac{\sqrt{3}}{2}\right)^2$

$$= \frac{1}{4} + \frac{3}{4} = 1$$

ii. By *ii.* on page 467

$$\tan(150°) = \frac{\sin(150°)}{\cos(150°)}$$

Verify this by determining the value of each member of the equation.

iii. Find the value of $\cos(105°)$.

Using *iv.* we know that

$$\cos(105°) = \cos((60 + 45)°)$$
$$= \cos(60°) \cdot \cos(45°) - \sin(60°) \cdot \sin(45°)$$
$$= \frac{1}{2} \cdot \frac{1}{\sqrt{2}} - \frac{\sqrt{3}}{2} \cdot \frac{1}{\sqrt{2}}$$
$$= \frac{1}{2\sqrt{2}} - \frac{\sqrt{3}}{2\sqrt{2}}$$
$$= \frac{1 - \sqrt{3}}{2\sqrt{2}} \text{ or } \frac{\sqrt{2} - \sqrt{6}}{4}$$

iv. By *vii.* and *viii.* on page 467 we know that

$$\cos(-30°) = \cos(30°) \text{ and } \sin(-30°) = -\sin(30°)$$

Verify both statements by determining the value of both members of the equations.

v. By *ix.* and *x.* we know that

$$\sin((90 - 30)°) = \cos(30°) \text{ and } \cos((90 - 120)°) = \sin(120°)$$

Verify both statements by determining the value of both members of the equations.

EXERCISES

1. Determine the value of each of the following if the symbol is defined.

a. $\cos(60°)$

b. $\cos(210°)$

c. $\cos^2(135°)$

d. $\sin(0°)$

e. $\sin(90°)$

f. $\sin(225°)$

g. $\cos(-30°)$

h. $\sin(-30°)$

i. $\tan(-180°)$

j. $\tan(90°)$

k. $\tan(135°)$

l. $\tan(120°)$

m. $\cos(15°)$ [HINT: $15 = 60 - 45$.]

n. $\sin(105°)$

o. $\sin(-15°)$

p. $\cos(-105°)$

q. $\cos(255°)$

r. $\sin(285°)$

2. True or false?

a. $\dfrac{\sin(32°)}{\cos(32°)} = \tan(32°)$

b. $-\cos(83°) = \cos(-83°)$

c. $\cos^2(16°) + \sin^2(16°) = \dfrac{\sin(85°)}{\cos(5°)}$

d. $\sin(-83°) = -\sin(83°)$

e. $\cos(180°) = -\sin(90°)$

f. $\cos(45°) = \sin(135°)$

g. $\sin(45°) = \cos(135°)$

h. $\cos(158°) = -\sin(22°)$

i. $\sin((30 + 60)°) = \sin(30°) + \sin(60°)$

j. $\cos(120°) = 2 \cdot \cos^2(60°) - 1$

k. $\sin(-120°) = 2 \cdot \sin(-60°) \cdot \cos(-60°)$

l. $\cos(240°) = \cos^2(120°) - \sin^2(120°)$

m. $\sin(255°) = \sin(300°) \cdot \cos(45°) + \cos(300°) \cdot \sin(45°)$

n. $\cos(285°) = \cos(315°) \cdot \cos(-30°) - \sin(315°) \cdot \sin(-30°)$

VOCABULARY

Use each of the following correctly in a sentence. Numerals in parentheses refer to pages where these words were used. If you are not sure of the meaning of any word, turn to the indicated pages.

adjacent leg (448)
cosine for degree-measure (467)
cosine ratio (451)
opposite leg (448)
similar triangles (447)

sine for degree-measure (467)
sine ratio (451)
tangent for degree-measure (467)
tangent ratio (451)
trigonometry (447)

REVIEW EXERCISES

1. Consider the right triangle ABC shown below at the right and then decide whether each statement below is true or false.

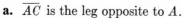

a. $\overline{AC}$ is the leg opposite to A.
b. $a^2 = c^2 - b^2$
c. $\sin(B) = \dfrac{a}{c}$
d. $\sin(A) = \cos(B)$
e. $\sin(A) + \cos(A) = 1$
f. If $a = 2$ and if $b = 3$, then $\sin(A) = \dfrac{2}{5}$.
g. If $a = 5$ and if $b = 7$, then $\tan(B) = \dfrac{7}{5}$.
h. If $\angle A$ is a $37°$ angle, then $\angle B$ is a $63°$ angle.
i. Angles A and B are supplementary.

2. A ship is sailing at an angle of $37°$ north of due east. It passes near an iceberg and continues for 14.2 miles. A second ship which is then due south of the first ship radios the first ship and learns of the danger. To the nearest tenth of a mile, how far to the east is the second ship from the iceberg?

3. Given right triangle ABC and that $\angle A$ is a $30°$ angle and that $\angle C$ is a right angle, determine each of the following.

a. $\sin(A)$
b. $\tan(A)$
c. $\cos(A)$
d. $\cos(B)$
e. $\tan(B)$
f. $\sin(B)$
g. The area of $\triangle ABC$ if $AB = 6$ inches.

4. Given isosceles right triangle DEF and that $\angle F$ is a right angle, determine each of the following.

a. $\sin(D)$
b. $\cos(D)$
c. $\tan(E)$
d. DE if $EF = 6$ cm.

5. True or false?

a. $\sin(150°) = \cos(60°)$
b. $\cos(150°) = \sin(60°)$
c. $\tan(20°) = \tan(380°)$
d. $\tan(50°) = \tan(-50°)$
e. $\cos(50°) = \cos(-50°)$
f. $\tan(90°)$ is undefined.

6. Determine the value of each of the following.

a. $\sin(-150°)$
b. $\tan(135°)$
c. $\cos(-120°)$
d. $\tan(180°)$
e. $\sin(240°)$
f. $\cos(225°)$
g. $\sin(105°)$
h. $\cos(15°)$

7. Given that for all real numbers a and b

$$\cos((a - b)°) = \cos(a°) \cdot \cos(b°) + \sin(a°) \cdot \sin(b°)$$

derive a formula for $\cos((x + y)°)$ in terms of $\cos(x°)$, $\sin(x°)$, $\cos(y°)$, and $\sin(y°)$.

8. Suppose that the degree-measures of angles K, T, and J are 30, 45, and 60, respectively. Determine the following:

a. $\sin(K)$
b. $\tan(K)$
c. $\cos(K)$
d. $\sin(T)$

e. $\tan(T)$
f. $\sin(J)$
g. $\cos(J)$
h. $\tan(J)$

9. What is the degree-measure of the acute angle A if $\sin(A) = \dfrac{\sqrt{3}}{2}$?

10. Solve each of the right triangles.

a.

b.

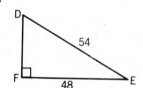

CHAPTER TEST

1. Given right triangle KLM with right angle M, answer the following.

a. Which leg is adjacent to L?
b. Determine $\cos(K)$ if $KL = 7$ and $LM = 3$.
c. Determine $\sin(K)$ if $\cos(L) = \frac{2}{3}$.
d. Determine $\tan(K)$ if $\cos(K) = \frac{5}{6}$.
e. Determine $\sin(K)$ if $\angle K$ is a 30° angle.
f. Determine $\cos(L)$ if $\triangle KLM$ is isosceles.
g. Determine $\tan(K)$ if $\angle L$ is a 30° angle.

2. Determine the value of each of the following.

a. $\cos(390°)$
b. $\sin(-45°)$
c. $\cos(0°)$
d. $\sin(90°)$
e. $\cos(-60°)$
f. $\sin(-210°)$

g. $\tan(180°)$
h. $\sin^2(300°) + \cos^2(300°)$
i. $\cos(135°)$
j. $\sin(240°)$
k. $\tan(-30°)$
l. $\tan(240°)$

3. Given that for all real numbers x and y

$$\sin((x + y)^\circ) = \sin(x^\circ) \cdot \cos(y^\circ) + \cos(x^\circ) \cdot \sin(y^\circ)$$

answer the following.

   a. Determine $\sin(105^\circ)$.
   b. Determine $\sin(165^\circ)$.
   c. Derive a formula for $\sin((m - n)^\circ)$ in terms of $\sin(m^\circ)$, $\sin(n^\circ)$, $\cos(m^\circ)$, and $\cos(n^\circ)$.
   d. Derive a formula for $\sin(2c^\circ)$ in terms of $\sin(c^\circ)$ and $\cos(c^\circ)$.

BIBLIOGRAPHY

Allendoerfer, C. and Oakley, C. *Fundamentals of Freshman Mathematics*. New York: McGraw-Hill Book Co., Inc., 1959. pp. 265–298.

Dubisch, R. *Trigonometry*. New York: Ronald Press Co., 1955. Chapters 2, 3, 4, 7.

Hogben, L. *Mathematics for the Million*. New York: W. W. Norton and Co., Inc., 1951. Chapter 6.

Moore, J. T. *Fundamental Principles of Mathematics*. New York: Holt, Rinehart and Winston, Inc., 1960. pp. 105–125, 172–210.

Sanford, V. *A Short History of Mathematics*. New York: Houghton Mifflin Co., 1930. pp. 291–307.

School Mathematics Study Group. *Elementary Functions*. New Haven: Yale University Press, 1961. pp. 225–242.

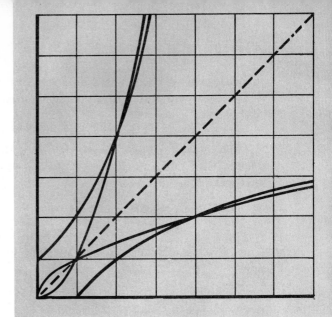

CHAPTER 15

Sequences and Series

ARITHMETIC PROGRESSIONS

Let us begin with a very simple sequence of numbers

$$1, 2, 3, \ldots, 98, 99, 100$$

This is the *sequence* of natural numbers from 1 through 100. Now consider the problem of finding the sum of these one hundred numbers. To try to compute this sum in the following way

$$1 + 2 = 3$$
$$1 + 2 + 3 = 6$$
$$1 + 2 + 3 + 4 = 10$$
$$1 + 2 + 3 + 4 + 5 = 15$$
$$\text{etc.}$$

would be quite a long and boring task. To avoid the drudgery involved in this method, we resort to a procedure which gives the desired result in seconds.

$$1 + \quad 2 + \quad 3 + \ldots + \quad 98 + \quad 99 + 100$$
$$100 + \quad 99 + \quad 98 + \ldots + \quad 3 + \quad 2 + \quad 1$$

$$\overline{101 + 101 + 101 + \ldots + 101 + 101 + 101}$$

473

Explain what was done in the display above. Do you see that 101×100 is equal to twice the sum of the natural numbers from 1 through 100? Since $101 \times 100 = 10{,}100$

$$1 + 2 + 3 + \ldots + 98 + 99 + 100 = 5{,}050$$

The above procedure presents us with a clue for determining sums of sequences of numbers similar to those above. To generalize this procedure, we first make some definitions.

■   *Definition of Arithmetic Progression*   A sequence of n numbers

$$a_1, a_2, a_3, \ldots, a_n$$

is called an *arithmetic progression* if and only if for some number d

$$a_2 = a_1 + d$$
$$a_3 = a_1 + 2d$$
$$a_4 = a_1 + 3d$$

$$\cdot$$
$$\cdot$$
$$\cdot$$

$$a_{n-1} = a_1 + (n-2)d$$
$$a_n = a_1 + (n-1)d$$

Each of the numbers a, $a + d$, $a + 2d$, and so on is called a *term* of the arithmetic progression; d is called the *common difference* of the progression.

EXERCISES

1.   Using a, $a + d$, $a + 2d$, $\ldots$, $[a + (n-3)d]$, $[a + (n-2)d]$, $[a + (n-1)d]$ as the form of an arithmetic progression, identify the first term, a, and the common difference, d, in each of the following arithmetic progressions.

Example: $6, 3, 0, \ldots, -21, -24, -27$
                 a is 6; d is -3.

  a. $2, 4, 6, \ldots, 98, 100$
  b. $3, 5, 7, \ldots, 191, 193, 195$
  c. $26, 22, 18, \ldots, -14, -18, -22$
  d. $5, 5\frac{1}{3}, 5\frac{2}{3}, \ldots, 19\frac{1}{3}, 19\frac{2}{3}, 20$
  e. $1, 1 + \sqrt{2}, 1 + 2\sqrt{2}, \ldots, 1 + 28\sqrt{2}, 1 + 29\sqrt{2}, 1 + 30\sqrt{2}$
  f. $1 + i, 1, 1 - i, \ldots, 1 - 13i, 1 - 14i, 1 - 15i$
  g. $3 + 4i, 2 + 2i, 1, \ldots, -15 - 32i, -16 - 34i, -17 - 36i$

2.   Present an argument showing that there are n terms in
     $$a, a + d, a + 2d, \ldots, [a + (n-3)d], [a + (n-2)d], [a + (n-1)d]$$

3.   Note that the nth term, a_n, of an arithmetic progression is equal to $[a + (n-1)d]$; that is, it is the first term, a, plus $(n-1)$ multiplied by the common difference, d. In each of the following progressions there are given the first three terms and the nth term. Determine the number of the last term, n.

Example: 5, 1, −3, ..., −103

Since the last term is −103 $a + (n - 1)d = -103$
and since $a = 5$ and $d = -4$ $5 + (n - 1)(-4) = -103$
$(n - 1)(-4) = -108$
$n - 1 = 27$
$n = 28$

Therefore, −103 is the 28th term.

a. 5, 11, 17, ..., 557

b. 1, −4, −9, ..., −139

c. 3, $3\frac{1}{2}$, 4, ..., 120

d. $2 - i, 1, i, \ldots, -18 + 19i$

e. $5 + \sqrt{3}, 5 + 3\sqrt{3}, 5 + 5\sqrt{3}, \ldots, 5 + 39\sqrt{3}$

ARITHMETIC SERIES

Let us now generalize the problem of determining the *sum* of an arithmetic progression. Suppose that

$$a_1, a_2, a_3, \ldots, a_{n-2}, a_{n-1}, a_n$$

is an arithmetic progression in which the first term is a_1 and the nth (last) term is a_n. Explain why $a_2 - a_1 = a_3 - a_2 = \ldots = a_n - a_{n-1}$.

■ *Definition of Arithmetic Series*   An *arithmetic series* is a sum shown in the form

$$a + (a + d) + (a + 2d) + \ldots + [a + (n - 1)d]$$

To find this sum, we use the same procedure we resorted to in determining the sum of the natural numbers from 1 through 100. Let S_n be the sum of the n terms of the series. Then

$$S_n = a_1 + a_2 + a_3 + \ldots + a_{n-2} + a_{n-1} + a_n$$

However, since $a_{n-1} = a_n - d$, $a_{n-2} = a_n - 2d$, and so forth, we may also write

$$S_n = (a_1) + (a_1 + d) + (a_1 + 2d) + \ldots + (a_n - 2d) + (a_n - d) + (a_n)$$
$$S_n = (a_n) + (a_n - d) + (a_n - 2d) + \ldots + (a_1 + 2d) + (a_1 + d) + (a_1)$$

Adding
$$2S_n = (a_1 + a_n) + (a_1 + a_n) + (a_1 + a_n) + \ldots + (a_1 + a_n) + (a_1 + a_n) + (a_1 + a_n)$$

$$n \text{ binomials}$$

Thus, $2S_n = n(a_1 + a_n)$ and $S_n = \dfrac{n(a_1 + a_n)}{2}$.

This formula enables us to determine the sum, S_n, of n terms of an arithmetic progression if we know the number of terms, n, the first term, a_1, and the last term, a_n.

Describe in words the formula for the sum of n terms of an arithmetic progression.

EXERCISES

1. Each series is described by n, the number of terms; a_1, the first term; and a_n, the last term. Determine S_n, the sum, in each case.

a. $n = 100$; $a_1 = 1$; $a_n = 20$

b. $n = 200$; $a_1 = 1$; $a_n = 200$

c. $n = 300$; $a_1 = 1$; $a_n = 300$

d. $n = 400$; $a_1 = 1$; $a_n = 400$

e. $n = 500$; $a_1 = 1$; $a_n = 500$

f. $n = 40$; $a_1 = -1$; $a_n = -40$

g. $n = 50$; $a_1 = 1$; $a_n = 99$

h. $n = 70$; $a_1 = 1$; $a_n = 139$

i. $n = 50$; $a_1 = 2$; $a_n = 100$

j. $n = 60$; $a_1 = 2$; $a_n = 120$

k. $n = 100$; $a_1 = 2$; $a_n = 200$

l. $n = 20$; $a_1 = 5$; $a_n = 100$

m. $n = 10$; $a_1 = 4$; $a_n = -32$

n. $n = 20$; $a_1 = 1 + \sqrt{2}$;
$a_n = 1 - 18\sqrt{2}$

o. $n = 50$; $a_1 = 2 + 3i$;
$a_n = -47 - 144i$

2. In the formula $S_n = \dfrac{n(a_1 + a_n)}{2}$ replace a_n by $[a_1 + (n-1)d]$ and simplify to obtain another formula for S_n.

3. Each series is described by giving n, a_1, and d. Determine the sum in each case, using the formula you obtained in problem **2.**

a. $n = 20$; $a_1 = 2$; $d = 3$

b. $n = 15$; $a_1 = 1$; $d = -4$

c. $n = 50$; $a_1 = 1$; $d = 2$

d. $n = 100$; $a_1 = 2$; $d = 2$

4. Verify that the nth positive odd number is equal to $2n - 1$ by replacing n by 1, 2, 3, and 4 to see that these replacements result in the first four odd numbers.

5. Use the formula $S_n = \dfrac{n(a_1 + a_n)}{2}$ to prove that the sum of the first n odd numbers is equal to n^2.

6. Verify that the nth positive even number is equal to $2n$. [HINT: See problem **4.**]

7. Use the formula $S_n = \dfrac{n(a_1 + a_n)}{2}$ to prove that the sum of the first n even numbers is equal to $n(n + 1)$.

8. The terms of an arithmetic progression which are between the first and the last terms are called *arithmetic means*. For example, in the arithmetic progression, 2, 5, 8, 11, 14, the three arithmetic means between 2 and 14 are 5, 8, and 11. Determine the following:

a. the one arithmetic mean between -5 and 1

b. the two arithmetic means between -1 and 14

c. the three arithmetic means between 1 and -1

d. the five arithmetic means between $-3\sqrt{2}$ and $15\sqrt{2}$

9. Find the value of x such that $x + 3, 2 - 3x, 6 - 2x$ will form an arithmetic progression. [HINT: $d = a_2 - a_1 = a_3 - a_2$.]

10. Find two values of m such that $\dfrac{1}{m}, 1, \dfrac{6}{m + 2}$ will form an arithmetic progression.

11. Jane decided on a system of saving money regularly during a thirty-day period. It called for saving 1¢ the first day and *increasing* the saving by 1¢ each successive day. In other words, she saved 1¢ the first day, 2¢ the second day, 3¢ the third day, and so on. How much money would Jane have saved at the end of thirty days?

12. A teacher's salary for the tenth year at Prosperous High School was $12,200. If his increases in salary were $600 each year, what was his salary for the first year?

13. A debt of $3600 is to be retired over a period of 3 years by making payments of $100 at the end of each month, plus the interest at the rate of 1% per month on the outstanding balance. How much interest will be paid by the time the debt is retired?

14. A manufacturer calculates that he will lose $20 if he makes only one unit of an item. When making more than one unit, his total profit will increase by $1 for each additional unit. What will his profit be after manufacturing 5,000 units?

15. Mr. Thrifty deposits $500 in his savings account on January 1. Each month thereafter he deposits $125 more than on the previous month.

   a. What was Mr. Thrifty's deposit on December 1 of the same year?

   b. What was the sum of his deposits made from January 1 through December 1?

   c. If at the end of each month he is mailed a check in the amount equal to $\frac{1}{2}\%$ of the balance in his account, how much money did he receive in the mail by the end of December?

GEOMETRIC PROGRESSIONS

Consider this simple sequence of numbers

$$1, 2, 4, \ldots, 1024, 2048, 4096$$

Undoubtedly, you discovered that each number in the sequence (after the first) is obtained by multiplying the preceding number by 2. It is an example of a geometric progression.

■   *Definition of Geometric Progression*   A sequence of numbers

$$a_1, a_2, a_3, \ldots, a_n$$

is called a *geometric progression* if and only if for some number $r \neq 0$

$$a_2 = a_1 r$$
$$a_3 = a_1 r^2$$
$$a_4 = a_1 r^3$$
$$\cdot$$
$$\cdot$$
$$\cdot$$
$$a_{n-1} = a_1 r^{n-2}$$
$$a_n = a_1 r^{n-1}$$

Each of the numbers a, ar, ar^2, and so on is called a *term* of the geometric progression; r is called the *common ratio* of the progression.

EXERCISES

1. Using

$$a, ar, ar^2, \ldots, ar^{n-3}, ar^{n-2}, ar^{n-1}$$

as the form of a geometric progression, identify a and r in each of the following partially displayed geometric progressions.

Example: 1, 3, 9, ...

a is 1; r is 3.

a. 2, 4, 8, ...

b. 5, −10, 20, ...

c. 2, 1, $\frac{1}{2}$, ...

d. 10, −2, $\frac{2}{5}$, ...

e. $\sqrt{2}$, 2, $2\sqrt{2}$, ...

f. 3, $-3\sqrt{3}$, 9, ...

g. 3, .6, .12, ...

h. i, −1, −i, 1, ...

i. $2i$, −2, −$2i$, ...

j. $1 + i$, $2i$, $-2 + 2i$, ...

2. Present an argument showing that there are n terms in

$$a, ar, ar^2, \ldots, ar^{n-3}, ar^{n-2}, ar^{n-1}$$

3. Tell which of the following sequences are the first three terms of *geometric progressions* and which are not.

a. 1, −1, 1, ...

b. 1, 2, 3, ...

c. $-\frac{1}{2}$, −1, −2, ...

d. $\sqrt{3}$, $2\sqrt{3}$, $3\sqrt{3}$, ...

e. 2^2, 3^2, 4^2, ...

f. $2 \cdot 4$, $2 \cdot 4^2$, $2 \cdot 4^3$, ...

g. i, −1, −i, ...

h. $2i$, $4i$, $6i$, ...

i. $\frac{1}{2}$, $\frac{1}{3}$, $\frac{1}{4}$, ...

j. $(\frac{1}{2})^2$, $(\frac{1}{3})^2$, $(\frac{1}{4})^2$, ...

k. .1, .01, .001, ...

l. 10, 100, 1000, ...

GEOMETRIC SERIES

Let us return to the example of the geometric progression which we used at the beginning of the last section.

$$1, 2, 4, \ldots, 1024, 2048, 4096$$

Suppose we attempt to determine the sum of the terms of this sequence. We could, of course, fill in the missing terms and add, but this would be a tedious task. We again resort to a device which simplifies the task. Let us call the sum of the numbers S. We multiply each number by the common ratio, which is 2 in this case, and subtract as shown at the top of the next page.

$$2S = \quad\ \ 2 + 4 + 8 + \ldots + 2048 + 4096 + 8192$$
$$S = 1 + 2 + 4 + 8 + \ldots + 2048 + 4096$$

$$2S - S = 8192 - 1$$
$$S = 8191$$

We can generalize this procedure, showing that it applies to every geometric series of n terms.

$$S = a + ar + ar^2 + \ldots + ar^{n-3} + ar^{n-2} + ar^{n-1}$$

Multiplying by r

$$rS = \quad\ \ ar + ar^2 + ar^3 + \ldots + ar^{n-2} + ar^{n-1} + ar^n$$
$$S \ = a + ar + ar^2 + ar^3 + \ldots + ar^{n-2} + ar^{n-1}$$

Subtracting, $Sr - S = ar^n - a$
$$S(r - 1) = a(r^n - 1)$$
$$S = \frac{a(r^n - 1)}{r - 1}$$

This formula enables us to find the sum, S, knowing the first term, a; the common ratio, r; and the number of terms, n, in a geometric progression.

EXERCISES

1. Find the sum of the indicated number of terms of each progression.

Example: $\frac{1}{3}, 1, 3, \ldots$; 8 terms.

$$S = \frac{a(r^n - 1)}{r - 1} = \frac{\frac{1}{3}(3^8 - 1)}{3 - 1} = \frac{\frac{1}{3}(6561 - 1)}{2} = \frac{6560}{6} = 1093\frac{1}{3}$$

a. $\frac{1}{2}, 2, 8, \ldots$; 8 terms   **d.** $\frac{1}{2}, -2, 8, \ldots$; 8 terms

b. $2, 1, \frac{1}{2}, \ldots$; 10 terms   **e.** $2, -1, \frac{1}{2}, \ldots$; 10 terms

c. $1, \frac{1}{3}, \frac{1}{9}, \ldots$; 6 terms   **f.** $10, -2, \frac{2}{5}, \ldots$; 6 terms

2. Give the next three terms of each of the following geometric progressions.

a. $2, 10, \ldots$ **e.** $\sqrt{2}, -2, \ldots$

b. $-1, 10, \ldots$ **f.** $1, \pi, \ldots$

c. $9, 3, \ldots$ **g.** $i, -1, \ldots$

d. $1, \sqrt{3}, \ldots$ **h.** $(1 - i), 2, \ldots$

3. Call the first term of a geometric progression a_1 and the nth term a_n. Then $a_n = a_1 r^{n-1}$. By appropriate substitutions, obtain a formula for the sum $S = \frac{a_1(r^n - 1)}{r - 1}$, which contains a_n in it. [HINT: $a_1 r^n = a_1 r^{n-1} \cdot r$.]

4. For each case, find all the values of x such that a beginning of a geometric progression is obtained. [HINT: There may be more than one value of x.]

     a. $\frac{1}{2}, x, 32, \ldots$ **b.** $\frac{1}{3}, x, \frac{1}{48}, \ldots$ **c.** $\sqrt{x-1}, \sqrt{x-2}, \sqrt{9x-9}, \ldots$

5. Solve the formula $S = \dfrac{a(r^n - 1)}{r - 1}$ for a in terms of the other variables.

6. Using the formula you obtained in problem **5,** determine the first term of a geometric progression of 5 terms if its sum is 127 and its common ratio is $\frac{1}{3}$.

7. If x, y, and z are the terms of a geometric progression, write an equation showing y in terms of x and z. [HINT: $a_2 \div a_1 = a_3 \div a_2 = r$.]

8. The terms of a geometric progression which are between the first and the last terms are called *geometric means*. Prove that a geometric mean of two numbers is a square root of the product of these two numbers.

9. Determine the positive middle term if the first and third terms of a three-term geometric progression are as follows:

    a. $1, \frac{1}{16}$ **b.** $\sqrt{3}, \; 27\sqrt{3}$ **c.** $-1, \; -144$ **d.** $-\frac{1}{3}, \; -243$

10. Determine the middle term if the first and third terms of a three-term geometric progression are as follows:

    a. $1 + i, \; 7 - i$ **b.** $i, \; 2i$ **c.** $1 + i, \; -1 - i$ **d.** $2i, \; -2i$

11. Determine the second and third terms of a four-term geometric progression, if the first and fourth terms are as follows:

    a. $\frac{1}{2}, 32$ **b.** $-1, 1$ **c.** $\sqrt{2}, 4$ **d.** $i, 1$

12. Determine which one of the following amounts to more money: **a.** a payment of $1 followed by 11 payments, each consecutive payment equaling twice the preceding one; or **b.** $5,000.

13. In problem **12,** by how many dollars does the larger amount exceed the smaller?

14. In January Mr. Adams writes ten letters, one letter to each of ten persons. The following month each of the ten persons who received a letter from Mr. Adams writes ten letters to ten other persons. The same process is repeated by each person receiving a letter in February. If the population of the earth is approximately three billion, how many months would it take for the majority of all people to receive one letter each?

15. The sum of $100 is invested at 5% compounded annually. This means that the interest is computed at the end of each year, added to the amount of investment, and the new amount draws interest the following year. Approximately how much interest does the $100 investment earn in 5 years? (Compute to nearest $.01.)

16. A depositor puts $100 each quarter into a savings fund which earns interest at 4% compounded quarterly. How much money is there in the fund at the end of 5 years? [HINT: Use logarithms.]

Summation notation

In dealing with series, we often are involved with expressions which are sums of many terms. To simplify writing, we shall introduce a more convenient notation. We use the Greek letter $\sum$ (read: sigma) as a summation symbol.

The examples below show how $\sum$ is used. Study each example.

Examples: i. $\displaystyle\sum_{k=1}^{5} k = 1 + 2 + 3 + 4 + 5$

ii. $\displaystyle\sum_{k=1}^{4} 3^k = 3^1 + 3^2 + 3^3 + 3^4$

iii. $\displaystyle\sum_{k=1}^{6} a_k = a_1 + a_2 + a_3 + a_4 + a_5 + a_6$

iv. $\displaystyle\sum_{k=1}^{n} a_k = a_1 + a_2 + \ldots + a_n$

v. $\displaystyle\sum_{k=1}^{4} k(k+1) = 1(1+1) + 2(2+1) + 3(3+1) + 4(4+1)$

vi. $\displaystyle\sum_{k=1}^{n} a_k r^{k-1} = a_1 r^0 + a_2 r^1 + a_3 r^2 + \ldots + a_n r^{n-1}$

vii. $\displaystyle\sum_{k=1}^{n} ab^k = ab + ab^2 + ab^3 + \ldots + ab^n$

The exercises below will provide you with an opportunity to practice the use of the summation symbol. Refer to the examples if you are not sure how $\sum$ is used.

EXERCISES

1. Write in an expanded form as in the examples above.

a. $\displaystyle\sum_{k=1}^{6} k$

b. $\displaystyle\sum_{k=1}^{5} 2k$

c. $\displaystyle\sum_{k=1}^{7} (2k-1)$

d. $\displaystyle\sum_{k=1}^{n} 2^k$

e. $\displaystyle\sum_{k=1}^{n} 5^{2k-1}$

f. $\displaystyle\sum_{k=1}^{5} c_k$

g. $\displaystyle\sum_{k=1}^{n} a^{k+1}$

h. $\displaystyle\sum_{k=1}^{5} 2k(k+1)$

i. $\displaystyle\sum_{k=1}^{n} a_k b_{k+1}$

j. $\displaystyle\sum_{k=1}^{n} ca^{2k-1}$

l. $\displaystyle\sum_{k=1}^{n} (a_k + d)$

n. $\displaystyle\sum_{k=1}^{n} \frac{k^2}{2k(2k-1)}$

k. $\displaystyle\sum_{k=1}^{n} \frac{k}{k+1}$

m. $\displaystyle\sum_{k=1}^{n} k^2(k+2)$

o. $\displaystyle\sum_{k=1}^{n} \frac{k^3}{k^2+2}$

2.   Expand $\displaystyle\sum_{k=1}^{n} ca_k$ and $\displaystyle c\sum_{k=1}^{n} a_k$, and show that $\displaystyle\sum_{k=1}^{n} ca_k = c\sum_{k=1}^{n} a_k$.

3.   By expanding, show that $\displaystyle\sum_{k=1}^{n} (a_k + b_k) = \sum_{k=1}^{n} a_k + \sum_{k=1}^{n} b_k$.

4.   Show that for all natural numbers m and n, such that $1 < m + 1 < n$, the following is true.

$$\sum_{k=1}^{n} a_k = \sum_{k=1}^{m} a_k + \sum_{k=m+1}^{n} a_k$$

5.   By expanding, show that

$$\sum_{k=1}^{n} (a_k + d) = nd + \sum_{k=1}^{n} a_k$$

INFINITE SEQUENCES AND LIMITS

So far we have considered only sequences with a finite number of terms. We now turn our attention to sequences in which the numbers of terms are not finite. One of the simplest such sequences is the sequence of all natural numbers

$$1, 2, 3, \ldots, n, \ldots$$

Is this sequence an infinite arithmetic progression?   An infinite geometric progression?

Let us examine two infinite sequences

$$1, \ \frac{1}{2}, \ \frac{1}{3}, \ \ldots, \ \frac{1}{n}, \ \ldots$$

$$1, 0, 1, 0, 1, 0, \ldots, 1, 0, \ldots$$

Each of these sequences is infinite.   There is one basic difference between them.

> In the first sequence, as we continue, the terms approach a certain number; what is this number?
>
> In the second sequence, this is not the case; the terms do not approach one certain number.

In the case of the first sequence $1, \frac{1}{2}, \frac{1}{3}, \ldots, \frac{1}{n}, \ldots$ in which

$$a_1 = 1 \qquad a_2 = \frac{1}{2} \qquad a_3 = \frac{1}{3} \qquad \cdots \qquad a_n = \frac{1}{n} \qquad \cdots$$

we say that a_n approaches a *limit*. In this case, the limit is 0. We write this as follows:

$$\lim_{n \to \infty} \frac{1}{n} = 0 \quad [\text{read: limit of } \frac{1}{n} \text{ as } n \text{ tends to infinity is 0}]$$

More generally, we say that a_n approaches a limit L as n becomes large, and we write

$$\lim_{n \to \infty} a_n = L$$

A sequence which has a limit is called a *convergent* sequence. Otherwise, it is called a *divergent* sequence.

EXERCISES

1. For each infinite sequence below, tell whether it is convergent or divergent. In the case of each convergent sequence, tell its limit.

a. $1, \frac{1}{2}, \frac{1}{4}, \frac{1}{8}, \ldots, \frac{1}{2^{n-1}}, \ldots$

c. $2, 4, 8, 16, \ldots, 2^n, \ldots$

b. $1, \frac{1}{3}, \frac{1}{9}, \frac{1}{27}, \ldots, \frac{1}{3^{n-1}}, \ldots$

d. $3, 9, 27, 81, \ldots, 3^n, \ldots$

e. $\left(1 + \frac{1}{2}\right), \left(1 + \frac{1}{3}\right), \left(1 + \frac{1}{4}\right), \left(1 + \frac{1}{5}\right), \ldots, \left(1 + \frac{1}{n+1}\right), \ldots$

f. $1 \cdot 2, 2 \cdot 3, 3 \cdot 4, 4 \cdot 5, \ldots, n(n+1), \ldots$

g. $\frac{1}{2}, \frac{2}{3}, \frac{3}{4}, \frac{4}{5}, \ldots, \frac{n}{n+1}, \ldots$

h. $\frac{1}{2}, \frac{4}{3}, \frac{9}{4}, \ldots, \frac{n^2}{n+1}, \ldots$

i. $\left(2 + \frac{1}{2}\right), \left(2 + \frac{2}{3}\right), \left(2 + \frac{3}{4}\right), \left(2 + \frac{4}{5}\right), \ldots, \left(2 + \frac{n}{n+1}\right), \ldots$

j. $2, -2, 2, -2, \ldots, 2, -2, \ldots, ((-1)^{n+1} \cdot (2)), \ldots$

2. For each *convergent* sequence in problem 1, write an equation using limit notation to show the limit. Problem 1a is done for you.

Example: $\qquad \lim_{n \to \infty} \frac{1}{2^{n-1}} = 0$

SUM OF AN INFINITE SERIES

Perhaps it seems strange to speak of a sum of an infinite series, when we know that there is no end to such a series. But we can conceive of the sum in terms of a limit. To illustrate, let us consider the infinite decimal $.\overline{3}$. It can be shown as an infinite series

$$.3 + .03 + .003 + .0003 + \cdots$$

To solve the problem of determining the number which is the sum of this *series*, we form a new *sequence*. We call the terms of this sequence s_1, s_2, s_3, and so on and obtain these terms as follows:

$s_1 = .3$	(the first partial sum)
$s_2 = .3 + .03 = .33$	(the second partial sum)
$s_3 = .3 + .03 + .003 = .333$	(the third partial sum)
$s_4 = .3 + .03 + .003 + .0003 = .3333$	(How many addends are needed
and so on	to find the fourth partial sum?)

What is s_5? You notice that the kth term of this sequence is the sum of the first k terms of the corresponding series. Such a sequence is called a sequence of partial sums of a given series. We now define the sum of an infinite series in terms of the sequence of its partial sums.

■ *Definition of Sum of Infinite Series*   The *sum of an infinite series* is the limit of the sequence of its partial sums.

Of course, this definition applies only to those series for which limits of their sequences of partial sums exist. Such series are called *convergent series*. Series for which limits do not exist are called *divergent series*.

To be able to determine the sums of convergent infinite series, we must know how to tell the limits of infinite sequences. You have already had some practice in doing this in the previous section, but no systematic way of going about it was developed. We shall state a number of properties of limits which will be helpful in accomplishing this task.

In the properties of limits of infinite convergent sequences which are listed below let

$$\lim_{n \to \infty} a_n = A \quad \text{and} \quad \lim_{n \to \infty} b_n = B$$

■ *Property of the Limit of the Product of a Constant and a Sequence*
$$\lim_{n \to \infty} (ka_n) = k \cdot \lim_{n \to \infty} a_n = kA$$

■ *Property of the Limit of the Sum of Two Sequences*
$$\lim_{n \to \infty} (a_n + b_n) = \lim_{n \to \infty} a_n + \lim_{n \to \infty} b_n = A + B$$

■ *Property of the Limit of the Difference of Two Sequences*
$$\lim_{n \to \infty} (a_n - b_n) = \lim_{n \to \infty} a_n - \lim_{n \to \infty} b_n = A - B$$

■ *Property of the Limit of the Product of Two Sequences*
$$\lim_{n \to \infty} (a_n b_n) = \lim_{n \to \infty} a_n \cdot \lim_{n \to \infty} b_n = AB$$

■ *Property of the Limit of the Quotient of Two Sequences*

$$\lim_{n \to \infty} \left(\frac{a_n}{b_n} \right) = \frac{\lim\limits_{n \to \infty} a_n}{\lim\limits_{n \to \infty} b_n} = \frac{A}{B} \quad (B \neq 0)$$

■ *Property of the Limit of a Constant* $\forall_{c \in R} \lim_{n \to \infty} c = c$

To clarify the meaning of these properties, let us consider two examples.

Examples: *i.* Find the limit of the sequence

$$3 \cdot \frac{1}{2}, \ 3 \cdot \frac{2}{3}, \ 3 \cdot \frac{3}{4}, \ \ldots, \ 3 \cdot \frac{n}{n+1}, \ \ldots$$

We have already decided that the limit of the sequence $\frac{1}{2}, \frac{2}{3}, \frac{3}{4}, \ \ldots, \frac{n}{n+1}, \ \ldots$ is 1; that is, $\lim\limits_{n \to \infty} \frac{n}{n+1} = 1$. [See problem **1g**, page 483.]

According to the property of the limit of the product of a constant and a sequence

$$\lim_{n \to \infty} \left(3 \cdot \frac{n}{n+1} \right) = 3 \cdot \left(\lim_{n \to \infty} \frac{n}{n+1} \right) = 3 \cdot 1 = 3$$

ii. Find the limit of the sequence

$$1 + \frac{1}{2}, \ \frac{1}{2} + \frac{2}{3}, \ \frac{1}{4} + \frac{3}{4}, \ \ldots, \ \frac{1}{2^{n-1}} + \frac{n}{n+1}, \ \ldots$$

Recall the sequence

$$1, \ \frac{1}{2}, \ \frac{1}{4}, \ \ldots, \ \frac{1}{2^{n-1}}, \ \ldots \text{ from exercise } \mathbf{1a} \text{ page 483.}$$

and the sequence

$$\frac{1}{2}, \ \frac{2}{3}, \ \frac{3}{4}, \ \ldots, \ \frac{n}{n+1}, \ \ldots \text{ exercise } \mathbf{1g} \text{ page 483.}$$

Note that each term of the given sequence is exactly the sum of the corresponding terms of the other two sequences. Therefore, according to the property of the limit of the sum of two sequences

$$\lim_{n \to \infty} \left(\frac{1}{2^{n-1}} + \frac{n}{n+1} \right) = \left(\lim_{n \to \infty} \frac{1}{2^{n-1}} \right) + \left(\lim_{n \to \infty} \frac{n}{n+1} \right)$$
$$= 0 + 1 = 1$$

Notice that we have asserted that $\lim\limits_{n \to \infty} \frac{n}{n+1} = 1$. Let us now prove that it is so.

Note that $\forall_{n \neq 0} \ \dfrac{n}{n+1} = \dfrac{\dfrac{n}{n}}{\dfrac{n+1}{n}} = \dfrac{1}{1 + \dfrac{1}{n}}$

Thus, $\lim\limits_{n \to \infty} \dfrac{n}{n+1} = \lim\limits_{n \to \infty} \dfrac{1}{1 + \dfrac{1}{n}} = \dfrac{\left(\lim\limits_{n \to \infty} 1 \right)}{\left(\lim\limits_{n \to \infty} \left(1 + \dfrac{1}{n} \right) \right)} = \dfrac{1}{\left(\lim\limits_{n \to \infty} 1 \right) + \left(\lim\limits_{n \to \infty} \dfrac{1}{n} \right)}$

$$= \frac{1}{1 + 0} = \frac{1}{1} = 1$$

Which properties did we make use of in this derivation?

EXERCISES

1. Assuming the six properties of limits stated on page 484 and that $\lim\limits_{n\to\infty}\left(\dfrac{1}{n}\right)=0$, determine each of the following:

a. $\lim\limits_{n\to\infty}\dfrac{1}{n^2}$

b. $\lim\limits_{n\to\infty}\left(\dfrac{1}{n}+\dfrac{1}{n^2}\right)$

c. $\lim\limits_{n\to\infty}\dfrac{1}{n+1}$

$$\left[\text{HINT: }\ \frac{1}{n+1}=\frac{\dfrac{1}{n}}{1+\dfrac{1}{n}}\ (n\neq o)\right]$$

d. $\lim\limits_{n\to\infty}\dfrac{1}{n^2+n}$

e. $\lim\limits_{n\to\infty}\dfrac{2n+1}{3n-2}$

f. $\lim\limits_{n\to\infty}\dfrac{3n^2+n-1}{4n^2+n+2}$

g. $\lim\limits_{n\to\infty}\dfrac{an^2+bn+c}{dn^2+en+f}$

2. Prove that
$$\lim_{n\to\infty}\frac{2n^2+7n-12}{4n^2-12n+25}=\lim_{n\to\infty}\frac{n^2-n-1}{2n^2+n+1}$$

3. For each infinite decimal

    i. show it as an infinite series (display the first four terms)

    ii. give the first four partial sums

Example: $.\overline{213}$

    i. $.213+.000213+.000000213+.000000000213+\ldots$

    ii. $s_1=.213$

        $s_2=.213213$
        $s_3=.213213213$
        $s_4=.213213213213$

a. $.\overline{1}$ **c.** $.\overline{207}$ **e.** $.9\overline{5}$

b. $.0\overline{2}$ **d.** $.1\overline{057}$ **f.** $.27\overline{43}$

SUM OF INFINITE GEOMETRIC SERIES

At the beginning of the last section we considered the infinite decimal $.\overline{3}$ in terms of the infinite series

$$.3+.03+.003+.0003+\ldots$$

Note that this is a geometric series, in which the first term is .3 and the common ratio is .1. The nth term in this series is

$$a_n=a_1\cdot r^{n-1}=.3\times(.1)^{n-1}$$

We were able to find the sums of finite geometric series by the use of the formula

$$S_n=\frac{a_1(r^n-1)}{r-1}$$

In the previous section we defined the sum of an infinite series to be the limit of the sequence of its partial sums. For a geometric sequence, the nth partial sum is given by the formula above. We apply this formula to the sequence

$$S_1 = .3 \qquad S_2 = .33 \qquad S_3 = .333 \qquad \dots$$

$$S_n = \frac{a_1(r^n - 1)}{r - 1} = \frac{.3[(.1)^n - 1]}{.1 - 1} = \frac{.3[(.1)^n - 1]}{-.9}$$

The sum of the series $.3 + .03 + .003 + .0003 + \dots$ is the limit of the partial sums

$$\lim_{n \to \infty} \frac{.3[(.1)^n - 1]}{-.9}$$

Using the properties of limits

$$\lim_{n \to \infty} \frac{.3[(.1)^n - 1]}{-.9} = \frac{\left(\lim_{n \to \infty} .3\right)\left(\lim_{n \to \infty} [(.1)^n - 1]\right)}{\left(\lim_{n \to \infty} (-.9)\right)}$$

$$= \frac{.3\left[\left(\lim_{n \to \infty} (.1)^n\right) - \left(\lim_{n \to \infty} 1\right)\right]}{-.9}$$

$$= \frac{.3(0 - 1)}{-.9} = \frac{-.3}{-.9} = \frac{3}{9} = \frac{1}{3}$$

Thus, $\lim_{n \to \infty} S_n = \frac{1}{3}$ for the series $.3 + .03 + .003 + \dots$.

A word of explanation of

$$\lim_{n \to \infty} (.1)^n = 0$$

is necessary. Note that $.1 = \frac{1}{10}$; therefore $\lim_{n \to \infty} (.1)^n = \lim_{n \to \infty} \left(\frac{1}{10}\right)^n$.

Now observe what happens as n takes on successively greater values.

$n = 1; \left(\frac{1}{10}\right)^n = \frac{1}{10}$ $\qquad\qquad$ $n = 4; \left(\frac{1}{10}\right)^n = \frac{1}{10,000}$

$n = 2; \left(\frac{1}{10}\right)^n = \frac{1}{100}$ $\qquad\qquad$ $n = 5; \left(\frac{1}{10}\right)^n = \frac{1}{100,000}$

$n = 3; \left(\frac{1}{10}\right)^n = \frac{1}{1000}$ $\qquad\qquad$ $n = 6; \left(\frac{1}{10}\right)^n = \frac{1}{1,000,000}$

$$\text{and so on}$$

From this pattern it is clear that the limit of the sequence

$$\frac{1}{10}, \frac{1}{100}, \frac{1}{1000}, \frac{1}{10,000}, \dots$$

is 0. Therefore, $\lim_{n \to \infty} (.1)^n = 0$.

The formula for the partial sums of a geometric progression is thus helpful in finding numerals of the form $\frac{a}{b}$ (a and b integers, $b \neq 0$) for numbers given in the form of infinite repeating decimals.

Let us now examine, in more general terms, the matter of the sum of an infinite geometric series, which is given by

$$\lim_{n \to \infty} S_n = \lim_{n \to \infty} \frac{a_1(r^n - 1)}{r - 1}$$

Using the properties of limits

$$\lim_{n \to \infty} S_n = \lim_{n \to \infty} \frac{a_1(r^n - 1)}{r - 1} = \frac{\left(\lim\limits_{n \to \infty} a_1\right)\left[\lim\limits_{n \to \infty} (r^n - 1)\right]}{\lim\limits_{n \to \infty} (r - 1)}$$

$$= \frac{a_1\left[\left(\lim\limits_{n \to \infty} r^n\right) - \left(\lim\limits_{n \to \infty} 1\right)\right]}{r - 1} = \frac{a_1}{r - 1}\left[\left(\lim\limits_{n \to \infty} r^n\right) - 1\right]$$

A close examination of the last expression will give us a clue as to when such a limit exists and when it does not exist.

    i. $\dfrac{a_1}{r - 1}$ exists for every series in which $r \neq 1$

    ii. $\lim\limits_{n \to \infty} r^n$ exists only for $|r| < 1$

Explain why $r = 0$ is meaningless in terms of a geometric series. What is $\lim\limits_{n \to \infty} r^n$ for $|r| < 1$ equal to? Do you agree that it is 0?

Therefore, if $|r| < 1$ then

$$\lim_{n \to \infty} \frac{a_1(r^n - 1)}{r - 1} = \frac{a_1}{r - 1}\left[\left(\lim_{n \to \infty} r^n\right) - 1\right] = \frac{a_1}{r - 1}(0 - 1) = \frac{a_1}{r - 1}(-1) = \frac{a_1}{1 - r}$$

Thus, the sum of an infinite geometric series with $|r| < 1$ is equal to $\dfrac{a_1}{1 - r}$.

EXERCISES

1. Find the sum of each infinite geometric series.

Example: $\dfrac{1}{2} + \dfrac{1}{4} + \ldots + \dfrac{1}{2^n} + \ldots$

$$S = \frac{a_1}{1 - r} = \frac{\dfrac{1}{2}}{1 - \dfrac{1}{2}} = \frac{\dfrac{1}{2}}{\dfrac{1}{2}} = 1$$

a. $\dfrac{1}{3} + \dfrac{1}{9} + \dfrac{1}{27} + \ldots$ **d.** $12 + 4 + \dfrac{4}{3} + \ldots$

b. $\dfrac{1}{2} - \dfrac{1}{4} + \dfrac{1}{8} - \ldots$ **e.** $10 - 1 + .1 - \ldots$

c. $1 - \dfrac{1}{4} + \dfrac{1}{16} - \ldots$ **f.** $100 - 10 + 1 - \ldots$

2. Tell for what values of x the infinite series $\dfrac{1}{x^2} + \dfrac{1}{x^3} + \dfrac{1}{x^4} + \ldots$ is convergent.

3. Tell for what values of x the infinite series

$$(x - 1)^0 + (x - 1)^1 + (x - 1)^2 + \dots$$

is convergent.

4. For each decimal, find a numeral of the form $\dfrac{a}{b}$ (a and b integers, $b \neq 0$).

    a. $.\overline{12}$ **b.** $.\overline{7}$ **c.** $.0\overline{15}$ **d.** $.9\overline{87}$

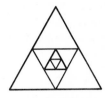

5. The sides of an equilateral triangle are bisected and the midpoints are connected as shown in the picture. This process is continued indefinitely. If the measure of a side of the largest triangle is 12'', find the sum of the perimeters of all the triangles so formed.

6. The sides of a square are bisected and the midpoints are connected to form a new square. If the measure of a side of the largest square is 9'', find the sum of the perimeters of all the squares so formed, if this process is continued indefinitely.

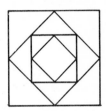

7. A steel ball dropped from the height of 100 feet rebounds on each bounce $\frac{9}{10}$ of the distance from which it fell. How many feet will the ball travel before coming to rest?

8. A rubber ball dropped from the height of 100 feet rebounds on each bounce $\frac{1}{2}$ of the distance from which it fell. How many feet will the ball travel before coming to rest?

9. A balloon contains 1000 cubic inches of air. The air is released by stages in the following manner: in the first stage 10% of the air is released, leaving 90% of the air in the balloon. In the second stage 10% of the remaining air is released, and so on. How many cubic inches of air are left in the balloon after the 8th stage?

Some special series

We shall give here a number of infinite series which find a great many uses in mathematics.

Example: Carry out the division to find that

$$\frac{1}{1 - x} = 1 + x + x^2 + x^3 + x^4 + \dots + x^{n-1} + \dots$$

For $|x| < 1$, this is the so-called *infinite power series*.

If $x = \dfrac{1}{2}$, we have

$$1 + \frac{1}{2} + \frac{1}{4} + \frac{1}{8} + \dots = \frac{1}{1 - \dfrac{1}{2}} = 2$$

Note that this is an infinite geometric series. What is the common ratio in this series? Note that we previously used the formula for the sum of an infinite geometric series to obtain the sum above.

You might have wondered at times how the tables of values of trigonometric functions are computed. This is done by resorting to infinite series. We shall give an example to illustrate this, but first we introduce a convenient abbreviation, which will simplify our writing. Whenever we need to show a product of consecutive natural numbers, such as

$$1 \times 2, \ 1 \times 2 \times 3, \ 1 \times 2 \times 3 \times 4, \ 1 \times 2 \times 3 \times 4 \times 5, \text{ and so on}$$

we use the following abbreviations

$$1 \times 2 = 2! \quad \text{[read: two factorial]}$$
$$1 \times 2 \times 3 = 3! \quad \text{[read: three factorial]}$$
$$1 \times 2 \times 3 \times 4 = 4!$$
$$1 \times 2 \times 3 \times 4 \times 5 = 5!$$

Thus, $1 \times 2 \times 3 \times \ldots \times (n-1) \times n = n!$ [$n!$ is read n factorial.]

Examples: *i.*   Find sin(2).

We use the expansion

$$\sin(x) = x - \frac{x^3}{3!} + \frac{x^5}{5!} - \frac{x^7}{7!} + \ldots + \frac{(-1)^{n-1}(x^{2n-1})}{(2n-1)!} + \ldots$$

In this expansion, x is a real number. If we want to approximate sin(2), we replace x by 2 in the series and use as many terms of the series as are necessary to obtain the accuracy we desire.

$$\sin(2) \doteq 2 - \frac{2^3}{3!} + \frac{2^5}{5!} - \frac{2^7}{7!}$$

We shall use just the first four terms of the series.

$$\frac{1}{3!} = \frac{1}{6} \doteq .166667$$

$$\frac{1}{5!} = \frac{1}{120} \doteq .008333$$

$$\frac{1}{7!} = \frac{1}{5040} \doteq .000198$$

$$\sin(2) \doteq 2 - (8 \times .166667) + (32 \times .008333) - (128 \times .000198)$$
$$= 2 - 1.333336 + .266656 - .025344$$
$$\doteq .90798$$

ii.   To compute approximations of e, the base of the *natural logarithm*, we use

$$e = 2 + \frac{1}{2!} + \frac{1}{3!} + \frac{1}{4!} + \ldots + \frac{1}{n!} + \ldots$$

EXERCISES

1. Use the series

$$e = 2 + \frac{1}{2!} + \frac{1}{3!} + \frac{1}{4!} + \cdots + \frac{1}{n!} + \cdots$$

and the first seven terms to compute an approximation of e to four decimal places. Use the following in your computations.

$$\frac{1}{2!} = \frac{1}{2} = .50000 \qquad\qquad \frac{1}{5!} = \frac{1}{120} \doteq .00833$$

$$\frac{1}{3!} = \frac{1}{6} \doteq .16667 \qquad\qquad \frac{1}{6!} = \frac{1}{720} \doteq .00139$$

$$\frac{1}{4!} = \frac{1}{24} \doteq .04167 \qquad\qquad \frac{1}{7!} = \frac{1}{5040} \doteq .00020$$

2. Use the series

$$e^x = 1 + x + \frac{x^2}{2!} + \frac{x^3}{3!} + \cdots + \frac{x^{n-1}}{(n-1)!} + \cdots$$

to compute an approximation of e^2 to four decimal places. [Use the values of factorials given in problem **1**.]

3. Use the series given in problem **2** to compute an approximation of $\sqrt{e}$ to four decimal places. [Recall that $\sqrt{e} = e^{\frac{1}{2}}$.]

4. Use the series

$$\cos(x) = 1 - \frac{x^2}{2!} + \frac{x^4}{4!} - \frac{x^6}{6!} + \cdots + \frac{(-1)^{n-1}x^{2n}}{(2n)!} + \cdots$$

to compute an approximation of $\cos(3)$ to four decimal places.

5. Compute $\displaystyle\sum_{k=2}^{5} (k!)$.

VOCABULARY

Use each of the following correctly in a sentence. Numerals in parentheses refer to pages where these words were used. If you are not sure of the meaning of any word, turn to the indicated pages.

arithmetic mean (476)
arithmetic progression (474)
arithmetic series (475)
common difference (474)
common ratio (478)
convergent sequence (483)
convergent series (484)
divergent sequence (483)
divergent series (484)
expansion (490)
factorial (490)

geometric mean (480)
geometric progression (477)
geometric series (478)
infinite power series (489)
infinite sequence (482)
limit (483)
natural logarithm (490)
sequence (473)
sigma, Σ (480)
term (474)

REVIEW EXERCISES

1. The nth term of an arithmetic progression is $a_n = [a + (n-1)d]$, where a is the first term, n is the number of terms and d is the common difference. In each of the following progressions there are given the first three terms and the nth term. Determine n, the number of the last term.

    a. $5, 9, 13, \ldots, 89$

    b. $3, 2\frac{1}{2}, 2, \ldots, -47$

    c. $1 + \sqrt{2}, -\sqrt{2}, -1 - 3\sqrt{2}, \ldots, -52 - 105\sqrt{2}$

    d. $1 + i, 1, 1 - i, \ldots, 1 - 61i$

2. $S_n = \dfrac{n(a_1 + a_n)}{2}$ is a formula for the sum of the first n terms of an arithmetic progression. Solve this formula for each of the following:

    a. n **b.** a_1 **c.** a_n

3. In each problem, the values of three variables appearing in the formula $S_n = \dfrac{n(a_1 + a_n)}{2}$ are given. Using the appropriate formula for each case, determine the value of the fourth variable.

    a. $a_1 = 1;\quad a_n = -71;\quad n = 13;\quad S_n = ?$

    b. $a_1 = 2;\quad n = 22;\quad S_n = -549;\quad a_{22} = ?$

    c. $a_1 = 1;\quad a_n = 13\frac{1}{2};\quad S_n = 194\frac{1}{2};\quad n = ?$

    d. $n = 25;\quad S_n = -900;\quad a_{25} = -63;\quad a_1 = ?$

4. Solve the formula $S_n = \dfrac{n[2a_1 + (n-1)d]}{2}$ for each of the following:

    a. a_1 **b.** d

5. Determine

    a. the one arithmetic mean between 1 and 17

    b. the two arithmetic means between 12 and -6

    c. the three arithmetic means between $\sqrt{2}$ and $9\sqrt{2}$

    d. the four arithmetic means between $-i$ and $5 + 4i$

6. Find the value of x such that $x + 1$, x, $3x$ will form an arithmetic progression.

7. A debt of \$12,000 is to be retired over a period of four years by making payments of \$250 at the end of each month, plus the interest at the rate of $\frac{1}{2}\%$ per month on the outstanding balance. How much interest will be paid by the time the debt is retired?

8. Tell which of the following sequences are the first three terms of *geometric* progressions and which are not.

    a. $1, 2, 3$ **c.** $\dfrac{1}{2}, -\dfrac{1}{2}, \dfrac{1}{2}$

    b. $1, 2, 4$ **d.** $5, 0, 0$

e. $1^2, 2^2, 3^2$

f. $5, 5\sqrt{3}, 15$

g. $\dfrac{1}{2}, \dfrac{1}{2^2}, \dfrac{1}{2^3}$

h. $-2, -1, -\dfrac{1}{2}$

i. $i, -1, -i$

j. $1+i, -1+i, -1-i$

9. Can any two numbers constitute the first two terms of some geometric progression? Explain your answer.

10. Find the sum of the indicated number of terms of each geometric progression.

  a. $2, -4, 8, \ldots$; 10 terms

  b. $6, 3, 1\frac{1}{2}, \ldots$; 10 terms

  c. $12, 4, 1\frac{1}{3}, \ldots$; 8 terms

  d. $1, .3, .09, \ldots$; 8 terms

  e. $1, -.3, .09, \ldots$; 8 terms

11. Give the next three terms of each of the following geometric progressions.

  a. $9, 18, \ldots$

  b. $\frac{1}{2}, -\frac{1}{6}, \ldots$

  c. $1, \sqrt{5}, \ldots$

  d. $2, e, \ldots$

  e. $\sin(x), \dfrac{\pi}{2} \cdot \sin(x), \ldots$

  f. $i, -1, \ldots$

12. If m, p, and r are the terms of a geometric progression, write an equation showing p in terms of m and r.

13. Determine the two geometric means between 1 and $-\frac{125}{8}$.

14. Mr. Save-it deposits \$50 each quarter in a savings account which earns interest at 5% compounded quarterly. How much money does he have in the savings account at the end of four years?

15. Write in an expanded form.

  a. $\displaystyle\sum_{k=1}^{5} k$

  b. $\displaystyle\sum_{k=1}^{5} 3k$

  c. $\displaystyle\sum_{k=1}^{n} 3^{3k-1}$

  d. $\displaystyle\sum_{k=1}^{n} a_k \cdot b^{k+1}$

  e. $\displaystyle\sum_{k=1}^{n} \dfrac{2k}{k+3}$

  f. $\displaystyle\sum_{k=1}^{n} \dfrac{k^2}{k(k+1)}$

16. For each infinite sequence below, tell whether it is convergent or divergent. In the case of each convergent sequence, tell its limit.

  a. $1, \dfrac{1}{4}, \dfrac{1}{16}, \dfrac{1}{64}, \ldots, \dfrac{1}{4^{n-1}}, \ldots$

  b. $1, 0, 1, 0, \ldots, 1, 0, \ldots$

  c. $\dfrac{1}{2}, \dfrac{3}{4}, \dfrac{5}{6}, \dfrac{7}{8}, \ldots, \dfrac{2n-1}{2n}, \ldots$

d. $1^2,\ 2^2,\ 3^2,\ 4^2,\ \ldots,\ n^2,\ \ldots$

e. $.1,\ .01,\ .001,\ .0001,\ \ldots,\ 10^{-n},\ \ldots$

f. $(1+.1),\ (1+.01),\ (1+.001),\ (1+.0001),\ \ldots,\ (1+10^{-n}),\ \ldots$

g. $2,\ -1,\ 2,\ -1,\ \ldots,\ 2,\ -1,\ \ldots$

h. $\left(\dfrac{1}{2}\right)^2,\ \left(\dfrac{1}{3}\right)^3,\ \left(\dfrac{1}{4}\right)^4,\ \left(\dfrac{1}{5}\right)^5,\ \ldots,\ \left(\dfrac{1}{n+1}\right)^{n+1},\ \ldots$

17. Show each infinite decimal below as an infinite series by displaying the first four terms.

   a. $.\overline{8}$ **b.** $.1\overline{05}$ **c.** $.2\overline{05}$ **d.** $.362\overline{509}$

18. For what values of x is the series $\dfrac{1}{x}+\dfrac{1}{x^3}+\dfrac{1}{x^5}+\ldots$ convergent?

CHAPTER TEST

1. Tell which of the following sequences are the first three terms of *arithmetic* progressions and which are not.

a. $1,\ -2,\ 1$ **e.** $\dfrac{1}{2},\ \dfrac{1}{3},\ \dfrac{1}{4}$

b. $10,\ 0,\ -10$ **f.** $-1,\ -5,\ -9$

c. $2^2,\ 4^2,\ 6^2$ **g.** $0,\ i,\ 2i$

d. $2\times 3,\ 2\times 4,\ 2\times 5$ **h.** $\dfrac{1}{i},\ \dfrac{1}{2i},\ \dfrac{1}{3i}$

2. Tell which of the following sequences are the first three terms of *geometric* progressions and which are not.

a. $1,\ -1,\ 1$ **e.** $-4,\ 2,\ -1$

b. $1,\ \dfrac{1}{3},\ \dfrac{1}{6}$ **f.** $\sqrt{3},\ 3,\ 3\sqrt{3}$

c. $2,\ 2^2,\ 2^3$ **g.** $i,\ -1,\ -i$

d. $2\times 3,\ 2\times 4,\ 2\times 5$ **h.** $2+i,\ 1+\dfrac{i}{2},\ \dfrac{1}{2}+\dfrac{i}{4}$

3. Find the value of n such that $n,\ n+1,\ 2n$ will form an arithmetic progression.

4. Find two values of m such that $m,\ m+1,\ 2m$ will form geometric progressions.

5. Determine the sum of an arithmetic progression for which $a_1=2$, $a_n=-25$, and $n=10$.

6. Determine the three arithmetic means between 10 and 0.

7. Determine the two geometric means between 30 and $\tfrac{10}{9}$.

8. Give the next two terms of each of the following geometric progressions.

   a. $1,\ \tfrac{1}{5},\ \ldots$ **b.** $2,\ 2^2,\ \ldots$ **c.** $2i,\ -1,\ \ldots$ **d.** $\pi,\ \pi^5,\ \ldots$

9. Find the sum of the indicated number of terms of each arithmetic progression.

   a. $1,\ -4,\ -9,\ \ldots;\quad 20$ terms   **c.** $i,\ 2i,\ 3i,\ \ldots;\quad 100$ terms

   b. $0,\ \tfrac{1}{3},\ \tfrac{2}{3},\ \ldots;\quad 15$ terms

10. Find the sum of the indicated number of terms of each geometric progression.

   a. $1, \frac{1}{2}, \frac{1}{4}, \ldots$;   10 terms

   b. $-1, 2, -4, \ldots$;   10 terms

   c. $1, .1, .01, \ldots$;   8 terms

11. Write in an expanded form.

   a. $\displaystyle\sum_{k=1}^{5} 7k$

   c. $\displaystyle\sum_{k=1}^{n} \frac{k}{2k+1}$

   b. $\displaystyle\sum_{k=1}^{n} a_k \cdot b^{k+2}$

   d. $\displaystyle\sum_{k=1}^{n} \frac{k^3}{k(k+1)(k+2)}$

12. For each infinite sequence below, tell whether it is convergent or divergent. In the case of each convergent sequence, tell its limit.

   a. $1, -1, 1, -1, \ldots, 1, -1, \ldots$

   b. $10^{-1}, 10^{-2}, 10^{-4}, 10^{-8}, \ldots, 10^{-(2^{n-1})}, \ldots$

   c. $-1, (-1)^2, (-1)^3, (-1)^4, \ldots, (-1)^n, \ldots$

   d. $\left(\frac{1}{2}\right)^2, \left(\frac{1}{2}\right)^4, \left(\frac{1}{2}\right)^6, \left(\frac{1}{2}\right)^8, \ldots, \left(\frac{1}{2}\right)^{2n}, \ldots$

BIBLIOGRAPHY

Rademacher, H. and Toeplitz, O.   *The Enjoyment of Mathematics.*   Princeton: Princeton University Press, 1957.   pp. 147-160.

Schiffer, M. M.   *Applied Mathematics in the High School.*   SMSG Studies in Mathematics, Volume X.   Stanford University, 1963.   pp. 73-75.

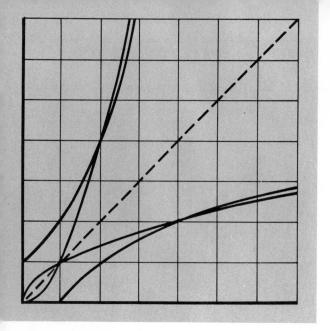

CHAPTER 16

Permutations, Combinations and the Binomial Theorem

LINEAR PERMUTATIONS

Let $A = \{\bigcirc, \triangle, \square\}$. In each of the following sets we have a different arrangement of the elements of set A.

$\{\bigcirc, \triangle, \square\}$	$\{\triangle, \bigcirc, \square\}$	$\{\square, \bigcirc, \triangle\}$
$\{\bigcirc, \square, \triangle\}$	$\{\triangle, \square, \bigcirc\}$	$\{\square, \triangle, \bigcirc\}$

Notice that you can list the elements of set A in six *different* orders. In how many different orders can you list the elements of the set $\{a, b\}$?

It is possible to find twenty-four different orders for listing the elements of the set $\{a, b, c, d\}$; six of these ways begin with the letter a; six ways begin with b; and so on. Write all twenty-four arrangements.

Each arrangement, or ordering, of the elements of a set is called a *linear permutation*[1] of that set of elements. For example, there are exactly six linear

---

[1] Not every permutation is linear. There are also circular permutations, which are discussed in the section on circular permutations in this chapter.

permutations of the elements of the set $\{\bigcirc, \triangle, \square\}$. What is the number of linear permutations of the set $\{x, y\}$? Of the set $\{p, q, r, s\}$?

We have learned that a set of two elements can be *permuted* in two ways, that a set of three elements can be permuted in six ways, and that a set of four elements can be permuted in twenty-four ways. You undoubtedly will be surprised to find that as the number of elements in a set increases, the number of permutations of its elements increases at an astonishing rate. Examine the following table.

Number of elements in a set	Number of permutations
3	6
4	24
5	120
10	3,628,800
15	1,307,674,368,000

Often we are interested in knowing the number of permutations of the elements of a finite set. Since the number of permutations of even a few elements is very large, as indicated by the above table, it is awkward to list all of the permutations of a set of elements to find out how many there are. It would be convenient to have a way of telling the number of permutations of n elements, n a natural number, which does not require listing all of the arrangements.

Let us examine the following problem. There are three roads — routes ①, ②, and ③ — which connect Circle City and Triangle Town; and there are two roads — routes ④ and ⑤ — connecting Triangle Town and Squareville. See figure 1.

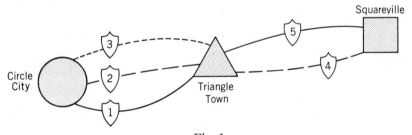

Fig. 1

Now, if we wish to travel from Circle City to Triangle Town, and then on to Squareville, we may choose one of several ways to get there. From figure 1, we see that we can travel from Circle City to Triangle Town by any one of three routes, and then for each one of these routes we have two choices for traveling on to Squareville. Hence, we have 3×2 or 6 possible ways in all. One of the six ways consists of taking route ① and then route ④. What are the other five ways?

Suppose there were four roads connecting Circle City and Triangle Town, and six roads connecting Triangle Town and Squareville. How many different ways are there to get from Circle City to Squareville by way of Triangle Town? The general principle which is involved here is called *The Fundamental Counting Principle* and is stated as follows:

■   *Fundamental Counting Principle*

If a first operation can be performed in k_1 ways, and after it is performed in any one of these ways, a second operation can be performed in k_2 ways, and after it is performed in any one of these ways, a third operation can be performed in k_3 ways, and so on for n operations (the replacements for n, k_1, k_2, k_3, ... being natural numbers), then, collectively, the n operations can be performed in $(k_1 \cdot k_2 \cdot k_3 \cdot \ldots \cdot k_n)$ ways.

Now, let us return to our original problem of finding the number of permutations of the n elements of a set. Suppose, for example, that we wish to determine the number of permutations of seven elements, say the elements of $\{a, b, c, d, e, f, g\}$. Let us indicate by frames the positions to be filled in one linear permutation. We note that the first position or frame can be filled in any one of seven ways; and, after it is filled, the second frame can be filled in any one of six ways, and so on. Observe that after the first six frames are filled, there is only one letter left for the last position. The number of possibilities for filling each of the seven frames is indicated as follows:

7	6	5	4	3	2	1

Now, applying the Fundamental Counting Principle, we see that the number of permutations of seven elements is given by

$$7 \cdot 6 \cdot 5 \cdot 4 \cdot 3 \cdot 2 \cdot 1$$

which, you recall, is equal to 7! What is the number of permutations of five elements? Of ten elements? Supply a proof for the following theorem, which is suggested by the answers to the previous questions.

Theorem 1 The number of permutations of n elements, n a natural number, is $n!$

Example: *i.*   How many different four-flag signals can be made by displaying four of seven available flags in a vertical line?

There are four positions to be filled. We have seven choices for the first, or top, position, six for the second, five for the third, and four for the fourth.

7
6
5
4

Hence, by the Fundamental Counting Principle there are $7 \cdot 6 \cdot 5 \cdot 4$, or 840, different signals that can be constructed.

Example: **ii.** How many different batting orders are possible for a nine-man baseball team?

By Theorem 1 it is possible to construct 9! different batting orders. What is 9! in ordinary decimal notation? [HINT: 8! = 40,320.]

EXERCISES

1. True or false?

a. $4 \cdot 3! = 4!$ **c.** $\dfrac{2!}{4!} = \dfrac{1}{2!}$ **e.** $\dfrac{(4!) \cdot (2!)}{3!} = 8$

b. $\dfrac{5!}{4!} = 5$ **d.** $(3!) \cdot (6!) = 9!$ **f.** $9 \cdot 8 \cdot 7! = 9!$

g. A set of four books can be arranged on a shelf in only four different ways.

h. It is possible to form 5! permutations of all the letters in the word "learn".

i. A student council of eight people can be seated in a row of eight seats in 56 different orders.

j. From a group of six people it is possible to form 240 different lists of candidates for the four offices: president, vice president, secretary and treasurer.

k. A coach with a seven-man basketball squad can form at most $\dfrac{7!}{2}$ different five-man teams.

2. How many different four-digit natural number numerals can be formed from the digits 1, 3, 5, 7, and 9 if no digit is repeated in a numeral?

3. How many four-digit natural number numerals can be formed using the digits 2, 4, 6, and 8 if a digit may be used more than once in a numeral?

4. How many natural number numerals of one or more digits can be formed using the digits 6, 7, 8, and 9 if a digit may be used more than once in a numeral and the number which is named is between 5 and 10,000?

5. How many different four-letter arrangements are there of the letters of the word "side"?

6. The football stadium at Athlete High School has nine gates; five are on the east side and four are on the west side.

a. In how many different ways can a person enter by an east gate and leave by a west gate?

b. In how many different ways can a person enter by a west gate and leave by an east gate?

c. In how many different ways can a person enter and leave the stadium?

7. How many different automobile license plates can be made using one letter followed by four digits?

8. How many different signals can be made from six different flags if each signal is to consist of six flags hung in a horizontal row?

9. How many different arrangements of five geometry books and three chemistry books can be made if all of the books are placed on a shelf in such a way that the geometry books are kept together and to the left of the chemistry books?

10. How many arrangements of three different mathematics books and seven different physics books can be made on a shelf with space for ten books if books on the same subject may not be separated?

11. In how many ways can a game of doubles in ping pong be arranged if each team is to be composed of a boy and a girl from a group of five boys and four girls?

12. An automobile manufacturer builds five different models of cars; each model is available in any one of four exterior colors, any one of three interior colors, and with or without white-wall tires. How many different appearing automobiles does the manufacturer make?

PERMUTATIONS—THE GENERAL CASE

We are now interested in finding the number of permutations of n objects using k of the objects at a time ($k \leq n$). If we use the symbol $P(n; k)$, where n and k are natural numbers, $n \geq k$, to designate the number of permutations of n objects, k at a time, then we already know that $P(n; n) = n!$ Why? We need to discover a way of finding the value of $P(n; k)$ in instances where $k < n$. Consider the following examples.

Examples: *i.* How many permutations can be formed from the letters in the word "Monday" if we use only three letters at a time?

By the Fundamental Counting Principle, the number of permutations is $6 \cdot 5 \cdot 4$ or 120. Thus, $P(6; 3) = 120$.

ii. How many permutations can we form from five objects using two objects at a time?

$$P(5; 2) = 5 \cdot 4 = 20$$

From your study of these examples, determine the value of $P(4; 3)$; the value of $P(7; 2)$.

Now, let us see if we can determine a formula for $P(n; k)$ for all natural numbers n and k, $k \leq n$. Notice that the *first* of the k objects must be selected from a collection of n objects; the *second* must be selected from the set of $(n - 1)$ remaining objects; the *third* must be selected from the set of $(n - 2)$ remaining objects, and so on; and finally, the kth, or last, object must be selected from the set of $[n - (k - 1)]$ or $(n - k + 1)$ objects then left. Therefore, by the Fundamental Counting Principle, we see that for natural numbers n and k, $k \leq n$

$$P(n; k) = n \cdot (n - 1) \cdot (n - 2) \cdot \ldots \cdot (n - k + 1)$$

We can obtain a better statement of this fact by making the following observations. First, notice that for all natural numbers n and k, $k < n$

$$n \cdot (n - 1) \cdot (n - 2) \cdot \ldots \cdot (n - k + 1) = \frac{n!}{(n - k)!}$$

We would like this to hold for $k = n$ also; that is, that

$$n \cdot (n - 1) \cdot (n - 2) \cdot \ldots \cdot (n - n + 1) = \frac{n!}{(n - n)!}$$

and, therefore, that
$$n! = \frac{n!}{0!}$$

But this is true if and only if $0! = 1$. Since, at present, the symbol $0!$ has no meaning, *let us define* $0! = 1$. We can now state the foregoing result in the desired fashion.

Theorem 2 $P(n; k) = \dfrac{n!}{(n - k)!}$ where n and k are natural numbers, $k \leq n$.

So far, our study of permutations has been restricted to sets of n distinct objects, n a natural number. The following examples involve situations in which not all of the n objects are different.

Example: i.   Find the number of *different* permutations of the letters of the word "seek."

Let us temporarily place subscripts on the e's to distinguish one from the other. We have, then, $4!$ or 24 permutations of the four letters s, e_1, e_2, and k. Of these 24 permutations, half will contain the e's in the order e_1, e_2; and the other half will contain them in the order e_2, e_1. [Why?] Without the subscripts, the two groups of permutations are indistinguishable. Hence, the number of distinct permutations is

$$\frac{4!}{2!} = \frac{24}{2} = 12$$

Example: ii.   Find the number of different permutations of the five letters of the word "puppy."

By placing subscripts on the p's, we obtain $5!$ permutations. Many of these $5!$ permutations differ only in the arrangement of the p's, however, and, hence, are indistinguishable. We, of course, are interested in counting only those arrangements which *are* distinguishable. Suppose there are R of them. Then for any one of these R permutations, say "pupyp," the three p's may be arranged in $3!$ ways without altering the permutation. These permutations are listed below.

$p_1up_2yp_3$	$p_2up_1yp_3$	$p_3up_1yp_2$
$p_1up_3yp_2$	$p_2up_3yp_1$	$p_3up_2yp_1$

Hence, we conclude that $3! \cdot R = 5!$ and, therefore, $R = \dfrac{5!}{3!} = 20$.

The twenty distinguishable permutations are

puppy	pypup	upypp	yppup	ppypu
pupyp	pyupp	uyppp	ypupp	ppyup
puypp	upppy	yuppp	ppupy	pppuy
pyppu	uppyp	ypppu	ppuyp	pppyu

Example: *iii.*   Find the number of different permutations of the six letters of the word "tattoo."

By placing subscripts on the t's and on the o's, we may obtain 6! permutations. However, many of these 6! permutations differ only in the arrangement of the t's or in the arrangement of the o's and, hence, are indistinguishable. We wish to count only those arrangements which are distinguishable. Suppose there are P of them. Then for any one of these P permutations the t's can be arranged in 3! ways without altering the permutation, and the o's can be arranged in 2! ways without affecting the permutation. We conclude that $2! \cdot 3! \cdot P = 6!$ and, therefore

$$P = \frac{6!}{2!3!} = 60$$

The reasoning used in the above examples may be extended to justify the following theorem.

Theorem 3 Consider a set of $n = k_1 + k_2 + \ldots + k_r$ objects of which k_1 are alike and of one kind, k_2 are alike and of a second kind, and so on, and, finally, k_r are alike and of an rth kind. Then the number, P, of different permutations of the n objects is

$$P = \frac{n!}{k_1! k_2! \ldots k_r!}$$

EXERCISES

1. True or false?

   a. $P(4; 4) = 4$

   b. $P(6; 4) = \dfrac{6!}{4!}$

   c. $P(3; 2) = 3$

   d. $P(6; 1) = 3 \cdot P(2; 1)$

   e. The number of permutations of seven different letters taken five at a time is $\dfrac{7!}{2!}$.

   f. The number of different permutations of the seven letters of the word "algebra" is $7!$.

   g. The number of different permutations of the four letters of the word "book" is $\dfrac{4!}{2!}$.

   h. The number of different permutations of the eleven letters of the word "permutation" is $\dfrac{11!}{2!}$.

   i. The number of different permutations of the eleven letters of the word "mathematics" is $\dfrac{11!}{2!2!}$.

2. How many different permutations can be made of the letters of the word "teeth"?

3. How many different permutations can be made of the letters of the word "scissors"?

4. A bookshelf has space for five books. If there are seven different books available, how many different arrangements can be made on the shelf?

5. A map of five states is to be colored using a different color for each state. How many different results are possible if there are nine colors available?

6. How many three-digit natural number numerals can be formed from the digits 1, 2, 3, 4, and 5 if no digit may appear more than once in any given numeral?

7. How many natural number numerals of one or more digits can be formed from the digits 1, 2, 3, 4, and 5 if no numeral may have a repeated digit?

8. Find the solution set for each of the following:

a. $P(3; k) = 3!$

b. $P(5; k) = 5!$

c. $P(n; 3) = 2 \cdot P(n - 1; 2)$

d. $P(n; 5) = 10 \cdot P(n - 1; 4)$

9. In how many different ways can two copies of a particular mathematics book and five copies of a particular science book be distributed to a group of seven students if each student is to receive a book?

10. How many different signals can be constructed by making a vertical display of eight flags if three of the flags are black, three are white and two are red?

Circular permutations

When we form a circular arrangement of objects, only the positions of the objects relative to one another are important. For example, there are 3! *linear permutations* of the letters of the set $\{x, y, z\}$:

$$x\,y\,z \qquad x\,z\,y \qquad y\,z\,x \qquad y\,x\,z \qquad z\,x\,y \qquad z\,y\,x$$

On the other hand, there are only two *circular permutations* of the elements of the set $\{x, y, z\}$. Notice that the arrangements

are all the same. Why? Similarly, the arrangements

also are all the same. Observe that, upon forming a circular permutation, it is immaterial where on the circle we locate the first object. After fixing the position of one of a set of n objects, n a natural number, we may then proceed to compute the number of permutations of the remaining $(n-1)$ objects as if they were in a straight line. Thus, we obtain the following theorem.

Theorem 4 The number of *circular* permutations of a set of n objects, n a natural number, is $(n-1)!$

Examples: *i.* In how many different orders can four people be seated at a round table?

By Theorem 4, the number of circular permutations of a set of four objects is

$$(4-1)! = 3! = 6$$

Show these six permutations on the pictures of six circles.

ii. A woman invites four of her friends to dinner. In how many different ways may she and her guests be arranged around a circular table?

The number of ways is $(5-1)! = 4! = 24$.

EXERCISES

1.   In how many different orders can six people take seats at a round table?

2.   In how many different orders can a football team form a circular huddle?

3.   In how many different orders can a group of four girls and four boys be seated at a round table if boys and girls must alternate?

4.   A gardener wishes to plant seven different flowers in a circular arrangement. In how many ways can this be done?

5.   How many seating arrangements are possible at a five-place table if seven people are available?

COMBINATIONS

In the section "Permutations — The General Case," we learned that $P(n; k)$, the number of permutations of n objects using k of the objects at a time, is given by

$$P(n; k) = \frac{n!}{(n-k)!}$$

A different, but related, problem arises if we wish to count the number of different k-member subsets which can be formed from an n-member set, k and n natural numbers, $k \leq n$. Consider, for example, the five member set

$$\{P, Q, R, S, T\}$$

The different three-member subsets of this set are listed on the next page.

| $\{P, Q, R\}$ | $\{P, Q, T\}$ | $\{P, R, T\}$ | $\{Q, R, S\}$ | $\{Q, S, T\}$ |
| $\{P, Q, S\}$ | $\{P, R, S\}$ | $\{P, S, T\}$ | $\{Q, R, T\}$ | $\{R, S, T\}$ |

Notice that there are ten three-member subsets of a five-member set. We call each of the above sets a *combination* of the five elements $P, Q, R, S,$ and T taken three at a time, and we use the symbol $\binom{5}{3}$ to name the total number of combinations of five elements taken three at a time. Thus, $\binom{5}{3} = 10$.

You already know that the letters in *each* of the above combinations can be permuted in $3!$ ways. If we permute the letters in each combination above, we obtain $3! \times \binom{5}{3}$ permutations. We obtain the same result of these permutations by forming all permutations of the five letters $P, Q, R, S,$ and T, taken three at a time. There are $\dfrac{5!}{2!}$ of these. Therefore

$$3! \cdot \binom{5}{3} = \frac{5!}{2!}$$

It follows that

$$\binom{5}{3} = \frac{5!}{3!2!}$$

Now let us examine the general case. For all natural numbers k and n, $k \le n$, the symbol $\binom{n}{k}$ denotes the number of k-member subsets of an n-member set. Furthermore

$$k! \cdot \binom{n}{k} = P(n;\ k)$$

Hence

$$\binom{n}{k} = \frac{P(n;\ k)}{k!}$$

And since

$$P(n;\ k) = \frac{n!}{(n-k)!}$$

$$\binom{n}{k} = \frac{\dfrac{n!}{(n-k)!}}{k!}$$

$$= \frac{n!}{k!(n-k)!}$$

To complete the discussion, let us consider the symbol $\binom{n}{0}$, n a non-negative integer. To be consistent, this symbol should represent the number of different 0-member subsets of an n-member set. How many *different* empty subsets can we form from a given n-member set, n a non-negative integer? Do you agree that there is only one empty set? If we replace k by 0 in

$$\binom{n}{k} = \frac{n!}{k!(n-k)!}$$

we get

$$\binom{n}{0} = \frac{n!}{0!(n-0)!}$$

$$= \frac{n!}{1 \cdot n!}$$

$$= \frac{n!}{n!} = 1$$

which is the desired result. Our findings are summarized in the following theorem.

Theorem 5 For non-negative integers k and n, $k \leq n$, $\binom{n}{k} = \frac{n!}{k!(n-k)!}$

Example: *i.*   Compute the value of $\binom{2}{0} + \binom{2}{1} + \binom{2}{2}$.

$$\binom{2}{0} + \binom{2}{1} + \binom{2}{2} = \frac{2!}{0!(2-0)!} + \frac{2!}{1!(2-1)!} + \frac{2!}{2!(2-2)!}$$

$$= \frac{2!}{0!2!} + \frac{2!}{1!1!} + \frac{2!}{2!0!}$$

$$= \frac{2!}{2!} + 2! + \frac{2!}{2!}$$

$$= 1 + 2! + 1$$

$$= 1 + 2 + 1$$

$$= 4$$

Example: *ii.*   A committee of three students is to be chosen from a group of seven students. In how many ways can the committee be formed?

We wish to determine the value of $\binom{7}{3}$, the number of combinations of seven things, taken three at a time. By Theorem 5

$$\binom{7}{3} = \frac{7!}{3!4!}$$

$$= \frac{7 \cdot 6 \cdot 5}{3!}$$

$$= 7 \cdot 5$$

$$= 35$$

Thus, there are 35 ways of forming a three-member committee from a group of seven students.

The values of $\binom{n}{k}$ for non-negative integers k and n, $k \leq n$, form an interesting pattern when they are arranged in a triangular array as in figure 2. What entries belong in the first unlisted row of figure 2?

$$\binom{0}{0}$$

$$\binom{1}{0} \qquad \binom{1}{1}$$

$$\binom{2}{0} \qquad \binom{2}{1} \qquad \binom{2}{2}$$

$$\binom{3}{0} \qquad \binom{3}{1} \qquad \binom{3}{2} \qquad \binom{3}{3}$$

$$\binom{4}{0} \qquad \binom{4}{1} \qquad \binom{4}{2} \qquad \binom{4}{3} \qquad \binom{4}{4}$$

$$\bullet \qquad \bullet \qquad \bullet \qquad \bullet \qquad \bullet \qquad \bullet$$

Fig. 2

Replacing the symbols in figure 2 by their values, we obtain the following array.

$$1$$

$$1 \qquad 1$$

$$1 \qquad 2 \qquad 1$$

$$1 \qquad 3 \qquad 3 \qquad 1$$

$$1 \qquad 4 \qquad 6 \qquad 4 \qquad 1$$

$$\square \qquad \square \qquad \square \qquad \square \qquad \square \qquad \square$$

Fig. 3

What entries belong in the boxes? Now compute the values of

$$\binom{5}{0} \qquad \binom{5}{1} \qquad \binom{5}{2} \qquad \binom{5}{3} \qquad \binom{5}{4} \qquad \binom{5}{5}$$

to see if you have discovered the pattern.

Returning to figure 2, locate the entries $\binom{2}{1}$, $\binom{2}{2}$ and $\binom{3}{2}$. Observe that

$$\binom{2}{1} + \binom{2}{2} = \binom{3}{2}$$

By examining figure 2, determine which of the following statements are true.

$$\binom{3}{0} + \binom{3}{1} = \binom{4}{1} \qquad\qquad \binom{2}{0} + \binom{2}{1} = \binom{3}{1}$$

$$\binom{3}{1} + \binom{3}{2} = \binom{4}{2} \qquad\qquad \binom{4}{3} + \binom{4}{4} = \binom{5}{4}$$

On the basis of your observations, do you think the following statement is true?

$$\binom{5}{2} + \binom{5}{3} = \binom{6}{3}$$

Compute and verify your answer.

You probably have concluded that for all non-negative integers k and n, $k \le n$

$$\binom{n}{k-1} + \binom{n}{k} = \binom{n+1}{k}$$

This is the case, indeed, and its proof is left to you. (See exercises on page 510, problem **17**.) This fact is called *Pascal's Rule*. The associated triangular array in figure 3 is called *Pascal's Triangle*. Observation of Pascal's Triangle also suggests that for all non-negative integers k and n, $k \le n$

$$\binom{n}{k} = \binom{n}{n-k}$$

You will be asked to supply a proof of this in problem **16**, page 510.

EXERCISES

1. True or false?

a. The symbol $\binom{5}{3}$ denotes the number of different three-member subsets that can be formed from a five-member set.

b. $\{a, b, c\}$ and $\{a, c, b\}$ are two of the different three-member subsets of $\{a, b, c, d\}$.

c. $\binom{0}{0} = 0$

d. $\binom{8}{8} = 1$

e. $\binom{4}{0} = \binom{4}{4}$

f. $\binom{6}{4} = \binom{6}{2}$

g. $\binom{7}{0} = \binom{9}{0}$

h. $\binom{9}{4} = \frac{9!}{4!}$

i. $\binom{7}{4} + \binom{7}{5} = \binom{8}{5}$

j. $\binom{3}{0} + \binom{3}{1} + \binom{3}{2} + \binom{3}{3} = 2 \cdot \binom{3}{0} + 2 \cdot \binom{3}{1}$

2. Simplify.

a. $\dbinom{4}{0} + \dbinom{4}{1} + \dbinom{4}{2} + \dbinom{4}{3} + \dbinom{4}{4}$

b. $\dbinom{7}{0} + \dbinom{7}{1} + \ldots + \dbinom{7}{6} + \dbinom{7}{7}$

c. $\dbinom{8}{0} + \dbinom{8}{1} + \ldots + \dbinom{8}{7} + \dbinom{8}{8}$

d. $\dbinom{9}{0} + \dbinom{9}{1} + \dbinom{9}{2} + \dbinom{9}{3} + \ldots + \dbinom{9}{8} + \dbinom{9}{9}$

e. $\dbinom{12}{12} + \dbinom{12}{11} + \ldots + \dbinom{12}{1} + \dbinom{12}{0}$

3. In a geometry class of twenty-five students, how many combinations of eight students can be selected to sit in the front row?

4. How many different lines are determined by a set of twelve points in a plane if no three of the points belong to the same straight line?

5. How many committees of twenty members can be formed from a set of twenty-five possible members?

6. In how many ways can a class of twenty students be separated into two groups, each of ten students?

7. A legislative body of thirteen people passes a law by a vote of seven to six. In how many different ways could this vote have resulted?

8. A student must do ten of fifteen problems on a final examination. In how many different ways can the student choose the ten problems?

9. The football team at Space University wishes to name two co-captains for their homecoming game. In how many ways can they be chosen from a squad of 55 players?

10. How many triangles are determined by the vertices of a regular octagon?

11. In how many ways can a set of four mathematics books and three biology books be selected from a set of six mathematics books and seven biology books?

12. From a standard deck of 52 cards
    a. how many different five-card hands can be formed?
    b. how many different five-card hands with at most two red cards (hearts or diamonds) can be formed?
    c. how many different five-card hands with at least four black cards (spades or clubs) can be formed?
    d. how many different five-card hands can be formed which contain all red cards or all black cards?

13. How many different sums of money can be formed from a penny, a nickel, a dime, a quarter and a half-dollar if each sum is determined by

    a. one coin?   **c.** three coins?   **e.** five coins?

    b. two coins?   **d.** four coins?

14. Find the solution set for each of the following:

    a. $\dbinom{n}{5} = \dbinom{n}{3}$ **b.** $\dbinom{n}{8} = \dbinom{n}{4}$ **c.** $\dbinom{n}{3} = \dbinom{n}{3}$

15. If a softball league consists of twelve teams, how many league games will be played during a season in which each team plays exactly two games with each of the other teams?

16. Prove that for all non-negative integers k and n, $k \le n$

$$\binom{n}{k} = \binom{n}{n-k}$$

17. Prove that for all non-negative integers k and n, $k \le n$

$$\binom{n}{k-1} + \binom{n}{k} = \binom{n+1}{k}$$

THE BINOMIAL THEOREM

The results of the previous section are related to the problem of finding the *expanded form* of $(x+y)^n$ for any natural number n. The expanded form of $(x+y)^n$ for several replacements of n are given below. Verify that each is correct.

$$(x+y)^1 = x+y$$
$$(x+y)^2 = x^2 + 2xy + y^2$$
$$(x+y)^3 = x^3 + 3x^2y + 3xy^2 + y^3$$
$$(x+y)^4 = x^4 + 4x^3y + 6x^2y^2 + 4xy^3 + y^4$$

Let us examine the pattern of coefficients in the above expansions. The pattern is displayed below.

$$
\begin{array}{ccccccc}
 & & & 1 & & 1 & \\
 & & 1 & & 2 & & 1 \\
 & 1 & & 3 & & 3 & & 1 \\
1 & & 4 & & 6 & & 4 & & 1
\end{array}
$$

Where have you seen this pattern before? The relationship we are seeking is easy to discover if we rewrite the expanded form of $(x+y)^4$ as

$$(x+y)^4 = \binom{4}{0}x^4 + \binom{4}{1}x^3y + \binom{4}{2}x^2y^2 + \binom{4}{3}xy^3 + \binom{4}{4}y^4$$

Notice that each term of the *expansion* is of the form $\binom{4}{k}x^{4-k}y^k$, and that the successive terms of the expansion may be obtained by replacing k, in order, by 0, 1, 2, 3, and 4. Verify that

$$(x + y)^5 = x^5 + 5x^4y + 10x^3y^2 + 10x^2y^3 + 5xy^4 + y^5$$

for all real number replacements of x and y. Is it true that

$$\forall_x \forall_y \; (x + y)^5 = \binom{5}{0}x^5 + \binom{5}{1}x^4y + \binom{5}{2}x^3y^2 + \binom{5}{3}x^2y^3 + \binom{5}{4}xy^4 + \binom{5}{5}y^5$$

Justify your answer. Is each term of the last expansion of the form $\binom{5}{k}x^{5-k}y^k$?

You probably have come to the conclusion that for any natural number n, each term of the expansion of $(x + y)^n$ is of the form $\binom{n}{k}x^{n-k}y^k$, the successive terms of the expansion being obtained by replacing k, in order, by 0, 1, 2, ..., n. This conclusion is correct, and is called the *Binomial Theorem*.

Theorem 6 (Binomial Theorem) If n is a natural number, then

$$\forall_x \forall_y \; (x + y)^n = \binom{n}{0}x^n + \binom{n}{1}x^{n-1}y + \binom{n}{2}x^{n-2}y^2 + \ldots + \binom{n}{n}y^n$$

Before we prove the Binomial Theorem, let us examine the following:

$$\begin{aligned}(x + y)^2 &= (x + y)(x + y) \\ &= x(x + y) + y(x + y) \\ &= x \cdot x + x \cdot y + y \cdot x + y \cdot y\end{aligned}$$

The above illustrates a procedure we could use to obtain the expansion of $(x + y)^2$. Notice that each term of the expansion is the product of either the x or the y from the factor $(x + y)$ and either the x or the y from the factor $(x + y)$; moreover, the expansion contains terms which represent all possible ways that this can be done. We see, then, that the expansion of $(x + y)^2$ must consist exclusively of x^2, y^2 and xy-terms.

Now let us see if we can determine the number of x^2, y^2 and xy terms that will appear in the expansion of $(x + y)^2$ without applying a procedure like that above. Suppose we first explore how many y^2-terms the expansion will contain. Notice that there are exactly two y's, one in each factor, from which to choose; and to form a y^2-term, we must use both of them. Hence the number of y^2-terms which will appear in the expansion of $(x + y)^2$ is $\binom{2}{2} = 1$. Next, let us explore how many xy-terms we can expect to appear in the expansion. In order to form an xy-term, we need one factor y, and there are two y's from which to choose. Hence, there are $\binom{2}{1}$ ways of choosing the y factor. Once the y factor has been selected — from one of the two $(x + y)$ factors — there is only one choice for the x-factor. Thus, by the Fundamental Counting Principle, we conclude that the number of xy-terms which will appear in the expansion of $(x + y)^2$ is $\binom{2}{1} \cdot \binom{1}{1} = \binom{2}{1} = 2$.

Finally, let us explore how many x^2-terms will appear in the expansion. By symmetry, since the expansion contains $\binom{2}{2}$ or one y^2-term, it must also contain precisely one x^2-term. Therefore, since $\binom{2}{2} = \binom{2}{0}$, we can claim that

$$(x + y)^2 = (x + y)(x + y)$$

$$= \binom{2}{0}x^2 + \binom{2}{1}xy + \binom{2}{2}y^2$$

Let us repeat the above argument to obtain the expansion of $(x + y)^3$ before going to the general case. Notice that the expanded form of

$$(x + y)^3 = (x + y)(x + y)(x + y)$$

must consist exclusively of x^3, x^2y, xy^2 and y^3-terms. Why? Our problem is to determine how many of each of these terms will appear in the expansion. Arguing as before, the expansion will contain $\binom{3}{3}$ y^3-terms, $\binom{3}{2} \cdot \binom{1}{1}$ or $\binom{3}{2}$ xy^2-terms, $\binom{3}{1} \cdot \binom{2}{2}$ x^2y-terms, and $\binom{3}{3}$ or $\binom{3}{0}$ x^3-terms. We conclude that

$$(x + y)^3 = \binom{3}{0}x^3 + \binom{3}{1}x^2y + \binom{3}{2}xy^2 + \binom{3}{3}y^3$$

On the basis of the preceding discussion, give the expansion for $(x + y)^4$; for $(x + y)^5$.

We are now prepared to consider the generalization for the Binomial Theorem. In general, the expansion of $(x + y)^n$, n a natural number, will consist exclusively of x^n, $x^{n-1}y$, $x^{n-2}y^2$, ..., xy^{n-1}, and y^n-terms. [Explain.]

the number of y^n-terms is $\binom{n}{n}$

the number of xy^{n-1}-terms is $\binom{n}{n-1}\binom{1}{1} = \binom{n}{n-1}$

the number of x^2y^{n-2}-terms is $\binom{n}{n-2}\binom{2}{2} = \binom{n}{n-2}$

the number of $x^{n-1}y$-terms is $\binom{n}{1} \cdot \binom{n-1}{n-1} = \binom{n}{1}$

and, finally, the number of x^n-terms is $\binom{n}{n} = \binom{n}{0}$

This concludes our generalization.

Now let us examine the statement of the Binomial Theorem to see what other facts we can discover. Notice that for any natural number n, there are $(n + 1)$ terms in the expansion of $(x + y)^n$. Explain why this is so. How many terms are there in the expansion of $(x + y)^3$? In the expansion of $(x + y)^9$? In the expansion of $(x + y)^{25}$? Notice also that the first term of the expansion of $(x + y)^n$ has no y factors; the second term has one y factor; the third term has two y factors; and so on. For instance, the third term in the expansion of $(x + y)^5$ will be the x^3y^2-term. How do we know that there are three x factors? Is the fifth term in the expansion the xy^4-term? Why or why not? What is the degree of each term in the expansion of $(x + y)^5$? Of each term in the expansion of $(x + y)^7$? Of each term in the expansion of $(x + y)^n$?

The coefficients in the expansion of $(x + y)^n$ also form an interesting pattern. Observe that the coefficient for the first term is $\binom{n}{0}$; for the second term is $\binom{n}{1}$; for the third term is $\binom{n}{2}$; and so on. Thus, for example, the coefficient of the fourth term of the expansion of $(x + y)^5$ is $\binom{5}{3}$. What is the coefficient of the fifth term? Of the sixth term?

Examples: i.   Expand $(x + y)^6$.

By the Binomial Theorem, $(x + y)^6$

$$= \binom{6}{0}x^6 + \binom{6}{1}x^5y + \binom{6}{2}x^4y^2 + \binom{6}{3}x^3y^3 + \binom{6}{4}x^2y^4 + \binom{6}{5}xy^5 + \binom{6}{6}y^6$$

$$= x^6 + 6x^5y + 15x^4y^2 + 20x^3y^3 + 15x^2y^4 + 6xy^5 + y^6$$

ii.   Expand $(x - y)^3$.

$$(x - y)^3 = [x + (-y)]^3$$

$$= \binom{3}{0}x^3 + \binom{3}{1}x^2 \cdot (-y) + \binom{3}{2}x \cdot (-y)^2 + \binom{3}{3} \cdot (-y)^3$$

$$= x^3 - 3x^2y + 3xy^2 - y^3$$

iii.   Expand $(x + 2y)^4$.

$$(x + 2y)^4 = [x + (2y)]^4$$

$$= \binom{4}{0}x^4 + \binom{4}{1}x^3 \cdot (2y) + \binom{4}{2}x^2 \cdot (2y)^2 + \binom{4}{3}x \cdot (2y)^3 + \binom{4}{4} \cdot (2y)^4$$

$$= 1 \cdot x^4 + 4x^3 \cdot 2y + 12x^2 \cdot 4y^2 + 4x \cdot 8y^3 + 1 \cdot 16y^4$$

$$= x^4 + 8x^3y + 48x^2y^2 + 32xy^3 + 16y^4$$

iv.   Prove that, for all natural numbers n

$$\binom{n}{0} + \binom{n}{1} + \binom{n}{2} + \ldots + \binom{n}{n} = 2^n$$

By the Binomial Theorem, if n is a natural number, then

$$\forall_x \forall_y \ (x + y)^n = \binom{n}{0}x^n + \binom{n}{1}x^{n-1}y + \ldots + \binom{n}{n}y^n$$

Hence, if we replace both x and y by 1, then for all natural numbers n

$$(1+1)^n = \binom{n}{0} \cdot 1^n + \binom{n}{1} \cdot 1^{n-1} \cdot 1 + \ldots + \binom{n}{n} \cdot 1^n$$

Simplifying, we obtain the desired result, namely

$$2^n = \binom{n}{0} + \binom{n}{1} + \ldots + \binom{n}{n}$$

$v.$ What is the eighth term in the expansion of $(x+y)^{12}$?

$$\binom{12}{7} x^5 y^7$$

EXERCISES

1. True or false?

a. $\forall_y \forall_z \ (y+z)^2 = \binom{2}{0}y^2 + \binom{2}{1}yz + \binom{2}{2}z^2$

b. $\forall_r \forall_s \ (r+s)^3 = \binom{3}{0}r^3 + \binom{3}{1}r^2s + \binom{3}{2}rs^2 + \binom{3}{3}s^3$

c. $\forall_a \forall_b \ (a-b)^3 = \binom{3}{0}a^3 - \binom{3}{1}a^2b + \binom{3}{2}ab^2 - \binom{3}{3}b^3$

d. $\forall_x \forall_y \ (2x+y)^3 = \binom{3}{0}x^3 + \binom{3}{1}x^2y + \binom{3}{2}xy^2 + \binom{3}{3}y^3$

e. $\forall_t \ (1+t)^4 = \binom{4}{0} + \binom{4}{1}t + \binom{4}{2}t^2 + \binom{4}{3}t^3 + \binom{4}{4}t^4$

f. The third term in the expansion of $(x+y)^6$ is $\binom{6}{2}x^3y^3$.

g. The second term in the expansion of $(a+b)^4$ is $\binom{4}{2}a^3b$.

h. The fourteenth term in the expansion of $(x+z)^{15}$ is $15xz^{14}$.

i. There are nine terms in the expansion of $(p+q)^{10}$.

j. The third and sixth terms of the expansion of $(x+y)^8$ have the same coefficient.

2. Write the expansion for each of the following. Simplify each term.

a. $(x-y)^7$

b. $(2x+y)^4$

c. $\left(x + \frac{1}{2}y\right)^5$

d. $(a-2b)^5$

e. $\left(\frac{1}{2}c - d\right)^4$

f. $(2r-s)^6$

g. $(2x+3y)^4$

h. $\left(3x - \frac{1}{2y}\right)^5$

i. $\left(\frac{1}{2}t + \frac{1}{3}v\right)^4$

j. $(m^2+n)^6$

k. $\left(\frac{1}{x} + \frac{1}{y}\right)^8$

l. $\left(\frac{x}{y} - 1\right)^5$

m. $\left(\frac{a}{2} - \frac{b}{3}\right)^4$

n. $(x + \sqrt{y})^{10}$

o. $\left(\frac{x^2}{2} + 2y^2\right)^5$

p. $\left(2y^3 - \frac{z^2}{2y}\right)^7$

3. Write the specified term in simplified form.

   a. the second term of $(3x + 2y)^5$

   b. the third term of $(\frac{1}{2}x + y)^6$

   c. the "middle" term of $(x^2 - y^2)^4$

   d. the fifth term of $(2 - 3t)^7$

   e. the sixth term of $(3\sqrt{x} + \sqrt[5]{y})^5$

4. Use the Binomial Theorem to obtain the expansion of

$$(x + y + z)^4$$

   (HINT: Note that $(x + y + z)^4 = [x + (y + z)]^4$.)

5. Use the Binomial Theorem to obtain the expansion of

$$(a + b + c + d)^3$$

VOCABULARY

Use each of the following correctly in a sentence. Numerals in parentheses refer to pages where these words were used. If you are not sure of the meaning of any word, turn to the indicated page.

Binomial Theorem (510)
circular permutation (503)
combination (504)
expanded form of $(x + y)^n$ (510)

Fundamental Counting Principle (498)
linear permutation (496)
Pascal's Rule (508)
Pascal's Triangle (508)

REVIEW EXERCISES

1. True or false?

   a. $7 \cdot 6! = 7!$

   b. $(3 \cdot 2)! = 3!$

   c. $\dfrac{6!}{3! \cdot 2!} = 1$

   d. $P(5; 5) = 5$

   e. $\dbinom{9}{8} = \dfrac{9!}{8!}$

   f. $P(7; 4) = \dfrac{7!}{4!}$

   g. $\dbinom{7}{0} = 1$

   h. $4! \cdot \dbinom{6}{4} = P(6; 4)$

   i. $\dbinom{6}{2} + \dbinom{6}{3} = \dbinom{7}{3}$

   j. $\forall_c \forall_d \ (c + d)^4 = \dbinom{4}{0}c^4 + \dbinom{4}{1}c^3 + \dbinom{4}{2}c^2 + \dbinom{4}{3}c + \dbinom{4}{4}$

2. Simplify.

   a. $\dfrac{100!}{2! \cdot 98!}$

   b. $\dbinom{27}{0}$

   c. $\dbinom{107}{1}$

   d. $4! \cdot 3!$

   e. $9 \cdot 8 \cdot 7!$

f. $\binom{7}{0} + \binom{7}{1} + \binom{7}{2} + \binom{7}{3} + \binom{7}{4} + \binom{7}{5} + \binom{7}{6} + \binom{7}{7}$

g. $\binom{5}{0}r^5 + \binom{5}{1}r^4s + \binom{5}{2}r^3s^2 + \binom{5}{3}r^2s^3 + \binom{5}{4}rs^4 + \binom{5}{5}s^5$

h. $\dfrac{7!}{2! \cdot 5!}$

i. $\binom{15}{4} + \binom{15}{5}$

j. $\binom{3}{0} \cdot x^3 - \binom{3}{1} \cdot x^2 \cdot \left(\dfrac{y}{4}\right) + \binom{3}{2} \cdot x \cdot \left(\dfrac{y}{4}\right)^2 - \binom{3}{3} \cdot \left(\dfrac{y}{4}\right)^3$

3. How many different signals can be made by displaying five of eight different flags in a horizontal line?

4. How many different seven-digit numerals for telephone numbers can be formed if the first digit cannot be zero?

5. How many different four-digit numerals can be formed using the digits 0, 1, 2, 3, 4, and 5?

6. How many different six-letter arrangements can be formed using all the letters of the word "symbol"?

7. How many different ten-letter arrangements can be formed using all the letters of the word "statistics"?

8. A girl invites nine of her friends to dinner. In how many different ways can she and her guests be seated around a circular table?

9. How many different ordinary decimal numerals can be made using the digits 1, 2, 3, 8 and 9 if no digit may be repeated in a numeral?

10. In how many ways can a five-person family be arranged in a line for a photograph if the father and mother wish to stand next to each other?

11. The University School cafeteria offers a three-item lunch tray consisting of one meat, one vegetable and one dessert. How many different choices of lunch trays are available if there are three choices of meat, five choices of vegetable, and eight choices of dessert?

12. How many triangles are determined by the vertices of a regular decagon?

13. How many different weights can be measured on a balance scale if a one-, a two-, a four-, an eight-, a sixteen-, and a thirty-two-gram weight are available?

14. How many permutations of the letters of the word "discovery" will end in the letter "d"?

15. How many different amounts of postage can be formed from a one-cent stamp, a three-cent stamp, a five-cent stamp, an eight-cent stamp and a ten-cent stamp using

    a. one or more of the stamps?   **c.** at least two of the stamps?

    b. exactly four of the stamps?   **d.** at most three of the stamps?

16. Find the solution set for each of the following:

    a. $P(4; k) = 4!$

    b. $P(n; 4) = 4 \cdot P(n - 1; 3)$

    d. $\binom{n}{4} = \binom{n}{2}$

    c. $\binom{n}{6} = \binom{n}{5}$

    e. $\binom{n}{4} = \binom{n}{4}$

17. Write the expansion for each of the following. Simplify each term.

    a. $(2 + 3i)^4$

    b. $(ax + b)^5$

    c. $(\sqrt{x} + \sqrt{y})^6$

    d. $(r^2 - t)^7$

18. Write the specified term in simplified form.

    a. the fourth term of $(2x + y)^5$

    b. the third term of $(m + n^2)^6$

    c. the "middle" term of $\left(\dfrac{a}{b} - 2\right)^6$

    d. the eighth term of $(\sqrt{x} + y)^{10}$

CHAPTER TEST

1. True or false?

    a. $4! \cdot 3! = 12!$

    b. $9 \cdot 8 \cdot 7! = 9!$

    d. $\binom{8}{5} + \binom{8}{6} = \binom{9}{7}$

    c. $P(7; 5) = \binom{7}{5} \cdot 5!$

    e. $\binom{237}{236} = 1$

    f. The number of different permutations of the letters of the word "tomorrow" is $8!$.

    g. $\binom{4}{0} + \binom{4}{1} + \binom{4}{2} + \binom{4}{3} + \binom{4}{4} = 2 \cdot \binom{4}{0} + 2 \cdot \binom{4}{1} + \binom{4}{2}$

    h. $\forall_a \forall_b \ (a + 2b)^3 = \binom{3}{0} \cdot a^3 + \binom{3}{1} \cdot a^2 \cdot (2b) + \binom{3}{2} \cdot a \cdot (2b)^2 + \binom{3}{3} \cdot (2b)^3$

    i. $\forall_r \ (r - 2)^4 = \binom{4}{0} \cdot r^4 + \binom{4}{1} \cdot r^3 \cdot 2 + \binom{4}{2} \cdot r^2 \cdot 2^2 + \binom{4}{3} \cdot r \cdot 2^3 + \binom{4}{4} \cdot 2^4$

    j. The fifth term in the expansion of $(x + y^2)^7$ is $\binom{7}{5} \cdot x^2 \cdot (y^2)^5$.

2. Simplify.

    a. $\binom{91}{89}$

    c. $\dfrac{8!}{2! \cdot 2!}$

    b. $\binom{17}{17}$

    d. $\binom{74}{0}$

    e. $P(6; 2)$

    f. $\binom{8}{0} + \binom{8}{1} + \binom{8}{2} + \binom{8}{3} + \binom{8}{4} + \binom{8}{5} + \binom{8}{6} + \binom{8}{7} + \binom{8}{8}$

    g. $\binom{12}{9} + \binom{12}{10}$

h. $\binom{4}{0}x^4 + \binom{4}{1}x^3 + \binom{4}{2}x^2 + \binom{4}{3}x + \binom{4}{4}$

i. $\dfrac{7!}{7}$

j. $\binom{5}{0} - \binom{5}{1}y + \binom{5}{2}y^2 - \binom{5}{3}y^3 + \binom{5}{4}y^4 - \binom{5}{5}y^5$

3. In how many ways can eight men be arranged in a

    a. line?   **b.** circle?

4. How many "call letters" for radio stations can be obtained by filling in the blanks in $W————$ with different letters not including W?

5. From a standard deck of 52 cards

    a. how many different five-card hands with exactly 3 black cards can be formed?

    b. how many different five-card hands with at most one black card can be formed?

    c. how many different five-card hands with at least 3 red cards can be formed?

6. In how many ways can four nickels, five dimes, and three quarters be distributed among twelve children if each child is to receive one coin?

7. Find the solution set for each of the following.

    a. $P(7; k) = 7!$ **c.** $\binom{n}{9} = \binom{n}{4}$

    b. $P(n; 7) = 5 \cdot P(n - 1; 6)$ **d.** $\binom{n}{10} = \binom{n}{10}$

8. Write the expansion for each of the following. Simplify each term.

    a. $(4x + y)^4$ **b.** $(3 - 2t)^5$

9. Use the Binomial Theorem to prove that for all natural numbers, n

$$\binom{n}{0} - \binom{n}{1} + \binom{n}{2} - \binom{n}{3} + \ldots \pm \binom{n}{n} = 0$$

BIBLIOGRAPHY

Commission on Mathematics. *Introductory Probability and Statistical Inference.* New York: College Entrance Examination Board, Revised Edition, 1959. Appendix II.

Sanford, V. *A Short History of Mathematics.* New York: Houghton Mifflin Co., 1930. pp. 177-181.

School Mathematics Study Group. *Intermediate Mathematics, Part II.* New Haven: Yale University Press, 1961. Chapter 14.

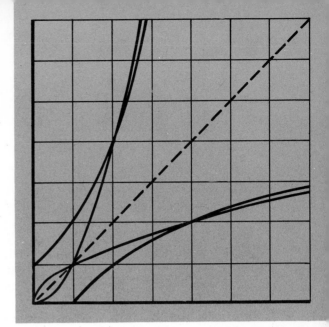

CHAPTER 17

Probability

SAMPLE SPACES AND PROBABILITY

Our study of probability will begin with an examination of several experiments. First, let us consider the experiment of tossing a coin. This experiment must result in one of two possible outcomes, a head (H) or a tail (T). The set of these two possible outcomes is then $\{H, T\}$. As a second example, let us examine the experiment of tossing a coin twice. In this experiment, the set of possible outcomes is $\{(H, H), (H, T), (T, H), (T, T)\}$. (H, H) means the occurrence of a head on both tosses. What outcome is specified by (H, T)? By (T, H)? By (T, T)?

■ *Definition of Sample Space of an Experiment*   The set of all possible outcomes of a given experiment is called the *sample space* of the experiment.

What is the sample space of the experiment of tossing a coin three times? How many elements does this sample space contain? How many elements are in the sample space of the experiment of tossing a coin four times?

We are interested in determining the likelihood of the occurrence of the various possible outcomes of an experiment. You will find that in many experiments one possible outcome is much more likely to occur than another. To verify this fact, imagine three cylindrical-shaped objects which look like those on the next page.

519

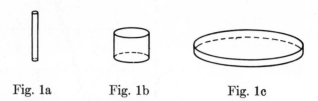

Fig. 1a   Fig. 1b   Fig. 1c

Suppose we design an experiment in which we drop
onto a flat surface an object similar to one of those pictured above, and then focus our attention on the position of the object when it comes to rest. To be more

specific, we shall be interested only in whether the object comes to rest on a flat
surface (position F at the right) or on its curved surface (position C at the right).

It should be clear that if we employ in our experiment an object similar in
size and shape to that in figure 1a above, the likelihood of outcome C is much
greater than the likelihood of outcome F. On the other hand, if we employ in our
experiment an object similar in size and shape to that in figure 1c, the likelihood of
outcome F is much greater than the likelihood of outcome C. Does it seem reasonable to expect that outcomes C and F have *approximately* the same likelihood of
occurrence in the case where an object is used in the experiment which is similar
in size and shape to that in figure 1b?

In our study of probability, we shall concentrate only on experiments in which
each outcome has the same likelihood of occurring on any given trial of the experiment. Much of what we will learn, however, applies also to experiments in which
outcomes are not equally likely.

Every subset of the sample space of an experiment is an *event*. We say that
the event has occurred as a result of a trial of the experiment if the outcome is some
element of the event. The *probability* of the occurrence of any one of the various
possible events associated with a given experiment is a measure of the likelihood
of the occurrence of that event. In order to obtain some meaningful measure of
the probability of various events associated with a particular experiment, we must
first assign some probability measure to each element in the sample space of the
experiment. In order to do this, we rely on our intuition. For example, consider
the experiment of tossing a coin twice. The sample space for this experiment is
$\{(H, H), (H, T), (T, H), (T, T)\}$. If we assume that each of the four possible
outcomes is equally likely, and if the experiment is repeated many times, then we
expect each outcome to occur about one-fourth of the time. It is this idea which
enables us to assign a probability measure to the elements of the sample space. We
say that the probability of the outcome (H, H), which we denote by $P(H, H)$, is $\frac{1}{4}$.
What is $P(H, T)$? $P(T, H)$? $P(T, T)$?

In general, we are often concerned with events which consist of more than one
element of the sample space. The procedure for assigning a probability measure
to such events can be discovered by resorting to an example. Suppose that for the
experiment of tossing a coin twice, we wish to describe the probability of the event,
E, of obtaining a head on one toss and a tail on the other toss; notice that both
(H, T) and (T, H) are elements of E. Since E contains two elements and since

there are a total of four elements in the sample space of the experiment, we conclude that $P(E) = \frac{2}{4}$ or $\frac{1}{2}$.

The foregoing intuitive notion about probability is embodied in the following:

■ *Definition of Probability of an Event* Given an experiment whose sample space S is finite and an event E, such that $E \subseteq S$. If we let $n(E)$ and $n(S)$ denote the number of elements in E and in S, respectively, and $P(E)$ denote the probability that E will occur as a result of a trial of the experiment, then $P(E) = \dfrac{n(E)}{n(S)}$.

There are two immediate consequences of the above-stated definition.

$$P(E) = 0 \text{ if and only if } E = \phi$$
$$0 \le P(E) \le 1 \text{ for every event } E$$

If an event $E = \phi$, then E is said to be *impossible* and $P(E) = 0$. On the other hand, an event E is said to be *certain* if $E = S$; in this case $P(E) = P(S) = 1$.

Study the following examples.

Examples: i. A ball is drawn at random from an urn which contains one black ball, one red ball, and one white ball. What is the probability that the drawn ball is red? black? white?

Let us begin by constructing a picture of the sample space.

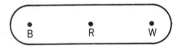

Since each outcome is equally likely, we see that $P(R) = \frac{1}{3}$. Similarly, $P(B) = \frac{1}{3}$ and $P(W) = \frac{1}{3}$.

ii. A ball is drawn at random from an urn which contains one black ball, two red balls, and three white balls. What is the probability that the ball which is drawn is black? red? white? We construct a picture of the sample space.

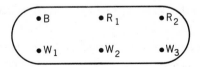

By the definition of probability of an event, $P(B) = \frac{1}{6}$; $P(R) = \frac{2}{6}$ or $\frac{1}{3}$; and $P(W) = \frac{3}{6}$ or $\frac{1}{2}$.

Examples: *iii.*   Consider the experiment of tossing an ordinary die.

      i. What is the sample space for the experiment?

$$\{1, 2, 3, 4, 5, 6\}$$

      ii. What is the probability that the top face will be the one with three dots?

$$\tfrac{1}{6}$$

      iii. What is the probability that the top face will contain an odd number of dots?

$$\tfrac{3}{6} \text{ or } \tfrac{1}{2}$$

      iv. What is the probability that the top face will have fewer than five dots?

$$\tfrac{4}{6} \text{ or } \tfrac{2}{3}$$

iv. A box contains twelve good transistors and three defective ones. If three transistors are drawn from the box at random, what is the probability that none are defective?

The number of three-member subsets which contain no defectives is $\dbinom{12}{3}$, and the total number of three-member subsets is $\dbinom{15}{3}$. Thus, by the definition of probability of an event, the probability that none are defective is

$$\frac{\dbinom{12}{3}}{\dbinom{15}{3}} = \frac{220}{455} = \frac{44}{91}$$

EXERCISES

1. True or false?

   a. If event E is impossible, then $P(E) = 0$.

   b. If event E is certain, then $P(E) = 1$.

   c. Each element of a sample space is a possible outcome.

   d. If S is a sample space and $E \subset S$, then $P(E) = \dfrac{n(E)}{S}$.

   e. If A and B are sets and $A \cap B = \phi$, then $n(A \cup B) = n(A) + n(B)$.

   f. If A and B are sets, then $n(A \cup B) = n(A) + n(B) - n(A \cap B)$.

   g. If S is a sample space, $A \subset S$, $n(A) = 2$, and $n(S) = 5$, then $P(A) = \tfrac{2}{5}$.

   h. If S is a sample space and $B \subset S$, then $\overline{B}$, the complement of B, is an event.

   i. If S is a sample space, $A \subset S$, $n(A) = r$, and $n(S) = t$, then $n(\overline{A}) = r - t$.

   j. If an experiment consists of selecting three light bulbs from a box of ten and testing them, then the sample space for this experiment contains $\dbinom{10}{3}$ elements.

2. Two letters are chosen at random from the set of letters in the word "true." List the sample space.

3. If a die is tossed, what is the probability that the number which "comes up" is **a.** odd? **b.** less than 6? **c.** greater than 6? **d.** greater than 0? **e.** less than 7? **f.** less than 1?

4. A marble is drawn at random from a bag which contains three white marbles, four green marbles, and one black marble. What is the probability that the marble is **a.** white? **b.** green? **c.** black? **d.** white or green? **e.** black or white?

5. If the letters e, a, m, g are arranged in a line at random, what is the probability that the arrangement will spell the word "game"?

6. One card is drawn at random from an ordinary deck of 52 cards. What is the probability of drawing **a.** a king? **b.** a spade? **c.** a red card?

7. The numerals from 0 to 9 inclusive are written on separate slips of paper, and the slips are placed in a box. One slip is drawn at random from the box. What is the probability that the numeral on the slip names **a.** an odd number? **b.** a number divisible by 2? **c.** a number divisible by 1? **d.** a composite number? **e.** a prime number? (Note that 0 and 1 are not prime numbers.)

8. A regular *octahedron* is a symmetrical solid with eight faces. Some of the faces of a particular octahedron are painted red and the rest are painted white. If, when the octahedron is rolled onto a flat surface, the probability of a white face landing on the bottom is three times the probability of a red face, how many faces are painted white?

9. A box of eight razor blades contains two defective blades. If two blades are drawn together from the box at random, what is the probability that **a.** neither of the two is defective? **b.** both are defective?

10. Give an argument in support of the following theorem.

Let E be any event in a finite sample space S.
Then $P(\overline{E}) = 1 - P(E)$.

THE ADDITION THEOREM

In practice, many probability problems are concerned with two or more of the events which occur as a result of a given experiment. For example, let E_1 and E_2 be two events associated with an experiment whose sample space is S. When an experiment is performed, we often wish to know the probability

    i. that both E_1 and E_2 will occur, or

    ii. that at least one of E_1 and E_2 will occur

Since events E_1 and E_2 are sets, $P(E_1 \cap E_2)$ is the probability that both E_1 and E_2 will occur as a result of a trial of the experiment. Why? Furthermore, $P(E_1 \cup E_2)$ is the probability that at least one of the events E_1 and E_2 will occur. Why?

In this section, we shall derive a formula for determining $P(E_1 \cup E_2)$. In order to develop some insight into the problem, however, let us first consider the experiment of rolling two dice. For the purpose of clarity, we will assume that one die is red, the other black. Here is the sample space for the experiment.

		E_1			E_2	
6	(1, 6)	(2, 6)	(3, 6)	(4, 6)	(5, 6)	(6, 6)
5	(1, 5)	(2, 5)	(3, 5)	(4, 5)	(5, 5)	(6, 5)
BLACK 4	(1, 4)	(2, 4)	(3, 4)	(4, 4)	(5, 4)	(6, 4)	$\leftarrow E_3$
3	(1, 3)	(2, 3)	(3, 3)	(4, 3)	(5, 3)	(6, 3)
2	(1, 2)	(2, 2)	(3, 2)	(4, 2)	(5, 2)	(6, 2)
1	(1, 1)	(2, 1)	(3, 1)	(4, 1)	(5, 1)	(6, 1)
	1	2	3	4	5	6

RED

Fig. 2

Suppose we let E_1 be the event of obtaining a "2" on the *red* die and E_2 be the event of obtaining a "5" on the *red* die. Note that $n(E_1) = 6$. How many elements does E_2 contain? Now suppose we are interested in $P(E_1 \text{ or } E_2) = P(E_1 \cup E_2)$. By the definition of probability we see that

$$P(E_1 \text{ or } E_2) = P(E_1 \cup E_2)$$
$$= \frac{n(E_1 \cup E_2)}{36}$$
$$= \frac{12}{36} \text{ or } \frac{1}{3}$$

Now notice that

$$P(E_1) = \frac{6}{36} = \frac{1}{6} \text{ and } P(E_2) = \frac{6}{36} = \frac{1}{6}$$

Hence

$$P(E_1) + P(E_2) = \frac{1}{6} + \frac{1}{6}$$
$$= \frac{1}{3}$$
$$= P(E_1 \cup E_2)$$

On the basis of the above results, one might guess that $P(A \cup B) = P(A) + P(B)$ for any two events A and B in a given sample space. Before we jump to such a conclusion, let us examine another problem. Suppose we let E_3 be the event of obtaining a "4" on the *black* die, and consider $P(E_2 \text{ or } E_3) = P(E_2 \cup E_3)$. By the definition of probability

$$P(E_2 \text{ or } E_3) = P(E_2 \cup E_3)$$
$$= \frac{n(E_2 \cup E_3)}{36}$$
$$= \frac{11}{36}$$

But observe that

$$P(E_2) = \frac{6}{36}, \quad P(E_3) = \frac{6}{36}$$

and

$$P(E_2) + P(E_3) = \frac{6}{36} + \frac{6}{36}$$
$$= \frac{12}{36}$$
$$\neq P(E_2 \cup E_3)$$

In order to complete our discussion, we must pause momentarily to consider $P(E_2 \text{ and } E_3) = P(E_2 \cap E_3)$. By examining figure 2 we see that $P(E_2 \cap E_3) = \frac{1}{36}$. Is it true, then, that $P(E_2 \cup E_3) = P(E_2) + P(E_3) - P(E_2 \cap E_3)$? In our previous example we learned that $P(E_1 \cup E_2) = P(E_1) + P(E_2)$. Is it incorrect to claim that

$$P(E_1 \cup E_2) = P(E_1) + P(E_2) - P(E_1 \cap E_2)$$

Explain. Our findings are no accident, as shown by the following theorem.

Theorem 1 (*Addition Theorem*) Let E and F be two events in a finite sample space S. Then

    i. if $E \cap F = \phi$, then $P(E \cup F) = P(E) + P(F)$

    ii. if $E \cap F \neq \phi$, then $P(E \cup F) = P(E) + P(F) - P(E \cap F)$

Proof $E \cup F$ is the set of elements which belong to E or to F or to both E and F, and $P(E \cup F) = \dfrac{n(E \cup F)}{n(S)}$.

PART I   Suppose $E \cap F = \phi$. Then $n(E \cup F) = n(E) + n(F)$.

Hence $P(E \cup F) = \dfrac{n(E) + n(F)}{n(S)}$

$$= \frac{n(E)}{n(S)} + \frac{n(F)}{n(S)}$$
$$= P(E) + P(F)$$

PART II   Suppose $E \cap F \neq \phi$. Then $n(E \cup F) = n(E) + n(F) - n(E \cap F)$.

Hence $P(E \cup F) = \dfrac{n(E) + n(F) - n(E \cap F)}{n(S)}$

$$= \frac{n(E)}{n(S)} + \frac{n(F)}{n(S)} - \frac{n(E \cap F)}{n(S)}$$
$$= P(E) + P(F) - P(E \cap F)$$

You should observe that the Addition Theorem can be condensed to read as follows: Let E and F be any two subsets of a finite sample space S, then

$$P(E \cup F) = P(E) + P(F) - P(E \cap F)$$

since, if $E \cap F = \phi$, $P(E \cap F) = 0$. We stated Theorem 1 in its longer form to assure complete clarity.

Example:

Consider the experiment of rolling a pair of dice, one red and one black. The sample space for this experiment is given in figure 2. Let

E_1 be the event of obtaining a "6" on the black die

E_2 be the event of obtaining a "1" on the black die

E_3 be the event of obtaining a "3" on the red die

E_4 be the event of obtaining with the pair of dice a *sum* of 3

Find: **a.** $P(E_1 \cup E_2)$ **c.** $P(E_2 \cup E_3)$ **e.** $P(E_4)$

       b. $P(E_1 \cup E_3)$ **d.** $P(E_1 \cap E_2)$

a. Since $E_1 \cap E_2 = \phi$

$$P(E_1 \cup E_2) = P(E_1) + P(E_2)$$

$$= \frac{6}{36} + \frac{6}{36}$$

$$= \frac{12}{36}$$

$$= \frac{1}{3}$$

b. Since $E_1 \cap E_3 \neq \phi$

$$P(E_1 \cup E_3) = P(E_1) + P(E_3) - P(E_1 \cap E_3)$$

$$= \frac{6}{36} + \frac{6}{36} - \frac{1}{36}$$

$$= \frac{11}{36}$$

c. Since $E_2 \cap E_3 \neq \phi$

$$P(E_2 \cup E_3) = P(E_2) + P(E_3) - P(E_2 \cap E_3)$$

$$= \frac{6}{36} + \frac{6}{36} - \frac{1}{36}$$

$$= \frac{11}{36}$$

d. Since $E_1 \cap E_2 = \phi$

$$P(E_1 \cap E_2) = 0$$

e. $P(E_4) = \dfrac{n(E_4)}{n(S)} = \dfrac{2}{36} = \dfrac{1}{18}$

EXERCISES

1. True or false?

   a. $P(A \cup B) = P(A) + P(B)$ if and only if A and B are *disjoint* events.

   b. If E is an event in a finite sample space S, then $P(E \cup \overline{E}) = 0$.

   c. If E is an event in a finite sample space S and $P(E) = \frac{3}{5}$, then $P(\overline{E}) = \frac{3}{5}$.

   d. If A and B are events in a finite sample space S and $A \cup B = S$, then $P(A \cup B) = 1$.

   e. If A and B are events in a finite sample space S, $A \cup B = S$, and $A \cap B \neq \phi$, then $P(A) + P(B) = 1$.

   f. If E and F are events in a finite sample space S and $P(E) + P(F) > 1$, then $E \cap F \neq \phi$.

   g. If E and F are events in a finite sample space S and $P(E) = \frac{1}{4}$, $P(F) = \frac{1}{3}$, and $P(E \cap F) = \frac{1}{12}$, then $P(E \cup F) = \frac{1}{2}$.

   h. If C and D are events in a finite sample space S, $P(C) = 1$, and $P(D) = 1$, then $C \cap D = \phi$.

   i. If H and K are events in a finite sample space S, $P(H) = 0$, and $P(K) = 1$, then $P(H \cup K) = 1$.

   j. If E and F are disjoint events in a finite sample space S, then $P(E \cap F) = 0$.

2. A marble is drawn at random from a bag which contains four white marbles, five green marbles, and two black marbles. What is the probability that the marble is **a.** white or green? **b.** white or black? **c.** green or black?

3. One card is drawn at random from an ordinary deck of 52 cards. What is the probability of drawing **a.** an ace or a king? **b.** a heart or a spade? **c.** a red card or a black card? **d.** an ace or a diamond?

4. One urn contains two red balls and two black balls, and a second urn contains three white balls and four black balls. If one ball is drawn at random from each urn, what is the probability that **a.** both balls will be white? **b.** both balls will be black? **c.** both balls will be the same color? **d.** the balls will have different colors?

5. The numerals from 1 to 21 are written on separate slips of paper, and the slips are placed in a box. One slip is drawn at random from the box. What is the probability that the numeral on the slip names a number **a.** which is either prime or divisible by 7? **b.** which is either composite or divisible by 7? **c.** which is divisible by 2 or by 6?

6. The following questions refer to the two-dice experiment. Let r denote the number of spots which appear on the red die, and let b denote the number of spots which appear on the black die. Find the probability that

   a. $r < 3$ or $b \geq 4$

   b. $r \geq 1$ or $b \leq 1$

   c. $r < 1$ or $b > 6$

   d. $r + b = 11$

   e. $r + b \neq 3$ [HINT: Apply the theorem stated in problem **10**, page 523.]

   f. $r + b < 10$

7. A box of coins contains five dimes and four nickels. If a clerk draws three coins at random, what is the probability that he will be able to make change for a quarter?

8. A man has four pairs of brown socks and six pairs of black socks. He also has two pairs of brown shoes and three pairs of black shoes. If, at random, he puts on one pair of these socks and one pair of these shoes, what is the probability that he is wearing socks and shoes of the same color?

9. The faces of each of two regular tetrahedra are numbered 1, 2, 3, 4. If two such tetrahedra are tossed, what is the probability that the sum 4 or 5 will come up?

10. In a class of thirty students, what is the probability that at least two of them will have birthdays falling on the same day of the same month?

THE MULTIPLICATION THEOREM

In order to make use of the Addition Theorem

$$P(E \cup F) = P(E) + P(F) - P(E \cap F)$$

we must be able to determine $P(E \cap F)$ for any two events E and F. We already have encountered problems where it was necessary to evaluate $P(E \cap F)$ for certain events E and F; in this section we shall derive a formula which is generally applicable. In order to do so, we must first consider the notion of *conditional probability*.

Consider the following experiment. A ball is drawn at random from an urn containing two red balls and three black balls; the color of the ball is recorded and the ball is returned to the urn; and, finally, a ball is again drawn at random from the urn. Suppose we let R_1 and R_2 denote the two red balls and B_1, B_2 and B_3 denote the three black balls. Since the urn contains a total of 5 balls, there are $\binom{5}{1} = 5$ different possible outcomes of the first draw. Since the ball is replaced, there are also $\binom{5}{1} = 5$ different possible outcomes of the second draw. Thus, by The Fundamental Counting Principle, we conclude that the sample space contains 5×5 or 25 elements. We may show the sample space S as follows:

		Second Draw				
		R_1	R_2	B_1	B_2	B_3
	R_1	$(\bullet, \bullet)$	$(\bullet, \bullet)$	$(\bullet, \bullet)$	$(\bullet, \bullet)$	$(\bullet, \bullet)$
First	R_2	$(\bullet, \bullet)$	$(\bullet, \bullet)$	$(\bullet, \bullet)$	$(\bullet, \bullet)$	$(\bullet, \bullet)$
Draw	B_1	$(\bullet, \bullet)$	$(\bullet, \bullet)$	$(\bullet, \bullet)$	$(\bullet, \bullet)$	$(\bullet, \bullet)$
	B_2	$(\bullet, \bullet)$	$(\bullet, \bullet)$	$(\bullet, \bullet)$	$(\bullet, \bullet)$	$(\bullet, \bullet)$
	B_3	$(\bullet, \bullet)$	$(\bullet, \bullet)$	$(\bullet, \bullet)$	$(\bullet, \bullet)$	$(\bullet, \bullet)$

Fig. 3

Notice that an ordered pair like (●, ●) corresponds to obtaining a red ball on each draw; an ordered pair like (●, ●) corresponds to obtaining a red on the first draw and a black on the second draw. What does an ordered pair like (●, ●) signify? What about an ordered pair like (●, ●)?

We are now prepared to examine a problem involving conditional probability. Let us determine the probability of the occurrence of a black ball on the second draw if a red ball occurred on the first draw; this is an example of a conditional probability. Suppose we let K be the subset of S which corresponds to obtaining a red on the first draw, and let H be the subset of S which corresponds to obtaining a black ball on the second draw; then the desired probability is denoted by the symbol $P(H|K)$ (READ: Probability of H given K). Since we wish to determine $P(H|K)$, the probability of obtaining a black ball on the second draw given that a red ball was obtained on the first draw, we confine our attention only to K, that subset of S each of whose elements corresponds to the occurrence of a red ball on the first draw.

$$K = \left\{ \begin{matrix} (●, ●) & (●, ●) & (●, ●) & (●, ●) & (●, ●) \\ (●, ●) & (●, ●) & (●, ●) & (●, ●) & (●, ●) \end{matrix} \right\}$$

By applying the definition of probability we find that $P(H|K) = \frac{6}{10}$. Now, by examining figure 3, we see that $P(H \cap K) = \frac{6}{25}$, and $P(K) = \frac{10}{25}$.

Is $P(H|K) = \dfrac{P(H \cap K)}{P(K)}$? That is, is $\dfrac{6}{25} \div \dfrac{10}{25} = \dfrac{6}{10}$? Thus, for the above example, we find that $P(H \cap K) = P(K) \cdot P(H|K)$. The argument presented in the foregoing example can be generalized to provide a proof of the following theorem.

Theorem 2 (*Multiplication Theorem*) Let E and F be two events in a finite sample space S. Then $P(E \cap F) = P(F) \cdot P(E|F)$.

If we return, momentarily, to the above example and examine the sample space S, we see that $P(H)$, the probability of obtaining a black ball on the second draw, is $\frac{15}{25} = \frac{6}{10}$. Notice that this value is the same as that obtained for $P(H|K)$; that is, $P(H|K) = P(H)$. This is often true of a conditional probability; in such a case, we say that the events H and K are *independent*. This fact together with the Multiplication Theorem enables us to conclude that if E and F are independent events, then

$$P(E \cap F) = P(E) \cdot P(F)$$

Example: Consider the two-dice experiment on page 524. If we let r denote the number of spots which appear on the red die, and b denote the number of spots which appear on the black die, then what is the probability that $r > 3$ *and* $b \leq 2$?

Let E be the event which corresponds to $r > 3$, and let F be the event which corresponds to $b \leq 2$. Our problem is to evaluate $P(E \cap F)$. By the Multiplication Theorem

$$P(E \cap F) = P(F) \cdot P(E|F)$$

Now observe that when two ordinary dice are tossed, how one die comes to rest will have no effect on how the other die will come to rest. Thus, the events are independent and therefore $P(E|F) = P(E)$; hence

$$P(E \cap F) = P(F) \cdot P(E)$$

Since $P(F) = \frac{1}{3}$ and $P(E) = \frac{1}{2}$, $P(E \cap F) = \frac{1}{2} \cdot \frac{1}{3} = \frac{1}{6}$. This result can also be obtained directly by examining the sample space of the experiment (figure 2) and applying the definition of probability.

Example:

An urn contains four red balls and seven black balls. Two balls are drawn, one after the other, from the urn, the first *not* being replaced before the second is drawn. What is the probability of obtaining

i. a red ball on each draw?

ii. a black ball on each draw?

iii. a black ball on the first draw and a red ball on the second draw?

iv. a red ball on the first draw and a black ball on the second draw?

v. a black ball on one draw and a red ball on the other draw?

Let E_1 be the event of obtaining a red ball on the first draw; E_2 be the event of obtaining a red ball on the second draw; E_3 be the event of obtaining a black ball on the first draw; and E_4 be the event of obtaining a black ball on the second draw.

i. We seek $P(E_1 \cap E_2)$.
$$P(E_1 \cap E_2) = P(E_2 \cap E_1)$$
$$= P(E_1) \cdot P(E_2|E_1) \text{ by Mult. Theorem}$$
$$\text{and} \quad P(E_1) = \frac{4}{11}$$

Now, $P(E_2|E_1)$ is the probability of obtaining a red ball on the second draw, given that a red ball was obtained on the first draw. When the second draw is to be made, there are ten balls in the urn, three of which are red if a red is obtained on the first draw. Accordingly, we conclude that $P(E_2|E_1) = \frac{3}{10}$. Thus,

$$P(E_1 \cap E_2) = \frac{4}{11} \cdot \frac{3}{10} = \frac{12}{110} = \frac{6}{55}.$$

ii. We seek $P(E_3 \cap E_4)$.
$$P(E_3 \cap E_4) = P(E_4 \cap E_3)$$
$$= P(E_3) \cdot P(E_4|E_3)$$
$$P(E_3) = \frac{7}{11}$$

$$P(E_4 | E_3) = \frac{6}{10}$$

Therefore, $P(E_3 \cap E_4) = \frac{7}{11} \cdot \frac{6}{10} = \frac{42}{110} = \frac{21}{55}$

iii. We seek $P(E_3 \cap E_2)$.

$$P(E_3 \cap E_2) = P(E_2 \cap E_3)$$
$$= P(E_3) \cdot P(E_2 | E_3)$$

$$P(E_3) = \frac{7}{11}$$

$$P(E_2 | E_3) = \frac{4}{10}$$

Therefore, $P(E_3 \cap E_2) = \frac{7}{11} \cdot \frac{4}{10} = \frac{28}{110} = \frac{14}{55}$

iv. We seek $P(E_1 \cap E_4)$.

$$P(E_1 \cap E_4) = P(E_4 \cap E_1)$$
$$= P(E_1) \cdot P(E_4 | E_1)$$

$$P(E_1) = \frac{4}{11}$$

$$P(E_4 | E_1) = \frac{7}{10}$$

Therefore, $P(E_1 \cap E_4) = \frac{4}{11} \cdot \frac{7}{10} = \frac{28}{110} = \frac{14}{55}$

v. We seek $P[(E_3 \cap E_2) \cup (E_1 \cap E_4)]$.

$$(E_3 \cap E_2) \cap (E_1 \cap E_4) = \phi$$

Hence, by the Addition Theorem

$$P[(E_3 \cap E_2) \cup (E_1 \cap E_4)] = P(E_3 \cap E_2) + P(E_1 \cap E_4)$$

From *iii.* and *iv.* above, $P(E_3 \cap E_2) = P(E_1 \cap E_4) = \frac{14}{55}$

Therefore, $P[(E_3 \cap E_2) \cup (E_1 \cap E_4)] = \frac{14}{55} + \frac{14}{55} = \frac{28}{55}$

EXERCISES

1. True or false?

   a. If A and B are events in a finite sample space S, then $P(A \cap B) = P(B \cap A)$.

   b. If A and B are events in a finite sample space S, then $P(A \cap B) = P(A) \cdot P(B | A)$.

   c. If A and B are events in a finite sample space S, then $P(A) \cdot P(B | A) = P(B) \cdot P(A | B)$.

   d. If A and B are events in a finite sample space S and if $P(A \cap B) = P(A) \cdot P(B)$, then $P(B) = P(A | B)$.

e. If A and B are events in a finite sample space S and if $P(A \cap B) = \frac{1}{2}$ and $P(B) = \frac{3}{4}$, then $P(A \mid B) = \frac{3}{8}$.

2. The following questions refer to the two-dice experiment. Let r denote the number of spots which appear on the red die, and b denote the number of spots which appear on the black die. Find the probability that

a. $r > 5$ *and* $b < 2$ **c.** r is prime *and* b is even

b. $r \geq 5$ *and* $b \leq 2$ **d.** r is odd *and* b is composite

3. An urn contains four green balls and one black ball. Two balls are drawn, one after the other, from the urn, the first not being replaced before the second is drawn. What is the probability of obtaining

a. a green ball on each draw?

b. a green ball on the first draw and a black ball on the second draw?

c. a black ball on the first draw and a green ball on the second draw?

d. a black ball on each draw?

4. Two cards are drawn, one after the other, from an ordinary deck of cards, the first card not being replaced before the second card is drawn. What is the probability that

a. both cards are clubs?

b. the first card is a heart and the second card is a club?

c. both cards are red?

d. one card is an ace and the other card is a queen?

5. Alice, Betty, and their brother Carl decide in the following manner who is to wash the supper dishes: Alice and Betty each select a natural number less than six; if the sum of their numbers is odd, then Alice loses and flips a coin with Carl. If the sum is even, then Betty loses and flips a coin with Carl. The loser of the coin toss must wash the dishes. What is the probability that Alice has to wash the dishes? that Betty has to wash the dishes? that Carl has to wash the dishes?

6. Suppose that a square, four inches on a side, is inscribed in a circle on a dart board. A dart is thrown, with no special skill, and lands inside the circle. What is the probability that the dart is inside the square?

VOCABULARY

Use each of the following correctly in a sentence. Numerals in parentheses refer to pages where these words were used. If you are not sure of the meaning of any word, turn to the indicated page.

Addition Theorem (525)

certain event (521)

conditional probability (528)

event (520)

impossible event (521)

independent event (529)

Multiplication Theorem (529)

probability (520)

sample space (519)

REVIEW EXERCISES

1. A card is drawn at random from an ordinary deck of 52 cards. What is the probability that the card is

    a. the queen of spades?

    b. a heart?

    c. black?

    d. a jack?

    e. not a diamond?

    f. red or black?

    g. green?

2. Suppose that before buying a carton of one dozen eggs, you inspect two eggs for cracks. If you find that either egg is cracked, you will not buy that particular carton of eggs. What is the probability that you will purchase a carton of eggs

    a. one of which is cracked?

    b. two of which are cracked?

    c. six of which are cracked?

    d. eleven of which are cracked?

3. The following questions refer to the two-dice experiment. Let r denote the number which appears on the red die, and let b denote the number which appears on the black die. Find the probability that

    a. $r > 1$ or $b < 6$

    b. $r \geq 4$ or $b > 4$

    c. $r + b = 5$

    d. $r + b \neq 10$

    e. $r + b > 8$

    f. $r > 3$ and $b \leq 4$

    g. r is composite and b is prime

4. An urn contains three black balls, two white balls, and one red ball. Two balls are drawn from the urn, one after the other. If the first ball is replaced before the second ball is drawn, find the probability that

    a. both balls are black

    b. both balls are white

    c. both balls are red

    d. neither ball is black

    e. neither ball is white

    f. neither ball is red

5. Repeat problem **4**, but without replacement; that is, assume that the first ball is *not* replaced before the second ball is drawn.

CHAPTER TEST

1. A regular *hexahedron* is a symmetrical solid with six faces. One of its faces is painted white, two are painted red, and the rest are painted blue. If the hexahedron is rolled onto a flat surface, what is the probability that it will come to rest on

    a. a white face?

    b. a blue face?

    c. a white face or a red face?

    d. a red face or a blue face?

    e. a white face and a blue face?

    f. a face?

2. A box of sixteen light bulbs contains one defective bulb. If together three light bulbs are drawn from the box at random, what is the probability that one of the bulbs is the defective one?

3. The following questions refer to the two-dice experiment. Let r denote the number which appears on the red die and let b denote the number which appears on the black die. Find the probability that

    a. $r < 5$ or $b \geq 5$ **c.** r is odd or b is even

    b. $r < 5$ and $b \geq 5$ **d.** r is odd and b is composite

4. Two cards are drawn, one after the other, from an ordinary deck of cards. If the first card is replaced before the second card is drawn, what is the probability that

    a. both cards are kings?   **c.** one card is red and one card is

    b. neither card is a spade?   black?

5. Repeat problem **4**, but without replacement; that is, assume that the first card is not replaced before the second card is drawn.

BIBLIOGRAPHY

Bergamini, D. *et al.*, *Mathematics*. New York: Time Incorporated, Life Science Library, 1963. Chapter 6.

Commission on Mathematics. *Introductory Probability and Statistical Inference, Revised Edition*. New York: College Entrance Examination Board, 1959. Chapters 4, 5.

Earl, B., Moore, J. and Smith, W. *Introduction to Probability* (A Programed Unit). New York: McGraw-Hill Book Co., Inc., 1963.

Kac, Mark. "Probability," *Scientific American*, September 1964. pp. 92-108.

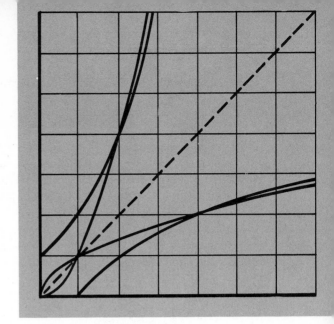

CHAPTER 18

Vectors

VECTORS, THEIR MAGNITUDES AND DIRECTIONS

In this chapter we shall be concerned with the study of those phenomena which possess two characteristics: magnitude and direction. Two examples of such phenomena are force acting on an object and velocity of a moving object. We shall develop a new concept, namely that of a *vector*, which will be helpful in this study.

Below are pictures of a few vectors.

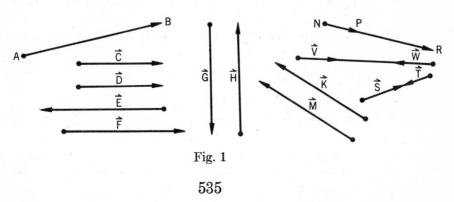

Fig. 1

535

We shall use names of two points to refer to a vector. For example, to designate the vector shown at the top of figure 1 we shall use the symbol $\overrightarrow{AB}$ (read: vector AB).

A is called the *initial* point of $\overrightarrow{AB}$

B is called the *terminal* point of $\overrightarrow{AB}$

Frequently, when we do not particularly care about the initial and the terminal point of a vector, we shall use only one letter to designate a vector. For example, one of the vectors in figure 1 on page 535 is designated by the symbol $\vec{C}$ (read: vector C). Identify this vector in the figure.

At the outset we stated that vectors are used to study phenomena possessing magnitude and direction. We shall therefore explain what we mean by the magnitude and direction of a vector. To do this, we define *magnitude* and clarify *direction* by examples.

■ *Definition of Magnitude of a Vector* For any points X and Y, the *magnitude* of $\overrightarrow{XY}$ is XY, the measure of $\overline{XY}$. The magnitude of $\overrightarrow{XY}$ is denoted by $|\overrightarrow{XY}|$.

Thus, if $AB = 5$ inches, the magnitude of $\overrightarrow{AB}$ is 5 inches; that is, $|\overrightarrow{AB}| = 5$ inches.

Now to learn what we mean by the direction of a vector, study the following statements and answer the questions while referring to figure 1.

$\vec{C}$ is a vector pointing in the easterly direction.

$\vec{D}$ is a vector pointing in what direction?

$\vec{C}$ and $\vec{D}$ are two vectors which have the *same direction*.

$\vec{G}$ is a vector pointing in the southerly direction.

What is the direction of $\vec{H}$?

$\vec{G}$ and $\vec{H}$ are two vectors which have *opposite directions*.

In figure 1 identify four more pairs of vectors which have the *same* direction. Identify four more pairs of vectors which have *opposite* directions.

Does it appear that $\vec{C}$ and $\vec{D}$ have the *same* magnitude; that is, that $|\vec{C}| = |\vec{D}|$? (See figure 1.)

Name two more pairs of vectors which appear to have the same magnitude.

EXERCISES

1. Draw pictures of the following vectors.

   a. $\vec{A}$ and $\vec{B}$, such that $|\vec{A}| = |\vec{B}| = 2$ inches and each has the northerly direction.

   b. $\vec{C}$ and $\vec{D}$, such that $|\vec{C}| = 1$ inch, $|\vec{D}| = 2$ inches, $\vec{C}$ has the southeasterly and $\vec{D}$ the northeasterly direction. Is it true that $2|\vec{C}| = |\vec{D}|$? Do $\vec{C}$ and $\vec{D}$ have opposite directions?

c. $\overrightarrow{EF}$ and $\overrightarrow{EG}$ (the two vectors have the same initial point), such that $|\overrightarrow{EF}| = |\overrightarrow{EG}| = 1.5$ inches and $\overrightarrow{EF}$ has the northeasterly and $\overrightarrow{EG}$ the northwesterly direction. What is the measure of $\angle FEG$ in degrees?

2. In figure 1 on page 535, $\overrightarrow{NP}$ and $\overrightarrow{PR}$ are subsets of the same line. They are therefore called *collinear vectors*.

    a. Do $\overrightarrow{NP}$ and $\overrightarrow{PR}$ have the same direction?

    b. Are $\overrightarrow{S}$ and $\overrightarrow{T}$ collinear vectors?

    c. Do $\overrightarrow{S}$ and $\overrightarrow{T}$ have the same direction?

    d. Are $\overrightarrow{V}$ and $\overrightarrow{W}$ collinear vectors?

    e. Do $\overrightarrow{V}$ and $\overrightarrow{W}$ have the same direction?

3. Make a picture of a horizontal line and on it mark pictures of the following:

    a. $\overrightarrow{AB}$ and $\overrightarrow{BC}$, each directed toward the right, such that $|\overrightarrow{AB}| = .5$ inch and $|\overrightarrow{BC}| = 1$ inch.

    b. $\overrightarrow{DC}$ directed toward the left and $|\overrightarrow{DC}| = 2$ inches.

4. Each of the following is a statement about the picture in problem **3.** Tell whether each statement is true or false. Make the necessary corrections in each false statement to obtain a true statement.

    a. The initial point of $\overrightarrow{AB}$ is the terminal point of $\overrightarrow{BC}$.

    b. The terminal point of $\overrightarrow{DC}$ is also the terminal point of $\overrightarrow{BC}$.

    c. $2|\overrightarrow{AB}| = |\overrightarrow{DC}|$

    d. $2|\overrightarrow{AB}| = |\overrightarrow{BC}|$

    e. $\frac{1}{2}|\overrightarrow{DC}| = |\overrightarrow{BC}|$

    f. $\overrightarrow{BC}$ and $\overrightarrow{DC}$ have the same direction.

    g. $\overrightarrow{AB}$ and $\overrightarrow{BC}$ have the same direction.

Ordered real number pairs and equivalent vectors

In order to study vectors more precisely, we shall consider them in relation to a coordinate system. Below is a picture of $\overrightarrow{MQ}$ whose initial point has the coordinates $(1, 2)$ and the terminal point $(5, 3)$.

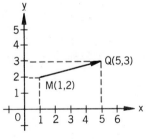

Fig. 2

Since vectors can be "scattered" over the entire plane, we shall focus our attention on those vectors whose initial point is the origin (0, 0). In order to do that we introduce the concept of *equivalence* of vectors.

■ *Definition of Equivalent Vectors* For any points X, Y, X', and Y', $\overrightarrow{XY}$ is *equivalent* to $\overrightarrow{X'Y'}$ if and only if $|\overrightarrow{XY}| = |\overrightarrow{X'Y'}|$ and $\overrightarrow{XY}$ and $\overrightarrow{X'Y'}$ have the same direction. To say that $\overrightarrow{XY}$ and $\overrightarrow{X'Y'}$ are equivalent, we write $\overrightarrow{XY} \overset{e}{=} \overrightarrow{X'Y'}$.

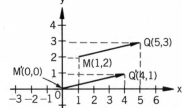

For the vector $\overrightarrow{MQ}$ in figure 2 we draw a picture of the vector $\overrightarrow{M'Q'}$, so that $\overrightarrow{M'Q'} \overset{e}{=} \overrightarrow{MQ}$ and the initial point of $\overrightarrow{M'Q'}$ is the origin. (See figure 3.)

Are there other vectors equivalent to $\overrightarrow{MQ}$?

Are there other vectors equivalent to $\overrightarrow{MQ}$ whose initial point is the origin?

Fig. 3

If your answer to the first question above was "yes" and to the last question "no," then you have probably concluded the following:

    i. Each vector has infinitely many vectors equivalent to it.

    ii. Each vector whose initial point is not the origin has one and only one (unique) vector which is equivalent to it and whose initial point is the origin.

■ *Definition of Standard Position for a Vector* A vector whose initial point is the origin is said to be in *standard position*.

Thus, when we study the set of vectors whose initial point is the origin, we are considering a special subset of all vectors, namely the subset of all vectors in standard position. Since each vector in standard position has the origin for its initial point, we can identify each such vector by its terminal point only. Thus, we have *a one-to-one correspondence between the set of all ordered real number pairs and the set of all vectors in standard position.* This is illustrated by means of three vectors in figure 4.

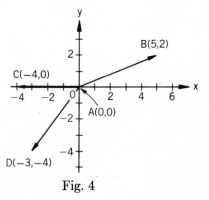

Fig. 4

Refer to figure 4 when reading the following examples.

Examples: *i.* The ordered pair $(5, 2)$ is associated with $\overrightarrow{AB}$, the vector from point $A(0, 0)$ (the origin) to point $B(5, 2)$.

ii. The ordered pair $(-4, 0)$ is associated with $\overrightarrow{AC}$. What is the initial point of $\overrightarrow{AC}$? What is the terminal point of $\overrightarrow{AC}$? What are the coordinates of these two points?

iii. The ordered pair $(-3, -4)$ is associated with $\overrightarrow{AD}$. Tell the initial point, the terminal point, and the coordinates of each of these two points for $\overrightarrow{AD}$.

In order to make the one-to-one correspondence between the set of ordered real number pairs and the set of vectors in standard position complete, we need to decide what vector will be associated with $(0, 0)$. It is the vector whose initial point and terminal point is $(0, 0)$. We shall call it a *zero vector*.

■   *Definition of Zero Vector*   Any vector whose initial point is the same as its terminal point is called a *zero vector*.

EXERCISES

1.   **a.** For each vector below draw a picture of the vector which is equivalent to it and whose initial point is the origin.

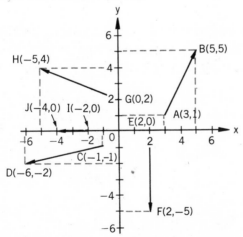

b. For each vector you pictured above, tell the ordered number pair which is associated with it.

2.   Each set of coordinates given is the initial and terminal point, respectively, of a vector. Without drawing pictures, tell the coordinates of the terminal point of each vector in standard position which is equivalent to the given vector.

Example: $(5, -3)$; $(-4, 1)$ The coordinates of the terminal point of the equivalent vector in standard position are $(-9, 4)$.

a. $(0, 3)$; $(5, 3)$

b. $(-1, 0)$; $(-7, 0)$

c. $(1, 1)$; $(6, 6)$

d. $(-2, -2)$; $(4, 4)$

e. $(1, 2)$; $(4, 5)$

f. $(1, -1)$; $(-1, 1)$

g. $(4, 0)$; $(0, -4)$

h. $(2, 5)$; $(-1, -6)$

i. $(1, 1)$; $(-5, -5)$

j. $(4, -6)$; $(-4, 6)$

k. $(5, 5)$; $(0, 0)$

l. $(-2, 8)$; $(0, 0)$

m. $(2, -6)$; (m, n)

n. (a, b); $(3, 5)$

o. (c, d); (p, r)

p. (x_1, y_1); (x_2, y_2)

3. What is the magnitude of a zero vector?

4. Can every point be considered to be a zero vector? Why or why not?

5. What is a zero vector in standard position?

ADDITION OF VECTORS

You have learned to find the vector in standard position which is equivalent to a given vector. Since there is a unique vector in standard position for every vector, we shall consider the addition of those vectors which are given in standard position. To add two vectors, we use the ordered number pairs which correspond to these vectors.

■ *Definition of Vector Sum*   If (a, b) corresponds to $\overrightarrow{MN}$ and (c, d) corresponds to $\overrightarrow{MP}$, then $\overrightarrow{MR}$ is the sum of $\overrightarrow{MN}$ and $\overrightarrow{MP}$, denoted by $\overrightarrow{MN} + \overrightarrow{MP} = \overrightarrow{MR}$, if and only if $\overrightarrow{MR}$ corresponds to $(a + c, b + d)$.

The sum of two vectors is a vector called the *resultant* of the two vectors. We use this definition to find the sum of two vectors shown in figure 5.

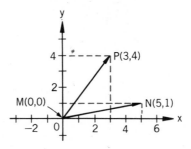

Fig. 5

In figure 5, $\overrightarrow{MN}$ corresponds to $(5, 1)$ and $\overrightarrow{MP}$ corresponds to $(3, 4)$. To find $\overrightarrow{MN} + \overrightarrow{MP}$, we use the definition of vector sum. We find the point to which $\overrightarrow{MN} + \overrightarrow{MP}$ corresponds: $(5 + 3, 4 + 1) = (8, 5)$. The complete picture of the two vectors and their sum is given in figure 6.

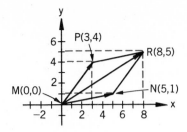

Fig. 6

In figure 6, $\overrightarrow{MR} = \overrightarrow{MN} + \overrightarrow{MP}$.

Now refer to this figure and answer the following questions.

Why is $\overleftrightarrow{NR}$ parallel to $\overrightarrow{MP}$?

Why is $\overleftrightarrow{PR}$ parallel to $\overrightarrow{MN}$?

Why is $MNRP$ a parallelogram?

Is $\overrightarrow{MR}$ a diagonal of parallelogram $MNRP$?

Thus, $\overrightarrow{MR}$, which is the sum of $\overrightarrow{MN}$ and $\overrightarrow{MP}$ is a diagonal of the parallelogram, in which $\overrightarrow{MN}$ and $\overrightarrow{MP}$ is one pair of adjacent sides.

We are now going to prove that, in general, if $P(0,0)$, $R(a,b)$, and $T(c,d)$ are three points, then the point $S(a+c,\ b+d)$ is the fourth vertex of a parallelogram with the other three points as its vertices ($bc \neq da$).

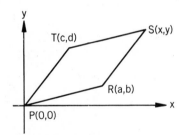

Fig. 7

Lines $\overleftrightarrow{PT}$ and $\overleftrightarrow{RS}$ have the same slope [why?]. The slope of $\overleftrightarrow{PT}$ is equal to $\dfrac{d}{c}$ [why?] and of $\overleftrightarrow{RS}$ to $\dfrac{y-b}{x-a}$.

Lines $\overleftrightarrow{PR}$ and $\overleftrightarrow{TS}$ have the same slope. The slope of $\overleftrightarrow{PR}$ is equal to $\dfrac{b}{a}$ and of $\overleftrightarrow{TS}$ to $\dfrac{y-d}{x-c}$.

From the above, we obtain the following two equations.

$$\frac{d}{c} = \frac{y-b}{x-a}$$

$$\frac{b}{a} = \frac{y-d}{x-c}$$

Verify the following operations which lead to an equivalent system of equations.

$$\begin{cases} dx - ad = cy - bc \\ bx - bc = ay - ad \end{cases}$$
$$\begin{cases} dx - cy = ad - bc \\ bx - ay = bc - ad \end{cases}$$

We solve the last system of equations using determinants.

$$x = \frac{\begin{vmatrix} ad - bc & -c \\ bc - ad & -a \end{vmatrix}}{\begin{vmatrix} d & -c \\ b & -a \end{vmatrix}} = \frac{-a(ad - bc) + c(bc - ad)}{-ad + bc}$$

$$= \frac{a(bc - ad) + c(bc - ad)}{bc - ad} = \frac{(a + c)(bc - ad)}{bc - ad} = a + c$$

$$y = \frac{\begin{vmatrix} d & ad - bc \\ b & bc - ad \end{vmatrix}}{bc - ad} = \frac{d(bc - ad) - b(ad - bc)}{bc - ad}$$

$$= \frac{d(bc - ad) + b(bc - ad)}{bc - ad} = \frac{(b + d)(bc - ad)}{bc - ad} = b + d$$

Thus, $(x, y) = (a + c, b + d)$, which is the pair of coordinates of point S, the point of intersection of $\overleftrightarrow{TS}$ and $\overleftrightarrow{RS}$.

Hence, the segment connecting the points $(0, 0)$ and $(a + c, b + d)$ is a diagonal of the parallelogram whose vertices are: $(0,0)$, (a, b), (c, d), and $(a + c, b + d)$.

We can now find geometrically the sum of any two vectors having a common initial point as is shown in figure 8.

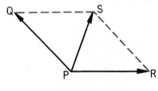

Fig. 8

$\overrightarrow{PQ} + \overrightarrow{PR} = \overrightarrow{PS}$. Explain why.

Pictorially, there is another way of obtaining $\overrightarrow{PS}$, the sum of $\overrightarrow{PQ}$ and $\overrightarrow{PR}$. In figure 8, consider $\overrightarrow{RS}$ which is equivalent to $\overrightarrow{PQ}$ (why?). The sum, $\overrightarrow{PS}$, is a vector whose initial point P is the initial point of $\overrightarrow{PR}$, the first of the two vectors to be added, and whose terminal point S is the terminal point of $\overrightarrow{RS}$, a vector equivalent to the second of the two vectors to be added.

This way of viewing addition of vectors is helpful in obtaining sums of collinear vectors. You should learn from the following examples how to add collinear vectors.

$$\overrightarrow{AB} + \overrightarrow{BC} = \overrightarrow{AC}$$

In the preceding picture, do $\overrightarrow{AB}$ and $\overrightarrow{BC}$ have the same direction? Is B, the terminal point of $\overrightarrow{AB}$, also the initial point of $\overrightarrow{BC}$?

Do $\overrightarrow{DE}$ and $\overrightarrow{FE}$ have opposite directions? To find the sum of $\overrightarrow{DE}$ and $\overrightarrow{FE}$, we draw a picture of $\overrightarrow{EF'}$ equivalent to $\overrightarrow{FE}$. Now the terminal point of $\overrightarrow{DE}$ is also the initial point of $\overrightarrow{EF'}$. Hence $\overrightarrow{DE} + \overrightarrow{FE} = \overrightarrow{DF'}$.

EXERCISES

1. Use a separate coordinate system for each pair of vectors. Draw a picture of each pair of vectors in standard position for each of the two ordered pairs given below.

a. $(1, 1); (2, 5)$ **f.** $(5, -2); (-4, 0)$

b. $(4, 3); (-3, 1)$ **g.** $(0, -5); (4, 1)$

c. $(1, 5); (-4, -5)$ **h.** $(0, 4); (-1, -6)$

d. $(-3, -3); (4, -1)$ **i.** $(-2, 0); (0, 3)$

e. $(-2, -4); (3, 0)$ **j.** $(5, 0); (0, -6)$

2. For each pair of vectors in problem **1**, sketch its resultant.

3. Copy each picture below on your paper. For each pair of vectors sketch the vector which is their sum.

a.   **b.**   **c.**   **d.**

4. For each picture below, name the vector which is the sum of the two pictured vectors.

a.

$\overrightarrow{PR} + \overrightarrow{RQ} = ?$

b.

$\overrightarrow{ST} + \overrightarrow{TV} = ?$

c.

$\overrightarrow{AB} + \overrightarrow{BB} = ?$

d.

$\overrightarrow{CD} + \overrightarrow{DC} = ?$

e.

$\overrightarrow{YZ} + \overrightarrow{ZX} = ?$

5. For any points A and B, we call $\overrightarrow{BA}$ the *additive inverse* of $\overrightarrow{AB}$. Justify this name.

6. Another symbol for $\overrightarrow{BA}$ is $-\overrightarrow{AB}$. Justify the reasonableness of this symbol.

7. Complete the following statement.
For any points A and B, $\overrightarrow{AB} + (-\overrightarrow{AB}) = $?

8. Show that the definition of vector sum applies to the collinear vectors in the coordinate system. Consider three cases.

CASE I: Two vectors have the same direction.

CASE II: Two vectors have opposite directions and have different magnitudes.

CASE III: Two vectors are additive inverses of each other.

MULTIPLICATION OF A SCALAR BY A VECTOR

In using vectors in physics it is frequently necessary to multiply a real number by a vector. Whenever this is done, we call the real number a *scalar*.

Study the examples of products of scalars and vectors given below.

Example: i.

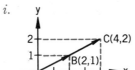

$2\overrightarrow{AB} = \overrightarrow{AC}$ Observe that $\overrightarrow{AB}$ corresponds to $(2,1)$, and $2\overrightarrow{AB}$ corresponds to $(4,2)$.

Example: ii.

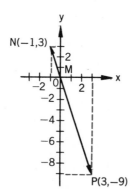

$-3\overrightarrow{MN} = \overrightarrow{MP}$ Observe that $\overrightarrow{MN}$ corresponds to $(-1,3)$, and $-3\overrightarrow{MN}$ corresponds to $(3,-9)$.

■ *Definition of Product of a Scalar and a Vector*   If $\overrightarrow{AB}$ is any vector and s is any real number, then $s\overrightarrow{AB} = \overrightarrow{AB}s = \overrightarrow{AC}$, where C is obtained as follows:

 i. If $s > 0$, then $C \in \overrightarrow{AB}$ ("$\overrightarrow{AB}$" means "ray from A through B") and $|\overrightarrow{AC}| = s|\overrightarrow{AB}|$.

 ii. If $s < 0$, then $C \in$ (the additive inverse of $\overrightarrow{AB}$) and $|\overrightarrow{AC}| = -s|\overrightarrow{AB}|$.

 iii. If $s = 0$, then $C = A$; that is $\overrightarrow{AC}$ is a zero vector.

EXERCISES

Make pictures of vectors obtained when multiplying each of the five vectors pictured below by 2, -1, $\frac{1}{2}$, and $-\frac{1}{3}$. Use a separate coordinate system for each of the four problems.

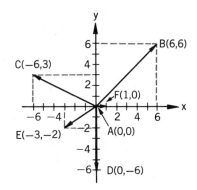

APPLICATIONS OF VECTORS

We now give some examples of the use of vectors in solving problems involving phenomena characterized by direction and magnitude.

Example: Find the resultant of the following two forces.

    $\overrightarrow{F_1}$ is a force of 200 lb. directed horizontally to the right and $\overrightarrow{F_2}$ is a force of 300 lb. directed vertically upward.

We first make a scale drawing of vectors representing the two forces.

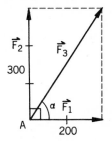

$\overrightarrow{F_3}$ is the resultant of the two forces.

We now determine the magnitude of $\vec{F_3}$ and the measure α of the angle whose sides are $\vec{F_1}$ and $\vec{F_3}$. Explain each step.

$$|\vec{F_3}| = \sqrt{200^2 + 300^2}$$
$$= \sqrt{40{,}000 + 90{,}000}$$
$$= \sqrt{130{,}000}$$
$$= \sqrt{13} \times \sqrt{10^4}$$
$$= 100\sqrt{13}$$
$$\doteq 100 \times 3.6$$
$$= 360$$

$$\tan(\alpha) = \frac{300}{200} = 1.5$$

$$\alpha \doteq 27°$$

Thus, $\vec{F_3}$ is a force of approximately 360 lb. acting in the direction of about 27° with the horizontal. This is the resultant of the forces $\vec{F_1}$ and $\vec{F_2}$ applied at point A.

Every vector can be *resolved* into its *horizontal and vertical components.* Examples *i.* and *ii.* below illustrate this.

Example: *i.* A ship sails in the northeasterly direction at 30 knots. (A knot is equal to 6080.20 feet per hour.) Find, in knots, the magnitude of the horizontal component in the easterly direction.

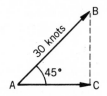

The picture on the left shows the ship's velocity vector $\overrightarrow{AB}$ and its horizontal easterly component $\overrightarrow{AC}$.

$$|\overrightarrow{AC}| = |\overrightarrow{AB}| \times \cos(45°) \doteq 30 \times .71 = 21.3 \doteq 21$$

Thus, the magnitude of the easterly component of $\overrightarrow{AB}$ is approximately 21 knots.

Example: *ii.* If a force has components as shown on the picture below, determine the magnitude and the direction of the force.

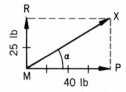

Given the horizontal component $\overrightarrow{MP}$ and the vertical component $\overrightarrow{MR}$, we are to determine $\overrightarrow{MX}$ by finding its magnitude and α.

Justify each step below.

$$|\overrightarrow{MX}| = \sqrt{40^2 + 25^2} = \sqrt{1600 + 625}$$
$$= \sqrt{2225} \doteq 47$$

$$\tan(\alpha) = \frac{25}{40} = .625; \; \alpha \doteq 32°$$

Thus, the force with the given components has the magnitude of approximately 47 lb. directed approximately at a 32° angle with the horizontal.

Example: *iii.* A wheelbarrow is held stationary on an inclined plane $\overleftrightarrow{AB}$ at C by a force $\overrightarrow{CD}$, which is parallel to the plane and a force $\overrightarrow{CE}$ perpendicular to $\overrightarrow{CD}$. The plane makes an angle of 15° with the horizontal and the weight of the wheelbarrow is 100 lb.; that is, $|\overrightarrow{CF}| = 100$. Determine $|\overrightarrow{CD}|$ and $|\overrightarrow{CE}|$.

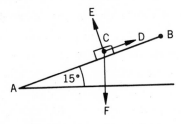

Since the wheelbarrow is balanced, $\overrightarrow{CE} + \overrightarrow{CD} + \overrightarrow{CF} = \overrightarrow{CC}$, which is a zero vector.

Establish the coordinate system as shown in the picture below.

The coordinates of the points D, E, and F are as follows:

$D\big(|\overrightarrow{CD}| \cdot \cos(15°), \; |\overrightarrow{CD}| \cdot \sin(15°)\big)$

$E\big(|\overrightarrow{CE}| \cdot \cos(105°), \; |\overrightarrow{CE}| \cdot \sin(105°)\big)$

$F(0, -100)$

Now since $\overrightarrow{CE} + \overrightarrow{CD} + \overrightarrow{CF} =$ zero vector, it follows that
$$0 + |\overrightarrow{CD}| \cdot \cos(15°) + |\overrightarrow{CE}| \cdot \cos(105°) = 0$$
$$-100 + |\overrightarrow{CD}| \cdot \sin(15°) + |\overrightarrow{CE}| \cdot \sin(105°) = 0$$

To simplify writing, we replace $|\overrightarrow{CD}|$ by x and $|\overrightarrow{CE}|$ by y and solve the system of equations

$$\begin{cases} x \cdot \cos(15°) + y \cdot \cos(105°) = 0 \\ x \cdot \sin(15°) + y \cdot \sin(105°) = 100 \end{cases}$$

$$x = \frac{\begin{vmatrix} 0 & \cos(105°) \\ 100 & \sin(105°) \end{vmatrix}}{\begin{vmatrix} \cos(15°) & \cos(105°) \\ \sin(15°) & \sin(105°) \end{vmatrix}}$$

$$= \frac{-100 \cdot \cos(105°)}{\cos(15°) \cdot \sin(105°) - \sin(15°) \cdot \cos(105°)}$$

$$= \frac{-100 \cdot \cos(105°)}{\sin((105 - 15)°)} = \frac{-100 \cdot \cos(105°)}{\sin(90°)} = 100 \cdot \sin(15°)$$

$$\doteq 100 \times .26 = 26$$

$$y = \begin{vmatrix} \cos(15°) & 0 \\ \sin(15°) & 100 \end{vmatrix} = 100 \cdot \cos(15°) \doteq 100 \times .97 = 97$$

Thus, $|\overrightarrow{CD}| \doteq 26$ lb. and $|\overrightarrow{CE}| \doteq 97$ lb.

EXERCISES

Solve each problem. If necessary, refer to the appropriate example above.

1. Find the resultant of the following two forces: force $\overrightarrow{G_1}$ of 120 lb. directed horizontally to the right and force $\overrightarrow{G_2}$ of 500 lb. directed vertically upward.

2. Find the resultant of the following two forces: force $\overrightarrow{K_1}$ of 200 lb. acting in the northeasterly direction and force $\overrightarrow{K_2}$ of 200 lb. acting in the northwesterly direction.

3. What is the resultant of two forces, if one is a force of n lb. and the other is a force of $\frac{1}{2}n$ lb. acting in the opposite direction of the first force? Compare the direction of the resultant with the direction of one of the two given forces.

4. An X-20 (Dyna-Soar) piloted space glider is flying in the southwesterly direction at 4000 mph. Compute the horizontal component of the glider's speed vector.

5. Which of the two forces given below has the longer horizontal component?

    a. Force of 100 lb. making an angle of 20° with the horizontal.

    b. Force of 100 lb. making an angle of 21° with the horizontal.

6. Which of the two forces given in problem **5** has the longer vertical component?

7. A wheelbarrow is held on an inclined plane $\overleftrightarrow{XY}$ at A by a force $\overrightarrow{AB}$ perpendicular to $\overrightarrow{AC}$ (see picture on the right). The plane makes an angle of 25° with the horizontal and the weight of the wheelbarrow is 150 lb.; that is, $|\overrightarrow{AD}| = 150$. Determine $|\overrightarrow{AB}|$ and $|\overrightarrow{AC}|$.

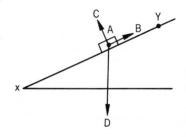

Inner product

We have defined addition of vectors and multiplication of a scalar by a vector. We now define *inner product* of two vectors.

■ *Definition of Inner Product* The *inner product*, $\vec{X} \cdot \vec{Y}$, of two non-zero vectors $\vec{X}$ and $\vec{Y}$ is the real number $|\vec{X}| \times |\vec{Y}| \times \cos(\alpha)$, where α is the measure of the angle between $\vec{X}$ and $\vec{Y}$. If $\vec{X}$ or $\vec{Y}$ is a zero vector, then the inner product is equal to the real number 0.

In order for this definition to be clear, we must define the measure of the angle between two vectors.

■ *Definition of Measure of the Angle Between Two Vectors* If $\vec{M}$ and $\vec{N}$ are any two non-zero vectors and if $\overrightarrow{AB} \overset{e}{=} \vec{M}$ and $\overrightarrow{AC} \overset{e}{=} \vec{N}$ and A is the origin of a coordinate system, then the measure of the angle between $\vec{M}$ and $\vec{N}$ is equal to the measure of the angle CAB.

Figure 9 illustrates this definition. The measure of the angle between $\vec{M}$ and $\vec{N}$ is α, $\overrightarrow{AB} \overset{e}{=} \vec{N}$ and $\overrightarrow{AC} \overset{e}{=} \vec{M}$.

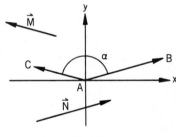

Fig. 9

Note that we are leaving the measure of an angle between two vectors undefined if at least one of the two vectors is a zero vector.

The inner product, $\vec{M} \cdot \vec{N}$, is sometimes called a *dot product*, and $\vec{M} \cdot \vec{N}$ is then read: $\vec{M}$ dot $\vec{N}$.

From your study of the cosine function, you will recall that $\cos(90°) = 0$. Since two vectors which make an angle of 90° are perpendicular to each other, we are now in a position to prove a theorem concerning perpendicularity of vectors.

Theorem 1 Two non-zero vectors $\vec{X}$ and $\vec{Y}$ are perpendicular if and only if $\vec{X} \cdot \vec{Y} = 0$.

Proof $\vec{X} \cdot \vec{Y} = |\vec{X}| \times |\vec{Y}| \times \cos(\alpha)$ by definition of inner product.

The product $|\vec{X}| \times |\vec{Y}| \times \cos(\alpha)$ is 0 if and only if at least one of its factors is 0. But $|\vec{X}| \neq 0$ and $|\vec{Y}| \neq 0$ [why?]. Therefore, $\cos(\alpha) = 0$. And $\cos(\alpha) = 0$ if and only if $\vec{X}$ and $\vec{Y}$ are perpendicular.

EXERCISES

1. Compute $\vec{X} \cdot \vec{Y}$ if $|\vec{X}| = 4$, $|\vec{Y}| = 7$ and

    a. $\alpha = 0°$ c. $\alpha = 45°$ e. $\alpha = 90°$

    b. $\alpha = 30°$ d. $\alpha = 60°$ f. $\alpha = 135°$

2. Determine the measure of the angle between $\vec{X}$ and $\vec{Y}$ if $|\vec{X}| = 3$, $|\vec{Y}| = 4$ and $\vec{X} \cdot \vec{Y}$ is equal to

    a. 0   c. -1 e. -2 g. 12

    b. 1   d. 2   f. 5   h. -12

COMMUTATIVE AND ASSOCIATIVE PROPERTIES OF VECTOR OPERATIONS

We shall now examine the three operations we introduced in connection with vectors in terms of the properties which these operations possess.

Theorem 2 Addition of vectors is commutative; that is

$$\forall_{\vec{X}} \forall_{\vec{Y}} \ \vec{X} + \vec{Y} = \vec{Y} + \vec{X}$$

Proof   Let $\vec{X}$ correspond to (a, b) and $\vec{Y}$ to (c, d)

             $\vec{X} + \vec{Y}$ corresponds to $(a + c, \ b + d)$

             $\vec{Y} + \vec{X}$ corresponds to $(c + a, \ d + b)$

             But $(a + c, \ b + d) = (c + a, \ d + b)$

             Hence, $\vec{X} + \vec{Y}$ and $\vec{Y} + \vec{X}$ both correspond to $(c + a, \ d + b)$ and, therefore, $\vec{X} + \vec{Y} = \vec{Y} + \vec{X}$

Do you think that the addition of vectors has the associative property? We can draw a picture which will convince us that the addition of vectors is an associative operation. Study the picture below and the accompanying statements to the left of it.

Given the three vectors: $\vec{A}$, $\vec{B}$, and $\vec{C}$, note that

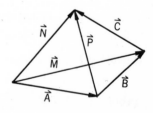

$$(\vec{A} + \vec{B}) + \vec{C} = \vec{M} + \vec{C} = \vec{N}$$
$$\vec{A} + (\vec{B} + \vec{C}) = \vec{A} + \vec{P} = \vec{N}$$

Therefore $(\vec{A} + \vec{B}) + \vec{C} = \vec{A} + (\vec{B} + \vec{C})$

You should see that this picture portrays the associativity of addition of vectors in general. Explain how this is related to the fact that we can find, for any three given vectors, equivalent vectors which are in the position shown in the picture above.

In considering multiplication, we need to examine the two kinds of products, the scalar-vector product and the inner product.

To illustrate associativity for all real numbers m and n and for every vector $\overrightarrow{X}$

$$m(n\overrightarrow{X}) = (mn)\overrightarrow{X}$$

We again resort to a picture and consider one example.

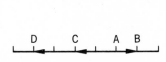

Let $m = 2$ and $n = -2$

Then $2(-2\overrightarrow{AB}) = 2(\overrightarrow{AC}) = \overrightarrow{AD}$

and $[2(-2)]\overrightarrow{AB} = -4\overrightarrow{AB} = \overrightarrow{AD}$

Thus, $2(-2\overrightarrow{AB}) = [2(-2)]\overrightarrow{AB}$

Give a proof of associativity of scalar-vector multiplication.

Now look at the definition of inner product and prove that the vector multiplication is commutative. This should be rather easy to do, since dot product is defined in terms of real numbers.

Since the dot product of two vectors is a real number, we do not need to investigate expressions like $(\overrightarrow{X} \cdot \overrightarrow{Y}) \cdot \overrightarrow{Z}$. Note that $(\overrightarrow{X} \cdot \overrightarrow{Y}) \cdot \overrightarrow{Z} = m\overrightarrow{Z}$, where m is some real number.

EXERCISES

1. Each of the quadrilaterals in the picture below is a parallelogram. $D, H, K,$ and F are the midpoints of $\overline{EC}, \overline{CB}, \overline{BA},$ and $\overline{AE}$, respectively.

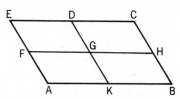

a. Express $\overrightarrow{GC}$ in terms of $\overrightarrow{HC}$ and $\overrightarrow{GH}$.

b. Express $\overrightarrow{FD}$ in terms of $\overrightarrow{GF}$ and $\overrightarrow{GD}$.

c. Express $\overrightarrow{GK}$ in terms of $\overrightarrow{GA}$ and $\overrightarrow{KA}$.

d. Express $\overrightarrow{FH}$ in terms of $\overrightarrow{FA}, \overrightarrow{AB},$ and $\overrightarrow{BH}$.

e. Express $\overrightarrow{AB}$ as the product of a vector and a scalar (real number).

f. Express $\overrightarrow{AG}$ as the product of a vector and a scalar.

g. Express $\overrightarrow{DE}$ as a product of a vector and a negative scalar (negative real number).

h. Name five vectors which are equivalent to $\overrightarrow{AK}$.

2. Using the vectors $\overrightarrow{AG}$ and $\overrightarrow{AC}$ in the picture for problem 1, illustrate the commutativity of multiplication of a vector by a scalar.

3. Asssume that, in the picture for problem **1**, $AF = FE = 2.0''$, $ED = DC = 3.0''$, and $\angle E$ is a 45° angle.

    a. Compute $\overrightarrow{FE} \cdot \overrightarrow{ED}$ to one decimal place.

    b. Compute $\overrightarrow{ED} \cdot \overrightarrow{DC}$.

    c. Compute $\overrightarrow{ED} \cdot \overrightarrow{DG}$ to one decimal place.

    d. How do the inner products $\overrightarrow{FE} \cdot \overrightarrow{ED}$ and $\overrightarrow{ED} \cdot \overrightarrow{DG}$ compare?

DISTRIBUTIVE PROPERTIES

We shall now state additional properties of operations with vectors. In these statements we shall use m and n as variables over the set of real numbers and $\vec{X}$, $\vec{Y}$, and $\vec{Z}$ as variables over the set of vectors.

■   *Left-hand Distributive Property of Real Numbers for Multiplication over a Vector Sum*

$$\forall_m \forall_{\vec{X}} \forall_{\vec{Y}} \ m(\vec{X} + \vec{Y}) = m\vec{X} + m\vec{Y}$$

■   *Right-hand Distributive Property of Vectors for Multiplication over a Real Number Sum*

$$\forall_m \forall_n \forall_{\vec{X}} \ (m + n)\vec{X} = m\vec{X} + n\vec{X}$$

■   *Left-hand Distributive Property of Vectors for Inner Product over Addition*

$$\forall_{\vec{X}} \forall_{\vec{Y}} \forall_{\vec{Z}} \ \vec{X} \cdot (\vec{Y} + \vec{Z}) = \vec{X} \cdot \vec{Y} + \vec{X} \cdot \vec{Z}$$

We shall now illustrate the use of vectors together with their operations in a proof of a theorem from geometry.

Theorem 3 In a parallelogram, diagonals bisect each other.

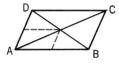

ABCD is a parallelogram.

Proof $\overrightarrow{AC} = \overrightarrow{AB} + \overrightarrow{BC}$ (by vector addition) and the terminal point of $\frac{1}{2}(\overrightarrow{AB} + \overrightarrow{BC})$ = midpoint of $\overline{AC}$ (by definition of midpoint and the correspondence between vectors and line segments).

$$\text{Let } \tfrac{1}{2}(\overrightarrow{AB} + \overrightarrow{BC}) = \overrightarrow{AF}$$

$\overrightarrow{BD} = \overrightarrow{BA} + \overrightarrow{AD}$ (by vector addition) and the terminal point of $\frac{1}{2}(\overrightarrow{BA} + \overrightarrow{AD})$ = midpoint of $\overline{BD}$ (same reasons as in first step.)

$$\text{Let } \tfrac{1}{2}(\overrightarrow{BA} + \overrightarrow{AD}) = \overrightarrow{BE}$$

Now the problem is to show that F and E are the same point.

NOTE: $\overrightarrow{AB} + \overrightarrow{BE} = \overrightarrow{AE}$ (by vector addition).

Now the problem is to show $\overrightarrow{AE} = \overrightarrow{AF}$.

$$\overrightarrow{AE} = \overrightarrow{AB} + \overrightarrow{BE} \text{ (by vector addition)}$$
$$= \overrightarrow{AB} + \tfrac{1}{2}(\overrightarrow{BA} + \overrightarrow{AD}) \text{ (recall that } \overrightarrow{BE} = \tfrac{1}{2}(\overrightarrow{BA} + \overrightarrow{AD}))$$
$$= \overrightarrow{AB} + \tfrac{1}{2}(-\overrightarrow{AB}) + \tfrac{1}{2}\overrightarrow{AD} \text{ (definition of additive inverse vector}$$
and distributivity of real numbers for multiplication over a
vector sum)
$$= \tfrac{1}{2}(\overrightarrow{AB} + \overrightarrow{AD}) \text{ (definition of addition and distributivity of}$$
real numbers for multiplication over vector sum)
$$\overset{\text{e}}{=} \tfrac{1}{2}(\overrightarrow{AB} + \overrightarrow{BC}) \text{ (given parallelogram, definition of } \overset{\text{e}}{=} \text{ vectors)}$$
$$= \overrightarrow{AF} \text{ since initial point of } \overrightarrow{AE} \text{ is } A \text{ and of } \tfrac{1}{2}(\overrightarrow{AB} + \overrightarrow{BC}) \text{ is } A.$$

∴ E and F must be the same point, i.e., the terminal point of the two vectors; and hence $\overrightarrow{BD}$ and $\overrightarrow{AC}$ bisect each other (by definition of midpoint).

EXERCISES

1. Given the following definition for the dot product, which is different from that given on page 549, prove the third Distributive Property stated on page 252.

If $\overrightarrow{G}$ corresponds to (a, b)

$\overrightarrow{H}$ corresponds to (c, d)

and $\overrightarrow{K}$ corresponds to (e, f)

then $\overrightarrow{G} + \overrightarrow{H}$ corresponds to $(a + c,\ b + d)$ and $\overrightarrow{G} \cdot \overrightarrow{H} = ac + bd$

2. If $\overrightarrow{G}$ corresponds to (a, b), then $c\overrightarrow{G}$ corresponds to (ca, cb). Using this and any additional assumptions stated in problem 1 which you find necessary, prove $\forall_m \forall_{\overrightarrow{X}} \forall_{\overrightarrow{Y}} (m\overrightarrow{X}) \cdot \overrightarrow{Y} = m(\overrightarrow{X} \cdot \overrightarrow{Y})$.

3. Using any assumptions stated in problem 1 and problem 2 which you find necessary, prove $\forall_m \forall_n \forall_{\overrightarrow{X}} \forall_{\overrightarrow{Y}} \forall_{\overrightarrow{Z}} \overrightarrow{X} \cdot (m\overrightarrow{Y} + n\overrightarrow{Z}) = m(\overrightarrow{X} \cdot \overrightarrow{Y}) + n(\overrightarrow{X} \cdot \overrightarrow{Z})$.

4. Prove that the medians of a triangle meet in a point which trisects each of the three medians.

5. Prove that the midpoints of the sides of any quadrilateral can be used to form a parallelogram.

VOCABULARY

Use each of the following correctly in a sentence. Numerals in parentheses refer to pages where these words were used. If you are not sure of the meaning of any word, turn to the indicated page.

additive inverse of a vector (544)
collinear vectors (537)
dot product (549)
equivalent vectors (538)
horizontal component (546)
initial point of a vector (536)
inner product (549)
magnitude of a vector (536)

resolving a vector (546)
resultant of two vectors (540)
scalar (544)
standard position (538)
terminal point of a vector (536)
vector sum (540)
vertical component (546)
zero vector (539)

REVIEW EXERCISES

1. For each vector below draw a picture of the vector which is equivalent to it and whose initial point is the origin.

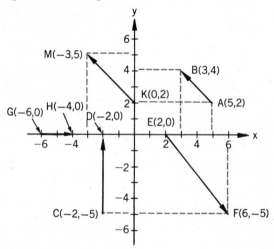

2. Each set of coordinates given below is the initial and terminal point, respectively, of a vector. Without drawing pictures, tell the coordinates of the terminal point of each vector in standard position which is equivalent to the given vector.

a. $(1, 1)$; $(-2, 3)$

b. $(0, 6)$; $(0, -4)$

c. $(5, 0)$; $(0, 2)$

d. $(-2, -3)$; $(1, 5)$

e. $(-1, 3)$; $(0, 0)$

f. $(2, 4)$; $(-1, -2)$

g. $(1, 7)$; (a, b)

h. (c, d); $(-1, 0)$

i. (a, b); (c, d)

j. (m_1, n_1); (m_2, n_2)

3. Copy each picture below on your paper. For each pair of vectors sketch the vector which is their sum.

a.

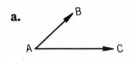

c.

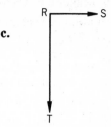

b.

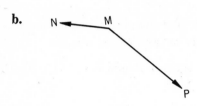

d.

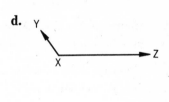

4. A ship sails in the southeasterly direction at 40 knots. Find, in knots, the magnitude of the vertical component in the southerly direction.

5. If a force has components as shown in the picture below, determine the magnitude and the direction of the force.

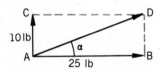

6. A stone weighing 300 lb. is held stationary on an inclined plane $\overleftrightarrow{AB}$ by two perpendicular forces, $\overrightarrow{CM}$ and $\overrightarrow{CD}$ (see picture below). The plane makes a 30° angle with the horizontal. Determine $|\overrightarrow{CM}|$ and $|\overrightarrow{CD}|$. [HINT: $|\overrightarrow{CN}| = 300$.]

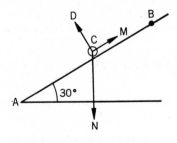

7. True or false?

a. The inner product of two non-zero vectors is a vector.

b. The product of a vector and a scalar is a scalar.

c. Two equivalent vectors have at least one common point.

d. Subtraction of vectors is not commutative.

e. Addition of vectors is associative.

f. $\forall_{\vec{X}} \ |\vec{X}| = |-\vec{X}|$

g. $\forall_{\text{point } A} \ |\overrightarrow{AA}| = 0$

h. Every vector has an equivalent vector in standard position.

i. In a triangle ABC, $\overrightarrow{AB} + \overrightarrow{BC} = \overrightarrow{CA}$.

j. If the measure of the angle between $\vec{A}$ and $\vec{B}$ is equal to $45°$, then $\vec{X} \cdot \vec{Y} < |\vec{X}| \cdot |\vec{Y}|$.

8. Compute $\vec{X} \cdot \vec{Y}$ if $|\vec{X}| = 6$, $|\vec{Y}| = 10$, and the measure of the angle between $\vec{X}$ and $\vec{Y}$ is equal to $25°$. Give your answer to two decimal places.

9. Determine the measure of the angle between $\vec{A}$ and $\vec{B}$ if $|\vec{A}| = 5$, $|\vec{B}| = 10$, and $\vec{X} \cdot \vec{Y}$ is equal to 25.

CHAPTER TEST

1. True or false?

a. There is a one-to-one correspondence between the set of vectors in a coordinate plane and the set of ordered real number pairs.

b. For some vectors, the initial point is the same as the terminal point.

c. Any two non-zero collinear vectors have the same direction.

d. The magnitude of every vector is a positive number.

e. Lines k and m are parallel and $\vec{A}$ and $\vec{B}$ are non-zero vectors. If $\vec{A} \subset k$ and $\vec{B} \subset m$, then $\vec{A}$ and $\vec{B}$ have either the same direction or opposite directions.

f. $\forall_A \forall_{B \neq A}$, if $|\overrightarrow{AB}| = |\overrightarrow{CD}|$, then $AB = CD$.

g. $\forall_A \forall_{B \neq A}$, if $AB = CD$, then $|\overrightarrow{AB}| = |\overrightarrow{CD}|$

h. $\forall_X \forall_Y \forall_{X'} \forall_{Y'}$, if $\overrightarrow{XY} \overset{e}{=} \overrightarrow{X'Y'}$, then $|\overrightarrow{XY}| = |\overrightarrow{X'Y'}|$.

i. For every $\vec{X}$ there is an infinite set of vectors, each of which is equivalent to $\vec{X}$.

j. A vector may be in standard position without having the origin for its initial point.

k. The magnitude of a vector in standard position which corresponds to $(1, 1)$ is $\sqrt{2}$.

l. The pair of coordinates of the terminal point of the vector in standard position, which is equivalent to $\overrightarrow{AB}$, $A(1, 3)$ and $B(-1, 4)$, is $(0, 1)$.

m. $\vec{A}$ and $\vec{B}$ are two vectors, each in standard position. If $\vec{A}$ corresponds to $(-2, 7)$ and $\vec{B}$ to $(3, -3)$, then $\vec{A} + \vec{B}$ corresponds to $(1, 4)$.

n. For all non-zero vectors $\vec{X}$ and $\vec{Y}$, $\vec{X} \cdot \vec{Y}$ is a vector.

o. $\forall_{\vec{X}} \forall_{n \epsilon R}\ n\vec{X}$ is a vector.

p. Every vector has an additive inverse, which is also a vector.

q. $\vec{M}$ is a vector in standard position. If $\vec{M}$ corresponds to $(4, -2)$, then $-2\vec{M}$ corresponds to $(-2, 1)$.

r. The horizontal component of a horizontal force is equal to this force.

s. $|\vec{AB}| = |\vec{AC}| = 1$. If $\angle BAC = 45°$, then $\vec{AB} \cdot \vec{AC} > 1$.

t. If $\vec{M}$ is perpendicular to $\vec{N}$, then $\vec{M} \cdot \vec{N} = 0$.

2. For each of the four vectors below, draw a picture of the vector which is equivalent to it and is in standard position.

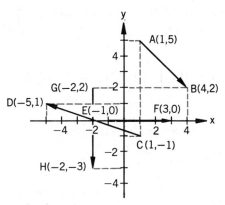

3. Given $A(-1, 5)$ and $B(0, -3)$. What are the coordinates of the terminal point of the vector in standard position which is equivalent to

    a. $\vec{AB}$?   **d.** $\vec{CA}$?

    b. $\vec{BA}$?   **e.** $\vec{BC}$?

    c. $\vec{AC}$, where C is the midpoint of $\vec{AB}$?   **f.** $\vec{CB}$?

4. For each pair of vectors, sketch their resultant.

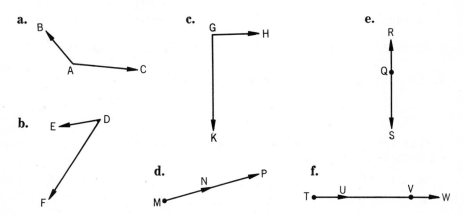

5. Four vectors in standard position have the following coordinates of their terminal points: $(1, 7)$; $(0, -4)$; $(-2, 3\frac{1}{2})$; and $(-1\frac{1}{2}, -2)$.
Give the coordinates of the terminal points of vectors obtained by multiplying each vector by the following scalars.

    a. 3   **b.** -2 **c.** $\sqrt{2}$ **d.** $-\frac{1}{2}$

6. Given $A(-1, -4)$ and $B(3, 5)$. What is the magnitude of $\overrightarrow{AB}$?

7. Give the magnitude and direction of the resultant of the following two forces: force $\overrightarrow{F_1}$ of 100 lb. acting in the southeasterly direction and force $\overrightarrow{F_2}$ of 250 lb. acting in the northwesterly direction.

8. Compute the magnitude of the horizontal and of the vertical component of $\overrightarrow{AD}$, given the data shown on the picture at the right.

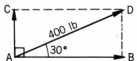

CUMULATIVE REVIEW

Chapters 13-18

1. Determine the value of each of the following:

    a. $\cos(0)$ **c.** $\cos\left(-\frac{\pi}{4}\right)$ **e.** $\cos(-\pi)$ **g.** $\sin\left(\frac{5\pi}{4}\right)$

    b. $\sin\left(\frac{\pi}{3}\right)$ **d.** $\tan(2\pi)$ **f.** $\tan(-\pi)$ **h.** $\sin(2\pi)$

2. Determine the value of each of the following:

    a. $\cos(45°)$ **c.** $\tan(30°)$ **e.** $\sin(120°)$

    b. $\sin(135°)$ **d.** $\cos(120°)$ **f.** $\tan(150°)$

3. Solve each equation for all values of $\theta(0 \le \theta < 2\pi)$.

    a. $2 \cdot \cos^2(\theta) = 1$ **c.** $\dfrac{1}{\sin(\theta)} = -2$

    b. $\tan(2\theta) = 1$ **d.** $\tan^2(\theta) - \tan(\theta) - 2 = 0$

4. If $\cos(\theta) = -\dfrac{3}{4}$ and $\dfrac{\pi}{2} < \theta < \pi$, determine $\sin(\theta)$ and $\tan(\theta)$.

5. Solve the right triangle pictured at the right.

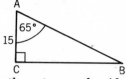

6. Tell which of the following sequences are the first three terms of *arithmetic* progressions and which are not.

    a. 2, 6, 18   **c.** $-2, 3\frac{1}{2}, 9$ **e.** $i, 2i, 4i$

    b. $1, -2, -5$ **d.** $2 + i, -i, -2 - 3i$ **f.** $-2i, 0, 2i$

7. Tell which of the following sequences are the first three terms of *geometric* progressions and which are not.

    a. $\tan(\theta)$, $\tan(2\theta)$, $\tan(4\theta)$ **c.** 2, 4, 16   **e.** i, -2, $-4i$

    b. $-1, 1, -1$ **d.** $\dfrac{1}{3}, \dfrac{1}{3^2}, \dfrac{1}{3^3}$ **f.** $\dfrac{1}{i}, -1, i$

8. Find the sum of the indicated number of terms of each arithmetic progression.

    a. $2, 1\frac{1}{2}, 1, \ldots$; 20 terms   **b.** $1+\sqrt{2}, 1+2\sqrt{2}, 1+3\sqrt{2}, \ldots$; 15 terms

9. Find the sum of the indicated number of terms of each geometric progression.

    a. $4, 2, 1, \ldots$; 10 terms   **b.** $1, .2, .04, \ldots$; 8 terms

10. Write in an expanded form.

    a. $\displaystyle\sum_{k=1}^{6} k$ **c.** $\displaystyle\sum_{k=1}^{n} \dfrac{3k}{k+2}$

    b. $\displaystyle\sum_{k=1}^{5} 4^{2k+1}$ **d.** $\displaystyle\sum_{k=1}^{n} \dfrac{k^3}{k(k^2+2)}$

11. For each infinite sequence below, tell whether it is convergent or divergent. In the case of each convergent sequence, tell its limit.

    a. $2, -\frac{1}{2}, 2, -\frac{1}{2}, \ldots, 2, -\frac{1}{2}, \ldots$

    b. $10^0, 10^{-2}, 10^{-4}, 10^{-6}, \ldots, 10^{-2(n-1)}, \ldots$

    c. $\frac{1}{2}, (\frac{1}{2})^2, (\frac{1}{2})^3, (\frac{1}{2})^4, \ldots, (\frac{1}{2})^n, \ldots$

    d. $-2, (-2)^2, (-2)^3, (-2)^4, \ldots, (-2)^n, \ldots$

12. Find the value of x such that $2x, x-1, \dfrac{x}{2}$ will form an arithmetic progression.

13. Find the value of x such that $x, \dfrac{x}{2}, 2x+1$ will form a geometric progression.

14. Simplify $\dfrac{100!}{98\ !}$.

15. How many different five-digit numerals can be formed using the digits 1, 2, 3, 4, 5, 6, and 7?

16. How many different four-letter arrangements can be formed using all the letters of the word "five"?

17. How many different eleven-letter arrangements can be formed using all the letters of the word "mathematics"?

18. In how many ways can six people be seated around a circular table?

19. Write the expansion for each of the following:

    a. $(2x+3)^5$ **b.** $(\sqrt{a}+2)^4$ **c.** $(a^3-n)^6$ **d.** $(2x^2-1)^7$

20. Simplify $\binom{6}{0} + \binom{6}{1} + \binom{6}{2} + \binom{6}{3} + \binom{6}{4} + \binom{6}{5} + \binom{6}{6}$.

21. Write the "middle" term of $(\sqrt{a} - x^2)^8$ in simplified form.

22. An ordinary die is tossed twice. What is the probability that

    a. a "6" will appear both times?

    b. the outcomes will be "1" and "2"?

    c. no "3" will appear either time?

    d. no "1" and no "2" will appear either time?

23. A card is drawn at random from an ordinary deck of 52 cards. What is the probability that the card is

    a. the king of diamonds?   **d.** red *or* black?

    b. a spade?   **e.** red *and* black?

    c. red?   **f.** an ace?

24. A coin is tossed four times. What is the probability that heads will come up four times?

25. A coin, which is biased in favor of heads 3 to 1, is tossed four times. What is the probability that heads will come up four times?

BIBLIOGRAPHY

National Council of Teachers of Mathematics. *Insights into Modern Mathematics.* Washington, 1957. pp. 145-199.

Norton, M. S. *Basic Concepts of Vectors.* St. Louis: Webster Publishing Co., 1963.

School Mathematics Study Group. *Intermediate Mathematics, Part II.* New Haven: Yale University Press, 1961. Chapter 11.

Table of Trigonometric Function Values

Angle Measure	Sin	Cos	Tan	Angle Measure	Sin	Cos	Tan
1°	.0175	.9998	.0175	46°	.7193	.6947	1.0355
2°	.0349	.9994	.0349	47°	.7314	.6820	1.0724
3°	.0523	.9986	.0524	48°	.7431	.6691	1.1106
4°	.0698	.9976	.0699	49°	.7547	.6561	1.1504
5°	.0872	.9962	.0875	50°	.7660	.6428	1.1918
6°	.1045	.9945	.1051	51°	.7771	.6293	1.2349
7°	.1219	.9925	.1228	52°	.7880	.6157	1.2799
8°	.1392	.9903	.1405	53°	.7986	.6018	1.3270
9°	.1564	.9877	.1584	54°	.8090	.5878	1.3764
10°	.1736	.9848	.1763	55°	.8192	.5736	1.4281
11°	.1908	.9816	.1944	56°	.8290	.5592	1.4826
12°	.2079	.9781	.2126	57°	.8387	.5446	1.5399
13°	.2250	.9744	.2309	58°	.8480	.5299	1.6003
14°	.2419	.9703	.2493	59°	.8572	.5150	1.6643
15°	.2588	.9659	.2679	60°	.8660	.5000	1.7321
16°	.2756	.9613	.2867	61°	.8746	.4848	1.8040
17°	.2924	.9563	.3057	62°	.8829	.4695	1.8807
18°	.3090	.9511	.3249	63°	.8910	.4540	1.9626
19°	.3256	.9455	.3443	64°	.8988	.4384	2.0503
20°	.3420	.9397	.3640	65°	.9063	.4226	2.1445
21°	.3584	.9336	.3839	66°	.9135	.4067	2.2460
22°	.3746	.9272	.4040	67°	.9205	.3907	2.3559
23°	.3907	.9205	.4245	68°	.9272	.3746	2.4751
24°	.4067	.9135	.4452	69°	.9336	.3584	2.6051
25°	.4226	.9063	.4663	70°	.9397	.3420	2.7475
26°	.4384	.8988	.4877	71°	.9455	.3256	2.9042
27°	.4540	.8910	.5095	72°	.9511	.3090	3.0777
28°	.4695	.8829	.5317	73°	.9563	.2924	3.2709
29°	.4848	.8746	.5543	74°	.9613	.2756	3.4874
30°	.5000	.8660	.5774	75°	.9659	.2588	3.7321
31°	.5150	.8572	.6009	76°	.9703	.2419	4.0108
32°	.5299	.8480	.6249	77°	.9744	.2250	4.3315
33°	.5446	.8387	.6494	78°	.9781	.2079	4.7046
34°	.5592	.8290	.6745	79°	.9816	.1908	5.1446
35°	.5736	.8192	.7002	80°	.9848	.1736	5.6713
36°	.5878	.8090	.7265	81°	.9877	.1564	6.3138
37°	.6018	.7986	.7536	82°	.9903	.1392	7.1154
38°	.6157	.7880	.7813	83°	.9925	.1219	8.1443
39°	.6293	.7771	.8098	84°	.9945	.1045	9.5144
40°	.6428	.7660	.8391	85°	.9962	.0872	11.4301
41°	.6561	.7547	.8693	86°	.9976	.0698	14.3007
42°	.6691	.7431	.9004	87°	.9986	.0523	19.0811
43°	.6820	.7314	.9325	88°	.9994	.0349	28.6363
44°	.6947	.7193	.9657	89°	.9998	.0175	57.2900
45°	.7071	.7071	1.0000	90°	1.0000	.0000	

Table of Mantissas

n	0	1	2	3	4	5	6	7	8	9
10	0000	0043	0086	0128	0170	0212	0253	0294	0334	0374
11	0414	0453	0492	0531	0569	0607	0645	0682	0719	0755
12	0792	0828	0864	0899	0934	0969	1004	1038	1072	1106
13	1139	1173	1206	1239	1271	1303	1335	1367	1399	1430
14	1461	1492	1523	1553	1584	1614	1644	1673	1703	1732
15	1761	1790	1818	1847	1875	1903	1931	1959	1987	2014
16	2041	2068	2095	2122	2148	2175	2201	2227	2253	2279
17	2304	2330	2355	2380	2405	2430	2455	2480	2504	2529
18	2553	2577	2601	2625	2648	2672	2695	2718	2742	2765
19	2788	2810	2833	2856	2878	2900	2923	2945	2967	2989
20	3010	3032	3054	3075	3096	3118	3139	3160	3181	3201
21	3222	3243	3263	3284	3304	3324	3345	3365	3385	3404
22	3424	3444	3464	3483	3502	3522	3541	3560	3579	3598
23	3617	3636	3655	3674	3692	3711	3729	3747	3766	3784
24	3802	3820	3838	3856	3874	3892	3909	3927	3945	3962
25	3979	3997	4014	4031	4048	4065	4082	4099	4116	4133
26	4150	4166	4183	4200	4216	4232	4249	4265	4281	4298
27	4314	4330	4346	4362	4378	4393	4409	4425	4440	4456
28	4472	4487	4502	4518	4533	4548	4564	4579	4594	4609
29	4624	4639	4654	4669	4683	4698	4713	4728	4742	4757
30	4771	4786	4800	4814	4829	4843	4857	4871	4886	4900
31	4914	4928	4942	4955	4969	4983	4997	5011	5024	5038
32	5051	5065	5079	5092	5105	5119	5132	5145	5159	5172
33	5185	5198	5211	5224	5237	5250	5263	5276	5289	5302
34	5315	5328	5340	5353	5366	5378	5391	5403	5416	5428
35	5441	5453	5465	5478	5490	5502	5514	5527	5539	5551
36	5563	5575	5587	5599	5611	5623	5635	5647	5658	5670
37	5682	5694	5705	5717	5729	5740	5752	5763	5775	5786
38	5798	5809	5821	5832	5843	5855	5866	5877	5888	5899
39	5911	5922	5933	5944	5955	5966	5977	5988	5999	6010
40	6021	6031	6042	6053	6064	6075	6085	6096	6107	6117
41	6128	6138	6149	6160	6170	6180	6191	6201	6212	6222
42	6232	6243	6253	6263	6274	6284	6294	6304	6314	6325
43	6335	6345	6355	6365	6375	6385	6395	6405	6415	6425
44	6435	6444	6454	6464	6474	6484	6493	6503	6513	6522
45	6532	6542	6551	6561	6571	6580	6590	6599	6609	6618
46	6628	6637	6646	6656	6665	6675	6684	6693	6702	6712
47	6721	6730	6739	6749	6758	6767	6776	6785	6794	6803
48	6812	6821	6830	6839	6848	6857	6866	6875	6884	6893
49	6902	6911	6920	6928	6937	6946	6955	6964	6972	6981
50	6990	6998	7007	7016	7024	7033	7042	7050	7059	7067
51	7076	7084	7093	7101	7110	7118	7126	7135	7143	7152
52	7160	7168	7177	7185	7193	7202	7210	7218	7226	7235
53	7243	7251	7259	7267	7275	7284	7292	7300	7308	7316
54	7324	7332	7340	7348	7356	7364	7372	7380	7388	7396

Table of Mantissas

n	0	1	2	3	4	5	6	7	8	9
55	7404	7412	7419	7427	7435	7443	7451	7459	7466	7474
56	7482	7490	7497	7505	7513	7520	7528	7536	7543	7551
57	7559	7566	7574	7582	7589	7597	7604	7612	7619	7627
58	7634	7642	7649	7657	7664	7672	7679	7686	7694	7701
59	7709	7716	7723	7731	7738	7745	7752	7760	7767	7774
60	7782	7789	7796	7803	7810	7818	7825	7832	7839	7846
61	7853	7860	7868	7875	7882	7889	7896	7903	7910	7917
62	7924	7931	7938	7945	7952	7959	7966	7973	7980	7987
63	7993	8000	8007	8014	8021	8028	8035	8041	8048	8055
64	8062	8069	8075	8082	8089	8096	8102	8109	8116	8122
65	8129	8136	8142	8149	8156	8162	8169	8176	8182	8189
66	8195	8202	8209	8215	8222	8228	8235	8241	8248	8254
67	8261	8267	8274	8280	8287	8293	8299	8306	8312	8319
68	8325	8331	8338	8344	8351	8357	8363	8370	8376	8382
69	8388	8395	8401	8407	8414	8420	8426	8432	8439	8445
70	8451	8457	8463	8470	8476	8482	8488	8494	8500	8506
71	8513	8519	8525	8531	8537	8543	8549	8555	8561	8567
72	8573	8579	8585	8591	8597	8603	8609	8615	8621	8627
73	8633	8639	8645	8651	8657	8663	8669	8675	8681	8686
74	8692	8698	8704	8710	8716	8722	8727	8733	8739	8745
75	8751	8756	8762	8768	8774	8779	8785	8791	8797	8802
76	8808	8814	8820	8825	8831	8837	8842	8848	8854	8859
77	8865	8871	8876	8882	8887	8893	8899	8904	8910	8915
78	8921	8927	8932	8938	8943	8949	8954	8960	8965	8971
79	8976	8982	8987	8993	8998	9004	9009	9015	9020	9025
80	9031	9036	9042	9047	9053	9058	9063	9069	9074	9079
81	9085	9090	9096	9101	9106	9112	9117	9122	9128	9133
82	9138	9143	9149	9154	9159	9165	9170	9175	9180	9186
83	9191	9196	9201	9206	9212	9217	9222	9227	9232	9238
84	9243	9248	9253	9258	9263	9269	9274	9279	9284	9289
85	9294	9299	9304	9309	9315	9320	9325	9330	9335	9340
86	9345	9350	9355	9360	9365	9370	9375	9380	9385	9390
87	9395	9400	9405	9410	9415	9420	9425	9430	9435	9440
88	9445	9450	9455	9460	9465	9469	9474	9479	9484	9489
89	9494	9499	9504	9509	9513	9518	9523	9528	9533	9538
90	9542	9547	9552	9557	9562	9566	9571	9576	9581	9586
91	9590	9595	9600	9605	9609	9614	9619	9624	9628	9633
92	9638	9643	9647	9652	9657	9661	9666	9671	9675	9680
93	9685	9689	9694	9699	9703	9708	9713	9717	9722	9727
94	9731	9736	9741	9745	9750	9754	9759	9763	9768	9773
95	9777	9782	9786	9791	9795	9800	9805	9809	9814	9818
96	9823	9827	9832	9836	9841	9845	9850	9854	9859	9863
97	9868	9872	9877	9881	9886	9890	9894	9899	9903	9908
98	9912	9917	9921	9926	9930	9934	9939	9943	9948	9952
99	9956	9961	9965	9969	9974	9978	9983	9987	9991	9996

Glossary

This is a list of important terms used in this book. A brief description, or an illustration, not necessarily a definition, is given for each term.

Absolute value (of a complex number). The real number $\sqrt{a^2 + b^2}$ is the absolute value of the complex number (a, b) or $a + bi$; it is indicated by the symbol $|(a, b)|$ or $|a + bi|$.

Absolute value (of a real number). The absolute value of a, symbolized by $|a|$, means the following: $|a| = a$ if $0 \leq a$ and $|a| = -a$ if $a < 0$.

Additive identity. A number n for which it is true that $\forall_x x + n = x$. For real numbers, 0 is the additive identity.

Additive inverse (of a number). The additive inverse of a number is the number which added to the original number gives the sum 0. If x is the additive inverse of y, then $x + y = 0$.

Additive inverse (of a vector). For any points A and B, $\overrightarrow{BA}$ is the additive inverse of $\overrightarrow{AB}$.

Adjacent leg. For any right triangle ABC with right angle C, the side $\overline{AC}$ is the leg adjacent to angle A.

Arithmetic means (of an arithmetic progression). The terms of an arithmetic progression, which are between the first and the last terms of the progression.

Arithmetic series. A sum shown in the form $a + (a + d) + (a + 2d) + \ldots + [a + (n - 1)d]$.

Associative Property of Multiplication, APM. $\forall_x \forall_y \forall_z (xy)z = x(yz)$.

Associative Property of Addition, APA. $\forall_x \forall_y \forall_z (x + y) + z = x + (y + z)$.

Axis (of a parabola). The line which passes through the vertex and through the focus of a parabola.

Base. In 7^9, 7 is the base. More generally, in x^y, x is the base.

Biconditional. A statement of the form "p if and only if q."

Binomial. A polynomial which has exactly two terms when written in simplest form.

Certain event. An event which is equal to the sample space.

Characteristic. If $\log(x) = c + m$ where c is an integer and $0 < m < 1$, then c is the characteristic of $\log(x)$. For example, $\log(5000) \doteq 3 + .6990$ and 3 is called the characteristic of $\log(5000)$.

Circle. The closed curve which is the set of all points in a plane equidistant from a given point.

Closed half-plane. The union of a half-plane and the line which determines it.

Closure. A set has closure under a given operation if the result of operating on any members of a set also belongs to the set. For example, the set of real numbers has closure under multiplication, since the product of any pair of real numbers is a real number.

Collinear vectors. Vectors which are subsets of the same line.

Combination (of a set of n elements taken k at a time). Any k-member subset of an n-member set, $k \leq n$.

Common difference (of an arithmetic progression). The number d used in the definition of an arithmetic progression.

Common ratio (of a geometric progression). The number r used in the definition of a geometric progression.

Commutative Property of Addition, CPA. $\forall_x \forall_y \, x + y = y + x$.

Commutative Property of Multiplication, CPM. $\forall_x \forall_y \, xy = yx$.

Complex number. Each ordered pair of real numbers is a complex number. The complex number (a, b) is sometimes expressed in another notation as $a + bi$.

Complex zero (of a polynomial). The complex number $a + bi$ is a complex zero of a polynomial $f(x)$ if and only if $f(a + bi) = 0$.

Composite number. A natural number which has more than two natural number divisors.

Conditional. A statement of the form "if p, then q" (also called *implication*).

Conic. The intersection of a plane and the surface of a right circular cone or of a right circular cylinder.

Conjugate (of a complex number). The complex number $(a, -b)$ is called the conjugate of the complex number (a, b). The conjugate of (a, b) is indicated by the symbol $\overline{(a, b)}$. In standard notation, the conjugate of $a + bi$ is indicated by the symbol $\overline{a + bi}$ and is the complex number $a - bi$.

Conjunction. A statement of the form "*p and q*."

Constant function. A function each ordered pair of which has the same second component.

Constant of proportionality (for variation). The real number c in the direct and inverse proportion functions.

Constant term (of $P(x)$). If $P(x) = a_0 x^n + a_1 x^{n-1} + a_2 x^{n-2} + \ldots + a_{n-1}x + a_n$, then a_n is the constant term of $P(x)$.

Contrapositive (of an implication). The contrapositive of $a \to b$ is $\sim b \to \sim a$.

Convergent sequence. A sequence which has a limit.

Convergent series. A series which has a limit.

Converse (of an implication). The converse of $a \to b$ is $b \to a$.

Coordinate system (in a plane). A one-to-one correspondence between all the points in a plane and all ordered pairs of real numbers.

Coordinate system (on a line). A one-to-one correspondence between all the points in a line and all real numbers.

Cosine (of an acute angle A). For any right triangle ABC with right angle C, $\cos(A) = \dfrac{AC}{AB}$, or the quotient of the measure of the leg adjacent to angle A and the measure of the hypotenuse.

Cosine (of θ). $\cos(\theta) = x$, where $(\theta, (x, y))$ belongs to the wrapping function.

Counterexample. An example which contradicts a statement.

Degree (of a polynomial function). If $f(x) = a_0 x^n + a_1 x^{n-1} + a_2 x^{n-2} + \ldots + a_{n-1}x + a_n \, (a_0 \neq 0)$, then n is the degree of $f(x)$.

Density. The property of a set of numbers in which there is a third number between any two given numbers. For example, the set of real numbers has the density property, or it is dense.

Dependent system (of linear equations in two variables). A system consisting of two equivalent equations.

Determinant. $\begin{vmatrix} 3 & -\sqrt{2} \\ 1 & 0 \end{vmatrix}$ is an example of a 2 by 2 (2 rows, 2 columns) determinant, and is equal to $3 \times 0 - 1 \times (-\sqrt{2})$ or $\sqrt{2}$.

Direct proportion (function). A function of the type $\{(x, y) \mid y = c \cdot x\}$ where c is a real number.

Directrix (of a parabola). The given line mentioned in the definition of a parabola.

Discrete (set). A set is discrete if and only if the number of elements between any two elements of the set is a natural number.

Disjunction. A statement of the form "*p or q.*"

Discriminant. The discriminant of a quadratic equation $ax^2 + bx + c = 0$, $a \neq 0$, is $b^2 - 4ac$.

Divergent sequence. A sequence which has no limit.

Divergent series. A series which has no limit.

Division algorithm. Given two polynomials $P(x)$ and $D(x)$, $D(x) \neq 0$, then exactly one of the following holds: *i.* there is a unique polynomial $Q(x)$ such that $P(x) = Q(x) \cdot D(x)$ *ii.* there are two unique polynomials $Q(x)$ and $R(x)$ such that $P(x) = Q(x) \cdot D(x) + R(x)$.

Domain (of a relation). The set of first components of the ordered pairs which comprise the relation.

Empty set (ϕ). The set which has no members.

Equivalent systems of equations. Two systems of equations having the same solution set.

Event. A subset of a sample space.

Exponent. In 3^5, 5 is the exponent. More generally, in x^y, y is the exponent.

Factor theorem. $(x - r)$ is a factor of $P(x)$ if and only if $P(r) = 0$.

Field. A set of elements with two operations which possesses the properties specified on page 23.

Finite set. A set is finite if the number of its elements can be expressed as a whole number.

Focus (of a parabola). The given point mentioned in the definition of parabola.

Fractional equation. Any equation which contains a non-polynomial rational expression in one or both of its members.

Function. A relation in which no two ordered pairs have the same first component.

Functional notation. A notation used for representing the second component of any ordered pair of a function.

Fundamental theorem of algebra. If $P(x)$ is a polynomial over the complex numbers and of degree greater than 0, then there is a complex number r for which $P(r) = 0$.

Greatest integer function. A function in which the second component of each ordered pair is the greatest integer which is less than the first component of that ordered pair.

Horizontal (line or segment). Property of lines and segments which are parallel to the x-axis.

Hypotenuse. The side of a right triangle which is opposite the right angle. For any right triangle ABC with right angle C, the side $\overline{AB}$ is the hypotenuse.

Identity function. A function which assigns each member of its domain to itself.

Implication. A statement of the form "if p, then q" (also called a *conditional*).

Impossible event. An event which is equal to the empty set.

Inconsistent system (of equations). A

system of equations which has the empty set for its solution set.

Independent events. Any two events, say E and F, such that $P(E|F) = P(E)$ and $P(F|E) = P(F)$.

Independent system (of linear equations in two variables). A system of equations which has an ordered pair of numbers for its solution.

Index. In $\sqrt[n]{x}$, n is the index.

Infinite set. A set which is not finite.

Inner product (of vectors). The inner product, $\vec{X} \cdot \vec{Y}$, of two non-zero vectors $\vec{X}$ and $\vec{Y}$ is the real number $|\vec{X}||\vec{Y}| \cos \alpha$, where α is the measure of the angle between $\vec{X}$ and $\vec{Y}$. If $\vec{X}$ or $\vec{Y}$ is a zero vector, then the inner product is equal to the real number 0 (also called *dot product*).

Integer. Any positive or negative whole number, or 0.

Integral domain. A set of elements with two operations which possesses the properties specified on page 17.

Integral polynomial. A polynomial which has only integers for its coefficients.

Integral zero (of a polynomial). If $P(r) = 0$ and r is an integer, then r is an integral zero of $P(x)$.

Integral zero theorem. If an integer r is a zero of an integral polynomial $P(x)$, then r is a factor of the constant term of $P(x)$.

Inverse (of a relation A). The relation obtained by interchanging the components of each of the ordered pairs in A.

Inverse (of an implication). The inverse of $a \rightarrow b$ is $\sim a \rightarrow \sim b$.

Inverse proportion (function). A function of the type $\left\{(x, y) \middle| y = c \cdot \dfrac{1}{x}\right\}$ where c is a non-zero real number.

Irrational number. A number which has no name of the form $\dfrac{a}{b}$ $(b \neq 0)$, a and b being integers. Example: $\sqrt{3}$.

Isomorphic. When two sets of elements "behave" exactly the same under their given operations, then we say that the two sets are isomorphic under those operations.

Left-Distributive Property of Multiplication over Addition, LDPMA.
$$\forall_x \forall_y \forall_z \ x(y + z) = (xy) + (xz)$$

Linear function. A function of the type $\{(x, y)|y = mx + b\}$, where m and b are real numbers, $m \neq 0$.

Linear permutation. A linear arrangement or ordering of the elements of a set.

Logarithmic function. The base-ten, or common, log function is $\{(x, y)|x > 0$ and $x = 10^y\}$. One member of this function is $(1000, 3)$; this may be indicated by the equation: $\log(1000) = 3$.

Magnitude (of a vector). For any points X and Y, the magnitude of $\overrightarrow{XY}$ is XY, the measure of $\overline{XY}$. The magnitude of $\overrightarrow{XY}$ is denoted by $|\overrightarrow{XY}|$.

Mantissa. If $\log(x) = c + m$ where c is an integer and $0 < m < 1$, then m is the mantissa of $\log(x)$. For example, $\log(5000) \doteq 3 + .6990$ and $.6990$ is called a mantissa.

Maximum value (of a quadratic function f). The greatest member of the range of f. Some quadratic functions do not have a maximum value.

Midpoint (of a segment). The point of a segment equidistant from the endpoints of the segment.

Minimum value (of a quadratic function f). The least number of the range of f. Some quadratic functions do not have a minimum value.

Monomial. A polynomial which has exactly one term when written in simplest form.

Multiplicative inverse. Given any real number $x \neq 0$, y is the multiplicative inverse of x if and only if $xy = 1$.

Natural number. Counting numbers: 1, 2, 3, 4, 5, 6, ...

Negation (of a statement). A statement prefixed by "it is not true that." The negation of p is symbolized by $\sim p$.

Oblique (line or segment). Property of lines and segments which are not parallel to either axis.

One-to-one correspondence. The pairing between the elements of two sets A and B, such that for each element in A there is a unique element in B, and conversely.

Open half-plane. The set of all points on one side of a line in a plane (also called *half-plane.*)

Opposite (of a number). The opposite of x is $-x$. It is also called the additive inverse of x.

Opposite leg. For any right triangle ABC with right angle C, the side $\overline{BC}$ is the leg opposite angle A.

Ordered integral domain. An integral domain in which the sum of a pair of positive elements is positive, and the product of a pair of positive elements is positive, and the trichotomy property holds.

Ordered pair of real numbers. A set containing only a pair of real numbers such that order is taken into account. If a, b, c, and d are real numbers, then (a, b) is the ordered pair of real numbers a and b; and $(a, b) = (c, d)$ if and only if $a = c$ and $b = d$.

Origin. The point which is the intersection of the x and y axes.

Parabola. The curve which is the set of all points in a plane equidistant from a given line and a given point (not on the given line), both in the plane.

Parallel (lines). Non-intersecting lines in the same plane.

Perfect square trinomial. A trinomial which is the square of a binomial.

Periodic function. Any function f is called periodic if for each x in the domain of f there exists a number p such that $f(x) = f(x + p)$. The number p is said to be a period of the function f. For example, the sine function is periodic and 2π is a period of the sine.

Perpendicular (lines). Intersecting lines whose union contains a right angle.

Plotting (a point). Locating the graph of a point in a plane, given the coordinates of the point.

Point-slope form (of an equation). An equation of the form: $y - y_1 = m(x - x_1)$. It is an equation of the straight line with slope m and passing through the point (x_1, y_1).

Polynomial (in n variables). Any expression which can be constructed from a set of n variables together with the real numbers, using only the operations of addition, subtraction, and multiplication. NOTE: A polynomial (in one variable, say x) is said to be written in simplest form if it is in the pattern
$$a_0 x^n + a_1 x^{n-1} + a_2 x^{n-2} + \cdots + a_{n-1} x + a_n$$

Power. x^n is the n-th power of x.

Prime number. A natural number which has exactly two natural number divisors.

Principal square root. The positive number whose square is equal to the given number. Example: 2 is the principal square root of 4, since $2 > 0$ and $2^2 = 4$.

Probability (of an event E in a finite sample space S). The ratio of the number of elements in set E to the number of elements in set S.

Product set (of two sets A and B). The set of all ordered pairs whose first components are elements of A and whose second components are elements of B.

Quadrant. Any one of the four portions of a plane which are interiors of the right angles formed by the axes.

Quadratic equation. Any equation which patterns in the form $ax^2 + bx + c = 0$ where a, b, and c are real numbers and $a \neq 0$.

Quadratic formula. A formula for finding the solution set of any quadratic equation. For the equation $ax^2 + bx + c = 0$, $x = \dfrac{-b \pm \sqrt{b^2 - 4ac}}{2a}$ is the quadratic formula.

Quadratic function. Any function of the type $\{(x, ax^2 + bx + c)\}$, where a, b, and c are real numbers and $a \neq 0$.

Quadratic inequality. Any inequality which patterns in either of the forms $ax^2 + bx + c > 0$ or $ax^2 + bx + c < 0$, where a, b, and c are real numbers, and $a \neq 0$.

Radical. $\sqrt[n]{x}$ is a radical.

Radical equation. An equation which contains a variable under a radical sign.

Radical sign. $\sqrt[n]{}$ is a radical sign.

Radicand. In $\sqrt[n]{x}$, x is the radicand.

Range (of a relation). The set of second components of the ordered pairs which comprise the relation.

Rational expression. A quotient of polynomials.

Rational number. A number which has a name of the form $\dfrac{a}{b}$ ($b \neq 0$), where a and b are integers.

Rational zero theorem. If $\dfrac{a}{b}$ ($b \neq 0$, a and b relatively prime integers) is a zero of the integral polynomial
$$P(x) = a_0 x^n + a_1 x^{n-1} + a_2 x^{n-2}$$
$$+ \cdots + a_{n-1} x + a_n$$
then a is a divisor of a_n and b is a divisor of a_0.

Real number. A rational or irrational number.

Reflexive (property of equality). $\forall_a \ a = a$.

Relation. A subset of a product set.

Remainder theorem. Given the polynomials $P(x)$, $D(x)$, and $(x - a)$, if $P(x) = D(x) \cdot (x - a) + R$ for some number R, then $R = P(a)$.

Repeating decimal. Example: $.316316316\ldots$.

Resolving a vector. Showing the horizontal and vertical components of a vector.

Resultant (of vectors). Resultant of two vectors is a vector which is the sum of the two vectors.

Sample space. The set of all possible outcomes of an experiment.

Scalar. A real number used in multiplication by a vector.

Scientific notation. Any numeral of the form $a \times 10^b$ where $1 \leq a < 10$ and b is an integer is said to be in scientific notation. 3420 and .00342 may be expressed in scientific notation as 3.42×10^3 and 3.42×10^{-3}, respectively.

Segment. Any set of points which contains two points and all points between these two points.

Sine (of an acute angle A). For any right triangle ABC with right angle C, $\sin(A) = \dfrac{BC}{AB}$, or the quotient of the measure of the leg opposite angle A and the measure of the hypotenuse.

Slope (of a line). The real number $\dfrac{y_1 - y_2}{x_1 - x_2}$ which measures the steepness of the line passing through the points (x_1, y_1) and (x_2, y_2).

Slope-intercept form (of an equation). An equation of the form: $y = mx + b$. It is an equation of the straight line with slope m and passing through the point $(0, b)$.

Standard form (of a complex number). A system of notation in which the complex number (a, b) is expressed as $a + bi$.

Standard position (of a vector). A vector is in standard position if its initial point is the origin of the coordinate system.

Substitution (property). If $a = b$, then a can be replaced by b and vice-versa in any statement, and the truth-value of the new statement is the same.

Symmetric (property of equality). $\forall_a \forall_b$, if $a = b$, then $b = a$.

System of equations. Two (or more) equations, the solution set for which is the solution set of the intersection of the equations.

Tangent (of an acute angle A). For any right triangle ABC with right angle C, $\tan(A) = \dfrac{BC}{AC}$, or the quotient of the measure of the leg opposite angle A and the measure of the leg adjacent to angle A.

Terminal point (of a vector). B is the terminal point of $\overrightarrow{AB}$.

Terminating decimal. A decimal which can be written with a finite number of digits. Example: .7601.

Transitive (property of equality). $\forall_a \forall_b \forall_c$, if $a = b$ and $b = c$, then $a = c$.

Trichotomy (property of real numbers). If x and y are real numbers, then only one of the following is true: (1) $x < y$; (2) $x = y$; (3) $x > y$.

Trinomial. A polynomial which has exactly three terms when written in simplest form.

Unique factorization theorem. Every polynomial $P(x)$ of degree $n \geq 1$ over the complex numbers can be factored uniquely into n linear factors, not all of which are necessarily distinct, and a constant factor which is the coefficient of the highest degree term of $P(x)$.

Unit circle. Any circle whose radius is one unit long.

Unit step function. Another name for the Greatest Integer Function.

Value (of a function f at x). The second component of the ordered pair in f whose first component is x.

Vector sum. If (a, b) corresponds to $\overrightarrow{MN}$ and (c, d) corresponds to $\overrightarrow{MP}$, then $\overrightarrow{MR}$ is the sum of $\overrightarrow{MN}$ and $\overrightarrow{MP}$, denoted by $\overrightarrow{MN} + \overrightarrow{MP} = \overrightarrow{MR}$, if and only if $\overrightarrow{MR}$ corresponds to $(a + c, b + d)$.

Vertex (of a parabola). The point of intersection of a parabola and its axis of symmetry.

Vertical (line or segment). Property of lines and segments which are parallel to the y-axis.

Wrapping function. The set of ordered pairs $(\theta, (x, y))$ where θ is the real number associated with the path (A, θ) along the unit circle whose center is at the origin and where (x, y) are the coordinates of the terminal point of the path (A, θ). One member of W, the wrapping function, is $\left(\dfrac{\pi}{3}, \left(\dfrac{1}{2}, \dfrac{\sqrt{3}}{2}\right)\right)$; this may be indicated by the equation

$$W\left(\frac{\pi}{3}\right) = \left(\frac{1}{2}, \frac{\sqrt{3}}{2}\right).$$

x-intercept (of a line). The first coordinate of the point at which any non-horizontal line intersects the x-axis.

y-intercept (of a line). The second coordinate of the point at which any non-vertical line intersects the y-axis.

Zero of a polynomial. r is a zero of a polynomial $P(x)$ if and only if $P(r) = 0$.

Zero vector. A vector which has the same initial point as terminal point.

Index

The figures in **bold-faced** type refer to the pages on which the words and expressions are described.

573